S

LINEAR PROGRAMMING

LINEAR PROGRAMMING

by

G. HADLEY

University of Chicago

ADDISON-WESLEY PUBLISHING COMPANY, INC.

READING, MASSACHUSETTS · PALO ALTO · LONDON

PREFACE

Only a little over a decade has passed since George Dantzig formulated the general linear programming problem and developed the simplex method for its solution. In this period, the growth of interest in, and the use of, linear programming has been remarkable. Rarely indeed has a new mathematical technique found such a wide range of practical applications, and simultaneously received so thorough a theoretical development in such a short period of time. The extensive interest in linear programming which has arisen has brought with it the need for texts at different levels of difficulty, suitable for readers of widely varying backgrounds and mathematical maturity. The present work is intended for those who desire to study the subject in some depth and detail. It attempts to provide a fairly rigorous and complete development of the theoretical and computational aspects of linear programming as well as a discussion of a number of practical applications.

Chapter 1 introduces the general linear programming problem and exhibits a series of graphical examples. Chapter 2 covers the mathematical background needed. In Chapter 3 the fundamental theoretical results required for the simplex method are derived. Chapter 4 provides a detailed development of the computational procedure of the simplex method. The two-phase technique is introduced in Chapter 5, which also includes a discussion of the solutions and requirements spaces. Chapter 6 presents Charnes' perturbation technique and the generalized simplex method for resolving the degeneracy problem. The revised simplex method is covered in Chapter 7. Chapter 8 is devoted to duality; included in this chapter are the dual simplex algorithm and the primal-dual algorithm. The solution of transportation problems is the concern of Chapter 9. A novel approach is used to derive the transportation algorithm from the simplex method. Generalized transportation problems are also covered in this chapter. Chapter 10 discusses network flow problems, the primal-dual algorithm for transportation problems, assignment problems, and the transhipment problem. Chapter 11 treats a number of special topics, such as sensitivity analysis, treatment of upper bounds for the general linear programming problem, the primal-dual algorithm for capacitated transportation problems, the decomposition principle, and the relationships between linear programming and zero-sum two-person games. The application of linear programming to practical problems in industry is discussed in Chapter 12, and applications to economic theory are considered in Chapter 13.

The level of presentation in this book assumes that the reader has a familiarity with certain elementary topics in linear algebra (including convex sets). The necessary background material is reviewed in Chapter 2. However, the reader who has had no previous introduction to the material may find this review too abbreviated. It is suggested that such readers study concurrently the author's *Linear Algebra*, which covers in detail the material needed. (Incidentally, the notation used is consistent throughout both volumes.) As an aid to those who are simultaneously attempting to gain some knowledge of linear algebra, the present book develops its major themes in considerable detail, especially in Chapters 3, 4, 5, 6. It might be pointed out that a knowledge of convex sets in n dimensions is not essential for reading the text. The sections dealing with these topics can be omitted without loss of continuity.

Although the text is fairly complete, there are several topics associated with linear programming which are not to be found here. Two such topics, namely, linear programming problems some of whose parameters may be random variables and the solution of the general linear programming problem in integers, are considered by the author to be special cases of nonlinear programming problems and are discussed in a separate volume entitled *Nonlinear and Dynamic Programming*. No account is given of the use of analog computers to solve linear programming problems. Some material in this subject was included in an original version of the manuscript, but was dropped because it was felt to be a diversion from the main theme, of interest only to a small number of readers. General considerations regarding the solution of linear programming problems on digital computers are examined in the text, but no attempt is made to describe coding procedures in detail since the method chosen depends too much on the characteristics of the computer to be employed. Similarly, no detailed description of the linear programming codes available for various computers is given since these would be almost immediately out of date.

The text contains sufficient material for a two-semester course in linear programming although it can easily be used for a one-semester or one-quarter course in the subject. For example, the author has taught a one-semester graduate course at MIT devoted to the theory of linear programming. The students entering the course had no background in linear algebra, and hence about the first seven weeks were devoted to covering selected topics from the first six chapters of the author's *Linear Algebra*. For the remainder of the semester the material covered consisted of Chapters 3, 4, 5 (through Section 5–4), 6 (through Section 6–6), 7, 8 (through Section 8–7), and 9 (through Section 9–12) of the present volume. At the University of Chicago, the author has taught a one-quarter course to graduate students who had a course in linear algebra. After a brief review (about two weeks) of linear algebra and some discussion of convex sets, the above-mentioned material, the first four sections of Chapter 11, and most of Chapter 12 of this book were covered in the remainder of the quarter. It should be pointed out that this quarter course normally required about twelve hours per week of work outside of class.

The present volume should also serve as a supplementary text for courses in mathematical economics, engineering mathematics, operations research, or other courses which attempt to provide a serious treatment of linear programming. Finally, because of its completeness, it should be useful as a reference and as a text for self-study.

At the end of each chapter there will be found a collection of problems for solution. Some of these problems emphasize numerical techniques, while others concentrate on theoretical points. Within each of these two classes, there is a considerable range of difficulty. The author considers the problems to be very important, and anyone studying this work should, at the very least, read all the problems. When linear programming problems are solved by hand, it is a good idea to use a desk calculator if at all possible, or at least a slide rule. In this way, the numbers computed will be obtained as decimals. Of course, if a large-scale digital computer is used, the answers obtained will also be in decimal form. It does not seem sound to get into the habit of solving problems by means of fractions instead of decimal numbers, since fractions become impossibly cumbersome unless the original coefficients are small integers. For this reason, most of the tableaux in the text are presented in decimal form, even though they could have been expressed more simply and accurately as fractions. When the decimal numbers given are not exact, each element in the tableaux is expressed with roughly the same relative error. The same number of decimal places does not appear in each element.

For their helpful suggestions, the author wishes to express his appreciation to Professors H. Houthakker and H. Wagner, who read an early version of the manuscript, and to Professors R. Dorfman and T. M. Whitin, who read a later version. The author is also indebted to one of his students, M. A. Simonnard, whose thesis laid the foundations for the method of development used in the initial sections of Chapter 9. Jackson E. Morris supplied most of the quotations which appear at the beginning of each chapter. The School of Industrial Management at the Massachusetts Institute of Technology generously provided secretarial assistance for typing the manuscript.

G.H.

CONTENTS

CHAPTER 1

INTRODUCTION

". . . Since a crooked figure may
Attest in little place a million;
Then let us, ciphers to this great account,
On your imaginary forces work,"

Shakespeare—Henry V.

1-1 Optimization problems. Problems which seek to maximize or minimize a numerical function of a number of variables (or functions), with the variables (functions) subject to certain constraints, form a general class which may be called *optimization problems*.

Many optimization problems were first encountered in the physical sciences and geometry. The quest for solutions led to applications of the differential calculus and to the development of the calculus of variations. These classical optimization techniques have been known for over 150 years. They have been applied with considerable success to the solution of many problems in the physical sciences and engineering. Later, the differential calculus was found to be very useful in economics, especially in developing the important results in the classical theory of production and consumption .

In the last ten or fifteen years, many new and important optimization problems have emerged in the field of economics and have received a great deal of attention. As a class, these problems may be referred to as programming problems. They are of so much interest because of their applicability to practical problems in government, military and industrial operations, as well as to problems in economic theory. In general, classical optimization techniques have been found to be of little assistance in solving these programming problems. Therefore, new methods had to be developed. In this book, we shall treat only a special but very important class of programming problems known as linear programming problems. We shall be concerned with the theory of linear programming, with numerical techniques for solving such problems, and with applications of the theory.

1-2 Programming problems. Broadly speaking, programming problems deal with determining optimal allocations of limited resources to meet given objectives; more specifically, they deal with situations where a number of resources, such as men, materials, machines, and land, are available, and are to be combined to yield one or more products. There

1

are, however, certain restrictions on all or some of the following broad categories, i.e.: on the total amount of each resource available, on the quantity of each product made, on the quality of each product. Even within these restrictions there will exist many feasible allocations. Out of all permissible allocations of resources, it is desired to find the one or ones which maximize or minimize some numerical quantity, such as profit or cost.

The actual conversion of resources to products may be a simple mixing operation, such as mixing raw stock gasolines to form various motor fuels, or a complicated production process involving many types of machines and operations. In certain cases, the resources and products can be identical. For example: We may be interested in finding the cheapest way of transporting a product from a number of origins to a number of destinations.

Linear programming deals with that class of programming problems for which all relations among the variables are linear. The relations must be linear both in the constraints and in the function to be optimized.

1–3 An example. Let us consider a shop with three types of machines, A, B, and C, which can turn out four products, 1, 2, 3, 4. Any one of the products has to undergo some operation on each of the three types of machines (lathes, drills, and milling machines, for example). We shall assume that the production is continuous, and that each product must first go on machine type A, then B, and finally C. Furthermore, we shall assume that the time required for adjusting the setup of each machine to a different operation, when production shifts from one product to another, is negligible. Table 1–1 shows: (1) the hours required on each machine type per unit of each product; (2) the total available machine hours per week; (3) the profit realized on the sale of one unit of any one of the products. It is assumed that the profit is directly proportional to the number of units sold. We wish to determine the weekly output for each product in order to maximize profits.

Examination of Table 1–1 shows that the item with the highest unit profit requires a considerable amount of time on machines A and C; the product with the second-best unit profit requires relatively little time on machine A and slightly less time on machine C than the item with the highest unit profit. The product with the lowest unit profit requires a considerable amount of time on machine B and relatively little time on C. This cursory examination indicates that the maximum profit will not be achieved by restricting production to a single article. It would seem that at least two of them should be made. It is not too obvious, however, what the optimal product mix should be.

Suppose x_j is the number of units of product j produced per week. It is of interest to find the values of x_1, x_2, x_3, x_4 which maximize the total

TABLE 1–1

DATA FOR EXAMPLE

Machine type	Products				Total time available per week
	1	2	3	4	
A	1.5	1	2.4	1	2000
B	1	5	1	3.5	8000
C	1.5	3	3.5	1	5000
Unit profit	5.24	7.30	8.34	4.18	

profit. Since the available machine time is limited, we cannot arbitrarily increase the output of any one product. Production must be allocated among products 1, 2, 3, 4 so that profits will be maximized without exceeding the maximum number of machine hours available on any one of the groups of machines.

Let us first consider the restrictions imposed by the availability of machine time. Machines of type A are in use a total of

$$1.5x_1 + x_2 + 2.4x_3 + x_4 \text{ hours per week,}$$

since 1.5 hours are required for each unit of product 1, and x_1 units of product 1 are produced; and so on for the remaining products. Also, the total time used is the sum of the times required to produce each product. The total amount of time used cannot be greater than 2000 hours. Mathematically, this means that

$$1.5x_1 + x_2 + 2.4x_3 + x_4 \leq 2000. \qquad (1\text{–}1)$$

It would not be correct to set the total hours used equal to 2000 for type A machines, since there may not be any combination of production rates that would use each of the three groups of machines to capacity. We do not wish to predict which machines will be used to capacity. Instead, we introduce a "less than or equal to" sign; the solution of the problem will indicate which machines will be used at full capacity.

For machines B and C we can write

$$x_1 + 5x_2 + x_3 + 3.5x_4 \leq 8000 \quad \text{(type } B \text{ machines)}, \qquad (1\text{–}2)$$

$$1.5x_1 + 3x_2 + 3.5x_3 + x_4 \leq 5000 \quad \text{(type } C \text{ machines)}. \qquad (1\text{–}3)$$

Since no more than the available machine time can be used, the variables x_j must satisfy the above three inequalities. Furthermore, we cannot produce negative quantities; that is, we have either a positive amount of any product or none at all. Thus the additional restrictions

$$x_1 \geq 0, \qquad x_2 \geq 0, \qquad x_3 \geq 0, \qquad x_4 \geq 0 \qquad (1\text{--}4)$$

require that the variables be non-negative.

We have now determined all the restrictions on the variables. If x_j units of product j are produced, the weekly profit z is

$$z = 5.24x_1 + 7.30x_2 + 8.34x_3 + 4.18x_4. \qquad (1\text{--}5)$$

We wish to find values of the variables which will satisfy restrictions (1–1) through (1–4) and maximize the profit (1–5).

The above example is clearly a programming problem. Moreover, it is a linear programming problem because the restrictions and the function to be maximized involve only linear relations among the variables.

In practice, it may not be true that the profit derived from the sale of any one product is directly proportional to the number of units sold. More generally, the profit will be some function of the quantities produced, i.e.,

$$z = f(x_1, x_2, x_3, x_4).$$

If this function is not of the form (1–5), we have a nonlinear rather than a linear programming problem. For example, if the profit function were of the form
$$z = 5.24x_1^{1/2} + 7.30x_2^{1/2} + 8.34x_3^{1/2} + 4.15x_4^{1/2}, \qquad (1\text{--}6)$$

then the determination of the variables which satisfy the constraints (1–1) through (1–4) and maximize Eq. (1–6) would be a special case of a nonlinear programming problem.

1–4 Linear programming. The preceding example illustrated how a linear programming problem and a particular case of a nonlinear programming problem can arise in practice. Linear programming is concerned with solving a very special type of problem—one in which all relations among the variables are linear both in the constraints and the function to be optimized. The general linear programming problem can be described as follows: *Given a set of m linear inequalities or equations in r variables, we wish to find non-negative values of these variables which will satisfy the constraints and maximize or minimize some linear function of the variables.*

Mathematically, this statement means: We have m inequalities or equations in r variables (m can be greater than, less than, or equal to r) of the form:

$$a_{i1}x_1 + a_{i2}x_2 + \cdots + a_{ir}x_r\{\geq, =, \leq\}b_i, \qquad i = 1, \ldots, m, \quad (1\text{--}7)$$

where for each constraint one and only one of the signs $\leq$, $=$, $\geq$ holds, but the sign may vary from one constraint to another. We seek values of the variables x_j satisfying (1–7) and

$$x_j \geq 0, \qquad j = 1, \ldots, r, \tag{1–8}$$

which maximize or minimize a linear function

$$z = c_1 x_1 + \cdots + c_r x_r. \tag{1–9}$$

The a_{ij}, b_i, c_j are assumed to be known constants.

We have thus formulated the general linear programming problem which, in mathematical terms, can be represented by (1–7) through (1–9). A programming problem is linear if, in the constraints and function to be optimized, the variables appear only as linear forms. A linear form involving n variables x_j is an expression of the type $a_1 x_1 + \cdots + a_n x_n + b$, where the a_j and b are constants. It is very important to see what the assumption of linearity implies. Intuitively, linearity implies that products of the variables, such as $x_1 x_2$, powers of variables, such as x_3^2, and combinations of variables, such as $a_1 x_1 + a_2 \log x_2$, cannot be allowed.

In more general terms, linearity can be characterized by certain additive and multiplicative properties. In the context of the above example, additivity means: If we use t_1 hours on machine A to make product 1, and t_2 hours to make product 2, the time on machine A devoted to products 1 and 2 is $t_1 + t_2$. In this case, the additivity property seems quite reasonable if the time required to convert from product 1 to 2 is negligible. However, not all physical processes behave in this way. If we mix several liquids of different chemical composition, it is, in general, not true that the total volume of the mixture is the sum of the volumes of the individual constituents. This is an example of a case where additivity may not hold.

The multiplicative property requires: (1) If it takes one hour to make a single item on a given machine, it takes ten hours to make ten parts; this also seems quite reasonable. (2) The total profit from selling a given number of units of a product is the unit profit times the number of units sold; this is not always true. In general, the profit is not directly proportional to the number of units sold even if the selling price is constant, since manufacturing costs per unit may vary with the number of units made. Thus the linearity implied in a linear programming problem is not always expected to be an absolutely accurate representation of the real world. Fortunately, the assumed linearity is often a close enough approximation of actual conditions so that it can provide very useful answers.

One other important restriction is inherent in a linear programming problem: It is assumed that the variables x_j can take on any values allowed by the restrictions (1–7) and (1–8); in other words, we cannot, for example, require that the variables assume only integral values. If the additional restriction is imposed that the variables must be integers, then, in general, we do not have any longer a linear programming problem. Actual situations often require that the variables be integers; such problems are frequently solved by linear programming, and the answers are rounded off to the nearest integers which satisfy the constraints. This may or may not be a valid approximation. In general, the approximation is good if the solution requires that a large number of units of each variable be used. Since, in the example discussed in Section 1–3, the production is assumed to be continuous, it is not necessary that the optimal x_j be integers. Of course, in practice no attempt would be made to schedule weekly production down to a fraction of a unit.

The assumption that the variables can vary continuously goes somewhat deeper than indicated in the previous paragraph. Fundamentally, everything in the real world comes in discrete units, and nothing is infinitely divisible. However, the basic building blocks (molecules, photons, etc.) are often so small in comparison with the quantities under consideration that for all practical purposes (i.e., to ten or fifteen decimal places), it can be assumed that the physical quantity is continuously variable. The real difficulty appears when the discrete units are not small in comparison with the magnitudes of the variables. In situations of this kind, one must be concerned about the discreteness of the variables.

The function to be optimized, (1–9), is called the *objective function*. Note that no constant term appears in the objective function, i.e., we do not write $z = \sum_{j=1}^{r} c_j x_j + c$. The reason for this is simple. The values of the x_j which optimize z are completely independent of any additive constant c. Hence, if there is such a constant, it can be ignored during the process of determining the best x_j, and added to z after the problem has been solved.

Mathematically, the constraints (1–8) which require that the variables x_j be non-negative do not differ from the constraints (1–7). However, when solving a linear programming problem, the non-negativity constraints are handled differently from the other constraints. For this reason, we shall refer to the non-negativity constraints as *non-negativity restrictions*, while the term *constraint* will be used to denote constraints other than the non-negativity restrictions. Thus when we say that there are m constraints on the problem, we mean that there are m constraints of the form (1–7). Then in addition, there are the non-negativity restrictions. This terminology will save some confusion later.

Any set of x_j which satisfies the constraints (1–7) will be called a *solution* to the linear programming problem. Any solution which satisfies the non-negativity restrictions is called a *feasible solution*. Any feasible solution which optimizes the objective function is called an *optimal feasible solution*. The task of solving a linear programming problem consists in finding an optimal feasible solution. Normally, there will be an infinite number of feasible solutions to a linear programming problem. Out of all these solutions, we must find one which optimizes the objective function.

1-5 The transportation problem; another example. In practice, linear programming has been of particular significance in its application to so-called transportation problems. To provide the reader with a little more feeling for the nature of linear programming, we shall discuss these briefly. Later two chapters will be devoted to solving transportation problems.

A typical transportation problem can be described as follows: Given amounts of a uniform product are available at each of a number of different origins (e.g., warehouses). We wish to send specified amounts of the product to each of a number of different destinations (e.g., retail outlets). The cost of shipping one unit amount from any one origin to any one destination is known. Assuming that it is possible to ship from any one warehouse to any one retail outlet, we are interested in determining the minimum-cost routing from the warehouses to the retail outlets.

We shall suppose that there are m origins and n outlets. Take x_{ij} to be the number of units shipped from origin i to destination j. Note that here it is convenient to use a double subscript since it simplifies the notation. For a given i (warehouse), there are n possible j-values (retail outlets to which units can be shipped). Hence we have a total of mn different x_{ij}. Since negative amounts cannot be shipped, we must have $x_{ij} \geq 0$ for all i, j.

Let a_i be the number of units of the product available at origin i and b_j the number of units required at destination j. We cannot ship more goods from any one origin than are available at that origin. Hence summing over all destinations, we have

$$\sum_{j=1}^{n} x_{ij} = x_{i1} + x_{i2} + \cdots + x_{in} \leq a_i, \qquad i = 1, \ldots, m. \quad (1\text{-}10)$$

There are m such constraints, one for each origin. We must supply each destination with the number of units desired; thus

$$\sum_{i=1}^{m} x_{ij} = x_{1j} + \cdots + x_{mj} = b_j, \qquad j = 1, \ldots, n. \quad (1\text{-}11)$$

The total amount received at any destination is the sum over the amounts received from each origin. The needs of the outlets can be satisfied if and only if

$$\sum_{i=1}^{m} a_i \geq \sum_{j=1}^{n} b_j. \quad (1\text{-}12)$$

We assume that this is the case.

If c_{ij} is the cost of shipping one unit from origin i to destination j, then the total cost of shipment is

$$z = \sum_{j=1}^{n} \sum_{i=1}^{m} c_{ij} x_{ij}$$
$$= (c_{11}x_{11} + c_{12}x_{12} + \cdots + c_{1n}x_{1n}) + (c_{21}x_{21} + \cdots + c_{2n}x_{2n})$$
$$+ \cdots + (c_{m1}x_{m1} + \cdots + c_{mn}x_{mn}). \tag{1–13}$$

The first term on the right of (1–13) is the cost of shipping from origin 1, the second the cost of shipping from origin 2, etc. We wish to find $x_{ij} \geq 0$ which satisfy the constraints (1–10), (1–11) and minimize (1–13).

We can now summarize the transportation problem as follows: Find $x_{ij} \geq 0$ which minimize

$$z = \sum_{j=1}^{n} \sum_{i=1}^{m} c_{ij} x_{ij}, \tag{1–14}$$

subject to

$$\sum_{j=1}^{n} x_{ij} \leq a_i, \qquad i = 1, \ldots, m,$$
$$\sum_{i=1}^{m} x_{ij} = b_j, \qquad j = 1, \ldots, n. \tag{1–15}$$

This is a linear programming problem in mn variables with $m + n$ constraints.

It will be observed that the constraints in the transportation problem have a particularly simple form. All the nonzero coefficients of the x_{ij} are ones. Furthermore, any given x_{ij} appears in two and only two of the constraints. Because of these special properties of the constraints, a transportation problem can be solved much more easily than a general linear programming problem of equivalent size. Historically, this simplification made it possible to solve transportation problems before it was possible to solve general linear programming problems. At this point, it is also worth mentioning that many practical problems which have nothing to do with transportation can be formulated as transportation problems.

1–6 Simple graphical examples. Linear programming problems which involve only two variables can be solved graphically. We shall illustrate the procedure by several examples. The geometrical interpretation of linear programming problems is very important, and we shall use it quite often in later work. An examination of the sorts of things which can occur in the simple cases involving only two variables provides a great deal of insight into what can happen in the more general case with any number of variables.

To begin let us find a geometric interpretation and solution for the following linear programming problem:*

$$3x_1 + 5x_2 \leq 15,$$

$$5x_1 + 2x_2 \leq 10,$$

$$x_1, x_2 \geq 0,$$

$$\max z = 5x_1 + 3x_2.$$

(1–16)

First, we shall find the sets of numbers (x_1, x_2) which are feasible solutions to the problem. We introduce an x_1x_2-coordinate system and note that any set of numbers (x_1, x_2) is a point in the x_1x_2-plane. All points (x_1, x_2) lying on or to the right of the x_2-axis have $x_1 \geq 0$. Similarly, all points lying on or above the x_1-axis have $x_2 \geq 0$. It follows that any point lying in the first quadrant has $x_1, x_2 \geq 0$ and hence satisfies the non-negativity restrictions. Any point which is a feasible solution must lie in the first quadrant.

To find the set of points in the first quadrant satisfying the constraints, we must interpret geometrically inequalities such as $3x_1 + 5x_2 \leq 15$. If the equal sign holds, that is $3x_1 + 5x_2 = 15$, we have the equation for

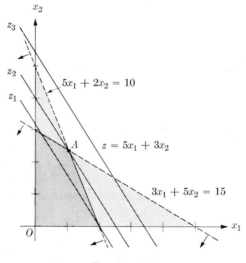

FIGURE 1–1

* To avoid monotonous repetition of the same group of words, we shall frequently represent linear programming problems in the abbreviated form (1–16); Eq. (1–16) should be read as follows: Find non-negative values of the variables x_1, x_2 which satisfy the constraints $3x_1 + 5x_2 \leq 15$, $5x_1 + 2x_2 \leq 10$, and which maximize the linear form $z = 5x_1 + 3x_2$.

a straight line, and any point on the straight line satisfies the equation. Now consider the point $(0, 0)$, i.e., the origin. We observe that $3(0) + 5(0) = 0 < 15$, so that the origin also satisfies the inequality. In fact, any point lying on or below the line $3x_1 + 5x_2 = 15$ satisfies $3x_1 + 5x_2 \leq 15$. However, no point lying above the line satisfies the inequality. Therefore, the set of points satisfying the inequality $3x_1 + 5x_2 \leq 15$ consists of all the points in the x_1x_2-plane lying on or below the line $3x_1 + 5x_2 = 15$. The points which satisfy the non-negativity restrictions and this inequality are all the points in the first quadrant lying on or below the line $3x_1 + 5x_2 = 15$. In precisely the same way, we see that all points satisfying $5x_1 + 2x_2 \leq 10$ and the non-negativity restrictions are all the points in the first quadrant lying on or below the line

$$5x_1 + 2x_2 = 10.$$

The set of points satisfying both $3x_1 + 5x_2 \leq 15$ and $5x_1 + 2x_2 \leq 10$, as well as the non-negativity restrictions, is the set of points in the darkly shaded region of Fig. 1–1. Any point in this region is a feasible solution, and only the points in this region are feasible solutions.

As yet we have said nothing about the objective function. To solve the linear programming problem, we must find the point or points in the region of feasible solutions which give the largest value of the objective function. Now for any fixed value of z, $z = 5x_1 + 3x_2$ is a straight line. Any point on this line will give the same value of z. For each different value of z, we obtain a different line. It is important to note that all the lines corresponding to different values of z are parallel. This follows because the slope of any line $z = c_1x_1 + c_2x_2$ is $-c_1/c_2$ and is independent of z. In our problem c_1, c_2 are fixed and the lines are parallel.

We should now be able to see how to solve the problem. We wish to find the line with the largest value of z which has at least one point in common with the region of feasible solutions. The parallel lines in Fig. 1–1 represent the objective function for three different values of z. It is clear that z_1 is not the maximum value of z because the line can be moved up, thus increasing z, while some of its points are still in the region of feasible solutions. On the other hand, although $z_3 > z_2$ and z_1, the line corresponding to z_3 has no point in common with the region of feasible solutions; hence no feasible solution can yield as large a value of z. Thus we see that z_2 is the maximum value of z, and the feasible solution which yields this value of z is the corner A of the region of feasible solutions.

The figure shows that the values of the variables for the optimal solution are approximately $x_1 = 1$, $x_2 = 2.4$. To find the exact values, we note that the point representing the optimal solution is the intersection of the lines $3x_1 + 5x_2 = 15$ and $5x_1 + 2x_2 = 10$. Solving these two equations

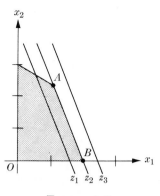

FIGURE 1–2

simultaneously, we find that $x_1 = 1.053$, $x_2 = 2.368$. Substitution of these values into the objective function shows that the maximum value of z is 12.37.

Now let us consider the problem:

$$3x_1 + 5x_2 \leq 15,$$

$$5x_1 + 2x_2 \leq 10,$$

$$x_1,\, x_2 \geq 0,$$

$$\max z = 2.5x_1 + x_2.$$

(1–17)

This problem is the same as the one just solved except for a slightly different objective function. The region of feasible solutions is the same as for the previous problem. Figure 1–2 shows the objective-function lines of (1–17) for three different values of z.

Clearly, z_2 is the maximum value of z. Now, however, the line representing the objective function lies along one edge of the polygon of feasible solutions. This means that there are no unique values of x_1, x_2 which maximize z; any point on the edge AB of the polygon gives the optimal value of z. The maximum value of z is unique, but there are an infinite number of feasible solutions which yield this value of z. Note that the corner which was optimal for the previous problem is also optimal for the present problem. Using these values of x_1, x_2, we find that max $z = 5.0$. For this problem, two corners, as well as any point on the line joining these two corners, are optimal solutions. When a linear programming problem has more than one optimal solution, we say that there are alternative optima; physically, this means that the resources can be combined in more than one way to maximize profit.

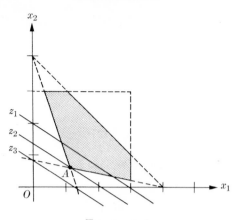

FIGURE 1–3

As an example of a problem for which the objective function is to be minimized consider:

$$x_1 + x_2 \leq 4,$$

$$6x_1 + 2x_2 \geq 8,$$

$$x_1 + 5x_2 \geq 4,$$

$$x_1 \leq 3, \qquad \qquad (1\text{–}18)$$

$$x_2 \leq 3,$$

$$x_1,\ x_2 \geq 0,$$

$$\min z = 2x_1 + 3x_2.$$

The geometrical interpretation of the problem is given in Fig. 1–3.

The minimum value of z is z_2. This minimum is found at a unique point, the point of intersection A of the lines $6x_1 + 2x_2 = 8$ and $x_1 + 5x_2 = 4$. Solving these two equations simultaneously, we see that the optimal solution is $x_1 = 8/7$, $x_2 = 4/7$, and min $z = 4$.

Linear programming problems involving three variables can also be presented geometrically; however, their graphical solution is more difficult. As an illustration, we shall graphically solve the following problem in three variables:

$$4x_1 + 6x_2 + 3x_3 \leq 24,$$

$$x_1 + 1.5x_2 + 3x_3 \leq 12,$$

$$3x_1 + x_2 \leq 12, \qquad \qquad (1\text{–}19)$$

$$x_1,\ x_2,\ x_3 \geq 0,$$

$$\max z = 0.5x_1 + 6x_2 + 5x_3.$$

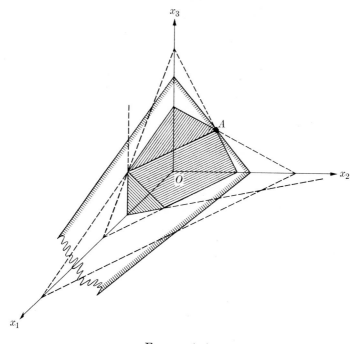

FIGURE 1–4

The region representing the feasible solutions is the shaded polyhedron in Fig. 1–4. We recall that an equation in three variables, such as $4x_1 + 6x_2 + 3x_3 = 24$, is a plane. When the equality sign is replaced by an inequality ($<$), the set of points satisfying this inequality is the collection of all points lying either above or below the plane. The set of points (x_1, x_2, x_3) which, when substituted into the objective function, yields a given value of z lies on the plane $z = 0.5x_1 + 6x_2 + 5x_3$. As z is varied, a series of parallel planes is obtained. The plane representing the largest value of z which has at least one point in common which the region of feasible solutions gives max z. The point or points from the region of feasible solutions which lie on this plane are the optimal solutions.

It is seen that the optimal solution occurs at corner A of the polyhedron of feasible solutions. At this point, the planes $4x_1 + 6x_2 + 3x_3 = 24$ and $x_1 + 1.5x_2 + 3x_3 = 12$ intersect. However, $x_1 = 0$ at A. Thus, by simultaneous solution of $6x_2 + 3x_3 = 24$ and $1.5x_2 + 3x_3 = 12$, x_2 and x_3 are found to be $x_2 = x_3 = 2\frac{2}{3}$; the optimal solution is $x_1 = 0$, $x_2 = x_3 = 2\frac{2}{3}$, and max $z = 29\frac{1}{3}$.

1–7 Some exceptional cases. The examples of the preceding section illustrate what may be called "properly behaved" linear programming

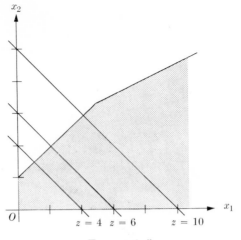

FIGURE 1-5

problems. Now we wish to show that there are certain exceptional cases which must be taken into consideration if a general technique for solving linear programming problems is to be developed.

Let us study the following problem:

$$x_1 - x_2 \geq -1,$$

$$-0.5x_1 + x_2 \leq 2,$$

$$x_1, x_2 \geq 0,$$

$$\max z = 2x_1 + 2x_2.$$

(1-20)

The region of feasible solutions is the shaded area of Fig. 1-5. Lines representing the objective function for several values of z are also drawn. Clearly, we have encountered a new phenomenon. The line representing the objective function can be moved forever parallel to itself in the direction of increasing z, and still have some points in the region of feasible solutions. Hence z can be made arbitrarily large, and the problem has no finite maximum value of z. In such a case we say that the problem has an unbounded solution.

We do not expect any linear programming problem representing some practical situation to have an unbounded solution, since this would imply, for example, the feasibility of an infinite profit. However, the limitation of resources and the impossibility of making arbitrarily large profits are precisely the reasons for our interest in using linear programming. Nonetheless, it occasionally happens that a mistake in the formula-

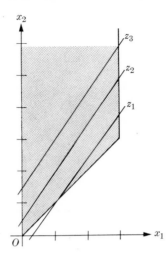

FIGURE 1-6

tion of an actual problem leads to an unbounded solution (the author has made such an error).

In the above example, both variables can be made arbitrarily large as z is increased. However, an unbounded solution does not necessarily imply that all the variables can be made arbitrarily large as z approaches infinity. This can be seen by solving the problem:

$$x_1 \leq 3,$$
$$x_1 - x_2 \leq 0,$$
$$x_1, x_2 \geq 0,$$
$$\max z = -3x_1 + 2x_2.$$

(1-21)

This problem is presented graphically in Fig. 1-6.

We have already noted that the set of variables which maximizes the objective function does not need to be unique. Now it may turn out that, although z has a finite maximum value, there are solutions giving this maximum z which have arbitrarily large values of the variables. This is illustrated by the following example:

$$x_1 - x_2 \geq -1,$$
$$-0.5x_1 + x_2 \leq 2,$$
$$x_1, x_2 \geq 0,$$
$$\max z = 2x_2 - x_1,$$

(1-22)

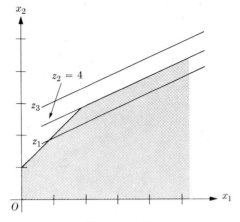

FIGURE 1-7

which is solved graphically in Fig. 1-7. This problem is not completely normal since there are solutions with arbitrarily large variables which yield the optimal value of z. The maximum value of z is 4. Furthermore, any point (x_1, x_2) lying on the edge of the region of feasible solutions, which extends to infinity, yields $z = 4$ and is therefore an optimal solution.

Thus far, every example has had a feasible solution. However, there is no automatic guarantee that all linear programming problems have feasible solutions. The next problem, shown graphically in Fig. 1-8, has no solution because the constraints are inconsistent:

$$x_1 + x_2 \leq 1,$$
$$2x_1 + 2x_2 \geq 4,$$
$$x_1, x_2 \geq 0,$$
$$\max z = 3x_1 - 2x_2.$$

$$(1-23)$$

There is no point (x_1, x_2) which satisfies both constraints.

The constraints can be consistent, and yet there may be no feasible solution because no point satisfying the constraints also satisfies the non-negativity restrictions. The following problem, illustrated geometrically in Fig. 1-9, gives an example of such a case:

$$x_1 - x_2 \geq 0,$$
$$3x_1 - x_2 \leq -3,$$
$$x_1, x_2 \geq 0,$$
$$\max z = x_1 + x_2.$$

$$(1-24)$$

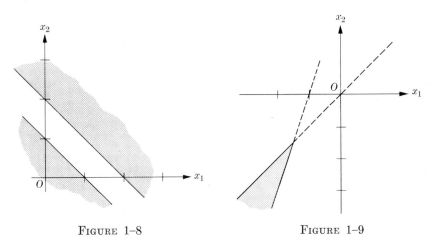

FIGURE 1–8   FIGURE 1–9

Any point in the shaded area satisfies the inequality constraints. However, since no solution has x_1, $x_2 \geq 0$, there is no feasible solution.

The reader should not feel that the examples presented in this section are of hypothetical interest only and never occur in the real world. While it is true that we do not expect any properly formulated practical problem to exhibit such behavior, it is equally true that a problem involving a large number of variables and constraints makes it extremely difficult to be sure that the constraints are indeed consistent, that there is a feasible solution, and that there is no unbounded solution. Because of this possibility of making mistakes in the formulation of problems, the exceptional cases discussed in this section can occur in practice. Hence the computational technique devised for solving a linear programming problem should be general enough to reveal the existence of an unbounded solution or the absence of a feasible solution. It would be most unfortunate if we had to ascertain that the problem actually possessed a finite maximum or minimum before we could proceed with the computation.

There is one other exceptional case, i.e., the problem with a single solution. However, it never presents any difficulty in practice because the possibility of its existence is evident as soon as the problem has been formulated. It can occur only if the number of equations in the constraints is at least equal to the number of variables. If the solution is feasible, it is optimal. If it is not feasible, the problem has no solution. A problem of this kind is of no interest as an optimization problem because there is no freedom; i.e., since there is only a single solution, there is nothing to be maximized or minimized.

1–8 The simplex method. Let us summarize some of the properties of the linear programming problems which were solved graphically in the preceding sections. Whenever feasible solutions existed, the region of feasible solutions had what in geometry is called the convexity property. This geometrical term means that the regions had no holes in them, i.e., they were solid, and there were no indentations in the boundary. The fact that a region is convex can be expressed simply by saying that the line joining any two points in the region also lies in the region. Furthermore, the boundaries of the regions were lines or planes. Finally, there were corners on the boundary, and there were edges joining the various corners.

In addition, it was seen that for any fixed value of z, the objective function could be represented by a line or a plane. We found the interesting result that whenever the maximum or minimum value of z was finite, at least one corner of the region of feasible solutions was an optimal solution. If the optimal solution was not unique, there were points other than corners that were optimal, but in any event at least one corner was optimal. The situation was different when the objective function could be made arbitrarily large. In this case, of course, no corner was optimal. As a matter of terminology unbounded solutions will not be called optimal. The term "optimal solution" will be taken to imply that the maximum or minimum value of z is finite.

Interestingly enough, these observations, which were derived from simple graphical examples, hold true for the general linear programming problem if we think of it as being represented geometrically in an r-dimensional space. The region of feasible solutions is a convex region, or convex set. It also has corners, or extreme points, as they are called in the more general case. In addition, if there is an optimal solution, at least one of the extreme points will be optimal.

The reader familiar with the methods of differential calculus and, in particular, with Lagrange multipliers, will probably feel that this technique can be applied to solve any linear programming problem. Unfortunately, this is not true. The difficulty stems from the fact that the optimal solutions lie on the boundary of the region of feasible solutions and, worse yet, at corners of the boundary. It may be recalled that the methods of differential calculus determine relative maxima and minima; they are of considerably less value when absolute maxima and minima are to be obtained. A discussion of the reasons for this failure of the classical methods would take us too far afield. In fact, if an optimal solution exists, the differential calculus does tell us that one of the extreme points is optimal. Unfortunately, it does not specify which extreme point is optimal.

Hence the idea of using the differential calculus to solve linear programming problems has to be discarded, and we must concentrate our efforts on developing a procedure which will exploit the special features of linear programming problems. No method has been found which will yield an optimal solution to a linear programming problem in a single step. It is really not surprising that all the techniques for solving such problems are iterative: If there are numerous constraints, it can be extremely difficult to find any feasible solution, not to mention an optimal solution. (The reader familiar with numerical analysis may recall that some of the most efficient techniques for solving sets of simultaneous linear equations are iterative.) The best-known and most widely used procedure for solving linear programming problems is called the simplex method, which was developed by George Dantzig in 1947. The term "simplex" has nothing to do with the method as it is now used; it had its origin in a special problem that was studied in the early development of the method.

The simplex method is an algebraic iterative procedure which will solve exactly (it is not an approximation method) any linear programming problem in a finite number of steps, or give an indication that there is an unbounded solution. The simplex method can be given a very simple geometrical interpretation in terms of the concepts that we have already introduced. We have stated above that if there is an optimal solution, one of the extreme points is optimal. There is only a finite number of extreme points. The simplex method is a procedure for moving step by step from a given extreme point to an optimal extreme point. At each step, it is possible to move only to what intuitively are adjacent extreme points. The simplex method moves along an "edge" of the region of feasible solutions from one extreme point to an adjacent one. Of all the adjacent extreme points, the one chosen is that which gives the greatest increase (or greatest decrease) in the objective function (in practice, for computational reasons, one usually does not determine the extreme point which gives the greatest change in the objective function; instead one bases the selection on a simpler criterion which is almost as good). At each extreme point, the simplex method tells us whether that extreme point is optimal, and if not, what the next extreme point will be. If at any stage the simplex method comes to an extreme point which has an edge leading to infinity, and if the objective function can be increased (or decreased) by moving along that edge, the simplex method informs us that there is an unbounded solution.

It was indicated above that the simplex method starts with a given extreme point. The question arises how to find an initial extreme point. In the examples of the previous two sections, it will be noted that the origin was often an extreme point of the region of feasible solution. If the origin is a feasible solution, it will be an extreme point because all variables are non-negative. Hence if $x_j = 0, j = 1, \ldots, r$, satisfies the constraints, we have immediately an initial extreme-point solution. However, as the minimization problem of Section 1–6 has illustrated, it is not necessarily true that the origin is an extreme point. In such a case, it is still possible to find an extreme point, but it involves considerably more work, as we shall see later.

1–9 Brief historical sketch. Programming problems first arose in economics, where the optimal allocation of resources has long been of interest to economists. More specifically, however, programming problems seem to be a direct outgrowth of the work done by a number of individuals in the 1930's. One outstanding theoretical model developed then was Von Neumann's linear model of an expanding economy [7],* which was part of the efforts of a number of Austrian and German economists and mathematicians who were studying generalizations of Walrasian equilibrium models of an economy [8]. A more practical approach was made by Leontief, who developed input-output models of the economy [5]. His work was concerned with determining how much various industries would have to produce to meet a specified bill of consumer demands. Input-output models did not actually involve any optimization; instead they required the solution of a system of simultaneous linear equations.

During World War II, a group under the direction of Marshall K. Wood worked on allocation problems for the United States Air Force. Generalizations of Leontief-type models were developed to allocate resources in such a way as to maximize or minimize some linear objective function. George B. Dantzig was a member of the Air Force group; he formulated the general linear programming problem and devised the simplex method of solution in 1947. His work was not generally available until 1951, when the Cowles Commission Monograph No. 13 was published [4].

After 1951, progress in the theoretical development and in practical applications of linear programming was rapid. Important theoretical contributions were made by David Gale, H. W. Kuhn, and A. W. Tucker, who had a major share in developing the theory of duality in linear programming. A. Charnes, who also did some important theoretical work, and W. W. Cooper took the lead in encouraging industrial applications of linear programming.

Problems of the linear-programming type had been formulated and solved before the pioneering work of Dantzig. In 1941 Hitchcock formulated and solved the transportation problem [1], which was independently solved by Koopmans in 1947 [3]. In 1942, Kantorovitch (Russian) also formulated the transportation problem [2], but did not solve it. The economist Stigler worked out a minimum-cost diet in 1945 [6]. Although this problem can be formulated as a linear programming problem, Stigler did not use this technique. It was not until Dantzig's work, however,

---

* Numbers in brackets refer to bibliographical references.

that the general linear programming problem was formulated as such, and a method devised for solving it.

1–10 The road ahead. The material in this book assumes that the reader has some familiarity with the theory of vector spaces, matrices, and convex sets. Chapter 2 summarizes the material needed. No attempt is made, however, to provide a rigorous or complete development. The reader who has had no previous acquaintance with linear algebra may find it desirable to study simultaneously a more complete development of the material. The author's companion volume, entitled *Linear Algebra*, was written for this purpose and is suggested as collateral reading.

Chapter 3 begins the formal development of linear programming and presents the fundamental results needed in the derivation of the simplex method. Chapters 4 and 5 consider the computational details of the simplex method and the geometrical interpretation in the so-called solutions and requirements space. The problem of degeneracy is studied in Chapter 6, where the perturbation technique and the generalized simplex method for resolving the theoretical problems associated with degeneracy are discussed. The revised simplex method is presented in Chapter 7. Chapter 8 considers duality and presents two additional techniques for solving linear programming problems, the dual simplex method and the primal-dual algorithm. The properties of transportation problems are investigated in Chapter 9. These properties allow the development of two special procedures for solving transportation problems, which are also presented in this chapter. Chapter 10 discusses network-flow problems and develops the efficient network-flow techniques for solving transportation problems. A number of miscellaneous topics, such as parametric programming and upper bounds, are covered in Chapter 11. Chapters 12 and 13 discuss applications of linear programming. Applications to industrial problems are considered in Chapter 12, and applications to economics in Chapter 13.

REFERENCES

1. F. L. HITCHCOCK, "The Distribution of a Product from Several Sources to Numerous Localities," *Journal Math. and Phys.*, **20**, 224–230, 1941.

2. L. KANTOROVITCH, "On the Translocation of Masses," *Comptes rendus (Doklady) de l'académie des sciences de l'USSR*, **37** No. 7–8, 199–201, 1942. English translation in: *Management Science*, **5**, 1, 1–4, 1958.

3. T. C. KOOPMANS, "Optimum Utilization of the Transportation System," *Proc. Int. Stat. Conf., 1947*, Washington, D.C., Vol. 5 (Vol. 5 reprinted as supplement to *Econometrica*, Vol. 17, 1949).

4. T. C. KOOPMANS, Ed., *Activity Analysis of Production and Allocation*. New York: Wiley, 1951.

5. W. W. Leontief, *The Structure of the American Economy, 1919–1939*, 2d ed. New York: Oxford, 1951.

6. G. J. Stigler, "The Cost of Subsistence," *Journal of Farm Econ.*, **27,** 303–314, 1945.

7. J. von Neumann, "Über ein ökonomisches Gleichungssystem und eine Verallgemeinerung des Brouwerschen Fixpunktsatzes," *Ergebnisse eines Mathematischen Kolloquiums*, **8,** 73–83 (1935–1936); English translation, "A Model of General Economic Equilibrium," *Rev. of Econ. Studies*, **13** (1), 1–9 (1945–1946).

8 L. Walras, *Elements of Pure Economics* (William Joffé transl.). London: Allen & Unwin, 1954.

Problems

Solve the linear programming problems 1–1 through 1–12 graphically and shade in the region representing the feasible solutions. Hint: By testing one point not on the line, it is always easy to determine which side of a line $a_1x_1 + a_2x_2 = b$ corresponds to $a_1x_1 + a_2x_2 \geq b$ (or $\leq b$). The origin is often a good point to test.

1–1.
$$2x_1 + 3x_2 \leq 6,$$
$$x_1 + 4x_2 \leq 4,$$
$$x_1,\ x_2 \geq 0,$$
$$\max z = x_1 + 1.5x_2.$$

1–2.
$$5x_1 + 10x_2 \leq 50,$$
$$x_1 + x_2 \geq 1,$$
$$x_2 \leq 4,$$
$$x_1,\ x_2 \geq 0,$$
$$\max z = x_1 + x_2.$$

1–3.
$$5x_1 + 10x_2 \leq 50,$$
$$x_1 + x_2 \geq 1,$$
$$x_2 \leq 4,$$
$$x_1,\ x_2 \geq 0,$$
$$\min z = 2x_1 + x_2.$$

1–4.
$$x_1 - x_2 \geq 0,$$
$$-0.5x_1 + x_2 \leq 1,$$
$$x_1,\ x_2 \geq 0,$$
$$\max z = x_2 - 0.75x_1.$$

1–5.
$$x_1 + 3x_2 \geq 3,$$
$$x_1 + x_2 \geq 2,$$
$$x_1,\ x_2 \geq 0,$$
$$\min z = 1.5x_1 + 2.5x_2.$$

1–6.
$$x_1 + x_2 \geq 1,$$
$$x_2 \leq 5,$$
$$x_1 \leq 6,$$
$$7x_1 + 9x_2 \leq 63,$$
$$x_1,\ x_2 \geq 0,$$
$$\max z = 10x_1 + 6.2x_2.$$

1–7.
$$2x_1 + x_2 \geq 1,$$
$$3x_1 + 4x_2 \geq 1.5,$$
$$x_1,\ x_2 \geq 0,$$
$$\min z = 6x_1 + 4x_2.$$

1–8.
$$x_1 - x_2 \geq 0,$$
$$x_1 - 5x_2 \geq -5,$$
$$x_1,\ x_2 \geq 0,$$
$$\min z = 2x_1 - 10x_2.$$

1–9.
$$x_1 + x_2 \leq 2,$$
$$-x_1 - 5x_2 \leq -10,$$
$$x_1,\ x_2 \geq 0,$$
$$\max z = -5x_2.$$

1–10.
$$x_1 - 0.5x_2 \geq 0,$$
$$x_1 - 5x_2 \geq -5,$$
$$x_1,\ x_2 \geq 0,$$
$$\min z = x_1 - 10x_2.$$

1-11.
$$x_1 + x_2 \leq 1,$$
$$-0.5x_1 - 5x_2 \leq -10,$$
$$x_1, x_2 \geq 0,$$
$$\max z = -5x_2.$$

1-12.
$$x_1 + x_2 \geq 1,$$
$$x_2 - 5x_1 \leq 0,$$
$$5x_2 - x_1 \geq 0,$$
$$x_1 - x_2 \geq -1,$$
$$x_1 + x_2 \leq 6,$$
$$x_1 \leq 3,$$
$$x_1, x_2 \geq 0,$$
$$\max z = 3x_1 + 2x_2.$$

1-13. Examine carefully the following pairs of problems: (a) 1-1 and 1-7; (b) 1-8 and 1-9; (c) 1-10 and 1-11. How are the solutions related? Each pair of problems forms what is called a set of dual problems. Note that both dual problems involve the same constants, but in rearranged order.

CHAPTER 2

MATHEMATICAL BACKGROUND

"What's the good of Mercator's
North Poles and Equators,
Tropics, Zones and Meridian Lines?"
So the Bellman would cry:
And the crew would reply
"They are merely conventional signs!"

Lewis Carroll, The Hunting of the Snark, Fit II.

2–1 Matrices. Our later discussions may be considerably simplified by the use of some elementary topics from the theory of linear algebra. Here we shall briefly present the material from linear algebra which will be needed. No attempt at a rigorous development will be made.*

MATRIX: *A matrix is defined to be a rectangular array of numbers and is written as follows:*

$$\mathbf{A} = \|a_{ij}\| = \begin{bmatrix} a_{11} & a_{12} \cdots a_{1n} \\ a_{21} & a_{22} \cdots a_{2n} \\ \vdots & \quad \vdots \\ a_{m1} & a_{m2} \cdots a_{mn} \end{bmatrix}. \tag{2-1}$$

The above array is called an m by n-matrix (written $m \times n$). Brackets [ ], parentheses ( ), or the form $\| \ \|$ is used to enclose the rectangular array of numbers. A matrix has no numerical value; it is simply a convenient way of representing arrays (tables) of numbers. The numbers in the array are called the elements of the matrix. A double subscript is used to denote the location of any given element. The first subscript gives the row and the second subscript the column in which the element is located. Thus a_{ij} is the element in row i and column j.

Matrices will usually be denoted by upper-case boldface roman letters ($\mathbf{A}$, $\mathbf{B}$, etc.), and elements by italicized lower-case letters (a_{ij}, b_{ij}, etc.), unless specific numbers are used. Note that in (2–1), the expressions $\mathbf{A}$ and $\|a_{ij}\|$ do not indicate how many rows or columns the matrix has. When only the typical element a_{ij} of the matrix is shown, we use $\|a_{ij}\|$ rather than (a_{ij}) or $[a_{ij}]$.

---

* The background material needed is developed in detail in the author's text *Linear Algebra*. References to sections in that work will be given in abbreviated form; for example, {LA 6–3} means Section 3 of Chapter 6.

We shall adopt the convention that brackets will be used to enclose matrices having at least two rows and two columns. Parentheses will be used to enclose a matrix of a single row. To simplify the printing in the text of matrices having a single column, they will be printed as a row and will be enclosed by brackets. In equations and in examples a matrix of a single column will sometimes be printed as a column for added clarity.

Any matrix which has the same number of rows as columns is called a square matrix. A square matrix with n rows and n columns is called an nth-order matrix.

Two matrices $\mathbf{A}$, $\mathbf{B}$ *are equal, written* $\mathbf{A} = \mathbf{B}$, *if and only if the corresponding elements are equal, that is,* $a_{ij} = b_{ij}$ *for every* i, j. *The sum* $\mathbf{C}$ *of a matrix* $\mathbf{A}$ *and a matrix* $\mathbf{B}$, *written* $\mathbf{C} = \mathbf{A} + \mathbf{B}$, *is a matrix whose elements are given by* $c_{ij} = a_{ij} + b_{ij}$. Two matrices $\mathbf{A}$, $\mathbf{B}$ cannot be added unless the number of rows in $\mathbf{A}$ is equal to the number of rows in $\mathbf{B}$ and the number of columns in $\mathbf{A}$ is equal to the number of columns in $\mathbf{B}$. It is obvious that matrix addition satisfies the commutative and associative laws, that is,

$$\mathbf{A} + \mathbf{B} = \mathbf{B} + \mathbf{A}, \tag{2–2}$$

$$\mathbf{A} + (\mathbf{B} + \mathbf{C}) = (\mathbf{A} + \mathbf{B}) + \mathbf{C} = \mathbf{A} + \mathbf{B} + \mathbf{C}, \tag{2–3}$$

since addition proceeds by elements and the laws hold for real numbers. *To multiply a matrix* $\mathbf{A}$ *by a real number* λ, *written* $\lambda\mathbf{A}$, *each element of* $\mathbf{A}$ *is multiplied by* λ. Thus $\lambda\mathbf{A} = \|\lambda a_{ij}\|$. Note that $\lambda\mathbf{A} = \mathbf{A}\lambda$. A real number will often be referred to as a scalar, and hence in forming $\lambda\mathbf{A}$, we say that $\mathbf{A}$ has been multiplied by the scalar λ.

EXAMPLES:

$$(1) \quad \mathbf{A} = \begin{bmatrix} 2 & 3 & 5 \\ 1 & 2 & 0 \end{bmatrix}, \quad \mathbf{B} = \begin{bmatrix} 4 & 7 & 6 \\ 0 & 2 & 1 \end{bmatrix};$$

$$\mathbf{A} + \mathbf{B} = \begin{bmatrix} 6 & 10 & 11 \\ 1 & 4 & 1 \end{bmatrix}.$$

$$(2) \quad \mathbf{A} = \begin{bmatrix} 5 & 4 \\ 3 & 9 \\ 8 & 1 \end{bmatrix}, \quad \lambda = 0.5; \quad \lambda\mathbf{A} = \begin{bmatrix} 2.5 & 2 \\ 1.5 & 4.5 \\ 4 & 0.5 \end{bmatrix}.$$

The product $\mathbf{AB}$ *of two matrices* $\mathbf{A}$, $\mathbf{B}$ *is defined if and only if the number of columns in* $\mathbf{A}$ *is equal to the number of rows in* $\mathbf{B}$. *If* $\mathbf{A}$ *is an* $m \times r$ *matrix* and **B** *is an* $r \times n$ *matrix, then the product* **C** $=$ **AB** *is defined, and* **C** *is an* $m \times n$ *matrix whose elements are computed from*

$$c_{ij} = \sum_{k=1}^{r} a_{ik}b_{kj}, \quad i = 1, \ldots, m; \quad j = 1, \ldots, n. \quad (2\text{-}4)$$

EXAMPLE:

$$\mathbf{A} = \begin{bmatrix} 2 & 1 \\ 3 & 2 \\ 4 & 5 \end{bmatrix}, \quad \mathbf{B} = \begin{bmatrix} 3 & 2 \\ 0 & 1 \end{bmatrix};$$

$$\mathbf{AB} = \begin{bmatrix} 2 & 1 \\ 3 & 2 \\ 4 & 5 \end{bmatrix} \begin{bmatrix} 3 & 2 \\ 0 & 1 \end{bmatrix} = \begin{bmatrix} 2(3) + 1(0) & 2(2) + 1(1) \\ 3(3) + 2(0) & 3(2) + 2(1) \\ 4(3) + 5(0) & 4(2) + 5(1) \end{bmatrix} = \begin{bmatrix} 6 & 5 \\ 9 & 8 \\ 12 & 13 \end{bmatrix}.$$

Note that **BA** is not defined.

Matrix multiplication satisfies the associative and distributive laws:

$$(\mathbf{AB})\mathbf{C} = \mathbf{A}(\mathbf{BC}) = \mathbf{ABC} \quad \text{(associative law)}, \quad (2\text{-}5)$$

$$\mathbf{A}(\mathbf{B} + \mathbf{C}) = \mathbf{AB} + \mathbf{AC} \quad \text{(distributive law)} \quad (2\text{-}6)$$

when the appropriate operations are defined. However, in general, matrix multiplication is not commutative, i.e., in general, **AB** and **BA** are not the same thing. The above example shows that **AB** and **BA** are not necessarily both defined. However, even when **AB** and **BA** are defined, they need not be identical.

2–2 Special matrices. In this section we wish to present a number of important definitions.

IDENTITY MATRIX: *The identity matrix of order* n, *written* **I** *or* $\mathbf{I}_n$, *is a square matrix having ones along the main diagonal (the diagonal running from upper left to lower right) and zeros elsewhere:*

$$\mathbf{I} = \begin{bmatrix} 1 & 0 & 0 \cdots 0 \\ 0 & 1 & 0 \cdots 0 \\ 0 & 0 & 1 \cdots 0 \\ \vdots & & \vdots \\ 0 & 0 & 0 \cdots 1 \end{bmatrix}. \quad (2\text{-}7)$$

If we write $\mathbf{I} = \|\delta_{ij}\|$, then

$$\delta_{ij} = \begin{cases} 1, & i = j, \\ 0, & i \neq j. \end{cases} \tag{2–8}$$

The symbol δ_{ij} defined by (2–8) is called the Kronecker delta. The symbol will always refer to the Kronecker delta unless otherwise specified. It is tacitly assumed that in (2–8) the indices i, j run from 1 to n. Frequently, we must deal with several identity matrices of different sizes. Differentiation of such matrices is facilitated by writing $\mathbf{I}_n$, where the subscript indicates the size of $\mathbf{I}$.

Direct multiplication shows that if $\mathbf{A}$ is an $m \times n$ matrix, then

$$\mathbf{I}_m\mathbf{A} = \mathbf{A}\mathbf{I}_n = \mathbf{A}. \tag{2–9}$$

If we write $\mathbf{I}_n\mathbf{I}_n = \mathbf{I}_n^2$, then $\mathbf{I}^2 = \mathbf{I}$ or, in general, $\mathbf{I}^k = \mathbf{I}$, $k = 1, 2, \ldots$.

For any scalar λ, the square matrix $\mathbf{S} = \|\lambda\delta_{ij}\| = \lambda\mathbf{I}$ is called a scalar matrix. The square matrix $\mathbf{D} = \|\lambda_i\delta_{ij}\|$ is called a diagonal matrix.

NULL MATRIX: *A matrix whose elements are all zero is called a null or zero matrix and is denoted by* $\mathbf{0}$.

A null matrix does not need to be square. When the operations are defined, we have

$$\mathbf{A} + \mathbf{0} = \mathbf{A} = \mathbf{0} + \mathbf{A}; \quad \mathbf{A} - \mathbf{A} = \mathbf{0}; \quad \mathbf{A}\mathbf{0} = \mathbf{0}; \quad \mathbf{0}\mathbf{A} = \mathbf{0}. \tag{2–10}$$

If a, b are real numbers, then $ab = 0$ implies that $a = 0$, or $b = 0$, or a and $b = 0$. But the matrix equation $\mathbf{AB} = \mathbf{0}$ does not imply that $\mathbf{A} = \mathbf{0}$ or $\mathbf{B} = \mathbf{0}$. It is easy to find non-null matrices whose product $\mathbf{AB} = \mathbf{0}$.

EXAMPLE:
$$\begin{bmatrix} 1 & 4 \\ 0 & 0 \end{bmatrix}\begin{bmatrix} 4 & 0 \\ -1 & 0 \end{bmatrix} = \begin{bmatrix} 0 & 0 \\ 0 & 0 \end{bmatrix}.$$

TRANSPOSE: *The transpose of a matrix* $\mathbf{A} = \|a_{ij}\|$ *is a matrix formed from* $\mathbf{A}$ *by interchanging rows and columns such that row i of* $\mathbf{A}$ *becomes column i of the transposed matrix. The transpose is denoted by* $\mathbf{A}'$; *if* $\mathbf{A}' = \|a'_{ij}\|$, $a'_{ij} = a_{ji}$.

From the definition of the transpose it is easy to prove the following relations:

$$(\mathbf{A} + \mathbf{B})' = \mathbf{A}' + \mathbf{B}', \tag{2–11}$$

$$(\mathbf{AB})' = \mathbf{B}'\mathbf{A}', \tag{2–12}$$

$$\mathbf{I}' = \mathbf{I}, \tag{2–13}$$

$$(\mathbf{A}')' = \mathbf{A}. \tag{2–14}$$

EXAMPLES:

(1) If $\mathbf{A} = \begin{bmatrix} 1 & 3 & 4 \\ 0 & 1 & 0 \end{bmatrix}$,   then $\mathbf{A}' = \begin{bmatrix} 1 & 0 \\ 3 & 1 \\ 4 & 0 \end{bmatrix}$.

(2) If $\mathbf{A} = \begin{bmatrix} 1 & 3 \\ 0 & 5 \end{bmatrix}$, $\mathbf{B} = \begin{bmatrix} 2 & 4 \\ 1 & 2 \end{bmatrix}$,

then $\mathbf{AB} = \begin{bmatrix} 5 & 10 \\ 5 & 10 \end{bmatrix}$, $(\mathbf{AB})' = \begin{bmatrix} 5 & 5 \\ 10 & 10 \end{bmatrix}$,

$\mathbf{A}' = \begin{bmatrix} 1 & 0 \\ 3 & 5 \end{bmatrix}$, $\mathbf{B}' = \begin{bmatrix} 2 & 1 \\ 4 & 2 \end{bmatrix}$, $\mathbf{B}'\mathbf{A}' = \begin{bmatrix} 5 & 5 \\ 10 & 10 \end{bmatrix} = (\mathbf{AB})'.$

SYMMETRIC MATRIX: *A symmetric matrix is a matrix* $\mathbf{A}$ *for which* $\mathbf{A}' = \mathbf{A}$.

A symmetric matrix must be square, and $a_{ij} = a_{ji}$ for all i, j. A skew-symmetric matrix is a matrix $\mathbf{A}$ for which $\mathbf{A} = -\mathbf{A}'$. A skew-symmetric matrix is also square and $a_{ij} = -a_{ji}$, all i, j. Hence the diagonal elements of a skew-symmetric matrix are zero.

2–3 Partitioning of matrices. We begin this section by defining a submatrix.

SUBMATRIX: *If we cross out all but* k *rows and* s *columns of an* $m \times n$ *matrix* $\mathbf{A}$, *the resulting* $k \times s$ *matrix is called a submatrix of* $\mathbf{A}$.

EXAMPLE: If we cross out rows 1, 3 and columns 2, 6 of the 4×6 matrix $\mathbf{A} = \|a_{ij}\|$, we are left with the 2×4 submatrix

$$\begin{bmatrix} a_{21} & a_{23} & a_{24} & a_{25} \\ a_{41} & a_{43} & a_{44} & a_{45} \end{bmatrix}.$$

For many reasons, a number of which will become clear later, it is at times useful to partition a given matrix into submatrices. Consider the matrix

$$\mathbf{A} = \begin{bmatrix} a_{11} & a_{12} & a_{13} \\ a_{21} & a_{22} & a_{23} \\ \hline a_{31} & a_{32} & a_{33} \\ a_{41} & a_{42} & a_{43} \end{bmatrix}. \tag{2–15}$$

By drawing the dotted lines shown we have partitioned $\mathbf{A}$ into four sub-matrices which are:

$$\mathbf{A}_{11} = \begin{bmatrix} a_{11} & a_{12} \\ a_{21} & a_{22} \end{bmatrix} ; \qquad \mathbf{A}_{21} = \begin{bmatrix} a_{31} & a_{32} \\ a_{41} & a_{42} \end{bmatrix} ;$$

$$\mathbf{A}_{12} = \begin{bmatrix} a_{13} \\ a_{23} \end{bmatrix} ; \qquad \mathbf{A}_{22} = \begin{bmatrix} a_{33} \\ a_{43} \end{bmatrix} . \tag{2–16}$$

Then $\mathbf{A}$ can be written:

$$\mathbf{A} = \begin{bmatrix} \mathbf{A}_{11} & \mathbf{A}_{12} \\ \mathbf{A}_{21} & \mathbf{A}_{22} \end{bmatrix} . \tag{2–17}$$

When $\mathbf{A}$ is written in the form (2–17), we say that $\mathbf{A}$ has been written as a partitioned matrix. Clearly there are many different ways in which $\mathbf{A}$ could be partitioned.

Frequently, partitioning is used to simplify operations with matrices, such as multiplication. If partitioning is to be of advantage, we would like to be able to multiply by "blocks" and have the rule for multiplication follow the usual rule. Thus, if $\mathbf{AB}$ is defined and $\mathbf{A}$ and $\mathbf{B}$ are partitioned as

$$\mathbf{A} = \begin{bmatrix} \mathbf{A}_{11} & \mathbf{A}_{12} \\ \mathbf{A}_{21} & \mathbf{A}_{22} \\ \mathbf{A}_{31} & \mathbf{A}_{32} \end{bmatrix} , \qquad \mathbf{B} = \begin{bmatrix} \mathbf{B}_{11} & \mathbf{B}_{12} \\ \mathbf{B}_{21} & \mathbf{B}_{22} \end{bmatrix} , \tag{2–18}$$

we wish to be able to write $\mathbf{AB}$ as

$$\mathbf{AB} = \begin{bmatrix} \mathbf{A}_{11}\mathbf{B}_{11} + \mathbf{A}_{12}\mathbf{B}_{21} & \mathbf{A}_{11}\mathbf{B}_{12} + \mathbf{A}_{12}\mathbf{B}_{22} \\ \mathbf{A}_{21}\mathbf{B}_{11} + \mathbf{A}_{22}\mathbf{B}_{21} & \mathbf{A}_{21}\mathbf{B}_{12} + \mathbf{A}_{22}\mathbf{B}_{22} \\ \mathbf{A}_{31}\mathbf{B}_{11} + \mathbf{A}_{32}\mathbf{B}_{21} & \mathbf{A}_{31}\mathbf{B}_{12} + \mathbf{A}_{32}\mathbf{B}_{22} \end{bmatrix} . \tag{2–19}$$

This will be correct if each product $\mathbf{A}_{ik}\mathbf{B}_{kj}$ is defined. In order that each such product be defined, the columns of $\mathbf{A}$ must be partitioned in "the same way" as the rows of $\mathbf{B}$.

A particularly useful form of partitioning is that in which each sub-matrix is a column of the given matrix (or a row of the given matrix). We shall find it convenient to denote matrices containing a single row (row matrices) or column (column matrices) by lower-case boldface letters rather than upper-case boldface letters. Each column of an $m \times n$ matrix $\mathbf{A}$ can be considered to be a submatrix of one column and m rows. The jth column of $\mathbf{A}$ will be denoted by $\mathbf{a}_j$. Thus $\mathbf{a}_j = [a_{1j}, \ldots, a_{mj}]$. Similarly, each row of $\mathbf{A}$ can be considered to be a submatrix of one row and n columns. The ith row of $\mathbf{A}$ will be denoted by $\mathbf{a}^i$ so that $\mathbf{a}^i = (a_{i1}, \ldots, a_{in})$. By partitioning into rows or columns we can write a matrix $\mathbf{A}$ as a row of column matrices, i.e., $\mathbf{A} = (\mathbf{a}_1, \ldots, \mathbf{a}_n)$, or as a column of row matrices, i.e., $\mathbf{A} = [\mathbf{a}^1, \ldots, \mathbf{a}^m]$.

Consider the matrix $\mathbf{C} = \mathbf{AB}$ where $\mathbf{C}$ is $m \times n$, $\mathbf{A}$ is $m \times r$, and $\mathbf{B}$ is $r \times n$. Then $c_{ij} = \sum_k a_{ik}b_{kj}$ or, if $\mathbf{c}_j$ is the jth column of $\mathbf{C}$, we have

$$\mathbf{c}_j = \left[\sum_k a_{1k}b_{kj}, \sum_k a_{2k}b_{kj}, \ldots, \sum_k a_{mk}b_{kj} \right] = \mathbf{Ab}_j, \qquad (2\text{-}20)$$

where $\mathbf{b}_j$ is the jth column of $\mathbf{B}$. Thus, if we write $\mathbf{B} = (\mathbf{b}_1, \ldots, \mathbf{b}_n)$, then $\mathbf{C} = (\mathbf{Ab}_1, \ldots, \mathbf{Ab}_n)$. Each column of $\mathbf{C}$ is computed by multiplying the corresponding column of $\mathbf{B}$ by $\mathbf{A}$.

2–4 Determinants. Associated with every square matrix $\mathbf{A}$ is a number which is called the determinant of $\mathbf{A}$. Only square matrices have determinants associated with them. Here we shall briefly summarize some useful properties of determinants without making any attempt to provide proofs. The complete development is found in {LA 3–10 through 3–17}.

A set of integers $1, \ldots, n$ are in "natural order" when they appear in the order $1, 2, 3, \ldots, n$. If two integers are out of natural order in a set of n integers, then a larger integer will precede a smaller one. For example, the natural order of the first five integers, beginning with 1, is $(1, 2, 3, 4, 5)$. When the integers 2 and 4 are interchanged, we obtain $(1, 4, 3, 2, 5)$. The set is now out of natural order because 4 precedes 3, 2, and 3 precedes 2. Any rearrangement of the natural order of n integers is called a *permutation* of these integers. The interchange of two integers, such as 2 and 4 in the above example, is called a *transposition*. The number of *inversions* in a permutation of n integers is the number of pairs of elements (not necessarily adjacent) in which a larger integer precedes a smaller one. In our example, there are three inversions: $(4, 3)$, $(4, 2)$, and $(3, 2)$. It should be noted that the number of inversions in any permutation is unique, and can be counted directly and systematically. A permutation is *even* when the number of inversions is even, and *odd* when the number of inversions is odd.

DETERMINANT: *The determinant of an nth-order matrix* $\mathbf{A} = \|a_{ij}\|$, *written* $|\mathbf{A}|$, *is defined to be the number computed from the following sum involving the* n^2 *elements in* $\mathbf{A}$:

$$|\mathbf{A}| = \sum(\pm)a_{1i}a_{2j} \ldots a_{nr}, \qquad (2\text{-}21)$$

the sum being taken over all permutations of the second subscripts. A term is assigned a plus sign if $(i, j, \ldots, r)$ *is an even permutation of* $(1, 2, \ldots, n)$, *and a minus sign if it is an odd permutation.*

Each term in (2–21) is the product of n elements from $\mathbf{A}$, one from each row and column. There are $n!$ such terms in (2–21). We shall find it convenient to refer to the determinant of an nth-order matrix as an nth-order, or $n \times n$, determinant. Often we shall write $|\mathbf{A}|$ as

$$|\mathbf{A}| = \begin{vmatrix} a_{11} & \cdots & a_{1n} \\ \vdots & & \vdots \\ a_{n1} & \cdots & a_{nn} \end{vmatrix}, \tag{2–22}$$

with straight lines denoting the determinant (instead of brackets).

EXAMPLE: From (2–21) the determinant of a third-order matrix $\mathbf{A} = \|a_{ij}\|$ is

$$|\mathbf{A}| = a_{11}a_{22}a_{33} - a_{12}a_{21}a_{33} + a_{12}a_{23}a_{31} - a_{13}a_{22}a_{31}$$
$$+ a_{13}a_{21}a_{32} - a_{11}a_{23}a_{32}. \tag{2–23}$$

The term $a_{11}a_{22}a_{33}$, in which the second subscripts are in their natural order, represents the identity permutation of the second subscripts, i.e., there are no inversions. The identity permutation is even.

It can be shown that the determinant of an nth-order matrix $\mathbf{A}$ can be written

$$|\mathbf{A}| = \sum_{j=1}^{n} a_{ij}A_{ij} \tag{2–24}$$

for every $i = 1, \ldots, n$, where A_{ij} is $(-1)^{i+j}$ times the determinant of the submatrix obtained from $\mathbf{A}$ by crossing off row i and column j; A_{ij} is called the cofactor of element a_{ij}. The expression (2–24) is called the cofactor expansion of $|\mathbf{A}|$ by row i. Note that for a matrix of a single element, $\mathbf{A} = (a_{11})$, Eq. (2–21) implies that $|\mathbf{A}| = a_{11}$. Thus if (2–24) is to hold for $n = 1$, we must define the cofactor of the element in a 1×1 matrix to be 1. It is also possible to expand in cofactors by columns. Thus

$$|\mathbf{A}| = \sum_{i=1}^{n} a_{ij}A_{ij}, \tag{2–25}$$

for every $j = 1, \ldots, n$.

EXAMPLES: (1) Expanding by row 2, we see that

$$|\mathbf{A}| = \begin{vmatrix} a_{11} & a_{12} & a_{13} \\ a_{21} & a_{22} & a_{23} \\ a_{31} & a_{32} & a_{33} \end{vmatrix} = a_{21}A_{21} + a_{22}A_{22} + a_{23}A_{23}, \tag{2–26}$$

and
$$A_{21} = (-1)^3 \begin{vmatrix} a_{12} & a_{13} \\ a_{32} & a_{33} \end{vmatrix} = (-1)(a_{12}a_{33} - a_{13}a_{32}),$$

$$A_{22} = (-1)^4 \begin{vmatrix} a_{11} & a_{13} \\ a_{31} & a_{33} \end{vmatrix} = a_{11}a_{33} - a_{13}a_{31},$$

$$A_{23} = (-1)^5 \begin{vmatrix} a_{11} & a_{12} \\ a_{31} & a_{32} \end{vmatrix} = -(a_{11}a_{32} - a_{12}a_{31}).$$

Substitution of the A_{ij} into (2–26) gives (2–23). We note that the co-factor expansion or (2–21) shows that

$$|\mathbf{B}| = \begin{vmatrix} b_{11} & b_{12} \\ b_{21} & b_{22} \end{vmatrix} = b_{11}b_{22} - b_{12}b_{21},$$

which is the expression learned in elementary algebra for a 2nd-order determinant.

(2) Expanding in cofactors by the first row, we see that

$$|\mathbf{I}_n| = (-1)^2 |\mathbf{I}_{n-1}|.$$

Thus

$$|\mathbf{I}_n| = 1.$$

The expansion by cofactors reduces the problem of evaluating an nth-order determinant to that of evaluating n determinants of order $n - 1$, i.e., the cofactors A_{ij}. Thus proceeding by steps, we arrive at an evaluation of $|\mathbf{A}|$. Application of the cofactor-expansion method to the cofactors reduces the task of evaluating each cofactor of order $n - 1$ to that of evaluating $n - 1$ determinants of order $n - 2$, etc. The expansion by cofactors is not a very efficient numerical procedure for evaluating determinants of high order. It is, however, of considerable theoretical value.

We find it useful to give a name to the kth-order determinants, $k = 1, \ldots, n - 1$, which appear in the step-by-step evaluation of $|\mathbf{A}|$ by cofactor expansion. They will be referred to as minors of $\mathbf{A}$. More precisely:

MINOR OF ORDER k: *For any* $m \times n$ *matrix* $\mathbf{A}$ *consider the* kth-order *submatrix* $\mathbf{R}$ *obtained by deleting all but some* k *rows and* k *columns of* $\mathbf{A}$. *Then* $|\mathbf{R}|$ *is called a* kth-order *minor of* $\mathbf{A}$.

Note that in the above definition $\mathbf{A}$ is not required to be a square matrix.

We shall now summarize some useful properties of determinants:

(1) An interchange of two columns in an nth-order matrix $\mathbf{A}$ changes the sign of $|\mathbf{A}|$.

(2) An interchange of two rows in an nth-order matrix $\mathbf{A}$ changes the sign of $|\mathbf{A}|$.

(3) $|\mathbf{A}'| = |\mathbf{A}|$.

(4) Multiplication of each element in the ith row (or ith column) of an nth-order matrix $\mathbf{A}$ by a scalar λ multiplies $|\mathbf{A}|$ by λ. Thus $|\lambda\mathbf{A}| = \lambda^n|\mathbf{A}|$, and hence $|-\mathbf{A}| = (-1)^n|\mathbf{A}|$.

(5) If every element in the ith row or ith column of $\mathbf{A}$ is zero, then $|\mathbf{A}| = 0$.

(6) Addition of a multiple of row k to row i $(i \neq k)$ or of a multiple of column k to column i $(i \neq k)$ of $\mathbf{A}$ does not change the value of $|\mathbf{A}|$.

(7) The determinant $|\mathbf{A}|$ vanishes if $\mathbf{A}$ has two rows or two columns which are the same, that is, $a_{ik} = a_{jk}$ (all k) or $a_{ik} = a_{ij}$ (all i).

(8) If $\mathbf{A}, \mathbf{B}$ are nth-order matrices, then $|\mathbf{AB}| = |\mathbf{A}|\,|\mathbf{B}|$, i.e., the determinant of the product is the product of the determinants.

Property (7) can be used to obtain an important result. Consider $\sum_j a_{ij}A_{kj}$. We are using the cofactors of row k and the elements of row i. This is exactly the cofactor expansion of the determinant of a matrix whose rows i and k are the same. Hence

$$\sum_j a_{ij}A_{kj} = \sum_j a_{ji}A_{jk} = 0 \qquad (i \neq k). \qquad (2\text{--}27)$$

Combining (2–27) with (2–24) and (2–25), we obtain

$$\sum_j a_{ij}A_{kj} = \sum_j a_{ji}A_{jk} = |\mathbf{A}|\,\delta_{ki}, \qquad (2\text{--}28)$$

where δ_{ki} is the Kronecker delta defined earlier.

It will be noted that (2–28) looks very much like a matrix product. If we set $a_{ij}^+ = A_{ji}$, then (2–28) becomes

$$\sum_j a_{ij}a_{jk}^+ = \sum_j a_{kj}^+a_{ji} = |\mathbf{A}|\,\delta_{ki}. \qquad (2\text{--}29)$$

Thus if

$$\mathbf{A}^+ = \|a_{ij}^+\| = \begin{bmatrix} A_{11} & A_{21} \cdots & A_{n1} \\ A_{12} & A_{22} \cdots & A_{n2} \\ \vdots & & \vdots \\ A_{1n} & A_{2n} \cdots & A_{nn} \end{bmatrix}, \qquad (2\text{--}30)$$

then Eq. (2–29) can be written in matrix form:

$$\mathbf{AA}^+ = \mathbf{A}^+\mathbf{A} = |\mathbf{A}|\mathbf{I}_n. \qquad (2\text{--}31)$$

The matrix $\mathbf{A}^+$ is called the adjoint of matrix $\mathbf{A}$. In fact, $\mathbf{A}^+$ is the transpose of the matrix obtained from $\mathbf{A}$ by replacing each element a_{ij} by its cofactor A_{ij}.

2–5 The matrix inverse. Another important concept in matrix theory is the matrix inverse. We define:

MATRIX INVERSE: *Given a square matrix* **A**. *If there exists a square matrix* **B** *which satisfies the relation*

$$AB = BA = I, \qquad (2\text{--}32)$$

then **B** *is called the inverse of* **A**.

Usually, the inverse of **A** is written $\mathbf{A}^{-1}$. Only square matrices have inverses.

We essentially obtained an explicit expression for the inverse of **A** in (2–31). If we write

$$\mathbf{A}^{-1} = \frac{1}{|\mathbf{A}|}\,\mathbf{A}^{+}, \qquad (2\text{--}33)$$

then from (2–31) we see that $\mathbf{A}^{-1}$ satisfies (2–32) and hence is the inverse of **A**. Note that $\mathbf{A}^{-1}$ in (2–33) exists only when $|\mathbf{A}| \neq 0$.

SINGULAR AND NONSINGULAR MATRICES: *The square matrix* **A** *is said to be singular if* $|\mathbf{A}| = 0$; *nonsingular if* $|\mathbf{A}| \neq 0$.

We have shown above that every nonsingular matrix has an inverse. It is also true that only nonsingular matrices have inverses.

EXAMPLES: (1) Let us compute the general formula for the inverse of a 2×2 nonsingular matrix **A**:

$$\mathbf{A} = \begin{bmatrix} a_{11} & a_{12} \\ a_{21} & a_{22} \end{bmatrix}; \qquad |\mathbf{A}| = a_{11}a_{22} - a_{12}a_{21}.$$

Then, since the cofactors are determinants of order one with values $A_{11} = a_{22}$, $A_{12} = -a_{21}$, $A_{21} = -a_{12}$, $A_{22} = a_{11}$, it follows that

$$\mathbf{A}^{+} = \begin{bmatrix} a_{22} & -a_{12} \\ -a_{21} & a_{11} \end{bmatrix}, \qquad \mathbf{A}^{-1} = \frac{1}{|\mathbf{A}|}\begin{bmatrix} a_{22} & -a_{12} \\ -a_{21} & a_{11} \end{bmatrix}.$$

(2) Assume that

$$\mathbf{A} = \begin{bmatrix} 1 & 0 \\ 2 & 3 \end{bmatrix}.$$

Then

$$|\mathbf{A}| = 3, \qquad \mathbf{A}^{+} = \begin{bmatrix} 3 & 0 \\ -2 & 1 \end{bmatrix}, \qquad \text{and} \qquad \mathbf{A}^{-1} = \begin{bmatrix} 1 & 0 \\ -\frac{2}{3} & \frac{1}{3} \end{bmatrix}.$$

(3) $\mathbf{II} = \mathbf{I}$; thus $\mathbf{I}^{-1} = \mathbf{I}$.

(4) If $\mathbf{A} = (a_{11})$, then $|\mathbf{A}| = a_{11}$, $\mathbf{A}^+ = (1)$, and $\mathbf{A}^{-1} = (1/a_{11})$, $a_{11} \neq 0$.

When a matrix is a single element, the inverse is also a single element, i.e., the reciprocal of that in $\mathbf{A}$. There is a complete correspondence between matrices of a single element and numbers. We shall not distinguish between the matrix $\mathbf{A} = (a_{11})$ and the number a_{11}.

The following is a list of useful properties of the inverse:

(1) The inverse of a nonsingular matrix is unique, i.e., there is only one matrix for which (2–32) holds. To prove this suppose that there existed two different inverses, $\mathbf{B}$ and $\mathbf{D}$, for $\mathbf{A}$. By assumption, $\mathbf{AB} = \mathbf{I}$. Hence $\mathbf{DAB} = \mathbf{DI} = \mathbf{D}$. However, by assumption, $\mathbf{DA} = \mathbf{I}$. Hence $\mathbf{B} = \mathbf{D}$.

(2) If we have two nth-order matrices $\mathbf{A}$ and $\mathbf{B}$ such that $\mathbf{AB} = \mathbf{I}$, then $\mathbf{A}$ and $\mathbf{B}$ are nonsingular, $\mathbf{A}^{-1} = \mathbf{B}$, $\mathbf{B}^{-1} = \mathbf{A}$, and $\mathbf{BA} = \mathbf{I}$. To prove this we note from property (8) of determinants that $|\mathbf{A}| \, |\mathbf{B}| = |\mathbf{I}| = 1$. Hence both $\mathbf{A}$ and $\mathbf{B}$ are nonsingular. Thus $\mathbf{A}^{-1}$ exists. Multiplying $\mathbf{AB} = \mathbf{I}$ on the left by $\mathbf{A}^{-1}$, we obtain $\mathbf{B} = \mathbf{A}^{-1}$ since $\mathbf{A}^{-1}\mathbf{A} = \mathbf{I}$. Consequently, from (2–32), $\mathbf{BA} = \mathbf{I}$.

(3) If $\mathbf{A}, \mathbf{B}$ are two nth-order nonsingular matrices, then $(\mathbf{AB})^{-1} = \mathbf{B}^{-1}\mathbf{A}^{-1}$. This is proved by noting that $\mathbf{ABB}^{-1}\mathbf{A}^{-1} = \mathbf{AIA}^{-1} = \mathbf{AA}^{-1} = \mathbf{I}$. By properties (1) and (2), the result follows.

(4) $(\mathbf{A}^{-1})^{-1} = \mathbf{A}$. This follows immediately from (2–32) because if $\mathbf{B}$ is the inverse of $\mathbf{A}$, $\mathbf{A}$ is also the inverse of $\mathbf{B}$.

(5) $(\mathbf{A}')^{-1} = (\mathbf{A}^{-1})'$.

(6) If $\mathbf{A}$ is nonsingular and $\mathbf{AB} = \mathbf{0}$, then $\mathbf{B} = \mathbf{0}$. To prove this multiply on the left by $\mathbf{A}^{-1}$. This gives $\mathbf{A}^{-1}\mathbf{AB} = \mathbf{A}^{-1}\mathbf{0}$ or $\mathbf{B} = \mathbf{0}$.

2–6 Computation of the inverse by partitioning. Suppose that we have an nth-order nonsingular matrix $\mathbf{M}$ which is partitioned as follows:

$$\mathbf{M} = \begin{bmatrix} \alpha & \beta \\ \gamma & \delta \end{bmatrix}, \tag{2–34}$$

where α is an $s \times s$ submatrix, β an $s \times m$ submatrix, γ an $m \times s$ submatrix, and δ an $m \times m$ submatrix ($n = m + s$). We use here Greek letters and no subscripts for the submatrices in order to simplify the formulas to follow. $\mathbf{M}^{-1}$ exists and will be partitioned in the same way as $\mathbf{M}$, that is,

$$\mathbf{M}^{-1} = \begin{bmatrix} \mathbf{A} & \mathbf{B} \\ \mathbf{C} & \mathbf{D} \end{bmatrix}, \tag{2–35}$$

where $\mathbf{A}$ is $s \times s$, $\mathbf{B}$ is $s \times m$, $\mathbf{C}$ is $m \times s$, and $\mathbf{D}$ is $m \times m$.

Assume that δ has an inverse, and that δ^{-1} is known. Then, since $MM^{-1} = I$,

$$\begin{bmatrix} \alpha & \beta \\ \gamma & \delta \end{bmatrix} \begin{bmatrix} A & B \\ C & D \end{bmatrix} = \begin{bmatrix} I_s & 0 \\ 0 & I_m \end{bmatrix}. \tag{2-36}$$

Four equations are obtained for the four unknown submatrices A, B, C, D:

$$\alpha A + \beta C = I_s, \qquad \alpha B + \beta D = 0,$$
$$\gamma A + \delta C = 0, \qquad \gamma B + \delta D = I_m. \tag{2-37}$$

Solving these for A, B, C, D, we obtain

$$A = (\alpha - \beta\delta^{-1}\gamma)^{-1}, \qquad B = -A\beta\delta^{-1},$$
$$C = -\delta^{-1}\gamma A, \qquad D = \delta^{-1} - \delta^{-1}\gamma B. \tag{2-38}$$

Since M^{-1} exists, the submatrices A, B, C, D exist. Hence, if δ^{-1} exists, all the operations can be carried out, and A, B, C, D can be computed from (2–38).

Imagine now that we wish to invert a matrix by the partitioning scheme introduced above. If we partition the matrix so that δ is of a size which can be inverted easily, then we shall find it difficult to obtain A if the order of the given matrix is fairly large. We are able to avoid this difficulty by applying the partitioning technique two or more times. Initially we partition the given matrix so that A is easy to compute. To find δ^{-1} we apply the partitioning technique one or more times to δ.

A special case that will be of interest to us arises when M in (2–34) has the form

$$M = \begin{bmatrix} I & Q \\ 0 & R \end{bmatrix}, \tag{2-39}$$

where R^{-1} exists and is known. Then from (2–38) we see that

$$M^{-1} = \begin{bmatrix} I & -QR^{-1} \\ 0 & R^{-1} \end{bmatrix}. \tag{2-40}$$

2–7 Power series expansion of $(I - A)^{-1}$. For the square matrix A, we shall write $AA = A^2$, $AAA = A^3$, etc. It is also convenient to write $A^0 = I$. Now note that

$$(I - A)(I + A + A^2 + \cdots + A^k) = I - A^{k+1}. \tag{2-41}$$

By

$$\lim_{k \to \infty} A^{k+1} = 0 \tag{2-42}$$

we shall mean that each element of $\mathbf{A}^{k+1}$ approaches zero as k becomes arbitrarily large. If (2–42) holds, then (2–41) becomes

$$(\mathbf{I} - \mathbf{A}) \sum_{k=0}^{\infty} \mathbf{A}^k = \mathbf{I} \quad \text{or} \quad (\mathbf{I} - \mathbf{A})^{-1} = \mathbf{I} + \mathbf{A} + \mathbf{A}^2 + \cdots \quad (2\text{–}43)$$

Thus if (2–42) holds, $(\mathbf{I} - \mathbf{A})^{-1}$ exists, and can be written as a matrix power series.

We shall now present an important set of conditions which guarantee that (2–42) holds. If for the matrix $\mathbf{A}$,

$$0 \leq a_{ij} < 1 \quad \text{for all } i, j \quad \text{and} \quad \sum_{i=1}^{n} a_{ij} < 1, \quad j = 1, \ldots, n, \quad (2\text{–}44)$$

then (2–42) holds. To prove this, let $a_{ij}^{(k)}$ be the ijth element of $\mathbf{A}^k$. Then by (2–44) there exists an r $(0 < r < 1)$ such that $\sum_i a_{ij} \leq r$ for all j. Hence if $\mathbf{A}^2 = \|a_{ij}^{(2)}\|$, then

$$a_{ij}^{(2)} = \sum_{k=1}^{n} a_{ik} a_{kj}; \quad \sum_{i=1}^{n} a_{ij}^{(2)} = \sum_{i=1}^{n} \sum_{k=1}^{n} a_{ik} a_{kj} \leq r^2, \quad \text{all } i, j, \quad (2\text{–}45)$$

so that $a_{ij}^{(2)} \leq r^2$. Continuing this process, we see that $a_{ij}^{(k)} \leq r^k$. Consequently, each $a_{ij}^{(k)}$ approaches zero as $k \to \infty$.

2–8 Vectors and euclidean spaces.

Matrices having a single row or column are often referred to as vectors. A matrix of a single row is called a row vector, and a matrix of a single column is called a column vector. Vectors will usually be denoted by lower-case boldface type. A vector $\mathbf{a} = (a_1, \ldots, a_n)$ or $\mathbf{a} = [a_1, \ldots, a_n]$ is called an n-component vector, and a_i, $i = 1, \ldots, n$, is said to be the ith component of $\mathbf{a}$.

Vectors can be given a geometric interpretation. Just as (a_1, a_2, a_3) can be considered to be a point in a three-dimensional space, so can $\mathbf{a} = (a_1, \ldots, a_n)$ be imagined to be a point in an n-dimensional space. There is no geometric distinction between row and column vectors. Geometrically, they are considered to be equivalent. The decision of writing a vector as a row or as a column is merely a matter of notational convenience. We shall more frequently use column vectors than row vectors, and hence a vector will, in general, be written $\mathbf{a} = [a_1, \ldots, a_n]$.

The operations of addition and multiplication by a scalar for vectors can be given a simple geometric interpretation in two and three dimensions. To illustrate these relations most clearly it is helpful to represent a vector by a directed line drawn from the origin to the point which characterizes the vector. An arrowhead is placed at the end point of the line. We shall often find it helpful to represent vectors geometrically by

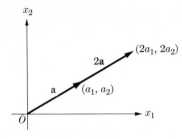

FIGURE 2–1

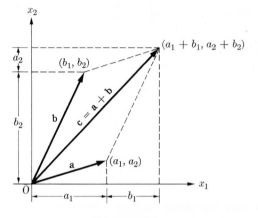

FIGURE 2–2

directed line segments. The operation of multiplication by a scalar is illustrated geometrically in Fig. 2–1, while addition is illustrated geometrically in Fig. 2–2. Note that if $\mathbf{c} = \mathbf{a} + \mathbf{b}$, then $\mathbf{c}$ is the diagonal of the parallelogram with sides $\mathbf{a}$, $\mathbf{b}$.

Certain vectors which are used frequently are given names, and hence we shall define them at the outset.

UNIT VECTOR: *A unit vector, denoted by* $\mathbf{e}_i$, *is a vector with unity as the value of its ith component and with all other components zero.*

For vectors with n components there are n unit vectors. They are:

$$\mathbf{e}_1 = [1, 0, \ldots, 0], \ \mathbf{e}_2 = [0, 1, 0, \ldots, 0], \ldots, \mathbf{e}_n = [0, 0, \ldots, 1].$$
$$(2\text{–}46)$$

NULL VECTOR: *The null vector, or zero vector, written* $\mathbf{0}$, *is a vector all of whose components are zero.*

SUM VECTOR: *A sum vector is a vector having unity as a value for each component; it will be written* **1**.

$$\mathbf{1} = (1, 1, \ldots, 1). \tag{2–47}$$

The sum vector will be used more often as a row vector than as a column vector. The matrix product of **1** and a column vector $\mathbf{a} = [a_1, \ldots, a_n]$ yields $\mathbf{1a} = \sum_i a_i$. This explains why **1** is called the sum vector.

We shall occasionally need vector inequalities. Given two n-component vectors **a** and **b**, then $\mathbf{a} \geq \mathbf{b}$ means $a_i \geq b_i$, $i = 1, \ldots, n$, and $\mathbf{a} \leq \mathbf{b}$ means $a_i \leq b_i$, $i = 1, \ldots, n$. Similarly, $\mathbf{a} > \mathbf{b}$ means $a_i > b_i$ for all i, and $\mathbf{a} < \mathbf{b}$ means $a_i < b_i$ for all i.

The scalar product of two n-component vectors **a**, **b** is defined to be the number

$$\sum_{i=1}^{n} a_i b_i. \tag{2–48}$$

This is true, irrespective of whether **a** and **b** are row or column vectors. If **a** is a row vector and **b** is a column vector, the scalar product is denoted by **ab**; if **a**, **b** are column vectors, the scalar product is denoted by $\mathbf{a'b}$; if **a**, **b** are row vectors, the scalar product is denoted by $\mathbf{ab'}$. In every case the notation for the scalar product is such that if it is interpreted as a matrix product, the result is (2–48).

We have observed that $\mathbf{a} = [a_1, \ldots, a_n]$ can be interpreted as a point in an n-dimensional space. As yet we have no coordinate system for this space. Now note that **a** can be written in terms of the unit vectors as follows:

$$\mathbf{a} = a_1\mathbf{e}_1 + a_2\mathbf{e}_2 + \cdots + a_n\mathbf{e}_n. \tag{2–49}$$

In two- and three-dimensional spaces, $\mathbf{e}_i$ is a point located a unit distance from the origin on the ith coordinate axis. Thus for our n-dimensional space, we use the unit vectors to define a coordinate system. We imagine that a coordinate axis is drawn from the origin through each unit vector. The origin is the null vector. For this coordinate system, a_i is the ith coordinate of the point **a**. Thus, when we write $\mathbf{a} = [a_1, \ldots, a_n]$, a special coordinate system is implied, i.e., the coordinate system defined by the unit vectors.

The distance between two points $\mathbf{a} = [a_1, \ldots, a_n]$ and $\mathbf{b} = [b_1, \ldots, b_n]$, written $|\mathbf{a} - \mathbf{b}|$, is defined to be

$$|\mathbf{a} - \mathbf{b}| = [(\mathbf{a} - \mathbf{b})'(\mathbf{a} - \mathbf{b})]^{1/2} = \left[\sum_{i=1}^{n} (a_i - b_i)^2\right]^{1/2}. \tag{2–50}$$

This is a direct generalization of the formula for distance in three dimensions. The distance from **0** to **a** is called the length or magnitude of **a**, and is symbolized by $|\mathbf{a}|$. The angle θ between two nonzero vectors is computed from

$$\cos \theta = \frac{\mathbf{a'b}}{|\mathbf{a}|\ |\mathbf{b}|}. \qquad (2\text{–}51)$$

It can be shown that $|\cos \theta| \le 1$, so that it is always possible to determine an angle θ lying between 0 and π. To show that $|\cos \theta| \le 1$ is equivalent to showing that

$$|\mathbf{a'b}| \le |\mathbf{a}|\ |\mathbf{b}| \qquad (2\text{–}52)$$

for any two n-component vectors **a**, **b**, where $|\mathbf{a'b}|$ is the absolute value of $\mathbf{a'b}$. This is called the Schwarz inequality, and the reader is asked to prove it in Problem 2–11. Two vectors are said to be orthogonal if $\mathbf{a'b} = 0$.

EUCLIDEAN SPACE: *An n-dimensional euclidean space, symbolized by E^n, is defined as the collection of all vectors (points) $\mathbf{a} = [a_1, \ldots, a_n]$. For these vectors, addition and multiplication by a scalar are defined by the rules for matrix operations. Furthermore, associated with any two vectors in the collection is a non-negative number, called the distance between two vectors; the distance is given by (2–50).*

Here we have a definition of the n-dimensional spaces that we shall be using. The familiar two- and three-dimensional spaces of elementary geometry were euclidean spaces.

2–9 Linear dependence. A vector **a** from E^n is said to be a linear combination of the vectors $\mathbf{a}_1, \ldots, \mathbf{a}_k$ from E^n if **a** can be written

$$\mathbf{a} = \lambda_1 \mathbf{a}_1 + \lambda_2 \mathbf{a}_2 + \cdots + \lambda_k \mathbf{a}_k \qquad (2\text{–}53)$$

for some set of scalars λ_i.

LINEAR DEPENDENCE: *A set of vectors $\mathbf{a}_1, \ldots, \mathbf{a}_m$ from E^n is said to be linearly dependent if there exist scalars λ_i not all zero such that*

$$\lambda_1 \mathbf{a}_1 + \lambda_2 \mathbf{a}_2 + \cdots + \lambda_m \mathbf{a}_m = \mathbf{0}. \qquad (2\text{–}54)$$

If the only set of λ_i for which (2–54) holds is $\lambda_1 = \lambda_2 = \cdots = \lambda_m = 0$, then the vectors are said to be linearly independent.

A set of vectors which is not linearly dependent must be linearly independent. If we let $\mathbf{a}_1 = [a_{11}, \ldots, a_{n1}], \ldots, \mathbf{a}_m = [a_{1m}, \ldots, a_{nm}]$, then on writing out the component form of (2–54), we obtain

$$a_{11}\lambda_1 + a_{12}\lambda_2 + \cdots + a_{1m}\lambda_m = 0,$$
$$\vdots \tag{2-55}$$
$$a_{n1}\lambda_1 + a_{n2}\lambda_2 + \cdots + a_{nm}\lambda_m = 0,$$

which is a set of n simultaneous linear equations in m unknowns, the λ_i. If there exists a solution to this set of equations with not all $\lambda_i = 0$, the given vectors are linearly dependent. Later we shall study systems of equations like (2–55).

Linear dependence and independence are properties of sets of vectors, and not of the individual vectors in the set. For a set containing a single vector $\mathbf{a}$, the definition of linear dependence says that $\mathbf{a}$ is linearly dependent if there exists a $\lambda \neq 0$ such that $\lambda\mathbf{a} = \mathbf{0}$. Thus the set containing a single vector is linearly independent if $\mathbf{a} \neq \mathbf{0}$, and linearly dependent if $\mathbf{a} = \mathbf{0}$.

If a set of vectors $\mathbf{a}_1, \ldots, \mathbf{a}_m$ from E^n contains two or more vectors, then the set is linearly dependent if and only if some one of the vectors is a linear combination of the others. To prove this suppose that one of the vectors, say $\mathbf{a}_m$, can be written as a linear combination of the others, i.e.,

$$\mathbf{a}_m = \sum_{i=1}^{m-1} \lambda_i \mathbf{a}_i \qquad \text{or} \qquad \sum_{i=1}^{m-1} \lambda_i \mathbf{a}_i - \mathbf{a}_m = \mathbf{0}. \tag{2-56}$$

Consequently, the vectors are linearly dependent. On the other hand, if the vectors are linearly dependent, then (2–54) holds, and at least one $\lambda_i \neq 0$. Suppose $\lambda_m \neq 0$. Thus we can write

$$\mathbf{a}_m = -\sum_{i=1}^{m-1} \frac{\lambda_i}{\lambda_m} \mathbf{a}_i, \tag{2-57}$$

and one of the vectors can be written as a linear combination of the others.

A vector $\mathbf{a}$ is said to be linearly dependent on a set of vectors $\mathbf{a}_1, \ldots, \mathbf{a}_m$ if $\mathbf{a}$ can be written as a linear combination of $\mathbf{a}_1, \ldots, \mathbf{a}_m$; otherwise, $\mathbf{a}$ is said to be linearly independent of $\mathbf{a}_1, \ldots, \mathbf{a}_m$. It can be noted immediately that the null vector is not linearly independent of any other vector or set of vectors since

$$\mathbf{0} = 0\mathbf{a}_1 + 0\mathbf{a}_2 + \cdots + 0\mathbf{a}_m. \tag{2-58}$$

No set of linearly independent vectors can contain the null vector.

It is clear that if a set of vectors is linearly independent, then any subset of these vectors is also linearly independent. Similarly, if any given set of vectors is linearly dependent, any larger set of vectors containing the given set of vectors is also linearly dependent. We say that the maximum number of linearly independent vectors in a set is k if in the set there is at least one subset of k vectors which are linearly independent, and if there is no linearly independent subset containing $k + 1$ vectors.

Suppose that $k < m$ is the maximum number of linearly independent vectors in a set of m vectors $\mathbf{a}_1, \ldots, \mathbf{a}_m$ from E^n. Then, given any linearly independent subset of k vectors in this set, every other vector in the set can be written as a linear combination of these k vectors. To see this label the vectors so that $\mathbf{a}_1, \ldots, \mathbf{a}_k$ are linearly independent. The set $\mathbf{a}_1, \ldots, \mathbf{a}_k, \mathbf{a}_r$ must be linearly dependent for any $r = k + 1, \ldots, m$. This implies that (2–54) holds and at least one $\lambda_i \neq 0$. However, λ_r cannot be zero, because this would contradict the fact that $\mathbf{a}_1, \ldots, \mathbf{a}_k$ are linearly independent. Hence $\mathbf{a}_r$ can be written as a linear combination of $\mathbf{a}_1, \ldots, \mathbf{a}_k$.

EXAMPLES: (1) The unit vectors for E^n, $\mathbf{e}_1, \ldots, \mathbf{e}_n$ are linearly independent since

$$\sum_{i=1}^{n} \lambda_i \mathbf{e}_i = [\lambda_1, \lambda_2, \ldots, \lambda_n] = \mathbf{0}$$

implies that $\lambda_1 = \lambda_2 = \cdots = \lambda_n = 0$.

(2) Any two non-null vectors $\mathbf{a}$, $\mathbf{b}$ are linearly dependent if $\lambda_1 \mathbf{a} + \lambda_2 \mathbf{b} = \mathbf{0}$, $\lambda_1, \lambda_2 \neq 0$ (why must both λ_1 and λ_2 differ from zero?), or $\mathbf{b} = \lambda \mathbf{a}$. Thus, two vectors are linearly dependent if one is a scalar multiple of the other. Geometrically, in E^2, this means that two vectors are linearly dependent if they lie on the same line through the origin. Because only vectors lying along the same line are linearly dependent in E^2, it follows that any two vectors not lying along the same line in E^2 are linearly independent. In E^2, any three vectors are linearly dependent

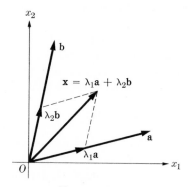

FIGURE 2–3

since one of the vectors can be written as a linear combination of the other two (see Fig. 2–3).

In E^3, any two vectors lie in a plane through the origin. Any vector which is a linear combination of these vectors will lie in this plane. Thus, if three vectors in E^3 are linearly dependent, they lie in a plane through the origin. Any three vectors in E^3 which do not lie in a plane through the origin are linearly independent. Any four vectors in E^3 must be linearly dependent.

2–10 Bases. The concept of a basis is very important in linear programming. We begin with the following definitions:

Spanning set: *A set of vectors* $\mathbf{a}_1, \ldots, \mathbf{a}_r$ *from* E^n *is said to span or generate* E^n *if every vector in* E^n *can be written as a linear combination of* $\mathbf{a}_1, \ldots, \mathbf{a}_r$.

From (2–49) we note that the unit vectors span E^n. A spanning set containing the smallest possible number of vectors must be linearly independent, since in a linearly dependent set at least one vector can be written as a linear combination of the others and hence is not needed in the spanning set.

Basis: *A basis for* E^n *is a linearly independent subset of vectors from* E^n *which spans the entire space.*

The unit vectors are a basis for E^n since they are linearly independent. A basis for E^n is by no means unique. As we shall see, there exists an infinite number of bases for E^n.

The representation of any vector in terms of a set of basis vectors is unique, that is, any vector in E^n can be written as a linear combination of a set of basis vectors in only one way. To prove this, let $\mathbf{b}$ be any vector in E^n, and let $\mathbf{a}_1, \ldots, \mathbf{a}_r$ be a set of basis vectors. Suppose that $\mathbf{b}$ can be written as a linear combination of the basis vectors in two different ways, namely:

$$\mathbf{b} = \sum_{i=1}^{r} \lambda_i \mathbf{a}_i; \qquad \mathbf{b} = \sum_{i=1}^{r} \lambda_i' \mathbf{a}_i. \tag{2–59}$$

Subtracting, we obtain $\sum_i (\lambda_i - \lambda_i')\mathbf{a}_i = \mathbf{0}$, and since the set of basis vectors is linearly independent, $\lambda_i - \lambda_i' = 0$, $i = 1, \ldots, r$, or $\lambda_i = \lambda_i'$.

We shall now investigate the conditions under which an arbitrary vector $\mathbf{b}$ from E^n can replace one of the vectors in a basis so that the new set of vectors is also a basis. The technique of replacing one vector in a basis by another such that the new set is also a basis is fundamental to the simplex technique for solving linear programming problems.

Given a set of basis vectors $\mathbf{a}_1, \ldots, \mathbf{a}_r$ *for* E^n *and any other vector* $\mathbf{b} \neq \mathbf{0}$ *from* E^n. *Then in the expression of* $\mathbf{b}$ *as a linear combination of the* $\mathbf{a}_i$,

$$\mathbf{b} = \sum_{i=1}^{r} \alpha_i \mathbf{a}_i, \tag{2-60}$$

if any vector $\mathbf{a}_i$ for which $\alpha_i \neq 0$ is removed from the set $\mathbf{a}_1, \ldots, \mathbf{a}_r$ and $\mathbf{b}$ is added to the set, the new collection of r vectors is also a basis for E^n. To prove this, note that at least one α_i in (2-60) is different from zero since $\mathbf{b} \neq \mathbf{0}$. Number the vectors so that $\alpha_r \neq 0$. We wish to show that the set $\mathbf{a}_1, \ldots, \mathbf{a}_{r-1}, \mathbf{b}$ is a basis for E^n. To show that the set $\mathbf{a}_1, \ldots, \mathbf{a}_{r-1}, \mathbf{b}$ is linearly independent, suppose the contrary, i.e., assume that

$$\sum_{i=1}^{r-1} \delta_i \mathbf{a}_i + \delta \mathbf{b} = \mathbf{0}, \tag{2-61}$$

and at least one δ_i or δ is not zero. Now δ cannot be zero in (2-61) because this would contradict the fact that the $\mathbf{a}_i, i = 1, \ldots, r - 1$, are linearly independent. However, using (2-60) to eliminate $\mathbf{b}$, we obtain

$$\sum_{i=1}^{r-1} (\delta_i + \alpha_i \delta) \mathbf{a}_i + \delta \alpha_r \mathbf{a}_r = \mathbf{0}, \tag{2-62}$$

and $\delta \alpha_r \neq 0$. However, this contradicts the fact that the $\mathbf{a}_i, i = 1, \ldots, r$, are linearly independent. Hence the set $\mathbf{a}_1, \ldots, \mathbf{a}_{r-1}, \mathbf{b}$ is linearly independent.

It is easy to see that any vector $\mathbf{x}$ in E^n can be written as a linear combination of $\mathbf{a}_1, \ldots, \mathbf{a}_{r-1}, \mathbf{b}$. Since the $\mathbf{a}_i, i = 1, \ldots, r$, form a basis, we can write

$$\mathbf{x} = \sum_{i=1}^{r} \gamma_i \mathbf{a}_i. \tag{2-63}$$

Eliminating $\mathbf{a}_r$ in (2-63) by means of (2-60), we obtain

$$\mathbf{x} = \sum_{i=1}^{r-1} \left(\gamma_i - \frac{\alpha_i}{\alpha_r} \gamma_r \right) \mathbf{a}_i + \frac{\gamma_r}{\alpha_r} \mathbf{b}, \tag{2-64}$$

which expresses $\mathbf{x}$ as a linear combination of $\mathbf{a}_1, \ldots, \mathbf{a}_{r-1}, \mathbf{b}$. Hence $\mathbf{a}_1, \ldots, \mathbf{a}_{r-1}, \mathbf{b}$ is a basis for E^n.

If in (2-60) $\mathbf{b}$ replaces a vector $\mathbf{a}_i$ for which $\alpha_i = 0$, then the new set of vectors is linearly dependent and does not form a basis for E^n. To prove this, take $\alpha_r = 0$ and replace $\mathbf{a}_r$ by $\mathbf{b}$. Then

$$\mathbf{b} - \sum_{i=1}^{r-1} \alpha_i \mathbf{a}_i = \mathbf{0}. \tag{2-65}$$

The vectors $\mathbf{a}_1, \ldots, \mathbf{a}_{r-1}, \mathbf{b}$ are linearly dependent.

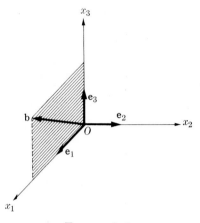

FIGURE 2–4

EXAMPLE: Imagine that we wish to insert the vector $\mathbf{b} = [3, 0, 4]$ into the basis $\mathbf{e}_1$, $\mathbf{e}_2$, $\mathbf{e}_3$ and remove one of the vectors in the basis. We have $\mathbf{b} = 3\mathbf{e}_1 + 0\mathbf{e}_2 + 4\mathbf{e}_3$. According to the preceding discussion, we can remove either $\mathbf{e}_1$ or $\mathbf{e}_3$ to obtain a new basis; that is, $\mathbf{e}_2$, $\mathbf{e}_3$, $\mathbf{b}$ or $\mathbf{e}_1$, $\mathbf{e}_2$, $\mathbf{b}$ will form a basis for E^3. We cannot remove the vector $\mathbf{e}_2$ and still maintain a basis. This is illustrated geometrically in Fig. 2–4. If $\mathbf{e}_2$ is removed, $\mathbf{e}_1$, $\mathbf{e}_3$, $\mathbf{b}$ all lie in the x_1x_3-plane and are linearly dependent. If either $\mathbf{e}_1$ or $\mathbf{e}_3$ is removed, the new set of vectors does not lie in a plane.

2–11 Number of vectors in a basis for E^n. The results obtained above lead us to suspect that every basis for E^n contains precisely n vectors. This is correct, as we shall now demonstrate.

We first prove that any two bases for E^n have the same number of basis vectors. Let $\mathbf{a}_1, \ldots, \mathbf{a}_u$ be one set of basis vectors for E^n and $\mathbf{b}_1, \ldots, \mathbf{b}_v$ be any other set of basis vectors. We wish to show that $u = v$. We can number the vectors $\mathbf{a}_i$ so that when $\mathbf{b}_v$ is expressed as a linear combination of the $\mathbf{a}_i$, $\mathbf{b}_v = \sum \lambda_i \mathbf{a}_i$, then $\lambda_u \neq 0$. Hence by the results of the previous section, $\mathbf{a}_1, \ldots, \mathbf{a}_{u-1}, \mathbf{b}_v$ is a basis for E^n. Now if we write

$$\mathbf{b}_{v-1} = \sum_{i=1}^{u-1} \delta_i \mathbf{a}_i + \delta \mathbf{b}_v, \tag{2–66}$$

at least one δ_i must be nonzero, for otherwise the set of $\mathbf{b}_j$ would not be linearly independent. Take $\delta_{u-1} \neq 0$; then $\mathbf{a}_1, \ldots, \mathbf{a}_{u-2}, \mathbf{b}_{v-1}, \mathbf{b}_v$ is a basis for E^n. This process can be continued until a basis is found which must take one of the following two forms:

$$\mathbf{a}_1, \ldots, \mathbf{a}_{u-v}, \mathbf{b}_1, \ldots, \mathbf{b}_v \quad \text{or} \quad \mathbf{b}_1, \ldots, \mathbf{b}_v.$$

There must be at least as many $\mathbf{a}_i$ as $\mathbf{b}_j$. Otherwise a state would be reached where one $\mathbf{b}_j$ was a linear combination of some of the others, contradicting the fact that the $\mathbf{b}_j$ are linearly independent. Hence $u \geq v$. However, one can start with the $\mathbf{b}_j$ and insert the $\mathbf{a}_i$. This would yield $v \geq u$. Therefore $u = v$, and we have proved the correctness of our assertion.

To determine the actual number of vectors in a basis for E^n, it is only necessary to find a basis and count the number of vectors in this basis. We have already shown that the n unit vectors form a basis for E^n. It immediately follows that every basis for E^n contains precisely n vectors.

We can now see that any set of n linearly independent vectors from E^n forms a basis for E^n. Let $\mathbf{a}_1, \ldots, \mathbf{a}_n$ be such a set of linearly independent vectors. To prove this result, we only need to start with the basis $\mathbf{e}_1, \ldots, \mathbf{e}_n$ and insert the $\mathbf{a}_i$. After n insertions, which can always be made (for the same reasons used in proving that two bases always have the same number of elements), we obtain a new basis $\mathbf{a}_1, \ldots, \mathbf{a}_n$. Thus it is obvious that any $n + 1$ vectors from E^n are linearly dependent.

Any $m < n$ linearly independent vectors from E^n form part of a basis for E^n, that is, if $\mathbf{a}_1, \ldots, \mathbf{a}_m$ from E^n are linearly independent, then $n - m$ additional vectors in E^n can be found such that $\mathbf{a}_1, \ldots, \mathbf{a}_m$ and the other $n - m$ vectors in E^n form a basis for E^n. Again, the proof depends on starting with a basis and inserting the $\mathbf{a}_i$ in precisely the same way as was done before. If we start with unit vectors as a basis, we see that the additional $n - m$ vectors used to fill out the basis can be unit vectors. As a specific example of this theorem, any non-null vector from E^n is part of a basis, and therefore there is an infinite number of bases for E^n.

We have characterized the dimension n of a euclidean space by the number of components in the set of vectors which form the space, that is, E^n is the set of all n-component vectors. We have shown that the maximum number of linearly independent vectors in E^n is n. In certain respects, it is more desirable to define the dimension of a space as the maximum number of linearly independent vectors in the space. This definition avoids connecting the dimension of a space to the number of components in the vectors forming the space. The advantage of this approach will become clear in the next section.

2–12 Vector spaces and subspaces.

VECTOR SPACE: *A vector space is a collection of vectors which is closed under the operations of addition and multiplication by a scalar.*

The expression "a set of vectors is closed under addition and multiplication by a scalar" means that if $\mathbf{a}$, $\mathbf{b}$ are in the collection, the sum $\mathbf{a} + \mathbf{b}$ is also in the collection, and if **a** is in the collection, λ**a** is in the collection for any scalar λ.

Note that distance need not be defined in a vector space. Also note that **0** is always an element of a vector space, and so is $-$**a** if **a** is. The totality of all n-component vectors is called an n-dimensional vector space and is denoted by V_n. Although E^n is clearly a vector space, it does not follow that any V_n is an E^n.

SUBSPACE: *A subspace S_n of V_n is defined to be a subset of V_n which is itself a vector space.*

The subscript n on S_n means that the vectors have n components, i.e., are elements of V_n. We define the dimension of S_n to be the maximum number of linearly independent vectors in S_n. We consider $S_n = V_n$ to be a subspace of V_n having dimension n, i.e., the subspace is all of V_n.

EXAMPLE: The set of vectors in E^3 lying in the plane $x_2 = x_3$ is a subspace of E^3, i.e., the set of all vectors $[x_1, x_2, x_2]$ (proof?). Now

$$[x_1, x_2, x_2] = x_1\mathbf{e}_1 + x_2[0, 1, 1],$$

and the dimension of the subspace is two. This is precisely what we want intuitively, since the vectors lie in a plane, i.e., in a two-dimensional space.

A clear geometric interpretation of subspaces in E^3 can be given. Any subspace of E^3 is either E^3 itself, a plane through the origin, a line through the origin, or just the origin itself (this is a subspace of a single element and has dimension 0).

A set of vectors from S_n is said to span or generate S_n if every vector in S_n can be written as a linear combination of this set of vectors. A linearly independent set of vectors from S_n which spans S_n is called a basis for S_n. If S_n has dimension k, then a basis for S_n will contain precisely k vectors. If S_n is a subspace of E^n having dimension k, then, except for notation, S_n is the same as E^k.

2–13 Rank. The n columns of an $m \times n$ matrix **A** can be considered to be vectors in E^m. Recall that the columns of **A** are denoted by $\mathbf{a}_j$.

RANK: *The rank (or more precisely the column rank) of an $m \times n$ matrix* **A**, *written $r(\mathbf{A})$, is the maximum number of linearly independent columns in* **A**.

EXAMPLE: The rank of an nth-order identity matrix is n since $\mathbf{I} = (\mathbf{e}_1, \ldots, \mathbf{e}_n)$, and the $\mathbf{e}_i$ are linearly independent.

It can be shown {LA 4–4} that the rank of **A** is k if and only if every minor of **A** having order $k + 1$ vanishes, while there is at least one minor of order k which does not vanish. This theorem provides a way to determine the rank of a matrix. We determine the order of the largest nonvanishing minor in $\mathbf{A}$, and this is the rank of $\mathbf{A}$. Although this method for determining the rank of a matrix is not too efficient computationally, it is of considerable theoretical importance. By means of this theorem it is also possible to find the maximum number of linearly independent vectors in a set $\mathbf{a}_1, \ldots, \mathbf{a}_r$ from E^n. We form the matrix $\mathbf{A} = (\mathbf{a}_1, \ldots, \mathbf{a}_r)$ and determine the order of the largest nonvanishing minor.

EXAMPLE:

$$\mathbf{A} = \begin{bmatrix} 2 & 0 & 7 \\ 3 & 3 & 6 \\ 2 & 2 & 4 \end{bmatrix}$$

has rank 2, since $|\mathbf{A}| = 0$, but there are several minors of order 2 which do not vanish.

The row rank of a matrix $\mathbf{A}$ can be defined as the maximum number of linearly independent rows in $\mathbf{A}$. It is easy to show that the row rank of $\mathbf{A}$ is equal to the column rank, i.e., the maximum number of linearly independent columns in $\mathbf{A}$ is equal to the maximum number of linearly independent rows. The rank of $\mathbf{A}$ is thus unique, and we need not distinguish between the row rank and column rank. To prove this it is only necessary to note that the row rank of $\mathbf{A}$ is equal to the column rank of $\mathbf{A}'$, and that the largest nonvanishing minor in $\mathbf{A}$ appears in $\mathbf{A}'$, and conversely.

The above results tell us that the columns (or rows) of an nth-order nonsingular matrix are linearly independent and form a basis for E^n. Also, an nth-order matrix whose columns (or rows) are a basis for E^n is nonsingular.

The following results are sometimes useful {LA 4–3}:
(1) $r(\mathbf{AB}) \leq \min [r(\mathbf{A}), r(\mathbf{B})]$. \hfill (2–67)
(2) If a matrix of rank k is multiplied in either order by a nonsingular matrix, the rank of the product is k.

2–14 Product form of the inverse. In the simplex method we have occasion to compute the inverse of a matrix for which only one column is different from that of a matrix whose inverse is known. Suppose that we have a nonsingular matrix $\mathbf{B} = (\mathbf{b}_1, \ldots, \mathbf{b}_n)$ and that $\mathbf{B}^{-1}$ is known. Now we replace column r of $\mathbf{B}$ with $\mathbf{a}$ and wish to compute the inverse of $\mathbf{B}_a = (\mathbf{b}_1, \ldots, \mathbf{b}_{r-1}, \mathbf{a}, \mathbf{b}_{r+1}, \ldots, \mathbf{b}_n)$. If the columns of $\mathbf{B}$ and $\mathbf{B}_a$ are viewed as two bases for E^n, then $\mathbf{B}_a$ is obtained from $\mathbf{B}$ by changing a single vector in the basis. Hence the results of Section 2–10 may be applied. Thus, if $\mathbf{a} = \sum_i y_i \mathbf{b}_i$, we know that $\mathbf{B}_a$ will be nonsingular if and only if $y_r \neq 0$. Assuming this to be the case, we note that

$$\mathbf{b}_r = \mathbf{B}_a \boldsymbol{\eta},$$

where

$$\boldsymbol{\eta} = \left[-\frac{y_1}{y_r}, \ldots, -\frac{y_{r-1}}{y_r}, \frac{1}{y_r}, -\frac{y_{r+1}}{y_r}, \ldots, -\frac{y_n}{y_r} \right]. \qquad (2\text{–}68)$$

Hence,

$$\mathbf{B} = \mathbf{B}_a \mathbf{E}, \qquad \mathbf{E} = (\mathbf{e}_1, \ldots, \mathbf{e}_{r-1}, \boldsymbol{\eta}, \mathbf{e}_{r+1}, \ldots, \mathbf{e}_n) \qquad (2\text{–}69)$$

or

$$\mathbf{B}_a^{-1} = \mathbf{E}\mathbf{B}^{-1}. \qquad (2\text{–}70)$$

Note that $\mathbf{E}$ is obtained from the identity matrix by replacing the rth column with $\boldsymbol{\eta}$. Also, to compute $\boldsymbol{\eta}$ we only need $\mathbf{y} = \mathbf{B}^{-1}\mathbf{a}$.

The above theory provides another way of computing the inverse of a nonsingular matrix $\mathbf{B} = (\mathbf{b}_1, \ldots, \mathbf{b}_n)$. We begin with the identity matrix $(\mathbf{I}^{-1} = \mathbf{I})$ and insert the columns of $\mathbf{B}$ one at a time. For example, we might begin by inserting the first column of $\mathbf{B}$ into $\mathbf{I}$, removing column 1 of $\mathbf{I}$, to yield $\mathbf{B}_1$. Then we might insert the second column of $\mathbf{B}$ into $\mathbf{B}_1$, removing column 2 of $\mathbf{B}_1$, to yield $\mathbf{B}_2$, etc. Then

$$\mathbf{B}^{-1} = \mathbf{E}_n \mathbf{E}_{n-1} \ldots \mathbf{E}_1, \qquad (2\text{–}71)$$

where

$$\mathbf{E}_i = (\mathbf{e}_1, \mathbf{e}_2, \ldots, \mathbf{e}_{i-1}, \boldsymbol{\eta}_i, \mathbf{e}_{i+1}, \ldots \mathbf{e}_n), \qquad (2\text{–}72)$$

$$\boldsymbol{\eta}_i = \left[-\frac{y_{1i}}{y_{ii}}, \ldots, -\frac{y_{i-1,i}}{y_{ii}}, \frac{1}{y_{ii}}, -\frac{y_{i+1,i}}{y_{ii}}, \ldots -\frac{y_{ni}}{y_{ii}} \right], \qquad (2\text{–}73)$$

and

$$\mathbf{y}_i = \mathbf{B}_{i-1}^{-1}\mathbf{b}_i, \qquad \mathbf{B}_i^{-1} = \mathbf{E}_i \mathbf{E}_{i-1}, \ldots \mathbf{E}_1 = \mathbf{E}_i \mathbf{B}_{i-1}^{-1}, \qquad i = 1, \ldots, n;$$

$$\mathbf{B}_0^{-1} = \mathbf{I}. \qquad (2\text{–}74)$$

We call (2–71) a product form of the inverse. Form (2–71) is not unique since different orders of insertion of the columns of $\mathbf{B}$ may be used and may indeed be required.

EXAMPLE: Consider a matrix $\mathbf{B} = (\mathbf{b}_1, \mathbf{b}_2, \mathbf{b}_3)$ whose inverse is

$$\mathbf{B}^{-1} = \begin{bmatrix} 2 & 0 & 4 \\ 5 & 1 & 6 \\ 7 & 9 & 3 \end{bmatrix}.$$

Let us replace the second column of $\mathbf{B}$ with $\mathbf{a} = [1, 8, 6]$ to yield the matrix $\mathbf{B}_a = (\mathbf{b}_1, \mathbf{a}, \mathbf{b}_3)$. To compute $\mathbf{B}_a^{-1}$ we first compute

$$\mathbf{y} = \mathbf{B}^{-1}\mathbf{a} = [26, 49, 97];$$

then we form the vector

$$\boldsymbol{\eta} = \left[-\frac{y_1}{y_2}, \frac{1}{y_2}, -\frac{y_3}{y_2} \right] = \left[-\frac{26}{49}, \frac{1}{49}, -\frac{97}{49} \right];$$

next we construct the matrix $\mathbf{E}$ by replacing the second column of $\mathbf{I}_3$ with $\boldsymbol{\eta}$, i.e.,

$$\mathbf{E} = \begin{bmatrix} 1 & -\frac{26}{49} & 0 \\ 0 & \frac{1}{49} & 0 \\ 0 & -\frac{97}{49} & 1 \end{bmatrix}.$$

Finally,

$$\mathbf{B}_a^{-1} = \mathbf{EB}^{-1} = \frac{1}{49} \begin{bmatrix} -32 & -26 & 40 \\ 5 & 1 & 6 \\ -142 & 344 & -435 \end{bmatrix}.$$

2–15 Simultaneous linear equations. A set (or system) of m simultaneous linear equations in n unknowns, $x_1, \ldots, x_n$, has the form

$$\begin{aligned} a_{11}x_1 + \cdots + a_{1n}x_n &= b_1, \\ &\vdots \\ a_{m1}x_1 + \cdots + a_{mn}x_n &= b_m, \end{aligned} \tag{2–75}$$

where the a_{ij}, b_i are known constants. If we write $\mathbf{A} = \|a_{ij}\|$, $\mathbf{x} = [x_1, \ldots, x_n]$, $\mathbf{b} = [b_1, \ldots, b_m]$, then using matrix notation, we see that (2–75) becomes simply $\mathbf{Ax} = \mathbf{b}$.

Let us study for the moment the case where $m = n$. Then if $r(\mathbf{A}) = n$ so that $|\mathbf{A}| \neq 0$, we obtain the unique solution $\mathbf{x} = \mathbf{A}^{-1}\mathbf{b}$. The solution is unique since the inverse is unique. We shall discuss later what happens if $r(\mathbf{A}) < n$. Using (2–30) and (2–33), we see that the solution $\mathbf{x} = \mathbf{A}^{-1}\mathbf{b}$ can be written in component form as

$$x_i = \frac{1}{|\mathbf{A}|} \sum_{j=1}^n A_{ji}b_j, \qquad i = 1, \ldots, n. \tag{2–76}$$

From the definition of a determinant, it will be observed that $\sum_j A_{ji}b_j$ is the determinant of the matrix formed from $\mathbf{A}$ by replacing column i

with **b**. Thus

$$x_1 = \frac{1}{|\mathbf{A}|} \begin{vmatrix} b_1 & a_{12} \dots a_{1n} \\ \vdots & \vdots \\ b_n & a_{n2} \dots a_{nn} \end{vmatrix} ; \ \dots \ ; \quad x_n = \frac{1}{|\mathbf{A}|} \begin{vmatrix} a_{11} \dots a_{1,n-1} & b_1 \\ \vdots & \vdots \\ a_{n1} \dots a_{n,n-1} & b_n \end{vmatrix} .$$

$$(2\text{--}77)$$

Equation (2–77) is called Cramer's rule for finding the solution to a system of n equations in n unknowns. It is not an efficient numerical procedure for finding solutions, but it is of considerable theoretical value.

A fairly efficient numerical procedure for solving a system of n equations in n unknowns is called the gaussian reduction scheme. It is perhaps the first thing one might think of in attempting to solve such a set of equations. Number the variables and equations in (2–75) (with $m = n$) so that $a_{11} \neq 0$. Divide the first equation by a_{11} and use the result to eliminate x_1 in equations $2, \dots, n$. This yields

$$\begin{aligned} x_1 + \hat{a}_{12}x_2 + \cdots + \hat{a}_{1n}x_n &= \hat{b}_1, \\ \hat{a}_{22}x_2 + \cdots + \hat{a}_{2n}x_n &= \hat{b}_2, \\ &\vdots \\ \hat{a}_{n2}x_2 + \cdots + \hat{a}_{nn}x_n &= \hat{b}_n, \end{aligned}$$

$$(2\text{--}78)$$

where

$$\hat{a}_{1j} = \frac{a_{1j}}{a_{11}}, \quad j = 2, \dots, n; \quad \hat{a}_{ij} = a_{ij} - \frac{a_{1j}}{a_{11}} a_{i1},$$

$$i = 2, \dots, n, \quad j = 2, \dots, n; \quad (2\text{--}79)$$

and

$$\hat{b}_1 = \frac{b_1}{a_{11}}, \quad \hat{b}_i = b_i - \frac{a_{i1}}{a_{11}} b_1, \quad i = 2, \dots, n.$$

Now divide the second equation of (2–78) by $\hat{a}_{22}$ (assume equations and variables are renumbered, if necessary, so that $\hat{a}_{22} \neq 0$) and eliminate x_2 in equations $3, \dots, n$. In a finite number of steps we arrive at a set of equations having the form (provided $|\mathbf{A}| \neq 0$)

$$\begin{bmatrix} 1 & h_{12} \dots h_{1n} \\ & 1 \ \dots h_{2n} \\ & & \ddots & \vdots \\ & & & 1 \end{bmatrix} \begin{bmatrix} x_1 \\ x_2 \\ \vdots \\ x_n \end{bmatrix} = \begin{bmatrix} g_1 \\ g_2 \\ \vdots \\ g_n \end{bmatrix} .$$

$$(2\text{--}80)$$

Then $x_n = g_n$, and by back substitution $x_{n-1} = g_{n-1} - h_{n-1,n} g_n$, etc.

Now let us return to (2–75) and consider the general case where m can differ from n. We allow m to be $>$, $=$, $<n$. To begin we wish to determine the conditions under which we know that there exists at least one solution to (2–75). In order to do this, we first introduce the $m \times (n + 1)$ matrix $\mathbf{A}_b = (\mathbf{A}, \mathbf{b})$; $\mathbf{A}_b$ is called the augmented matrix for the system and is formed by annexing to $\mathbf{A}$ the vector $\mathbf{b}$ which becomes column $n + 1$. It will be noted that $r(\mathbf{A}_b) \geq r(\mathbf{A})$ since every minor in $\mathbf{A}$ also appears in $\mathbf{A}_b$. It is now easy to see that if $r(\mathbf{A}_b) > r(\mathbf{A})$, then there does not exist a solution to (2–75). This follows since if $r(\mathbf{A}_b) = k > r(\mathbf{A})$, every set of k linearly independent columns from $\mathbf{A}_b$ must contain $\mathbf{b}$. Hence $\mathbf{b}$ cannot be written as a linear combination of the columns of $\mathbf{A}$, i.e., there do not exist x_j such that $\sum_j x_j \mathbf{a}_j = \mathbf{b}$. On the other hand, if $r(\mathbf{A}_b) = r(\mathbf{A}) = k$, then there exists a set of k columns from $\mathbf{A}$ such that every column in $\mathbf{A}_b$, and in particular $\mathbf{b}$, can be written as a linear combination of these k columns. Hence there exists at least one solution to (2–75) and, in fact, a solution with no more than k of the variables different from zero. The set of equations (2–75) is called consistent if there is at least one solution; otherwise it is said to be inconsistent.

EXAMPLE: The equations

$$3x_1 + 4x_2 = 7,$$
$$2.25x_1 + 3x_2 = 1$$

are inconsistent, and there is no solution since $r(\mathbf{A}) = 1$ and $r(\mathbf{A}_b) = 2$. If the first equation is multiplied by $\frac{3}{4}$, the left-hand side becomes the left-hand side of the second equation. However, the right-hand side of the first equation does not become the right-hand side of the second equation. Geometrically, the equations represent two parallel lines which do not intersect.

Let us now study a system of equations of the form (2–75) for the case where $r(\mathbf{A}) = r(\mathbf{A}_b) = k < m$. To be specific, number the equations so that the first k rows of the matrix $\mathbf{A}$ are linearly independent. Then, denoting the rows of $\mathbf{A}_b$ by $(\mathbf{a}^i, b_i)$, one can write any row with index $r > k$ as a linear combination of the first k rows, i.e.,

$$(\mathbf{a}^r, b_r) = \sum_{i=1}^{k} \lambda_{ir}(\mathbf{a}^i, b_i), \qquad r = k + 1, \ldots, m, \qquad (2\text{–}81)$$

or

$$\mathbf{a}^r = \sum_{i=1}^{k} \lambda_{ir}\mathbf{a}^i; \qquad b_r = \sum_{i=1}^{k} \lambda_{ir}b_i, \qquad r = k + 1, \ldots, m. \qquad (2\text{–}82)$$

Now suppose that $\mathbf{x}$ satisfies the first k equations of (2–75), i.e., $\mathbf{a}^i\mathbf{x} = b_i$,

$i = 1, \ldots, k$. Then

$$\mathbf{a}^r \mathbf{x} = \sum_{i=1}^{k} \lambda_{ir} \mathbf{a}^i \mathbf{x} = \sum_{i=1}^{k} \lambda_{ir} b_i = b_r, \qquad r = k+1, \ldots, m. \quad (2\text{-}83)$$

Thus any $\mathbf{x}$ which satisfies k equations $\mathbf{a}^i \mathbf{x} = b_i$ for which the corresponding rows of $\mathbf{A}$ are linearly independent satisfies all m equations. In other words, all but k equations may be ignored in the process of seeking solutions to (2–75). We say that $m - k$ of the equations are redundant, i.e., they do not place any additional constraints on the variables.

We have assumed that the first k rows of the matrix $\mathbf{A}$ are linearly independent. Denote by $\mathbf{A}_1$ the submatrix formed from the first k rows and columns of $\mathbf{A}$. Then we can write the first k equations of (2–75) as

$$\mathbf{A}_1 \mathbf{x}_\alpha + \mathbf{R} \mathbf{x}_\beta = \mathbf{b}^*, \qquad (2\text{-}84)$$

where $\mathbf{x}_\alpha = [x_1, \ldots, x_k]$, $\mathbf{x}_\beta = [x_{k+1}, \ldots, x_n]$, $\mathbf{b}^* = [b_1, \ldots, b_k]$, and $\mathbf{R}$ contains the last $n - k$ columns of the first k rows of $\mathbf{A}$. Any $\mathbf{x} = [\mathbf{x}_\alpha, \mathbf{x}_\beta]$ which satisfies (2–84) satisfies all m equations (2–75). Now assume that the variables have been numbered so that $\mathbf{A}_1$ is nonsingular; then we can write

$$\mathbf{x}_\alpha = \mathbf{A}_1^{-1} \mathbf{b}^* - \mathbf{A}_1^{-1} \mathbf{R} \mathbf{x}_\beta. \qquad (2\text{-}85)$$

Hence given any $\mathbf{x}_\beta$, we can solve uniquely for $\mathbf{x}_\alpha$ in terms of $\mathbf{x}_\beta$. Therefore, arbitrary values can be assigned to the $n - k$ variables in $\mathbf{x}_\beta$; values for the remaining k variables in $\mathbf{x}$ can be found so that $\mathbf{x} = [\mathbf{x}_\alpha, \mathbf{x}_\beta]$ is a solution to (2–75). All solutions to (2–75) can be generated by assigning all possible values to the set of variables in $\mathbf{x}_\beta$. Thus, if $n > k$, there will be an infinite number of different solutions to (2–75). We have shown, therefore, that a set of equations $\mathbf{Ax} = \mathbf{b}$ has either no solution, a unique solution, or an infinite number of solutions.

Let $\mathbf{x}_1$ be any solution to (2–75). Then any other solution $\mathbf{x}_2$ to (2–75) can be written $\mathbf{x}_2 = \mathbf{x}_1 + \mathbf{y}$, $\mathbf{y} = \mathbf{x}_2 - \mathbf{x}_1$. Note that $\mathbf{y}$ satisfies $\mathbf{Ay} = \mathbf{0}$. A set of linear equations $\mathbf{Ax} = \mathbf{0}$ is said to be homogeneous. We have shown that every solution to (2–75) can be obtained from one solution to (2–75) plus all solutions to the set of homogeneous equations. It is easy to demonstrate that the set of all solutions to $\mathbf{Ax} = \mathbf{0}$ is a subspace of E^n. The dimension of this subspace can be shown to be $n - k$, where $r(\mathbf{A}) = k$ {LA 5–6}. Then the dimension of the space generated by the solutions to (2–75) must also have dimension $n - k$. However, if $\mathbf{b} \neq \mathbf{0}$, the space is not a subspace of E^n because $\mathbf{0}$ is not a solution. The space generated by the solution to (2–75) with $\mathbf{b} \neq \mathbf{0}$ is called an affine subspace. This space is translated away from the origin because $\mathbf{b} \neq \mathbf{0}$.

EXAMPLE: The solutions to $a_1x_1 + a_2x_2 + a_3x_3 = b$ lie on a plane. This plane does not pass through the origin unless $b = 0$.

2–16 Basic solutions. We now wish to study solutions to a set of m equations $\mathbf{Ax} = \mathbf{b}$ in $n > m$ unknowns, which have as many of the variables equal to zero as possible. From the previous section we know that if $r(\mathbf{A}) = k$ and we select any k linearly independent columns from $\mathbf{A}$, we can assign arbitrary values to the $n - k$ variables not associated with these columns. The remaining k variables will be uniquely determined in terms of the $n - k$ variables. Thus for such a system, we can set $n - k$ variables to zero; the remaining k variables will, in general, be different from zero since the equations must be satisfied (in certain cases, however, one or more of these k variables will be zero). To be specific, we shall assume that $r(\mathbf{A}) = r(\mathbf{A}_b) = m$. This implies that none of the equations is redundant.

BASIC SOLUTION: *Given a system of m simultaneous linear equations in n unknowns, $\mathbf{Ax} = \mathbf{b}$ (m < n) and $r(\mathbf{A}) = m$. If any $m \times m$ non-singular matrix is chosen from $\mathbf{A}$, and if all the $n - m$ variables not associated with the columns of this matrix are set equal to zero, the solution to the resulting system of equations is called a basic solution. The m variables which can be different from zero are called basic variables.*

Let us choose m linearly independent columns from $\mathbf{A}$ and form a matrix $\mathbf{B}$ whose columns are the columns selected from $\mathbf{A}$. Then we can write a basic solution as $\mathbf{x}_B = \mathbf{B}^{-1}\mathbf{b}$, where all variables not associated with the columns from $\mathbf{A}$ in $\mathbf{B}$ are set equal to zero.

How many basic solutions are possible in a system of m equations and n unknowns? The answer is the number of combinations of n things taken m at a time, that is, $n!/m!(n - m)!$, and this is the maximum number of basic solutions. To obtain all these solutions, every set of m columns from $\mathbf{A}$ would have to be linearly independent.

DEGENERACY: *A basic solution to $\mathbf{Ax} = \mathbf{b}$ is degenerate if one or more of the basic variables vanish.*

It is easy to prove the following {LA 5–8}:

(1) A necessary and sufficient condition for the existence and non-degeneracy of all possible basic solutions of $\mathbf{Ax} = \mathbf{b}$ is the linear independence of every set of m columns from the augmented matrix $\mathbf{A}_b = (\mathbf{A}, \mathbf{b})$.

(2) A necessary and sufficient condition for any given basic solution $\mathbf{x}_B = \mathbf{B}^{-1}\mathbf{b}$ to be nondegenerate is the linear independence of $\mathbf{b}$ and every set of $m - 1$ columns from $\mathbf{B}$.

If we have a solution to (2–75) which involves precisely m nonzero variables, and if this solution is unique, then it must be a basic solution.

To prove this it is only necessary to show that the columns of **A** associated with the nonzero variables are linearly independent. If they were dependent, then some one of them, say k, could be expressed as a linear combination of the others. This would, however, contradict the fact that the solution is unique because, for any arbitrary value of x_k, values of the other $m - 1$ variables could be found (the zero variables remaining zero) that maintain a solution.

EXAMPLE: Let us find all basic solutions for

$$x_1 + 2x_2 + x_3 = 4,$$
$$2x_1 + x_2 + 5x_3 = 5.$$

The maximum possible number of basic solutions is $3!/2!1! = 3$.

First we set $x_3 = 0$ and solve for x_1 and x_2, obtaining $x_1 = 2$, $x_2 = 1$. Next we set $x_2 = 0$ and solve for x_1 and x_3, obtaining $x_1 = 5$, $x_3 = -1$. Finally, we set $x_1 = 0$ and solve for x_2 and x_3, obtaining $x_2 = \frac{5}{3}$, $x_3 = \frac{2}{3}$. Thus all three basic solutions exist and are nondegenerate.

2–17 Linear transformations. The algebra of matrices is often referred to as the algebra of linear transformations. Let **A** be an $m \times n$ matrix. Then for any vector **x** in E^n, the vector $\mathbf{y} = \mathbf{Ax}$ can be considered to be a vector in E^m. To each vector or point **x** in E^n there corresponds a point $\mathbf{y} = \mathbf{Ax}$ in E^m. The point $\mathbf{y} = \mathbf{Ax}$ is called the image of **x**. We say that **A** maps E^n into all or part of E^m. The relation $\mathbf{y} = \mathbf{Ax}$ is also said to transform each point in E^n into a point in E^m. A matrix transformation of the form $\mathbf{y} = \mathbf{Ax}$ is said to be a linear transformation. A matrix or linear transformation has the property of preserving addition under the transformation: If $\mathbf{y}_1 = \mathbf{Ax}_1$ and $\mathbf{y}_2 = \mathbf{Ax}_2$, then if $\mathbf{y}_3 = \mathbf{A}(\mathbf{x}_1 + \mathbf{x}_2)$, it follows that $\mathbf{y}_3 = \mathbf{y}_1 + \mathbf{y}_2$. Also a matrix or linear transformation preserves multiplication by a scalar, i.e., if $\mathbf{y} = \mathbf{Ax}$ and $\hat{\mathbf{y}} = \mathbf{A}(\lambda\mathbf{x})$, then $\hat{\mathbf{y}} = \lambda\mathbf{y}$.

If **A** is an $m \times r$ matrix and **B** is an $r \times n$ matrix, the relation $\mathbf{y} = \mathbf{ABx}$ can be viewed as a sequence of linear transformations. The matrix **B** takes a point in E^n into a point in E^r, and **A** takes the point in E^r into a point in E^m.

2–18 Point sets. On various occasions, we have used the notion of a set, for example, a set of n component vectors. The notion of a set is so basic that it is somewhat difficult to give its definition in terms of more fundamental ideas. The following expressions are synonymous: (1) a set of elements, (2) a collection of objects, (3) a number of things. A set consists of a finite or infinite number of elements. Sets will be denoted by capital letters, for example, A, B. The elements of the set will be denoted by a_i, b_i, etc. Braces $\{\ \}$ enclose the elements belonging to a set. Thus the set A containing elements a_i can be written $A = \{a_i\}$.

Two sets A and B are equal, $A = B$, if they contain precisely the same elements. The notation $a_i \in A$ indicates that a_i is an element of A, and $b_i \notin A$ means that b_i is not an element of A. A subset B of a set A is a set all of whose elements are in A. However, not all elements of A need to be in the subset B; B is a proper subset of A if A contains at least one element which is not in B. The notation $B \subset A$ or $A \supset B$ indicates that B is a subset of A. *The intersection of a finite number of sets $A_1, \ldots, A_k$, written $A_1 \cap A_2 \cap \cdots \cap A_k$, is the set containing all elements common to $A_1, \ldots, A_k$. The union of a finite number of sets $A_1, \ldots, A_k$, written $A_1 \cup A_2 \cup \cdots \cup A_k$, is the set containing all elements in at least one of the sets $A_1, \ldots, A_k$.*

Point sets are sets whose elements are points or vectors in E^n. Since our approach here will be mainly geometric, we shall often refer to vectors as points in E^n. Our future discussions will be limited to point sets. These sets may contain either a finite or infinite number of elements. Usually, however, they will contain an infinite number of elements. Point sets are often defined by some property or properties which the set of points satisfy. In E^2, for example, let us consider the set of points lying inside a circle of unit radius with center at the origin, that is, the set of points satisfying the inequality $x_1^2 + x_2^2 < 1$. A convenient representation for the set X is $X = \{[x_1, x_2] | x_1^2 + x_1^2 < 1\}$. In general, the notation

$$X = \{\mathbf{x} | \mathbf{P}(\mathbf{x})\} \qquad (2\text{–}86)$$

will indicate that the set of points $X = \{\mathbf{x}\}$ has the property (or properties) $\mathbf{P}(\mathbf{x})$. In the above example, the property $\mathbf{P}$ is the inequality $x_1^2 + x_2^2 < 1$. If there are no points with property $\mathbf{P}$, then the set (2–86) contains no elements, and is called empty or vacuous. We shall always assume that there is at least one element in a set unless otherwise stated.

A hypersphere in E^n with center at $\mathbf{a}$ and radius $\epsilon > 0$ is defined to be the set of points $X = \{\mathbf{x} | |\mathbf{x} - \mathbf{a}| = \epsilon\}$, i.e., the equation for a hypersphere in E^n is $\sum_{i=1}^{n} (x_i - a_i)^2 = \epsilon^2$, which is a circle in E^2 and a sphere in E^3. *The inside of a hypersphere with center at $\mathbf{a}$ and radius ϵ is the set of points $X = \{\mathbf{x} | |\mathbf{x} - \mathbf{a}| < \epsilon\}$. An ϵ-neighborhood about the point $\mathbf{a}$ is defined as the set of points lying inside the hypersphere with center at $\mathbf{a}$ and radius ϵ. A point $\mathbf{a}$ is an interior point of the set A if there exists an ϵ-neighborhood about $\mathbf{a}$ which contains only points of the set A.* An interior point of A must be an element of A. *A point $\mathbf{a}$ is a boundary point of the set A if every ϵ-neighborhood about $\mathbf{a}$ (regardless of how small $\epsilon > 0$ may be) contains points which are in the set and points which are not in the set.* A boundary point of A does not have to be an element of A. *A set A is an open set* *if it contains only interior points. A set A is a closed set if it contains all its boundary points.* A set may be neither open nor closed, i.e., it may contain some but not all of its boundary points. *A set is said to be strictly bounded if there exists a positive number r such that for every* $\mathbf{a} \in A$, $|\mathbf{a}| < r$. A strictly bounded set lies inside a hypersphere of radius r with center at the origin. *The set A is bounded from below if there exists an* $\mathbf{r}$ *with each component finite such that for all* $\mathbf{a} \in A$, $\mathbf{r} \leq \mathbf{a}$. A set which is bounded from below has a lower limit on each component of every point in the set.

2–19 Lines and hyperplanes. Consider the line in E^2 shown in Fig. 2–5. This line passes through the points $\mathbf{x}_1$ and $\mathbf{x}_2$, and the vector $\mathbf{x}_2 - \mathbf{x}_1$ is parallel to the line. It follows from the law for addition of vectors that for any point $\mathbf{x}$ on the line, there exists a λ such that $\mathbf{x} = \mathbf{x}_1 + \lambda(\mathbf{x}_2 - \mathbf{x}_1) = \lambda\mathbf{x}_2 + (1 - \lambda)\mathbf{x}_1$. *In E^n, we define the line through the two points* $\mathbf{x}_1$ *and* $\mathbf{x}_2$, $\mathbf{x}_1 \neq \mathbf{x}_2$, *to be the set of points*

$$X = \{\mathbf{x} | \mathbf{x} = \lambda\mathbf{x}_2 + (1 - \lambda)\mathbf{x}_1, \text{ all real } \lambda\}. \tag{2–87}$$

In Fig. 2–5 note that as λ varies between 0 and 1, that part of the line joining $\mathbf{x}_1$ to $\mathbf{x}_2$ is traced out. *In E^n, the line segment joining points* $\mathbf{x}_1$ *and* $\mathbf{x}_2$ *is defined to be the set of points*

$$X = \{\mathbf{x} | \mathbf{x} = \lambda\mathbf{x}_2 + (1 - \lambda)\mathbf{x}_1, \ 0 \leq \lambda \leq 1\}. \tag{2–88}$$

In E^2, $c_1x_1 + c_2x_2 = z$ is a line for given values of c_1, c_2, and z, while in E^3, $c_1x_1 + c_2x_2 + c_3x_3 = z$ is a plane. *In E^n we say that the set of*

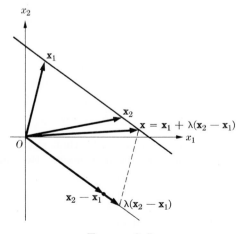

FIGURE 2–5

points $\mathbf{x}$ *satisfying*

$$c_1 x_1 + c_2 x_2 + \cdots + c_n x_n = z \qquad (\text{not all } c_i = 0) \qquad (2\text{--}89)$$

defines a hyperplane for given values of the c_i and z. If we write $\mathbf{c} = (c_1, \ldots, c_n)$, then the hyperplane (2–89) can be written $\mathbf{cx} = z$. In a linear programming problem the set of all $\mathbf{x}$ yielding a given value of the objective function is a hyperplane.

A hyperplane passes through the origin if and only if $z = 0$. Thus a hyperplane through the origin can be written $\mathbf{cx} = 0$. Note that this relation implies that $\mathbf{c}$ is orthogonal to every vector $\mathbf{x}$ in the hyperplane. When $z \neq 0$, then if $\mathbf{x}_1, \mathbf{x}_2$ satisfy (2–89), i.e., lie on the hyperplane, $\mathbf{c}(\mathbf{x}_2 - \mathbf{x}_1) = 0$. Thus, in general, $\mathbf{c}$ is called a vector normal to the hyperplane; $\pm \mathbf{c}/|\mathbf{c}|$ are called unit normals. Two hyperplanes are said to be parallel if they have the same unit normal. Thus the hyperplanes $\mathbf{c}_1 \mathbf{x} = z_1$ and $\mathbf{c}_2 \mathbf{x} = z_2$ are parallel if $\mathbf{c}_1 = \lambda \mathbf{c}_2$, $\lambda \neq 0$.

Consider the hyperplane $\mathbf{cx} = z_0$. Then consider the set of points $\mathbf{x}_0 + \lambda \mathbf{c}'$, $\lambda > 0$, $\mathbf{cx}_0 = z_0$ ($\mathbf{c}$ is a row vector, so $\mathbf{c}'$ is a column vector). Note that these points lie on the hyperplane $\mathbf{cx} = z_1$, where $z_1 = z_0 + \lambda |\mathbf{c}|^2 > z_0$. Points lying on the hyperplane $\mathbf{cx} = z_1$ satisfy $\mathbf{cx} > z_0$. Intuitively we say that the hyperplane $\mathbf{cx} = z_1$ is obtained by moving $\mathbf{cx} = z_0$ parallel to itself in the direction of $\mathbf{c}$.

A hyperplane $\mathbf{cx} = z$ divides all of E^n into three mutually exclusive and collectively exhaustive sets. These are: (1) $X_1 = \{\mathbf{x} | \mathbf{cx} < z\}$, (2) $X_2 = \{\mathbf{x} | \mathbf{cx} = z\}$, (3) $X_3 = \{\mathbf{x} | \mathbf{cx} > z\}$. *The sets X_1, X_3 are called open half-spaces.* In E^2 and E^3, a half-space is all of E^2 or E^3 lying on one side of a line or plane, respectively. The sets $X_4 = \{\mathbf{x} | \mathbf{cx} \leq z\}$ and $X_5 = \{\mathbf{x} | \mathbf{cx} \geq z\}$ are called closed half-spaces. Note that $X_4 \cap X_5 = X_2$.

Hyperplanes are closed sets. In fact, every point on the hyperplane is a boundary point, and no point not on the hyperplane can be a boundary point. *Also, closed half-spaces are closed sets.* On the other hand, open half-spaces are open sets.

2–20 Convex sets. We begin by defining some important concepts.

CONVEX SET: *A set X is convex if for any points $\mathbf{x}_1, \mathbf{x}_2$ in the set, the line segment joining these points is also in the set.*

This definition implies that if $\mathbf{x}_1, \mathbf{x}_2 \in X$, then every point $\mathbf{x} = \lambda \mathbf{x}_2 + (1 - \lambda)\mathbf{x}_1$, $0 \leq \lambda \leq 1$, must also be in the set. By convention, we say that any set containing only one point is convex. The expression $\lambda \mathbf{x}_2 + (1 - \lambda)\mathbf{x}_1$, $0 \leq \lambda \leq 1$, is often referred to as a convex combination of $\mathbf{x}_1, \mathbf{x}_2$ (for a given λ). Intuitively, a convex set cannot have any "holes" in it; it is "solid," and not "re-entrant," i.e., its boundaries are always "flat" or "bent away" from the set.

EXTREME POINT: *A point* **x** *is an extreme point of a convex set if and only if there do not exist other points* $\mathbf{x}_1$, $\mathbf{x}_2$, $\mathbf{x}_1 \neq \mathbf{x}_2$, *in the set such that* $\mathbf{x} = \lambda\mathbf{x}_2 + (1 - \lambda)\mathbf{x}_1$, $0 < \lambda < 1$.

Note that strict inequalities are imposed on λ. The definition stipulates that an extreme point cannot be "between" any other two points of the set. Clearly, an extreme point is a boundary point of the set, for otherwise it would be between some other two points. Not all boundary points of a convex set are necessarily extreme points. Some boundary points may lie between two other boundary points.

EXAMPLES: (1) A triangle and its interior form a convex set. The vertices of the triangle are its only extreme points.

(2) The set $X = \{[x_1, x_2] | x_1^2 + x_2^2 \leq 1\}$ is convex. Every point on the circumference is an extreme point.

(3) The set in Fig. 2–6 is not convex since the line joining $\mathbf{x}_1$ and $\mathbf{x}_2$ does not lie entirely within the set. The set is re-entrant.

(4) The polygons in Fig. 2–7 are convex sets, and the extreme points are the vertices. Point $\mathbf{x}_1$ is not an extreme point because it can be represented as a convex combination of $\mathbf{x}_2$ and $\mathbf{x}_3$, with $0 < \lambda < 1$.

A hyperplane is a convex set. To prove this it is only necessary to note that if $\mathbf{x}_1$ and $\mathbf{x}_2$ are on the hyperplane, that is, $\mathbf{c}\mathbf{x}_1 = z$, $\mathbf{c}\mathbf{x}_2 = z$, then $\mathbf{x} = \lambda\mathbf{x}_2 + (1 - \lambda)\mathbf{x}_1$ is on the hyperplane since

$$\mathbf{c}\mathbf{x} = \mathbf{c}[\lambda\mathbf{x}_2 + (1 - \lambda)\mathbf{x}_1] = \lambda\mathbf{c}\mathbf{x}_2 + (1 - \lambda)\mathbf{c}\mathbf{x}_1 = \lambda z + (1 - \lambda)z = z.$$
$$(2\text{–}90)$$

Similarly, *open and closed half-spaces are convex sets.*

The intersection of two convex sets is also convex. To prove this consider the convex sets X_1, X_2 and let $\mathbf{x}_1$, $\mathbf{x}_2$ be any two points in $X_3 = X_1 \cap X_2$ (if there is only one point in X_3, then X_3 is automatically convex). Thus $\lambda\mathbf{x}_2 + (1 - \lambda)\mathbf{x}_1 \in X_1$ for $0 \leq \lambda \leq 1$ and $\lambda\mathbf{x}_2 + (1 - \lambda)\mathbf{x}_1 \in X_2$ for

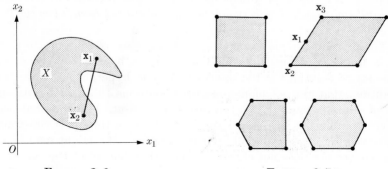

FIGURE 2–6   FIGURE 2–7

$0 \leq \lambda \leq 1$. Hence $\lambda \mathbf{x}_2 + (1 - \lambda)\mathbf{x}_1 \in X_1 \cap X_2 = X_3$, and X_3 is convex. *If X_1 and X_2 are closed sets, then $X_3 = X_1 \cap X_2$ is also closed.* To see this, it is only necessary to note that every boundary point of X_3 is a boundary point of X_1 or X_2. However, X_1, X_2 are closed; hence X_3 contains all its boundary points and is closed. More generally *the intersection of any finite number of convex sets is convex, and if each of the sets is closed, the intersection is also closed.*

The above results show that *the intersection of a finite number of hyperplanes, or half-spaces, or of both is a convex set.* Furthermore, the intersection of a finite number of hyperplanes, or closed half-spaces, or of both is a closed convex set. This result has an immediate application to linear programming. In Chapter 1 we saw that the constraints on a linear programming problem can be written

$$\sum_{j=1}^{r} a_{ij}x_j \{\leq = \geq\} b_i, \qquad i = 1, \ldots, m. \qquad (2\text{--}91)$$

If we let $\mathbf{a}^i = (a_{1i}, \ldots, a_{ri})$, then (2–91) becomes $\mathbf{a}^i \mathbf{x} \{\leq = \geq\} b_i$, $i = 1, \ldots, m$. Each one of the constraints requires that the allowable $\mathbf{x}$ be in some given closed half-space in E^r or, if the strict equality holds, lie on some given hyperplane. In addition, there are the non-negativity restrictions $x_j \geq 0$, $j = 1, \ldots, r$. If we write $\mathbf{a}^{m+j} = \mathbf{e}'_j$, then $x_j \geq 0$ becomes $\mathbf{a}^{m+j}\mathbf{x} = \mathbf{e}'_j\mathbf{x} \geq 0$. Each of the non-negativity restrictions also requires that the allowable $\mathbf{x}$ be in some closed half-space. The region of E^r defined by $x_j \geq 0$, $j = 1, \ldots, r$, is called the non-negative orthant of E^r. Now we can see that any feasible solution $\mathbf{x}$ must simultaneously be an element of each of the sets

$$X_i = \{\mathbf{x}|\mathbf{a}^i\mathbf{x}(\leq = \geq)b_i\}, \qquad i = 1, \ldots, m + r, \qquad (2\text{--}92)$$

where $b_i = 0$, $i = m + 1, \ldots, m + r$. Thus the set of feasible solutions is the intersection of the $m + r$ sets X_i. Therefore, *the set of feasible solutions to a linear programming problem (if a feasible solution exists) is a closed convex set.* Furthermore, this set is bounded from below (by $\mathbf{0}$) since $\mathbf{x} \geq \mathbf{0}$.

The preceding analysis also shows that the set of solutions to a system of m linear equations in n unknowns, $\mathbf{Ax} = \mathbf{b}$, is a closed convex set. The set of solutions is the intersection of m hyperplanes. It is true, in addition, that the set of non-negative solutions to $\mathbf{Ax} = \mathbf{b}$, that is, the set of solutions with $\mathbf{x} \geq \mathbf{0}$, is a closed convex set. Later we shall see that it is advantageous to convert any inequalities in the set of constraints to equations by introducing additional variables. We might note here that this conversion does not change the fact that the set of feasible solutions is a convex set.

We have already defined a convex combination of two points. This definition can easily be generalized to the concept of a convex combination of m points. *A convex combination of a finite number of points* $\mathbf{x}_1, \ldots, \mathbf{x}_m$ *is defined as a point*

$$\mathbf{x} = \sum_{i=1}^{m} \mu_i \mathbf{x}_i, \quad \mu_i \geq 0, \quad i = 1, \ldots, m; \quad \sum_{i=1}^{m} \mu_i = 1. \quad (2\text{--}93)$$

It is very easy to prove directly from the definition of a convex set that the set of all convex combinations of a finite number of points $\mathbf{x}_1, \ldots, \mathbf{x}_m$ is a convex set.

CONVEX POLYHEDRON: *The set of all convex combinations of a finite number of points is called the convex polyhedron spanned by these points.*

The convex polyhedron spanned by $n + 1$ points in E^n which do not lie on a hyperplane is called a simplex. In E^2, a triangle and its interior form a simplex. The three points which generate the simplex are the vertices of the triangle.

2–21 Convex sets and hyperplanes. In this section we state four important theorems which are useful in linear programming, decision theory, and game theory.

THEOREM I: *Given any closed convex set X, a point $\mathbf{y}$ either belongs to the set X or there exists a hyperplane which contains $\mathbf{y}$ such that all of X is contained in one open half-space produced by that hyperplane.*

This theorem is proved in {LA 6–6}. It is geometrically obvious in E^2 and E^3, as Fig. 2–8 illustrates. If $\mathbf{y}$ is not in the set X, we can pass a line through $\mathbf{y}$ such that all of X lies in one open half-space produced by the line.

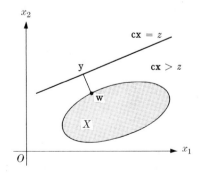

FIGURE 2–8

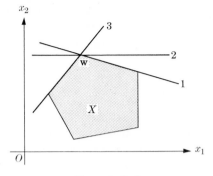

FIGURE 2–9

Given a boundary point **w** *of a convex set* X; *then* **cx** $= z$ *is called a supporting hyperplane at* **w** *if* **cw** $= z$ *and if all of* X *lies in one closed half-space produced by the hyperplane,* that is, **cu** $\geq z$ for all **u** $\in X$ or **cu** $\leq z$ for all **u** $\in X$.

THEOREM II: *If* **w** *is a boundary point of a closed convex set, then there is at least one supporting hyperplane at* **w**. This theorem is proved in {LA 6–6}. There may be more than a single supporting hyperplane at **w**. Consider, for example, Fig. 2–9.

We have already shown that the set of feasible solutions to a linear programming problem is a closed convex set, and that the function to be optimized is a hyperplane. This hyperplane is moved parallel to itself over the convex set of feasible solutions until z is made as large as possible (if z is being maximized) while still having at least one point **x** on the hyperplane in the convex set of feasible solutions.

Hence, if a given hyperplane corresponds to the optimal value of z, then no point on the hyperplane can be an interior point of the convex set of feasible solutions (recall that unbounded solutions are not called optimal). To see this, let us suppose that $z =$ **cx** is an optimal hyperplane, and that one of its points $\mathbf{x}_0$ is an interior point of the set. We select an $\epsilon > 0$ such that every point in this ϵ-neighborhood of $\mathbf{x}_0$ is in X. The point $\mathbf{x}_1 = \mathbf{x}_0 + (\epsilon/2)(\mathbf{c}'/|\mathbf{c}|)$ is in X, and $\mathbf{cx}_1 = z + (\epsilon/2)|\mathbf{c}| > z$. This contradicts the fact that z is the maximum value of the objective function. Thus, if $\mathbf{x}_0$ is an optimal solution to a linear programming problem, it must be a boundary point of the convex set of feasible solutions, and if $z =$ **cx**$_0$, then **cx** $= z$ is a supporting hyperplane to the convex set of feasible solutions at $\mathbf{x}_0$.

THEOREM III: *A closed convex set which is bounded from below has extreme points in every supporting hyperplane.*

This theorem is especially important in linear programming because it says that if there is an optimal solution, then at least one extreme point of the convex set of feasible solutions will be an optimal solution. The number of extreme points is finite (proof of this will be presented later). Hence, if we had the means of selecting the extreme points of the convex set of feasible solutions, only a finite number of points would have to be examined to find an optimal solution to the problem. This is the basis of the simplex method. We move from one extreme point to a new one until an optimal solution is found.

We shall now prove Theorem III. The hyperplane $\mathbf{cx} = z$ will be assumed to be a supporting hyperplane at $\mathbf{x}_0$ to the closed convex set X which is bounded from below. The intersection of X and $S = \{\mathbf{x} | \mathbf{cx} = z\}$ will be denoted by T. The intersection is not empty because $\mathbf{x}_0 \in T$; furthermore, since X and S are closed convex sets, so is T; T is also bounded from below since X is.

Let us show that any extreme point of T is also an extreme point of X. If $\mathbf{t}$ is any point in T, and if $\mathbf{t} = \lambda\mathbf{x}_2 + (1 - \lambda)\mathbf{x}_1$, $0 < \lambda < 1$, where $\mathbf{x}_1, \mathbf{x}_2 \in X$, then $\mathbf{x}_1, \mathbf{x}_2 \in T$. This follows from the fact that $\mathbf{ct} = \lambda\mathbf{cx}_2 + (1 - \lambda)\mathbf{cx}_1 = z$, and $\mathbf{cx}_1 \geq z$, $\mathbf{cx}_2 \geq z$ because $\mathbf{cx} = z$ is a supporting hyperplane. Noting that $\lambda > 0$, $1 - \lambda > 0$, we see that $\mathbf{ct} = z$ requires that $\mathbf{cx}_1 = z$, $\mathbf{cx}_2 = z$, that is, $\mathbf{x}_1, \mathbf{x}_2 \in T$. Thus, if $\mathbf{t}$ is an extreme point of T, there do not exist other points $\mathbf{x}_1, \mathbf{x}_2$ in X such that $\mathbf{t}$ can be written as a convex combination of these points with $0 < \lambda < 1$. Hence an extreme point of T is an extreme point of X.

We still must prove that T actually has an extreme point; this will be done by constructing an extreme point. Out of all the points in T, choose the one with the smallest (algebraic) first component. There is at least one such point since T is closed and bounded from below.

If there are more than one point with a smallest first component, choose the point or points with the smallest first and second components. If a unique point is not obtained, choose the point with the smallest first, second, and third components, etc. Finally, a unique point will be obtained, since only one point can have all its components of minimum algebraic value.

The unique point $\mathbf{t}^*$ determined by the above process is an extreme point. If $\mathbf{t}^*$ were not an extreme point, we could write

$$\mathbf{t}^* = \lambda\mathbf{t}_1 + (1 - \lambda)\mathbf{t}_2, \quad 0 < \lambda < 1, \quad \mathbf{t}_1, \mathbf{t}_2 \in T, \quad \mathbf{t}_1 \neq \mathbf{t}_2. \quad (2\text{--}94)$$

Suppose the unique $\mathbf{t}^*$ was determined on minimizing the jth component. Denote the ith component of $\mathbf{t}^*$, $\mathbf{t}_1$, $\mathbf{t}_2$ by t_i^*, t_{i1}, t_{i2}, respectively. Then from (2–94) and the definition of $\mathbf{t}^*$, it follows that $t_i^* = t_{i1} = t_{i2}$, $i = 1, \ldots, j - 1$. Then the jth component of (2–94) requires that

$t_j^* > \min [t_{j1}, t_{j2}]$ or $t_j^* = t_{j1} = t_{j2}$. Either of these alternatives contradicts the fact that t_j^* is the unique minimum for the jth component when the first $j - 1$ components are at their minimum values. Consequently $\mathbf{t}^*$ cannot be represented as a convex combination of any other two points in T $(0 < \lambda < 1)$. Hence $\mathbf{t}^*$ is an extreme point, and the theorem is proved.

THEOREM IV: *If a closed, strictly bounded convex set X has a finite number of extreme points, any point in the set can be written as a convex combination of the extreme points, that is, X is the set of all convex combinations of its extreme points.*

This theorem is proved in {LA 6–8}.

EXAMPLE: Suppose that we wish to write any point $\mathbf{w}$ inside a triangle as a convex combination of the vertices (extreme points) $\mathbf{x}_1$, $\mathbf{x}_2$, $\mathbf{x}_3$, that is, $\mathbf{w} = \sum \mu_i \mathbf{x}_i$, $\mu_i \geq 0$, $\sum \mu_i = 1$. The situation is illustrated in Fig. 2–10. First, draw a line from $\mathbf{x}_2$ through $\mathbf{w}$. It will intersect the opposite side of the triangle at $\mathbf{v}$. Then $\mathbf{w} = \lambda_1 \mathbf{x}_2 + (1 - \lambda_1)\mathbf{v}$, $0 \leq \lambda_1 \leq 1$. However, $\mathbf{v} = \lambda_2 \mathbf{x}_1 + (1 - \lambda_2)\mathbf{x}_3$. Thus

$$\mathbf{w} = \lambda_1 \mathbf{x}_2 + (1 - \lambda_1)\lambda_2 \mathbf{x}_1 + (1 - \lambda_1)(1 - \lambda_2)\mathbf{x}_3.$$

Let $\mu_1 = \lambda_2(1 - \lambda_1)$, $\mu_2 = \lambda_1$, $\mu_3 = (1 - \lambda_1)(1 - \lambda_2)$. Clearly, each $\mu_i \geq 0$, and $\mu_1 + \mu_2 + \mu_3 = 1$. The desired expression is $\mathbf{w} = \sum \mu_i \mathbf{x}_i$.

From the definition of a convex polyhedron and from Theorem IV, it follows that every closed strictly bounded convex set with a finite number of extreme points is a convex polyhedron. Convex sets with a finite number of extreme points are essentially convex polyhedrons. However, they may have the form shown in Fig. 1–5, that is, they may not be strictly bounded.

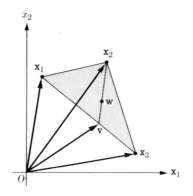

FIGURE 2–10

EDGE: *Let* $\mathbf{x}_1$, $\mathbf{x}_2$ *be distinct extreme points of the convex set* X. *The line joining them is called an edge of the convex set if it is the intersection of* X *with a supporting hyperplane. If* $\mathbf{x}^*$ *is an extreme point, and if there exists another point* $\mathbf{x} \in X$ *such that the line* $\mathbf{x}^* + \lambda(\mathbf{x} - \mathbf{x}^*)$, *all* $\lambda \geq 0$, *is in* X *and is the intersection of* X *with a supporting hyperplane, then this line is said to be an edge of the set which originates at* $\mathbf{x}^*$ *and extends to infinity.*

ADJACENT EXTREME POINTS: *Two distinct extreme points* $\mathbf{x}_1$, $\mathbf{x}_2$ *of the convex set* X *are called adjacent if the line segment joining them is an edge of the convex set.*

2–22 Convex cones. *A cone* C *is a set of points with the following property: If* $\mathbf{x}$ *is in the set, so is* $\mu\mathbf{x}$ *for all* $\mu \geq 0$. The cone generated by a set of points $X = \{\mathbf{x}\}$ is the set

$$C = \{\mathbf{y} | \mathbf{y} = \mu\mathbf{x}, \text{ all } \mu \geq 0, \text{ and all } \mathbf{x} \in X\}. \qquad (2\text{--}95)$$

In E^2, E^3, a cone as a set of points is often identical with the usual geometrical concept of a cone. Note that a cone is never a strictly bounded set (except in the trivial case where $\mathbf{0}$ is the only element in the cone). The point $\mathbf{0}$ is an element of any cone and is called the vertex of the cone. *The negative* C^- *of a cone* $C = \{\mathbf{u}\}$ *is the set of points* $C^- = \{-\mathbf{u}\}$. Naturally, C^- is a cone if C is. *The sum of two cones* $C_1 = \{\mathbf{u}\}$, $C_2 = \{\mathbf{v}\}$, *written* $C_1 + C_2$, *is the set of all points* $\mathbf{u} + \mathbf{v}$, $\mathbf{u} \in C_1$, $\mathbf{v} \in C_2$. The sum $C_1 + C_2$ is a cone. *If* $C = \{\mathbf{u}\}$ *is a cone, then* C^+, *the cone polar to* C, *is the collection of points* $\{\mathbf{v}\}$ *such that* $\mathbf{v}'\mathbf{u} \geq 0$ *for each* $\mathbf{v}$ *in the set, and all* $\mathbf{u} \in C$. It is easy to see that C^+ is a cone. Intuitively, a polar cone is the collection of all vectors which form a nonobtuse angle with all the vectors in C. Note that each $\mathbf{v} \in C^+$ must form a nonobtuse angle with every vector in C.

A cone is a convex cone if it is a convex set. It can be proved {LA 6–9} that a set of points is a convex cone if and only if the sum $\mathbf{v}_1 + \mathbf{v}_2$ is in the set when $\mathbf{v}_1$, $\mathbf{v}_2$ are, and if $\mu\mathbf{v}$ is in the set when $\mathbf{v}$ is for any $\mu \geq 0$. The sum of two convex cones is also convex. The cone generated by a convex set is a convex cone. The dimension of a convex cone C is defined to be the maximum number of linearly independent vectors in C.

Given a single point $\mathbf{a} \neq \mathbf{0}$, *a half-line, or ray, is defined as the set* $L = \{\mathbf{y} | \mathbf{y} = \mu\mathbf{a}, \text{ all } \mu \geq 0\}$. Note that a half-line is a convex cone. *A convex polyhedral cone* C *is the sum of a finite number of half-lines, i.e.,* $C = \sum_{i=1}^{r} L_i$. In this definition the term "sum" is used in the sense of sums of cones. If the point $\mathbf{a}_i \neq \mathbf{0}$ generates the half-line L_i, then a convex polyhedral cone is the collection of points

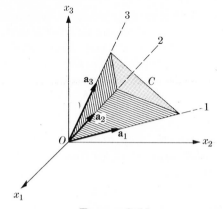

FIGURE 2–11

$$\mathbf{y} = \sum_{i=1}^{r} \mu_i \mathbf{a}_i, \qquad \text{all } \mu_i \geq 0, \qquad i = 1, \ldots, r. \qquad (2\text{–}96)$$

The cone generated by a convex polyhedron is a convex polyhedral cone.

EXAMPLE: Figure 2–11 shows the convex polyhedral cone generated by the half-lines 1, 2, 3. Note that any cross section of the polyhedral cone is a convex polyhedron.

If $\mathbf{A}$ is an $n \times r$ matrix $\mathbf{A} = (\mathbf{a}_1, \ldots, \mathbf{a}_r)$, then the set of points $\mathbf{y} = \mathbf{Ax} = \sum x_j \mathbf{a}_j$, all $\mathbf{x} \geq \mathbf{0}$, is a convex polyhedral cone in E^n. The columns $\mathbf{a}_j$ of $\mathbf{A}$ generate the half-lines whose sum yields the polyhedral cone. Thus we see that there is a non-negative solution to the set of equations $\mathbf{Ax} = \mathbf{b}$ if and only if $\mathbf{b}$ is an element of the convex polyhedral cone generated by the columns of $\mathbf{A}$.

Any given finite number of points $\mathbf{a}_1, \ldots, \mathbf{a}_r$ from E^n can be thought of as generating a convex polyhedral cone C. If the maximum number of linearly independent points in the set $\mathbf{a}_1, \ldots, \mathbf{a}_r$ is n, then the set generates a cone of dimension n. Suppose that we have in E^n an n-dimensional cone generated by $\mathbf{a}_1, \ldots, \mathbf{a}_r$. Out of the set $\mathbf{a}_1, \ldots, \mathbf{a}_r$ let us choose any $n-1$ linearly independent points $\mathbf{b}_1, \ldots, \mathbf{b}_{n-1}$. These points determine a unique hyperplane $\mathbf{cx} = 0$ through the origin in E^n. It may or may not be true that all of the cone C will lie in one of the closed half-spaces $\mathbf{cx} \geq 0$ or $\mathbf{cx} \leq 0$.

If C does lie in one closed half-space produced by $\mathbf{cx} = 0$, we make the following definitions: *The set of points $H_F = \{\mathbf{v} | \mathbf{cv} \geq 0\}$ is an extreme supporting half-space for the n-dimensional convex polyhedral cone C generated by the points $\mathbf{a}_1, \ldots, \mathbf{a}_r$ if C lies in the half-space H_F and $n-1$ linearly independent points from the set $\mathbf{a}_1, \ldots, \mathbf{a}_r$ lie on the hyperplane $\mathbf{cv} = 0$.* The hyperplane $\mathbf{cv} = 0$ is then called an extreme supporting hyperplane for the convex polyhedral cone C. It is important to note the difference between an extreme supporting hyperplane for a convex polyhedral cone and a supporting hyperplane for any convex set as defined earlier. An extreme supporting hyperplane must have $n - 1$ linearly independent points of the cone lying on it, while a supporting hyperplane need not have more than a single point in common with the set.

It is clear that the intersection F of an extreme supporting hyperplane $\mathbf{cv} = 0$ and the polyhedral cone C yields a collection of points which are on the boundary of C. Furthermore, F is itself a convex polyhedral cone generated by the points from $\mathbf{a}_1, \ldots, \mathbf{a}_r$ which lie on the hyperplane $\mathbf{cv} = 0$. We call F a subcone of C; F has dimension $n - 1$ since there are precisely $n - 1$ linearly independent points in F. In Fig. 2–11 any two of the vectors $\mathbf{a}_1$, $\mathbf{a}_2$, $\mathbf{a}_3$ uniquely determine a plane through the origin such that the cone C is contained in one half-space produced by the plane. Also, any two points from $\mathbf{a}_1$, $\mathbf{a}_2$, $\mathbf{a}_3$ are linearly independent, and hence the resulting hyperplane is an extreme supporting hyperplane. The intersection of C with any one of the three extreme supporting hyperplanes yields a face of the cone C. This face is a cone—the cone F discussed above. In general, *we call the $(n - 1)$-dimensional convex polyhedral cone F which is the intersection of an n-dimensional polyhedral cone C in E^n with an extreme supporting hyperplane a facet or face of the cone C.*

An n-dimensional convex polyhedral cone in E^n generated by $\mathbf{a}_1, \ldots, \mathbf{a}_r$ can have only a finite number of extreme supporting hyperplanes since there are at most $r!/(n - 1)!(r - n + 1)!$ sets of $n - 1$ linearly independent points in the set $\mathbf{a}_1, \ldots, \mathbf{a}_r$. Not every n-dimensional convex polyhedral cone in E^n needs to have an extreme supporting hyperplane. The convex polyhedral cone may be all of E^n, and thus cannot lie in any half-space of E^n.

The following result is sometimes useful: If a convex polyhedral cone C in E^n contains no vector $\mathbf{x} < \mathbf{0}$, then C^+ contains a vector $\mathbf{y} \geq \mathbf{0}$, $\mathbf{y} \neq \mathbf{0}$.

References

1. G. Birkhoff and S. A. MacLane, *A Survey of Modern Algebra.* New York: Macmillan, 1941.

2. G. Hadley, *Linear Algebra.* Reading, Mass.: Addison-Wesley, 1961.

3. J. G. Kemeny, H. Mirkil, J. L. Snell, G. L. Thompson, *Finite Mathematical Structures.* Englewood Cliffs: Prentice-Hall, 1959.

4. T. C. Koopmans, ed., *Activity Analysis of Production and Allocation.* New York: John Wiley and Sons, 1951. Chapter XVIII. "Theory of Convex Polyhedral Cones" by Murray Gerstenhaber.

5. R. M. Thrall and L. Tornheim, *Vector Spaces and Matrices.* New York: Wiley, 1958.

Problems

2–1. Find the products $\mathbf{AB}$ and $\mathbf{BA}$ (when they are defined):

(a) $\mathbf{A} = \begin{bmatrix} a_{11} & a_{12} \\ a_{21} & a_{22} \end{bmatrix}$, $\qquad \mathbf{B} = \begin{bmatrix} b_{11} & b_{12} \\ b_{21} & b_{22} \end{bmatrix}$;

(b) $\mathbf{A} = \begin{bmatrix} 1 & 2 & 4 & 5 \\ 3 & 1 & 0 & 2 \end{bmatrix}$, $\qquad \mathbf{B} = \begin{bmatrix} 1 \\ 4 \\ 8 \\ 9 \end{bmatrix}$;

(c) $\mathbf{A} = \begin{bmatrix} 1 & 3 & 4 \\ 2 & 0 & 7 \\ 5 & 6 & 9 \end{bmatrix}$, $\qquad \mathbf{B} = \begin{bmatrix} 10 & 2 & 0 \\ 7 & 1 & 3 \\ 4 & 5 & 6 \end{bmatrix}$;

(d) $\mathbf{A} = [1, 0, 7, 8]$, $\mathbf{B} = (2, 4, 9, 6)$.

2–2. Obtain the inverse of the following matrix:

$$\mathbf{A} = \begin{bmatrix} 10 & 1 & 2 \\ 3 & 9 & 7 \\ 2 & 1 & 6 \end{bmatrix}.$$

What is a product form of the inverse?

2–3. Show that if $\mathbf{A}$ is the partitioned matrix

$$\mathbf{A} = \begin{bmatrix} \mathbf{A}_{11} & \mathbf{A}_{12} \\ \mathbf{A}_{21} & \mathbf{A}_{22} \end{bmatrix}, \qquad \text{then} \qquad \mathbf{A}' = \begin{bmatrix} \mathbf{A}'_{11} & \mathbf{A}'_{21} \\ \mathbf{A}'_{12} & \mathbf{A}'_{22} \end{bmatrix}.$$

2–4. Given a nonsingular matrix $\mathbf{B} = (\mathbf{b}_1, \ldots, \mathbf{b}_n)$. Show that $\mathbf{B}^{-1}\mathbf{b}_i = \mathbf{e}_i$. Also, show that $\mathbf{B}\mathbf{e}_i = \mathbf{b}_i$.

2–5. Show that

$$\begin{vmatrix} \mathbf{I}_m & \mathbf{R} \\ \mathbf{0} & \mathbf{I}_n \end{vmatrix} = 1.$$

2–6. Using $\mathbf{A}^{-1} = (1/|\mathbf{A}|)\mathbf{A}^+$, compute the inverse of the following matrices:

(a) $\mathbf{A} = \begin{bmatrix} 2 & 1 \\ 3 & 4 \end{bmatrix}$; (b) $\mathbf{A} = \begin{bmatrix} 4 & 1 & 2 \\ 0 & 1 & 0 \\ 8 & 4 & 5 \end{bmatrix}.$

2–7. Do the following vectors form a basis for E^3?

(a) $\mathbf{a}_1 = [3, 0, 2]$, $\mathbf{a}_2 = [7, 0, 9]$, $\mathbf{a}_3 = [4, 1, 2]$;

(b) $\mathbf{a}_1 = [1, 1, 0]$, $\mathbf{a}_2 = [3, 0, 1]$, $\mathbf{a}_3 = [5, 2, 1]$;

(c) $\mathbf{a}_1 = [1, 5, 7]$, $\mathbf{a}_2 = [4, 0, 6]$, $\mathbf{a}_3 = [1, 0, 0]$.

2–8. Show how the change of basis technique (discussed in Section 2–10) can be used to express a vector in terms of some arbitrary basis by starting with the unit vectors as a basis and then proceeding to insert the vectors of the arbitrary basis. How is this related to the product form of the inverse? Illustrate by expressing $\mathbf{b} = [6, 4, 1]$ in terms of $\mathbf{a}_1 = [3, 1, 2]$, $\mathbf{a}_2 = [1, 3, 9]$, and $\mathbf{a}_3 = [2, 8, 5]$.

2–9. Given the basis vectors $\mathbf{e}_1 = [1, 0, 0]$, $[0, 1, 1]$, $\mathbf{e}_3 = [0, 0, 1]$ for E^3. Which vectors can be removed from the basis and be replaced by $\mathbf{b} = [4, 3, 6]$ while still maintaining a basis? Illustrate this geometrically.

2–10. In the text it was shown under what circumstances a vector could be removed from a basis and replaced by another vector in such a way that the new set of vectors was also a basis. Suppose now that we wish to form a new basis by removing two vectors from a basis and replacing them by two other vectors. Try to derive the conditions under which the new set of vectors will be a basis. What are the difficulties? Is it easier to insert the two vectors one at a time or both together?

2–11. Prove the Schwarz inequality $|\mathbf{a}'\mathbf{b}| \leq |\mathbf{a}| \, |\mathbf{b}|$. Hint:

$$|\lambda\mathbf{a} + \mathbf{b}|^2 = \lambda^2|\mathbf{a}|^2 + 2\lambda\mathbf{a}'\mathbf{b} + |\mathbf{b}|^2 \geq 0 \qquad \text{for all } \lambda.$$

Thus the quadratic equation $|\lambda\mathbf{a} + \mathbf{b}|^2 = 0$ cannot have two different real roots.

2–12. Find the rank of the following matrices:

(a) $\mathbf{A} = \begin{bmatrix} 2 & 4 \\ 1 & 2 \end{bmatrix}$, (b) $\mathbf{A} = \begin{bmatrix} 3 & 2 \\ 1 & 1 \end{bmatrix}$, (c) $\mathbf{A} = \begin{bmatrix} 1 \\ 0 \end{bmatrix}$,

(d) $\mathbf{A} = \begin{bmatrix} 3 & 2 & 1 \\ 4 & 6 & 2 \\ 0 & 0 & 0 \end{bmatrix}$, (e) $\mathbf{A} = \begin{bmatrix} 3 & 2 & 1 \\ 3 & 2 & 1 \\ 0 & 0 & 0 \end{bmatrix}$, (f) $\mathbf{A} = \begin{bmatrix} 4 & 5 & 3 \\ 2 & 0 & 7 \\ 9 & 1 & 8 \end{bmatrix}$.

2–13. Consider the vectors:

$\mathbf{a}_1 = \begin{bmatrix} 1 \\ 0 \end{bmatrix}$, $\mathbf{a}_2 = \begin{bmatrix} 3 \\ 4 \end{bmatrix}$, $\mathbf{a}_3 = \begin{bmatrix} -3 \\ -4 \end{bmatrix}$, $\mathbf{a}_4 = \begin{bmatrix} -1 \\ 2 \end{bmatrix}$, $\mathbf{a}_5 = \begin{bmatrix} -1 \\ -4 \end{bmatrix}$, $\mathbf{a}_6 = \begin{bmatrix} 1 \\ 4 \end{bmatrix}$,

$\mathbf{b}_1 = \begin{bmatrix} 5 \\ 6 \end{bmatrix}$, $\mathbf{b}_2 = \begin{bmatrix} 2 \\ -4 \end{bmatrix}$, $\mathbf{b}_3 = \begin{bmatrix} 1 \\ 4 \end{bmatrix}$.

Plot these vectors. Do all possible basic solutions exist for the following sets of equations? How many do exist? Are they nondegenerate?

$$(\mathbf{a}_2, \mathbf{a}_3, \mathbf{a}_4, \mathbf{a}_6)\mathbf{x} = \mathbf{b}_1, \qquad (\mathbf{a}_2, \mathbf{a}_4, \mathbf{a}_5, \mathbf{a}_6)\mathbf{x} = \mathbf{b}_2,$$

$$(\mathbf{a}_2, \mathbf{a}_4, \mathbf{a}_6)\mathbf{x} = \mathbf{b}_3, \qquad (\mathbf{a}_1, \mathbf{a}_2, \mathbf{a}_4, \mathbf{a}_5)\mathbf{x} = \mathbf{b}_1.$$

In Problems 2–14 through 2–16, find all existing basic solutions. Do all possible basic solutions actually exist?

2–14. $x_1 + 2x_2 + 3x_3 + 4x_4 = 7,$
$\quad 2x_1 + x_2 + x_3 + 2x_4 = 3.$

2–15. $8x_1 + 6x_2 + 13x_3 + x_4 + x_5 = 6,$
$\quad 9x_1 + x_2 + 2x_3 + 6x_4 + 10x_5 = 11.$

2–16. $2x_1 + 3x_2 + 4x_3 + x_4 = 2,$
$\quad x_1 + x_2 + 7x_3 + x_4 = 6,$
$\quad 3x_1 + 2x_2 + x_3 + 5x_4 = 8.$

2–17. Which of the following sets are convex?

(a) $X = \{[x_1, x_2] | 3x_1^2 + 2x_2^2 \leq 6\}$;
(b) $X = \{[x_1, x_2] | x_1 \geq 2, x_1 \leq 3\}$;
(c) $X = \{[x_1, x_2] | x_1 x_2 \leq 1, x_1 \geq 0, x_2 \geq 0\}$;
(d) $X = \{[x_1, x_2] | x_2 - 3 \geq -x_1^2, x_1 \geq 0, x_2 \geq 0\}$.

2–18. Sketch the convex polyhedra generated by the following sets of points:

(a) $(0, 0), (1, 0), (0, 1), (1, 1)$;
(b) $(3, 4), (5, 6), (0, 0), (2, 2), (1, 0), (2, 5), (4, 7)$;
(c) $(-1, 2), (3, -4), (4, 4), (0, 0), (6, 5), (7, 1)$.

2–19. Consider the triangle with vertices $(0, 0), (2, 0), (1, 1)$. Express the point $(0.5, 0.5)$ as a convex combination of the extreme points. Do the same for point $(0.3, 0.2)$.

2–20. What difficulties would arise in the process of solving a linear programming problem if the constraints were open (i.e., have a $>$ or $<$ sign) rather than closed half-spaces. Would the absolute maximum or minimum actually be taken on at a point in the set of feasible solutions?

CHAPTER 3

THEORY OF THE SIMPLEX METHOD

". . . it leads
A long, steep journey, through sunk
gorges, o'er mountains in snow."

Matthew Arnold.

3–1 Restatement of the problem. The general linear programming problem was formulated in Chapter 1 as follows: We wish to find values for a set of r variables x_j satisfying m linear inequalities or equalities (the constraints) of the form

$$a_{i1}x_1 + a_{i2}x_2 + \cdots + a_{ir}x_r \{\leq = \geq\}b_i, \qquad i = 1, \ldots, m, \qquad (3\text{--}1)$$

where one and only one of the signs $\leq$, $=$, $\geq$ holds for each constraint, but the sign can vary from one constraint to another. Furthermore, the variables are to be non-negative, $x_j \geq 0, j = 1, \ldots, r$ (the non-negativity restrictions), and are to maximize or minimize a linear form

$$z = c_1x_1 + c_2x_2 + \cdots + c_rx_r. \qquad (3\text{--}2)$$

All the a_{ij}, b_i, c_j are assumed to be known constants.

Recall that any set of x_j which satisfies the set of constraints (3–1) is called a solution. Any solution which satisfies the non-negativity restrictions is called a feasible solution. Any feasible solution which maximizes or minimizes the z of (3–2) is called an optimal feasible solution. We are trying to develop a procedure for finding an optimal feasible solution.

In this chapter, the theoretical foundations of the simplex method will be considered in some detail. The simplex method is fundamentally a rather simple procedure for solving a linear programming problem. However, some of the difficulties pointed out in Chapter 1 and the necessity of showing that the simplex method will lead to a solution in a finite number of steps create certain problems whose elimination requires a considerable amount of discussion. This discussion is apt to give the impression that the simplex technique is much more difficult than it really is. Hence we suggest that the reader studying this chapter and Chapters 4, 5, 6, and 7 attempt to keep in mind the basic simplicity of the simplex method. It should also be recognized, however, that a thorough comprehension of the subject, which is necessary for an intelligent use of the technique, requires a discussion of the finer points.

71

3-2 Slack and surplus variables. In general, it is much more convenient to work with equations than with inequalities. For this reason, it is desirable to convert any inequalities in the constraints (3-1) into equations, so that a system of simultaneous linear equations is obtained. This conversion can be carried out very simply by introducing some additional variables, which are called slack and surplus variables.

In the majority of the practical linear programming problems which will be formulated in this text, we shall find that the b_i of (3-1) are all nonnegative. From a strictly theoretical point of view, however, the b_i can have any sign. Later we shall find it advantageous to have all $b_i \geq 0$. Hence, at the outset, the necessary transformations will be made to ensure that each $b_i \geq 0$.

Suppose that in the original formulation of some constraint i, $b_i < 0$. Multiplying both sides of this constraint by -1, we obtain

$$-a_{i1}x_1 - a_{i2}x_2 - \cdots - a_{ir}x_r \{\geq = \leq\} - b_i. \qquad (3\text{-}3)$$

(Note that if the constraint has an inequality sign, the direction of the inequality is reversed after multiplying by (-1); that is, $-5 < -1$, and $(-1)(-5) > (-1)(-1)$.) Multiplication by (-1) yields $-b_i > 0$. Thus it is a simple matter to convert all the constraints into ones with $b_i \geq 0$. Hereafter, we shall assume that (3-1) represents a set of constraints with each $b_i \geq 0$.

We would now like to convert the set of constraints (3-1) into a set of simultaneous linear equations. To simplify problems of notation, let us agree to number the constraints in the following order: (1) Constraints with $\leq$ signs; (2) constraints with $\geq$ signs; (3) constraints which were originally formulated as equations.

Consider first the constraints having $\leq$ signs: A typical constraint of this category (say constraint h) can be written

$$\sum_{j=1}^{r} a_{hj}x_j \leq b_h. \qquad (3\text{-}4)$$

Let us introduce a new variable $x_{r+h} \geq 0$, where

$$x_{r+h} = b_h - \sum_{j=1}^{r} a_{hj}x_j \geq 0. \qquad (3\text{-}5)$$

We call x_{r+h} a slack variable, because b_h can be considered to be the maximum amount available of resource h, and for any set of x_j, $\sum a_{hj}x_j$ is the amount actually used. The difference between the amount available and the amount actually used is the slack (such as slack machine time).

Equation (3–5) can then be written

$$\sum_{j=1}^{r} a_{hj}x_j + x_{r+h} = b_h. \qquad (3\text{–}6)$$

By introducing an additional variable, the slack variable, we have converted the inequality (3–4) into an equality, (3–6). Furthermore, we note that for any set of x_j (not necessarily non-negative) satisfying the inequality (3–4), x_{r+h} must be non-negative.

Next consider inequalities having a $\geq$ sign: A typical inequality in this set (say constraint k) can be written

$$\sum_{j=1}^{r} a_{kj}x_j \geq b_k. \qquad (3\text{–}7)$$

Then define a new variable $x_{r+k} \geq 0$ by

$$x_{r+k} = \sum_{j=1}^{r} a_{kj}x_j - b_k. \qquad (3\text{–}8)$$

The variable x_{r+k} is called a surplus variable, because b_k can be considered to be the minimum amount of a product to be manufactured (or of a resource to be used), and for any set of x_j, $\sum a_{kj}x_j$ is the actual amount manufactured (or resource used). The difference between the quantity actually produced and the minimum to be produced is the surplus over and above the minimum. Equation (3–8) can be rearranged to read

$$\sum_{j=1}^{r} a_{kj}x_j - x_{r+k} = b_k. \qquad (3\text{–}9)$$

The inequality (3–7) has been converted into an equality by the introduction of a surplus variable. For any set of x_j satisfying the inequality (3–7), x_{r+k} is non-negative.

Thus, proceeding by steps, we have converted the original constraints (3–1) into a set of simultaneous linear equations of the form

$$\sum_{j=1}^{r} a_{hj}x_j + x_{r+h} = b_h, \qquad h = 1, \ldots, u, \qquad (3\text{–}10\text{a})$$

$$\sum_{j=1}^{r} a_{kj}x_j - x_{r+k} = b_k, \qquad k = u+1, \ldots, v, \qquad (3\text{–}10\text{b})$$

$$\sum_{j=1}^{r} a_{pj}x_j = b_p, \qquad p = v+1, \ldots, m. \qquad (3\text{–}10\text{c})$$

Constraints with a $\leq$ sign will be converted to the form (3–10a), those with a $\geq$ sign to the form (3–10b), and those having an equality sign will remain unchanged. We then have m simultaneous equations in n unknowns. The number of variables will be between r and $r + m$, depending upon the number of slack and surplus variables which must be introduced.

Note that if the original set of constraints (3–1) contained inequalities with $\leq$ and $\geq$ signs, multiplication by -1 would convert all inequalities with $\geq$ signs to inequalities with $\leq$ signs, with the result that only slack variables would be introduced. Similarly, every inequality could be converted to one having a $\geq$ sign, and then only surplus variables would be introduced. However, it is not possible to carry out either one of the above transformations and still maintain all $b_i \geq 0$. In the general case, when all $b_i \geq 0$, the introduction of both slack and surplus variables is necessary.

The set of constraint equations (3–10) can be written in matrix form as

$$\mathbf{Ax} = x_1\mathbf{a}_1 + \cdots + x_n\mathbf{a}_n = \mathbf{b}, \qquad (3\text{–}11)$$

where the $\mathbf{a}_j$ are the columns of $\mathbf{A}$. A slack or surplus variable x_{r+i} appears only in equation i, where it was introduced to remove an inequality. Thus the column of $\mathbf{A}$ corresponding to x_{r+i} is $\mathbf{e}_i$ if x_{r+i} is a slack variable, and $-\mathbf{e}_i$ if x_{r+i} is a surplus variable. The vector $\mathbf{e}_i$ is, of course, the ith m-component unit vector.

The matrix $\mathbf{A}$ can then be written (recall that by our convention, equations containing slack variables come first)

$$\mathbf{A} = \begin{bmatrix} a_{11} & a_{12} & \cdots & a_{1r} & 1 & 0 & \cdots & 0 & 0 \\ a_{21} & a_{22} & \cdots & a_{2r} & 0 & 1 & \cdots & 0 & 0 \\ \vdots & & & & & & & & \vdots \\ a_{v-1,1} & a_{v-1,2} & \cdots & a_{v-1,r} & 0 & 0 & \cdots -1 & 0 \\ a_{v1} & a_{v2} & \cdots & a_{vr} & 0 & 0 & \cdots & 0 & -1 \\ \vdots & & & & & & & & \vdots \\ a_{m1} & a_{m2} & \cdots & a_{mr} & 0 & 0 & \cdots & 0 & 0 \end{bmatrix} . \qquad (3\text{–}12)$$

EXAMPLE: Convert

$$2x_1 + 3x_2 \leq 6,$$
$$x_1 + 7x_2 \geq 4,$$
$$x_1 + x_2 = 3$$

into a set of equalities. Introducing a slack variable $x_3 \geq 0$ into the first constraint, we obtain

$$2x_1 + 3x_2 + x_3 = 6.$$

A surplus variable $x_4 \geq 0$ is introduced into the second constraint to yield

$$x_1 + 7x_2 - x_4 = 4.$$

The third constraint is already in equation form. The resulting set of linear equations can then be written in matrix form:

$$\begin{bmatrix} 2 & 3 & 1 & 0 \\ 1 & 7 & 0 & -1 \\ 1 & 1 & 0 & 0 \end{bmatrix} \begin{bmatrix} x_1 \\ x_2 \\ x_3 \\ x_4 \end{bmatrix} = \begin{bmatrix} 6 \\ 4 \\ 3 \end{bmatrix}.$$

Thus far we have proceeded to convert the inequalities in the constraints into equalities by introduction of slack and surplus variables, without mentioning the effects of this conversion on the function to be maximized or minimized. Let us now consider the function to be optimized. Originally, we had

$$z = \sum_{j=1}^{r} c_j x_j. \tag{3–13}$$

The number c_j is often called the "price" associated with the variable x_j. (Of course, it is not a price in every case.) As yet we have said nothing about the price to be associated with a slack or surplus variable. Suppose that we assign a price of zero to every slack and surplus variable. Then the conversion of the constraints to a system of simultaneous linear equations does not change the function to be optimized:

$$z = c_1 x_1 + \cdots + c_r x_r + 0 x_{r+1} + \cdots + 0 x_{r+v} = \sum_{j=1}^{r} c_j x_j. \tag{3–14}$$

We claim that optimizing (3–14) subject to the constraints expressed by the set of simultaneous linear equations (3–11) with $x_j \geq 0$ $(j = 1, \ldots, n)$ is completely equivalent to optimizing (3–2) subject to (3–1) with $x_j \geq 0$ $(j = 1, \ldots, r)$. To prove this, note first that if we have any feasible solution to the original constraints (3–1), then our method of introducing slack and surplus variables will yield a set of non-negative slack and/or surplus variables such that (3–11) is satisfied, with all variables non-negative. Conversely, if we have a feasible solution $\mathbf{x}$ to (3–11), then the first r components of $\mathbf{x}$ yield a feasible solution to (3–1). Thus, there is a one-to-one correspondence between the feasible solutions to the original set of constraints (3–1) and the feasible solutions to the set of simultaneous linear equations (3–11).

Next it will be observed that if $\mathbf{x}^* = [x_1^*, \ldots, x_n^*] \geq \mathbf{0}$ is a feasible solution to (3–11) which optimizes (3–14), then the first r components of $\mathbf{x}^*$, that is, $x_1^*, \ldots, x_r^*$, are an optimal solution to (3–1) and (3–2), with the same optimum z^*. To see this let us suppose that for Eqs. (3–1) and (3–2) a different solution, say $\hat{x}_1, \ldots, \hat{x}_r$, gives an improved value of z, say $\hat{z}$, over $x_1^*, \ldots, x_r^*$; then we need to note only that there are non-negative slack and/or surplus variables $\hat{x}_{r+1}, \ldots, \hat{x}_n$ such that $\hat{x}_1, \ldots, \hat{x}_n$ is a feasible solution to (3–11), with $\hat{z}$ as the value of z. This contradicts the fact that z^* was the optimal z for (3–11) and (3–14). Similarly, by annexing the slack and surplus variables to any optimal solution to (3–1) and (3–2), we obtain an optimal solution to (3–11) and (3–14). Thus we conclude that if slack and surplus variables having a zero price are introduced to convert the original set of constraints into a set of simultaneous linear equations, the resulting problem has the same set of optimal solutions as the original one.

The preceding discussion has shown that the general linear programming problem can be reformulated as follows: Find a vector

$$\mathbf{x} = [x_1, \ldots, x_n] \geq \mathbf{0}$$

satisfying a set of m simultaneous linear equations

$$\mathbf{Ax} = x_1\mathbf{a}_1 + \cdots + x_n\mathbf{a}_n = \mathbf{b}, \tag{3–15}$$

and maximizing or minimizing the objective function

$$z = c_1x_1 + \cdots + c_nx_n = \mathbf{cx}. \tag{3–16}$$

The vector $\mathbf{b}$ is often referred to as the requirements vector, and the $\mathbf{a}_j$ are called activity vectors. As noted previously, the c_j in the objective function are called the prices associated with the variables x_j.

The above formulation of a linear programming problem will be used in discussing the theory of linear programming.

3–3 Preliminary remarks on the theory of the simplex method. In Chapter 1, we discussed the geometrical interpretation of linear programming problems in two and three dimensions. We observed that the set of feasible solutions to a linear programming problem described mathematically by (3–1) and (3–2) formed a convex region or convex set (if there was a feasible solution). Furthermore, when an optimal solution existed (recall that unbounded solutions are not called optimal), at least one corner, or extreme point, of the convex region was optimal. In Chapter 2, we showed that, in general, the set of feasible solutions to (3–1) or (3–15) is a convex set, and if an optimal solution exists, at least one of the extreme points is optimal. For the examples in two and three dimensions, there was only a finite number of extreme points. We suggested in Chapter 2 that, in spaces of higher dimensions, the number of extreme points is also finite (we did not prove this; the proof will follow from the result of the present chapter). Hence, if we had a way of finding analytically the extreme points of the convex set of feasible solutions, only a finite number of solutions would need to be examined to find an optimal solution (if an optimal solution exists). We shall prove below the interesting result that the extreme points of the convex set of feasible solutions are basic feasible solutions to (3–15). (Review the discussion of basic solutions in Chapter 2.) Thus an optimal solution to a linear programming problem will be contained in the set of basic feasible solutions to (3–15). It was shown in Chapter 2 that there is only a finite number of basic solutions (and this in turn shows that there is only a finite number of extreme points).

To determine an optimal basic feasible solution, we might attempt to find all basic solutions (including those which are not feasible) and then select one which yields the optimal value of the objective function. There is only a finite number of basic solutions, and hence, in theory, this could be done. However, this procedure is extremely inefficient, because the number of basic solutions increases very rapidly as the number of variables is increased. Even a very modest problem involving four constraints and eight variables could require the solution of $8!/4!4! = 70$ sets of four simultaneous equations in four unknowns. In addition, an examination of the basic solutions alone would never determine whether the problem had an unbounded solution.

Naturally, we would like to find an explicit expression for an optimal solution which would allow the numerical values to be computed directly (or point out that the solution was unbounded), without using an iterative procedure. As indicated in Chapter 1, no such expression has been developed. Since the more efficient techniques used in solving sets of simultaneous linear equations are iterative procedures, it is not surprising that iterative techniques have been found to be the most efficient means for solving linear programming problems.

Thus our present efforts have to be concentrated on developing an iterative method of solution which lies between the two extremes outlined above, i.e., between the extremes of examining all basic solutions and of obtaining an explicit expression for an optimal solution. The simplex method referred to in the first chapter is such a method; it proceeds in systematic steps from an initial basic feasible solution to other basic feasible solutions and finally, in a finite number of steps, to an optimal basic feasible solution, in such a way that the value of the objective function at each step (iteration) is better (or at least not worse) than at the preceding step. Because z is improved (or at least not worsened) at each step, the number of basic feasible solutions that must be examined before an optimal solution is found is usually much smaller than the total number of existing basic solutions. The simplex method also indicates whether there is an unbounded solution.

Instead of beginning with the proof that an extreme point of the convex set of feasible solutions is a basic feasible solution, we shall find it of advantage to approach the general linear programming problem from the strictly algebraic point of view. The reason for this lies in the fact that the general linear programming problem must be solved by algebraic methods. Although the geometric interpretation by means of convex sets contributes considerably to an intuitive understanding of linear programming, it is not possible to solve geometrically any but the most trivial linear programming problems. In developing the algebraic theory, we automatically formulate the basic features of the simplex method. In addition, the algebraic approach, which is completely independent of geometrical considerations, nevertheless provides deeper insight into the geometrical results. After the algebraic treatment of the theory, we shall return to the geometric interpretation and prove that an extreme point of the convex set of feasible solutions is a basic feasible solution. Since the algebraic approach is independent of geometrical concepts, the reader need not be familiar with the material on convex sets in order to understand it.

The algebraic theory that we are about to consider was first developed by George Dantzig (published in Chapter XXI of Koopman's *Activity Analysis of Production and Allocation* [5]). Our assumptions and our order of development will differ somewhat from Dantzig's presentation. However, the final results will be essentially the same.

First, we wish to comment briefly on some of the assumptions that will be made during our algebraic development: We shall assume that for the set of constraints (3–15),

$$r(\mathbf{A}) = r(\mathbf{A}_b), \qquad \mathbf{A}_b = (\mathbf{A}, \mathbf{b}); \qquad (3\text{–}17)$$

i.e., the rank of the matrix of the coefficients is equal to the rank of the augmented matrix. If this is not true, the constraint equations are inconsistent, and there is no solution to the linear programming problem. In addition, it will be assumed that

$$r(\mathbf{A}) = m, \qquad (3\text{–}18)$$

where m is the number of constraint equations. This restriction implies that there are at least as many variables as equations. If, in the original formulation, there were more equations than variables, then some of the equations would be redundant and could be omitted. If the number of variables is the same as the number of equations, (3–18) requires that there be a unique solution. If this unique solution is feasible, it is the optimal solution, and if it is not feasible, then no solution exists. However, in practice, we are not interested in cases where the problem admits of only one solution, for then linear programming is not needed. In the typical case, there are more variables than equations. Then (3–18) ensures that none of the equations is redundant. When a practical problem is properly formulated, (3–18) is usually expected to hold; in other words, we expect that the constraints will be consistent, and that each constraint will add some new restriction to the problem.

During the actual process of formulating a linear programming problem with a considerable number of variables and constraints, it becomes extremely difficult to be sure that the constraints are indeed independent (or even consistent in some cases). It would be most unfortunate if, before applying the simplex method, we had to determine whether (3–18) held. It can be difficult to compute the rank of a large matrix. Hence we hope that the simplex method will tell us whether (1) there is a feasible solution and (2) any redundancy exists in the constraints. This can indeed be done. In fact, although the original set of constraints may not satisfy (3–18), we shall always begin the simplex method with a set of constraints which does satisfy (3–18). This set may not be the set of constraints (3–15), but a set of constraints having the same number of equations and some additional variables. These additional variables are introduced into the original constraints (3–15) in such a way that (3–18) holds. By applying the simplex method to the augmented set of constraints we finally determine whether the original set of constraint equations possesses a feasible solution, and whether there is any redundancy.

To sum up the above discussion, we shall develop the algebraic foundations of the simplex method, assuming that (3–18) holds for the constraints (3–15). This is what we expect to happen in the typical case. If we cannot determine immediately whether (3–18) holds, then we apply the simplex procedure to a new set of constraints for which (3–18) does hold. Ultimately, we find whether the original set of constraints has a feasible solution and whether any constraint is redundant. In addition, we actually find a feasible solution if there is one, and determine which constraints are redundant. We can drop the redundant constraints and then apply the algebraic theory to the new set of constraints. Equation (3–18) will hold for this new set. Consequently, the restriction (3–18) is really no restriction at all. It is introduced only to simplify the theoretical discussion.

Note: There are several aspects of the condition (3–18) that merit further comment. First of all, the fact that $r(\mathbf{A}) = m$ does not imply that a feasible solution to $\mathbf{Ax} = \mathbf{b}$ exists. However, as indicated above, the simplex method will always tell us whether there is a feasible solution to the set of constraint equations. Furthermore, even when (3–18) holds and the set of constraint equations is consistent, we cannot conclude that the original set of constraint inequalities was consistent. Consider

$$2x_1 + 3x_2 \leq 6, \qquad 2x_1 + 3x_2 \geq 7.$$

These two inequalities are clearly inconsistent. When slack and surplus variables are added, we obtain

$$2x_1 + 3x_2 + x_3 = 6,$$

$$2x_1 + 3x_2 - x_4 = 7.$$

This set of equations is consistent. One solution is

$$x_3 = 6, \qquad x_4 = -7, \qquad x_1 = x_2 = 0.$$

The difficulty arises because the slack and surplus variables are not all non-negative. It will be remembered that any solution to the set of constraint equations (3–15) is a solution to the original constraint inequalities (3–1) if and only if all slack and surplus variables are non-negative. If there is no solution to (3–15) having all slack and surplus variables non-negative, then the set of constraints (3–1) is inconsistent.

3–4 Reduction of any feasible solution to a basic feasible solution. In this section, we wish to show that if there is a feasible solution to the constraint equations (3–15), then there is a basic feasible solution. Recall that if $\mathbf{Ax} = \mathbf{b}$ has a solution and $r(\mathbf{A}) = m$, then $\mathbf{b}$ can be written as a linear combination of m linearly independent columns of $\mathbf{A}$; hence there is a solution with no more than m variables different from zero. Now we wish to extend this result and demonstrate that if there is a feasible solution to (3–15), then there exists a feasible solution with at most m variables different from zero, which is furthermore a basic solution. In addition, we shall actually show how to construct a basic feasible solution from any given feasible solution.

Later, for reasons already outlined, we shall restrict our attention to basic feasible solutions to linear programming problems. The results of this section ensure that if a feasible solution exists, then there is at least one basic feasible solution, and hence there do not exist cases where a linear programming problem has a feasible solution but no basic feasible solution. We shall now formally restate and prove this result.

Given a set of m simultaneous linear equations in n unknowns $(n \geq m)$, $\mathbf{Ax} = \mathbf{b}$, *with* $r(\mathbf{A}) = m$. *Then if there is a feasible solution* $\mathbf{x} \geq \mathbf{0}$, *there is a basic feasible solution.** To prove this, assume that there exists a feasible solution with $p \leq n$ positive variables. Number the variables so that the

---

* We shall always think of a set of equations $\mathbf{Ax} = \mathbf{b}$ as a set of constraints for some linear programming problem. Hence, we shall call any solution which satisfies $\mathbf{x} \geq \mathbf{0}$ a feasible solution. Outside of the linear programming context, a solution $\mathbf{x} \geq \mathbf{0}$ would be called a non-negative solution to the set of equations.

first p variables are positive. Then the feasible solution can be written

$$\sum_{j=1}^{p} x_j \mathbf{a}_j = \mathbf{b}, \tag{3–19}$$

and hence

$$x_j > 0 \quad (j = 1, \ldots, p); \quad x_j = 0 \quad (j = p + 1, \ldots, n). \tag{3–20}$$

Now the vectors $\mathbf{a}_j$ associated with the positive variables may be linearly independent or dependent.

Consider first the case where the set of $\mathbf{a}_j$ $(j = 1, \ldots, p)$ is linearly independent. Then $p \le m$. If $p = m$, the given solution is automatically a nondegenerate basic feasible solution. Since $r(\mathbf{A}) = m$, we know from Chapter 2 that if $p < m$, then there are $m - p$ columns of $\mathbf{A}$ which, together with the p columns, form a basis for E^m and yield a nonsingular matrix. Thus we can form a degenerate basic feasible solution with $m - p$ of the basic variables equal to zero.

It remains to examine the case where the vectors $\mathbf{a}_j$ $(j = 1, \ldots, p)$ are linearly dependent. We shall show that under these circumstances it is possible to reduce the number of positive variables step by step until the columns associated with the positive variables are linearly independent.

When the $\mathbf{a}_j$ $(j = 1, \ldots, p)$ are linearly dependent, there exist α_j not all zero such that

$$\sum_{j=1}^{p} \alpha_j \mathbf{a}_j = \mathbf{0}. \tag{3–21}$$

Using (3–21), we proceed to reduce some x_r in

$$\sum_{j=1}^{p} x_j \mathbf{a}_j = \mathbf{b}, \quad x_j > 0 \quad (j = 1, \ldots, p), \tag{3–22}$$

to zero. The type of analysis employed here will appear a number of times in our discussion of linear programming, and the reader should make a special effort to understand it.

Suppose that any vector $\mathbf{a}_r$ of the p vectors in (3–21) for which $\alpha_r \neq 0$ is expressed in terms of the remaining $p - 1$ vectors. Thus

$$\mathbf{a}_r = -\sum_{j \neq r} \frac{\alpha_j}{\alpha_r} \mathbf{a}_j. \tag{3–23}$$

Substituting (3–23) into (3–22), we obtain

$$\sum_{\substack{j=1 \\ j \neq r}}^{p} \left(x_j - x_r \frac{\alpha_j}{\alpha_r} \right) \mathbf{a}_j = \mathbf{b}. \tag{3–24}$$

Here we have a solution with not more than $p - 1$ nonzero variables. However, we are not sure that all these variables are non-negative. In general, if we choose $\mathbf{a}_r$ arbitrarily, some variables may be negative. It is interesting to note that if $\mathbf{a}_r$ is properly selected, the $p - 1$ variables in (3–24) will be non-negative.

To see how to choose $\mathbf{a}_r$, observe that we wish to obtain

$$x_j - x_r \frac{\alpha_j}{\alpha_r} \geq 0 \qquad (j = 1, \ldots, p), \qquad j \neq r. \qquad (3\text{–}25)$$

For any j for which $\alpha_j = 0$, (3–25) will be satisfied automatically. When $\alpha_j \neq 0$, division by α_j must yield

$$\frac{x_j}{\alpha_j} - \frac{x_r}{\alpha_r} \geq 0 \qquad \text{if } \alpha_j > 0, \qquad (3\text{–}26\text{a})$$

$$\frac{x_j}{\alpha_j} - \frac{x_r}{\alpha_r} \leq 0 \qquad \text{if } \alpha_j < 0. \qquad (3\text{–}26\text{b})$$

The inequality sign in (3–26b) is reversed because we have divided by a negative number. Equation (3–26) can be interpreted to mean that x_r/α_r must not be greater than any x_j/α_j which is >0, and not less than any x_j/α_j which is <0. This requirement suggests a way of choosing the vector $\mathbf{a}_r$ such that the $p - 1$ variables in (3–24) will be non-negative. Suppose that we select the vector $\mathbf{a}_r$, using*

$$\frac{x_r}{\alpha_r} = \min_j \left\{ \frac{x_j}{\alpha_j}, \quad \alpha_j > 0 \right\}. \qquad (3\text{–}27)$$

Then each variable in (3–24) will be non-negative, and a feasible solution with no more than $p - 1$ nonzero variables has been found.

Equation (3–27) implies that we first compute all x_j/α_j for which $\alpha_j > 0$ and then select the smallest one. The variable corresponding to this smallest x_j/α_j is then driven to zero by the substitution (3–23). The α_j are, of course, those given by (3–21). We have to consider at most p values of x_j/α_j. There must always be at least one $\alpha_j > 0$ since none of the $\mathbf{a}_j = \mathbf{0}$; if all $\alpha_j \leq 0$, we simply multiply (3–21) by (-1) and obtain new $\alpha_j \geq 0$.

We have constructed a solution with not more than $p - 1$ positive variables; all other variables are zero. If the columns associated with the

---

* Instead of (3–27), the expression

$$\frac{x_r}{\alpha_r} = \max_j \left\{ \frac{x_j}{\alpha_j}, \alpha_j < 0 \right\}$$

could have been used to select $\mathbf{a}_r$. This choice will also satisfy (3–26). However, the vector chosen in this way will not be the same as that obtained from (3–27).

positive variables are linearly independent, we have reduced the problem to one which has already been examined, and we know that a basic feasible solution exists. If the columns associated with the positive variables are linearly dependent, we can repeat the same procedure and reduce one of the positive variables to zero. Ultimately, we shall arrive at a solution such that the columns corresponding to the positive variables are linearly independent (why?), and we know that there is a basic feasible solution.

It is not necessarily true that the minimum in (3–27) will be unique. There may be two or more x_j/α_j with the same minimum value. In such a case, instead of reducing the number of nonzero variables by one, we drive to zero all variables x_j for which x_j/α_j has the minimum value. Because of the possibility that the minimum is not unique, we had to mention in the preceding paragraph that after the first reduction not more than $p - 1$ variables will be different from zero. There may be less than $p - 1$ positive variables.

EXAMPLE: Consider the system of equations

$$x_1\mathbf{a}_1 + x_2\mathbf{a}_2 + x_3\mathbf{a}_3 = \mathbf{b};$$

$$\mathbf{a}_1 = [2, 3], \qquad \mathbf{a}_2 = [1, 1], \qquad \mathbf{a}_3 = [4, 5], \qquad \mathbf{b} = [11, 14].$$

A feasible solution is

$$2\mathbf{a}_1 + 3\mathbf{a}_2 + \mathbf{a}_3 = \mathbf{b}.$$

The rank of the matrix $\mathbf{A} = (\mathbf{a}_1, \mathbf{a}_2, \mathbf{a}_3)$ is 2. Hence a basic feasible solution exists with no more than two variables different from zero. Note that

$$\mathbf{a}_1 + 2\mathbf{a}_2 - \mathbf{a}_3 = \mathbf{0},$$

so that in the notation of (3–21), $\alpha_1 = 1$, $\alpha_2 = 2$, $\alpha_3 = -1$. To reduce the number of positive variables, the variable to be driven to zero is found, according to our above discussion, from

$$\frac{x_r}{\alpha_r} = \min_j \left\{ \frac{x_j}{\alpha_j}, \ \alpha_j > 0 \right\} = \min \left\{ \frac{2}{1}, \frac{3}{2} \right\} = \frac{3}{2}.$$

Thus we can eliminate the vector $\mathbf{a}_2$ for which $x_2/\alpha_2 = 3/2$ and obtain a new solution with not more than two non-negative variables. By (3–24) the values of the new variables $\hat{x}_j$ are

$$\hat{x}_j = x_j - \frac{x_r}{\alpha_r}\alpha_j; \qquad \hat{x}_1 = 2 - \frac{3}{2}(1) = \frac{1}{2}; \qquad \hat{x}_3 = 1 - \frac{3}{2}(-1) = \frac{5}{2}.$$

Only two variables are different from zero. Furthermore, $\mathbf{a}_1$, $\mathbf{a}_3$ are linearly independent. The basic feasible solution is

$$\hat{x}_1 \mathbf{a}_1 + \hat{x}_3 \mathbf{a}_3 = \mathbf{b}.$$

This result can be checked since

$$\tfrac{1}{2}[2, 3] + \tfrac{5}{2}[4, 5] = [11, 14].$$

If $\mathbf{a}_1$ is eliminated instead of $\mathbf{a}_2$, then x_1 is driven to zero. However, the new solution is not feasible. This can be easily verified: For $\mathbf{a}_1$, $x_1/\alpha_1 = 2$, and the new values of the nonzero variables are

$$\hat{x}_2 = 3 - 2(2) = -1; \qquad \hat{x}_3 = 1 - 2(-1) = 3.$$

This solution is basic but not feasible, which shows that a feasible solution cannot be maintained if an arbitrary $\mathbf{a}_j$ $(\alpha_j > 0)$ is eliminated.

Now suppose that the criterion given in the footnote on page 82 is used to select the vector which is to be eliminated. Only one α_j, namely α_3, is negative; thus $\mathbf{a}_3$ should be removed. For $\mathbf{a}_3$, $x_3/\alpha_3 = -1$, and the new variables are

$$\hat{x}_1 = 2 - (-1)(1) = 3, \qquad \hat{x}_2 = 3 - (-1)(2) = 5;$$

these yield indeed a basic feasible solution which is different from that obtained above.

3–5 Some definitions and notations. Before proceeding with the theory we shall introduce some definitions and notations that will be used a great deal in future developments. The notation may at first seem unnecessarily complex; however, its usefulness will become clear as the simplex method is developed. Since all quantities have one or two subscripts, it is important that the meaning of these subscripts be thoroughly understood.

The constraints of a linear programming problem are now written as a set of m simultaneous linear equations in n unknowns,

$$\mathbf{Ax} = \mathbf{b}. \tag{3–28}$$

The jth column of the $m \times n$ matrix $\mathbf{A}$ is denoted by $\mathbf{a}_j$ $(j = 1, \ldots, n)$. We shall deal almost exclusively with basic solutions to this set of constraints. Let us form a matrix $\mathbf{B}$ whose columns are any m linearly independent columns from $\mathbf{A}$. These columns of $\mathbf{B}$ form a basis for E^m. Matrix $\mathbf{B}$ will be used exclusively to indicate an $m \times m$ nonsingular matrix whose columns are m linearly independent columns from $\mathbf{A}$. We shall sometimes refer to $\mathbf{B}$ as the basis matrix and to the columns of $\mathbf{A}$ in $\mathbf{B}$ as the columns of $\mathbf{A}$ in the basis. The columns of $\mathbf{B}$ will be denoted by $\mathbf{b}_1, \ldots, \mathbf{b}_m$. It is important to note here that $\mathbf{b}_1$ may be any column of $\mathbf{A}$, say $\mathbf{a}_{17}$; the same applies to the other columns of $\mathbf{B}$. The numbering of the columns of $\mathbf{B}$ does not indicate which vector from $\mathbf{A}$ corresponds to that column. Hence we must know from other sources which columns of $\mathbf{A}$ correspond to the columns in $\mathbf{B}$.

Any column $\mathbf{a}_j$ of $\mathbf{A}$ can be written as a linear combination of the columns of $\mathbf{B}$. The following notation will be used to represent such a linear combination:

$$\mathbf{a}_j = y_{1j}\mathbf{b}_1 + \cdots + y_{mj}\mathbf{b}_m = \sum_{i=1}^{m} y_{ij}\mathbf{b}_i = \mathbf{B}\mathbf{y}_j; \qquad (3\text{–}29)$$

or

$$\mathbf{y}_j = \mathbf{B}^{-1}\mathbf{a}_j; \qquad \mathbf{y}_j = [y_{1j}, \dots, y_{mj}]. \qquad (3\text{–}30)$$

A knowledge of the vector $\mathbf{y}_j$ allows us to express $\mathbf{a}_j$ as a linear combination of the columns of $\mathbf{B}$. The ith component of $\mathbf{y}_j$ is y_{ij}. Note that the subscript j refers to the vector $\mathbf{a}_j$, and the subscript i refers to the column of $\mathbf{B}$ which y_{ij} multiplies in (3–29). The vector $\mathbf{y}_j$ will, of course, change if the columns of $\mathbf{A}$ which make up $\mathbf{B}$ are changed. We repeat that the subscript i does not indicate which vector from $\mathbf{A}$ is in column i of $\mathbf{B}$.

Any basis matrix $\mathbf{B}$ determines a basic solution to $\mathbf{A}\mathbf{x} = \mathbf{b}$. This basic solution, defined by an m-component vector $\mathbf{x}_B$, is

$$\mathbf{x}_B = \mathbf{B}^{-1}\mathbf{b}, \qquad \mathbf{x}_B = [x_{B1}, \dots, x_{Bm}]. \qquad (3\text{–}31)$$

It will always be implicitly understood that all $n - m$ variables not associated with the columns of $\mathbf{A}$ appearing in $\mathbf{B}$ are zero. The subscript i means that x_{Bi} corresponds to column $\mathbf{b}_i$ of $\mathbf{B}$; however, it does not indicate which variable x_j of (3–28) x_{Bi} is. If $\mathbf{a}_{17}$ is in column 2 of $\mathbf{B}$, then $x_{B2} = x_{17}$. By knowing which vectors from $\mathbf{A}$ are the columns of $\mathbf{B}$ we are able to determine the variables of $\mathbf{x}$ referred to by the x_{Bi}. If $x_{Bi} > 0$, we shall say that $\mathbf{b}_i$ is in the basis at a positive level, and if $x_{Bi} = 0$, $\mathbf{b}_i$ is in the basis at a zero level. Recall from Chapter 2 that the variables x_{Bi} are called the basic variables, and the remaining $n - m$ variables are called the nonbasic variables. Also recall that a basic solution is said to be degenerate if one or more of the basic variables vanish. The variables "in the basic solution" are the basic variables.

Corresponding to any $\mathbf{x}_B$, we define an m-component row vector $\mathbf{c}_B$ containing the prices of the basic variables as:

$$\mathbf{c}_B = (c_{B1}, \dots, c_{Bm}). \qquad (3\text{–}32)$$

The components of $\mathbf{c}_B$ are c_{Bi}, and the subscript i means that c_{Bi} is the price of variable x_{Bi}. If $\mathbf{a}_{17}$ is in column 2 of $\mathbf{B}$, then $c_{B2} = c_{17}$.

For any basic feasible solution, the value of the objective function z is given by

$$z = \mathbf{c}_B \mathbf{x}_B, \qquad (3\text{--}33)$$

since all nonbasic variables vanish.

Next we shall consider an equation similar in structure to (3–29). A new variable z_j is defined by

$$z_j = y_{1j}c_{B1} + \cdots + y_{mj}c_{Bm} = \sum_{i=1}^{m} y_{ij}c_{Bi} = \mathbf{c}_B \mathbf{y}_j. \qquad (3\text{--}34)$$

For each $\mathbf{a}_j$ in $\mathbf{A}$, there is a z_j; the z_j corresponding to $\mathbf{a}_j$ changes as the columns of $\mathbf{A}$ in $\mathbf{B}$ are changed. Later an economic interpretation will be given to z_j.

EXAMPLE: The above definitions and notation will be applied to the following linear programming problem:

$$\sum_{j=1}^{5} x_j \mathbf{a}_j = \mathbf{b}, \qquad \text{all } x_j \geq 0; \qquad (3\text{--}35)$$

$$\mathbf{a}_1 = [4, 1], \qquad \mathbf{a}_2 = [2, 2], \qquad \mathbf{a}_3 = [1, 3], \qquad \mathbf{a}_4 = [1, 0],$$

$$\mathbf{a}_5 = [0, -1], \qquad \mathbf{b} = [2, 1];$$

$$\max z = 2x_1 + x_2 + 3x_3.$$

The variables x_4, x_5 can be considered to be slack and surplus variables, respectively. The prices corresponding to these variables are zero.

The vectors $\mathbf{a}_1$, $\mathbf{a}_3$ are linearly independent and form a basis for E^2. They can be used to form a basic solution. A basis matrix $\mathbf{B}$ will be formed by inserting $\mathbf{a}_3$ into the first column of $\mathbf{B}$, and $\mathbf{a}_1$ into the second column of $\mathbf{B}$, so that

$$\mathbf{B} = (\mathbf{b}_1, \mathbf{b}_2) = \begin{bmatrix} 1 & 4 \\ 3 & 1 \end{bmatrix},$$

and $\mathbf{b}_1 = \mathbf{a}_3$, $\mathbf{b}_2 = \mathbf{a}_1$. The basic solution with all variables except x_1, x_3 equal to zero is feasible, and is given by

$$\mathbf{x}_B = \mathbf{B}^{-1}\mathbf{b} = -\frac{1}{11}\begin{bmatrix} 1 & -4 \\ -3 & 1 \end{bmatrix}\begin{bmatrix} 2 \\ 1 \end{bmatrix} = \frac{1}{11}\begin{bmatrix} 2 \\ 5 \end{bmatrix} = \begin{bmatrix} x_{B1} \\ x_{B2} \end{bmatrix},$$

with $x_2 = x_4 = x_5 = 0$. The variables in the basis are $x_{B1} = x_3$, $x_{B2} = x_1$. The prices corresponding to these variables are $c_{B1} = c_3 = 3$, $c_{B2} = c_1 = 2$. Thus for this basic solution,

$$\mathbf{c}_B = (3, 2).$$

Any other vector $\mathbf{a}_j$ in $\mathbf{A}$ can be written as a linear combination of the basis vectors. This requires computation of the $\mathbf{y}_j$ for $\mathbf{a}_j$. Consider $\mathbf{a}_2$; we obtain from (3–30)

$$\mathbf{y}_2 = \mathbf{B}^{-1}\mathbf{a}_2 = -\frac{1}{11}\begin{bmatrix} 1 & -4 \\ -3 & 1 \end{bmatrix}\begin{bmatrix} 2 \\ 2 \end{bmatrix} = \frac{1}{11}\begin{bmatrix} 6 \\ 4 \end{bmatrix} = \begin{bmatrix} y_{12} \\ y_{22} \end{bmatrix},$$

$$\mathbf{a}_2 = y_{12}\mathbf{b}_1 + y_{22}\mathbf{b}_2 = y_{12}\mathbf{a}_3 + y_{22}\mathbf{a}_1.$$

The value of z_2 [defined in general by (3–34)] corresponding to $\mathbf{a}_2$ is given by

$$z_2 = \mathbf{c}_B\mathbf{y}_2 = 3\left(\frac{6}{11}\right) + 2\left(\frac{4}{11}\right) = \frac{26}{11}.$$

For this basic feasible solution, the value of z is given by

$$z = \mathbf{c}_B\mathbf{x}_B = 3\left(\frac{2}{11}\right) + 2\left(\frac{5}{11}\right) = \frac{16}{11}.$$

3–6 Improving a basic feasible solution. Suppose that a basic feasible solution to the linear programming problem (3–15), (3–16) is given by $\mathbf{x}_B = \mathbf{B}^{-1}\mathbf{b}$. The value of the objective function for this solution is $z = \mathbf{c}_B\mathbf{x}_B$. In addition, we assume that for this basic solution the $\mathbf{y}_j = \mathbf{B}^{-1}\mathbf{a}_j$ and $z_j = \mathbf{c}_B\mathbf{y}_j$ are known for every column $\mathbf{a}_j$ of $\mathbf{A}$ not in $\mathbf{B}$.

We now wish to examine the possibility of finding another basic feasible solution with an improved value of z. We shall confine our attention to those basic feasible solutions in which only one column of $\mathbf{B}$ is changed; i.e., we remove one column of $\mathbf{B}$ and replace it by some other vector from $\mathbf{A}$. In Chapter 2, we discussed the method of changing a single vector in a basis. For this case, it is very easy to determine whether the new set of vectors forms a basis. We saw that if

$$\mathbf{a}_j = \sum_{i=1}^{m} y_{ij}\mathbf{b}_i,$$

then $\mathbf{a}_j$ can replace any vector $\mathbf{b}_r$ for which $y_{rj} \neq 0$, and the new set of vectors will still form a basis. Let us then select any $\mathbf{a}_j$ not in $\mathbf{B}$ for which at least one $y_{ij} \neq 0$ and insert it into the basis matrix $\mathbf{B}$. If we decide to remove column $\mathbf{b}_r$ of $\mathbf{B}$ ($y_{rj} \neq 0$) and replace it by $\mathbf{a}_j$, it follows that

$$\mathbf{b}_r = \frac{1}{y_{rj}}\mathbf{a}_j - \sum_{\substack{i=1 \\ i \neq r}}^{m} \frac{y_{ij}}{y_{rj}}\mathbf{b}_i. \tag{3–36}$$

The original basic feasible solution can be written

$$\sum_{i=1}^{m} x_{Bi}\mathbf{b}_i = \mathbf{b}. \qquad (3\text{-}37)$$

Eliminating $\mathbf{b}_r$ by (3–36), we obtain for the new basic solution

$$\sum_{\substack{i=1 \\ i \neq r}}^{m} \left(x_{Bi} - x_{Br}\frac{y_{ij}}{y_{rj}} \right) \mathbf{b}_i + \frac{x_{Br}}{y_{rj}} \mathbf{a}_j = \mathbf{b}. \qquad (3\text{-}38)$$

The new basic solution must also be feasible. This requires that

$$x_{Bi} - x_{Br}\frac{y_{ij}}{y_{rj}} \geq 0, \qquad i \neq r, \qquad (3\text{-}39\text{a})$$

$$\frac{x_{Br}}{y_{rj}} \geq 0. \qquad (3\text{-}39\text{b})$$

We cannot remove any $\mathbf{b}_r$ with $y_{rj} \neq 0$ and expect that (3–39) will hold. In fact, we immediately see from (3–39b) that if $x_{Br} \neq 0$, we must have $y_{rj} > 0$. Interestingly enough, we can now show that if $\mathbf{a}_j$ has at least one $y_{ij} > 0$, and if the proper column of $\mathbf{B}$ is removed and replaced by $\mathbf{a}_j$, then the new basic solution will be feasible. Note that if $y_{rj} > 0$ and $y_{ij} \leq 0$ ($i \neq r$), then (3–39a) is automatically satisfied for this i. Thus we only need to be concerned with the $y_{ij} > 0$. We must select from the $\mathbf{b}_i$ with $y_{ij} > 0$ the vector $\mathbf{b}_r$ to be removed in such a way that (3–39a) holds. When $y_{ij} > 0$, the requirement (3–39a) can be written

$$\frac{x_{Bi}}{y_{ij}} - \frac{x_{Br}}{y_{rj}} \geq 0.$$

It is now clear that if we determine the column r of $\mathbf{B}$ to be replaced by means of

$$\frac{x_{Br}}{y_{rj}} = \min_{i} \left\{ \frac{x_{Bi}}{y_{ij}}, \; y_{ij} > 0 \right\} = \theta, \qquad (3\text{-}40)$$

then the new basic solution will be feasible.

Let us summarize what we have said above and, at the same time, introduce some additional notation. We begin with a nonsingular matrix

$$\mathbf{B} = (\mathbf{b}_1, \ldots, \mathbf{b}_m),$$

whose columns are m columns from $\mathbf{A}$. It is assumed that $\mathbf{x}_B = \mathbf{B}^{-1}\mathbf{b}$ is a basic feasible solution to the linear programming problem. We then select an arbitrary column $\mathbf{a}_j$ from $\mathbf{A}$ which is not in $\mathbf{B}$. If $\mathbf{a}_j$ has one or more $y_{ij} > 0$, $\mathbf{y}_j = \mathbf{B}^{-1}\mathbf{a}_j$, we have shown that we can remove some column from $\mathbf{B}$, replace it by $\mathbf{a}_j$, and thereby obtain a new basic feasible solution. It is not possible to select arbitrarily the column of $\mathbf{B}$ to be removed if the new basic solution is to be feasible. However, if the selection is done by means of Eq. (3–40), then the new basic solution will be feasible. Let us denote by $\hat{\mathbf{B}} = (\hat{\mathbf{b}}_1, \ldots, \hat{\mathbf{b}}_m)$ the new nonsingular matrix obtained from $\mathbf{B}$ by removing $\mathbf{b}_r$ and replacing it by $\mathbf{a}_j$. The columns of the new matrix are given by

$$\hat{\mathbf{b}}_i = \mathbf{b}_i, \qquad i \neq r; \qquad \hat{\mathbf{b}}_r = \mathbf{a}_j. \tag{3–41}$$

If the new basic feasible solution is denoted by $\hat{\mathbf{x}}_B$, then $\hat{\mathbf{x}}_B = \hat{\mathbf{B}}^{-1}\mathbf{b}$; from (3–38) we obtain the values of the new basic variables in terms of the original ones and the y_{ij}, that is,

$$\hat{x}_{Bi} = x_{Bi} - x_{Br}\frac{y_{ij}}{y_{rj}}, \qquad i \neq r, \tag{3–42a}$$

$$\hat{x}_{Br} = \frac{x_{Br}}{y_{rj}}. \tag{3–42b}$$

At this point the reader should be careful to take note that we have obtained a new basic feasible solution to the set of constraints (3–15) by changing one of the variables in the basic solution. Consequently, the $m - 1$ variables that could be different from zero in the original basic solution can still differ from zero in the new basic solution. However, in general, the actual values of the variables will change, and their new values are given by (3–42a). On the other hand, the new variable, $\hat{x}_{Br}$, corresponding to the rth position is different from that in the previous solution. For example, if $\mathbf{a}_3$ were $\mathbf{b}_r$ (thus implying $x_{Br} = x_3$) and $\mathbf{a}_7$ replaced $\mathbf{b}_r$, that is, $\mathbf{a}_3$, then $\hat{x}_{Br} = x_7$. A different variable appears in the rth position, while in all others there are the same variables (usually with different values). The original variable in the rth position is driven to zero.

We shall now turn to some of the more subtle points of the above discussion. Note, first of all, that the minimum in (3–40) may not be unique. There may be two or more different columns of $\mathbf{B}$ for which the same minimum value is obtained. In this case, we can remove any one of the columns for which the minimum is taken on, and the new basic solution is feasible. It is important to observe what happens to the new variables still in the basic solution corresponding to the columns for which the θ of (3–40) was the same as that for the removed column. From (3–42a), we immediately see that since $x_{Bi}/y_{ij} = x_{Br}/y_{rj}$, $\hat{x}_{Bi} = 0$ for those columns that have the same value of θ as the removed column. In other words, if the minimum in (3–40) is not unique, the new basic feasible solution will be degenerate. In the new basis, all new basic variables will vanish for those columns that have the same θ in (3–40) as the eliminated column.

Next let us study what happens if the θ of (3–40) is zero. Examination of Eq. (3–40) demonstrates that θ can be zero only if $x_{Br} = 0$, that is, if we start out with a degenerate basic solution. In this case, (3–42) immediately shows that $\hat{x}_{Bi} = x_{Bi}$ $(i \neq r)$, $\hat{x}_{Br} = 0$. The values of the variables common to the old and new solutions do not change, and the new variable is at a zero level. Hence the new basic feasible solution is also degenerate. It does not follow that the new basic feasible solution will always be degenerate if the original one was. If $y_{ij} < 0$ for every x_{Bi} which is zero in the original basic solution, none of these variables enter into the computation of (3–40). Then θ will be positive, and the new solution will be nondegenerate, although we started out with a degenerate solution, provided that r is uniquely determined.

We might go one step further and note that the only reason for our requirement $y_{rj} > 0$ is to ensure that $x_{Br}/y_{rj} \geq 0$. However, if $x_{Br} = 0$, then it is not necessary that $y_{rj} > 0$. If in the initial basic solution there is some basic variable $x_{Br} = 0$ and $y_{rj} \neq 0$, then we can remove column r of $\mathbf{B}$ and replace it by $\mathbf{a}_j$. No computation like (3–40) is needed; since $x_{Br} = 0$, the new values of the variables will be the same as the old ones and hence will be non-negative. These finer points discussed in the last three paragraphs will be of some use in later developments.

Our main interest was in finding a new basic feasible solution with an improved value of the objective function. Having found a new basic feasible solution, we must determine whether z is improved. The value of the objective function for the original basic feasible solution is $z = \mathbf{c}_B \mathbf{x}_B = \sum c_{Bi} x_{Bi}$. The new value of the objective function $\hat{z}$ is given by $\hat{z} = \hat{\mathbf{c}}_B \hat{\mathbf{x}}_B = \sum \hat{c}_{Bi} \hat{x}_{Bi}$. Note that $\hat{c}_{Bi} = c_{Bi}$ $(i \neq r)$ and $\hat{c}_{Br} = c_j$, since only the price of the new variable entering the basis changes. Therefore, using (3–42), we obtain

$$\hat{z} = \sum_{\substack{i=1 \\ i \neq r}}^{m} c_{Bi}\left(x_{Bi} - x_{Br}\frac{y_{ij}}{y_{rj}}\right) + \frac{x_{Br}}{y_{rj}}c_j. \tag{3–43}$$

In the summation it is desirable to include the $i = r$ term which is

$$c_{Br}\left(x_{Br} - x_{Br}\frac{y_{rj}}{y_{rj}}\right) = 0.$$

Because the term is 0, we can add it without changing $\hat{z}$. Thus

$$\hat{z} = \sum_{i=1}^{m} c_{Bi}\left(x_{Bi} - x_{Br}\frac{y_{ij}}{y_{rj}}\right) + \frac{x_{Br}}{y_{rj}}c_j,$$

or

$$\hat{z} = \sum_{i=1}^{m} c_{Bi} x_{Bi} - \frac{x_{Br}}{y_{rj}}\sum_{i=1}^{m} c_{Bi} y_{ij} + \frac{x_{Br}}{y_{rj}}c_j. \tag{3–44}$$

Note, however, that $\sum c_{Bi} y_{ij}$ is exactly what we defined to be z_j. The expression for $\hat{z}$ reduces to

$$\hat{z} = z + \frac{x_{Br}}{y_{rj}}(c_j - z_j) = z + \theta(c_j - z_j). \tag{3–45}$$

Here we have obtained a very interesting result. The new value of the objective function is the original value plus the quantity $\theta(c_j - z_j)$. Now $z_j = \mathbf{c}_B \mathbf{y}_j$, and it is known for the original basic solution (note that z_j refers to the original basic solution, not the new one), and c_j is the price associated with the newly introduced variable x_j. Assume now that we wish to maximize z. If $\theta(c_j - z_j) > 0$, then $\hat{z} > z$, and we have obtained an increase in z. Since $\theta \geq 0$, we cannot have $\hat{z} > z$ unless $c_j - z_j > 0$ (or $z_j - c_j < 0$). Hence a restriction is placed on the choice of the vector $\mathbf{a}_j$ to be inserted into the new basis. Up to the present, this vector has been arbitrary. We have just shown that if we choose any vector $\mathbf{a}_j$ for which $c_j - z_j > 0$ and at least one $y_{ij} > 0$, we can obtain a new basic solution with $\hat{z} \geq z$. If our original basic solution was not degenerate, then $\theta > 0$, and we have a definite increase in z, that is, $\hat{z} > z$. When the initial basic solution is degenerate and we choose a vector $\mathbf{a}_j$ for which $c_j - z_j > 0$ and at least one $y_{ij} > 0$, we then may or may not have an increase in z, depending on whether $\theta > 0$. In any event, when $c_j - z_j > 0$, we are sure that $\hat{z}$ is not less than z. By inspection of (3–45), we see that if we insert the variable x_j into the basic solution and drive the variable corresponding to the rth column of $\mathbf{B}$ to zero, we gain θc_j. However, the introduction of x_j causes the remaining variables to change their values, and this causes a change of $-\theta z_j$ in z. Hence $c_j - z_j$ may be thought of intuitively as the change in z per unit increase in the value of x_j when all other nonbasic variables are maintained at a zero level and the basic variables are allowed to change, as they must in order to maintain a solution.

If we are minimizing rather than maximizing z, it is obvious that $\mathbf{a}_j$ must have $c_j - z_j < 0$, in order that $\hat{z} \leq z$.

We can summarize the above discussion as follows:

Given a basic feasible solution $\mathbf{x}_B = \mathbf{B}^{-1}\mathbf{b}$ to the set of constraints $\mathbf{Ax} = \mathbf{b}$ for a linear programming problem, with the value of the objective function for this solution being $z = \mathbf{c}_B\mathbf{x}_B$. If for any column $\mathbf{a}_j$ in $\mathbf{A}$, but not in $\mathbf{B}$, the condition $c_j > z_j$ or $z_j - c_j < 0$ holds, and if at least one $y_{ij} > 0$, $i = 1, \ldots, m$, then it is possible to obtain a new basic feasible solution by replacing one of the columns in $\mathbf{B}$ by $\mathbf{a}_j$, and the new value of the objective function $\hat{z}$ satisfies $\hat{z} \geq z$. Furthermore, if the given basic solution is not degenerate, $\hat{z} > z$. Similarly, if for some $\mathbf{a}_j$ in $\mathbf{A}$, but not in $\mathbf{B}$, $c_j < z_j$ or $z_j - c_j > 0$ and at least one $y_{ij} > 0$, then it is possible to obtain a new basic feasible solution by replacing one of the columns in $\mathbf{B}$ by $\mathbf{a}_j$, and the new value of the objective function $\hat{z}$ satisfies $\hat{z} \leq z$. Also, if the given basic solution is not degenerate, $\hat{z} < z$.

EXAMPLE: Consider the following linear programming problem:

$$x_1\mathbf{a}_1 + x_2\mathbf{a}_2 + x_3\mathbf{a}_3 = \mathbf{b}, \qquad x_j \geq 0, \quad j = 1, 2, 3,$$

$$\max z = c_1x_1 + c_2x_2 + c_3x_3;$$

$$\mathbf{a}_1 = [3, 3], \qquad \mathbf{a}_2 = [2, 4],$$

$$\mathbf{a}_3 = [2, 1], \qquad \mathbf{b} = [8, 7],$$

$$c_1 = 3, \qquad c_2 = 2, \qquad c_3 = 1.$$

Let us form the basis matrix $\mathbf{B}$ with $\mathbf{a}_3$ in column 1 and $\mathbf{a}_2$ in column 2, i.e.,

$$\mathbf{B} = \begin{bmatrix} 2 & 2 \\ 1 & 4 \end{bmatrix},$$

$$\mathbf{B}^{-1} = \frac{1}{6}\begin{bmatrix} 4 & -2 \\ -1 & 2 \end{bmatrix}.$$

The corresponding basic solution is feasible since

$$\mathbf{x}_B = \mathbf{B}^{-1}\mathbf{b} = \frac{1}{6}\begin{bmatrix} 4 & -2 \\ -1 & 2 \end{bmatrix}\begin{bmatrix} 8 \\ 7 \end{bmatrix} = \begin{bmatrix} 3 \\ 1 \end{bmatrix}.$$

For this basic feasible solution,

$$\mathbf{y}_1 = \mathbf{B}^{-1}\mathbf{a}_1 = \begin{bmatrix} 1 \\ \frac{1}{2} \end{bmatrix}, \qquad \mathbf{c}_B = (1, 2),$$

$$z_1 = \mathbf{c}_B\mathbf{y}_1 = 2, \qquad z_1 - c_1 = 2 - 3 = -1,$$

$$z = \mathbf{c}_B\mathbf{x}_B = 1(3) + 2(1) = 5.$$

According to the theory developed above, we should be able to replace one of the columns in $\mathbf{B}$ by $\mathbf{a}_1$ and obtain a new basic feasible solution with an improved value of the objective function, since $z_1 - c_1 < 0$, $y_{ij} > 0$, $i = 1, 2$, and the given basic feasible solution is not degenerate.

We determine the vector to be removed, using

$$\frac{x_{Br}}{y_{r1}} = \min_i \left(\frac{x_{Bi}}{y_{i1}}, y_{i1} > 0\right) = \min\left(\frac{3}{1} = \frac{x_{B1}}{y_{11}}; \frac{1}{1/2} = \frac{x_{B2}}{y_{21}}\right) = 2 = \frac{x_{B2}}{y_{21}}.$$

The minimum is taken on for $r = 2$, and the second column of $\mathbf{B}$, that is, $\mathbf{a}_2$ is removed. Thus

$$\hat{z} = z + \frac{x_{Br}}{y_{rj}}(c_1 - z_1) = z + 2 = 7 > z = 5.$$

We can easily check this result by finding $\hat{\mathbf{x}}_B$, $\hat{\mathbf{c}}_B$ and using $\hat{z} = \hat{\mathbf{c}}_B \hat{\mathbf{x}}_B$:

$$\hat{\mathbf{B}} = \begin{bmatrix} 2 & 3 \\ 1 & 3 \end{bmatrix}, \qquad \hat{\mathbf{B}}^{-1} = \frac{1}{3} \begin{bmatrix} 3 & -3 \\ -1 & 2 \end{bmatrix};$$

$$\hat{\mathbf{x}}_B = \frac{1}{3} \begin{bmatrix} 3 & -3 \\ -1 & 2 \end{bmatrix} \begin{bmatrix} 8 \\ 7 \end{bmatrix} = \begin{bmatrix} 1 \\ 2 \end{bmatrix};$$

$$\hat{\mathbf{c}}_B = (1, 3), \qquad \hat{z} = \hat{\mathbf{c}}_B \hat{\mathbf{x}}_B = 7.$$

The value of $\hat{z}$ verifies that obtained above. We have found a new basic feasible solution with $\mathbf{a}_3$, $\mathbf{a}_1$ in the basis, and $\hat{z} > z$.

3–7 Unbounded solutions. In the foregoing discussion we assumed that if we inserted $\mathbf{a}_j$ into the basis and removed some column to form a new basis, there was at least one $y_{ij} > 0$, $i = 1, \ldots, m$. Let us now consider what happens if we insert an $\mathbf{a}_j$ for which all $y_{ij} \leq 0$, $i = 1, \ldots, m$. It has been noted in the previous section that if a new basic solution is to be obtained on inserting such an $\mathbf{a}_j$, then $\mathbf{a}_j$ must enter the basis at a negative or a zero level (since y_{rj} will be negative), thus implying that the new basic solution will not be feasible unless $\mathbf{a}_j$ enters at a zero level. Now, instead of trying to obtain a new basic solution, we shall study the solutions which can be formed by allowing $m + 1$ variables (x_j and the x_{Bi}'s) to be different from zero. We have the basic feasible solution

$$\sum_{i=1}^{m} x_{Bi} \mathbf{b}_i = \mathbf{b}, \tag{3–46}$$

with the value of the objective function being $z = \mathbf{c}_B \mathbf{x}_B$. Suppose that we add and subtract $\theta \mathbf{a}_j$, θ any scalar, in (3–46) to obtain

$$\sum_{i=1}^{m} x_{Bi} \mathbf{b}_i - \theta \mathbf{a}_j + \theta \mathbf{a}_j = \mathbf{b}; \tag{3–47}$$

but

$$-\theta \mathbf{a}_j = -\theta \sum_{i=1}^{m} y_{ij} \mathbf{b}_i. \tag{3–48}$$

If (3–48) is substituted into (3–47), we obtain

$$\sum_{i=1}^{m} (x_{Bi} - \theta y_{ij}) \mathbf{b}_i + \theta \mathbf{a}_j = \mathbf{b}. \tag{3–49}$$

When $\theta > 0$, then $x_{Bi} - \theta y_{ij} \geq 0$ since, by assumption, $y_{ij} \leq 0$, $i = 1, \ldots, m$; therefore (3–49) is a feasible solution in which $m + 1$ variables can be different from zero. However, it is not, in general, a basic solution. Note that (3–49) is feasible for any $\theta \geq 0$.

Next we shall compute the value of $\hat{z}$ for the feasible (nonbasic) solution (3–49):

$$\hat{z} = \sum c_i \hat{x}_i = \sum_{i=1}^{m} c_{Bi}(x_{Bi} - \theta y_{ij}) + c_j \theta = z + \theta(c_j - z_j). \quad (3\text{–}50)$$

Then by making θ sufficiently large $\hat{z}$ can be made arbitrarily large if $c_j - z_j > 0$, and arbitrarily small if $c_j - z_j < 0$. We can summarize the above development, as follows:

Given any basic feasible solution to a linear programming problem. If for this solution there is some column $\mathbf{a}_j$ not in the basis for which

$$z_j - c_j < 0 \quad \text{and} \quad y_{ij} \leq 0 \quad (i = 1, \ldots, m), \quad (3\text{–}51)$$

then there exist feasible solutions in which $m + 1$ variables can be different from zero, with the value of the objective function being arbitrarily large. In such a case, the problem has an unbounded solution if the objective function is to be maximized. Similarly, if for some $\mathbf{a}_j$,

$$z_j - c_j > 0 \quad \text{and} \quad y_{ij} \leq 0 \quad (i = 1, \ldots, m), \quad (3\text{–}52)$$

then there exist feasible solutions, in which $m + 1$ variables can be different from zero, with the value of the objective function being arbitrarily small. In such a case, the problem has an unbounded solution if z is to be minimized.

The preceding statement is a rather pleasant surprise, because it gives us some information about the annoying problem of unbounded solutions. In fact, it will be seen that the above results enable us to determine always whether a linear programming problem has an unbounded solution. As indicated in Chapter 1, we do not expect real-world problems to possess unbounded solutions. In fact, linear programming is useful because there are limiting factors which prevent us from making the function to be optimized arbitrarily large. However, some mistake in the formulation of a linear programming problem may at times lead to an unbounded solution. For this reason, it is most desirable to have a computational technique which will show whether there is an unbounded solution. It would be dangerous if a technique selected only the basic feasible solution with the largest value of the objective function, for in such a case the problem might actually have an unbounded solution and we would not know it. Fortunately, with the help of the information developed above, the simplex method does indicate whether there is an unbounded solution.

EXAMPLE: If in the preceding example $\mathbf{a}_1 = [-3, -3]$, then

$$\mathbf{y}_1 = \mathbf{B}^{-1}\mathbf{a}_1 = \frac{1}{6}\begin{bmatrix} 4 & -2 \\ -1 & 2 \end{bmatrix}\begin{bmatrix} -3 \\ -3 \end{bmatrix} = \begin{bmatrix} -1 \\ -\frac{1}{2} \end{bmatrix};$$

$$z_1 - c_1 = -5.$$

An unbounded solution exists. If $\theta\mathbf{a}_1$, $\theta > 0$, is added to and subtracted from the basic feasible solution $\mathbf{a}_2 + 3\mathbf{a}_3 = \mathbf{b}$, we obtain

$$\theta\mathbf{a}_1 + \left(1 + \frac{\theta}{2}\right)\mathbf{a}_2 + (3 + \theta)\mathbf{a}_3 = \mathbf{b}.$$

This is feasible so long as $\theta > 0$, and

$$\hat{z} = z + \theta(c_1 - z_1) = z + 5\theta.$$

If θ is increased sufficiently, $\hat{z}$ can be made arbitrarily large. The feasible solution will have three variables different from 0.

3–8 Optimality conditions. Let us consider a linear programming problem for which we wish to maximize the objective function. Section 3–6 has shown that if we start with a basic feasible solution and if there is a vector $\mathbf{a}_j$ not in the basis with $z_j - c_j < 0$ and at least one $y_{ij} > 0$, $i = 1, \ldots, m$, then there exists another basic feasible solution with the new value $\hat{z}$ of the objective function at least as large as the old value, z. If degeneracy is not present, then $\hat{z} > z$.

For the moment, we shall assume that we never encounter degeneracy. Under these circumstances, we can move from one basis to another, changing one vector at a time, so long as there is some $\mathbf{a}_j$ not in the basis with $z_j - c_j < 0$ and at least one $y_{ij} > 0$. At each step, z is increased. This process cannot continue indefinitely because there is only a finite number of bases. In the absence of degeneracy, no basis can ever be repeated because z increases at each step, and the same basis cannot yield two different values of z. However, the process can terminate in only one of two ways:

(1) One or more $z_j - c_j < 0$, and for each $z_j - c_j < 0$, $y_{ij} \leq 0$ for all $i = 1, \ldots, m$.
(2) All $z_j - c_j \geq 0$ for the columns of $\mathbf{A}$ not in the basis.

If the process terminates with condition (1), we know that there is an unbounded solution. This leads us to suspect that if the process terminates with condition (2), we have an optimal basic solution. This is indeed the case, as we shall now show.

Assume that we have a basic feasible solution $\mathbf{x}_B = \mathbf{B}^{-1}\mathbf{b}$ to a linear programming problem $\mathbf{Ax} = \mathbf{b}$, $\mathbf{x} \geq \mathbf{0}$, $\max z = \mathbf{cx}$, and that the value of the objective function for this solution is $z_0 = \mathbf{c}_B \mathbf{x}_B$. In addition, suppose that $z_j - c_j \geq 0$ for every column $\mathbf{a}_j$ of $\mathbf{A}$ not in the basis matrix $\mathbf{B}$. It is easy to demonstrate that, subject to the constraints $\mathbf{A}\mathbf{x} = \mathbf{b}$ and the non-negativity restrictions $\mathbf{x} \geq \mathbf{0}$, z_0 is the maximum value of the objective function $z = \mathbf{c}\mathbf{x}$.

Let

$$x_j \geq 0, \quad j = 1, \ldots, n; \qquad x_1\mathbf{a}_1 + \cdots + x_n\mathbf{a}_n = \mathbf{b}, \quad (3\text{--}53)$$

be any feasible solution to $\mathbf{A}\mathbf{x} = \mathbf{b}$. The corresponding value of the objective function, denoted by z^*, is

$$z^* = c_1 x_1 + \cdots + c_n x_n. \qquad (3\text{--}54)$$

Any vector $\mathbf{a}_j$ in $\mathbf{A}$ can be written as a linear combination of the basis vectors in $\mathbf{B}$:

$$\mathbf{a}_j = \sum_{i=1}^{m} y_{ij} \mathbf{b}_i. \qquad (3\text{--}55)$$

On substituting (3–55) into (3–53), we obtain

$$x_1 \sum_{i=1}^{m} y_{i1} \mathbf{b}_i + \cdots + x_n \sum_{i=1}^{m} y_{in} \mathbf{b}_i = \mathbf{b},$$

or

$$\left[\sum_{j=1}^{n} x_j y_{1j} \right] \mathbf{b}_1 + \cdots + \left[\sum_{j=1}^{n} x_j y_{mj} \right] \mathbf{b}_m = \mathbf{b}. \qquad (3\text{--}56)$$

Recall, however, that the expression of any vector in terms of the basis vectors is unique. We must conclude that

$$x_{Bi} = \sum_{j=1}^{n} x_j y_{ij}, \quad i = 1, \ldots, m. \qquad (3\text{--}57)$$

Next we turn our attention to z^*. By hypothesis, $z_j \geq c_j$ for every column of $\mathbf{A}$ not in the basis. For those columns of $\mathbf{A}$ that are in the basis,

$$\mathbf{y}_j = \mathbf{B}^{-1}\mathbf{a}_j = \mathbf{B}^{-1}\mathbf{b}_i = \mathbf{e}_i \qquad (3\text{--}58)$$

if $\mathbf{a}_j$ is in column i of $\mathbf{B}$. Hence $z_j = \mathbf{c}_B \mathbf{y}_j = \mathbf{c}_B \mathbf{e}_i = c_{Bi} = c_j$. Thus, for the columns of $\mathbf{A}$ in the basis, it is always true that $z_j - c_j = 0$. We conclude that for the case under consideration $z_j \geq c_j$ for *every* column in $\mathbf{A}$. Consequently, using $z_j \geq c_j$ in (3–54), we see that

$$z_1 x_1 + \cdots + z_n x_n \geq z^* \qquad (3\text{--}59)$$

since each $x_j \geq 0$. Now we use the definition

$$z_j = \sum_{i=1}^{m} c_{Bi} y_{ij}$$

in (3–59) and obtain

$$\left[\sum_{j=1}^{n} x_j y_{1j} \right] c_{B1} + \cdots + \left[\sum_{j=1}^{n} x_j y_{mj} \right] c_{Bm} \geq z^*.$$

However, because of (3–57), we have

$$z_0 = x_{B1} c_{B1} + \cdots + x_{Bm} c_{Bm} \geq z^*. \tag{3–60}$$

This proves that z_0 is at least as large as the objective function for any other feasible solution, and therefore z_0 is the maximum value of the objective function.

We can summarize the above results in the following statements:

Given a basic feasible solution $\mathbf{x}_B = \mathbf{B}^{-1}\mathbf{b}$ *with* $z_0 = \mathbf{c}_B\mathbf{x}_B$ *to the linear programming problem* $\mathbf{Ax} = \mathbf{b}$, $\mathbf{x} \geq \mathbf{0}$, $\max z = \mathbf{cx}$ *such that* $z_j - c_j \geq 0$ *for every column* $\mathbf{a}_j$ *in* $\mathbf{A}$. *Then* z_0 *is the maximum value of* z *subject to the constraints, and the basic feasible solution is an optimal basic feasible solution.*

Given a basic feasible solution $\mathbf{x}_B = \mathbf{B}^{-1}\mathbf{b}$ *with* $z_0 = \mathbf{c}_B\mathbf{x}_B$ *to the linear programming problem* $\mathbf{Ax} = \mathbf{b}$, $\mathbf{x} \geq \mathbf{0}$, $\min z = \mathbf{cx}$ *such that* $z_j - c_j \leq 0$ *for every column* $\mathbf{a}_j$ *in* $\mathbf{A}$. *Then* z_0 *is the minimum value of* z *subject to the constraints, and the basic feasible solution is an optimal basic feasible solution.*

Note that our proof did not depend on any requirement that the basic feasible solution $\mathbf{x}_B$ be nondegenerate. If all $z_j - c_j \geq 0$, then $\mathbf{x}_B$ is an optimal solution regardless of whether or not it is degenerate.

Any linear programming problem falls into one of three mutually exclusive and collectively exhaustive categories: (a) There is no feasible solution; (b) there is an optimal solution; (c) the objective function is unbounded. If there is a feasible solution and hence a basic feasible solution, only two possibilities remain: There is either an optimal solution or an unbounded solution. If we are given a basic feasible solution which is not optimal, the above results have shown that, in the absence of degeneracy, we can proceed step by step, changing a single vector in the basis at a time, and reach either condition (1) or condition (2) in a finite number of steps. Condition (1) indicates that there is an unbounded solution, and condition (2) that we have an optimal basic feasible solution. These are the only two alternatives, and hence all possibilities have been accounted for.

Note that in the absence of degeneracy, we have proved that if there is an optimal solution, one of the basic feasible solutions will be optimal. This is a very important result. Stated in another way, it means that an optimal solution to a linear programming problem never need have more than m nonzero variables. We have also shown that, in the absence of degeneracy, there will be an optimal basic feasible solution having all $z_j - c_j \geq 0$.

EXAMPLE: Consider the basic feasible solution characterized by the basis $\hat{\mathbf{B}}$ ($\hat{\mathbf{B}} = \begin{bmatrix} 2 & 3 \\ 1 & 3 \end{bmatrix}$, $\hat{\mathbf{B}}^{-1} = (1/3)\begin{bmatrix} 3 & -3 \\ -1 & 2 \end{bmatrix}$) (see example, p. 92). The only vector not in the basis is $\mathbf{a}_2$. For this vector

$$\mathbf{y}_2 = \hat{\mathbf{B}}^{-1}\mathbf{a}_2 = \frac{1}{3}\begin{bmatrix} 3 & -3 \\ -1 & 2 \end{bmatrix}\begin{bmatrix} 2 \\ 4 \end{bmatrix} = \begin{bmatrix} -2 \\ 2 \end{bmatrix};$$

$$z_2 - c_2 = \hat{\mathbf{c}}_B\mathbf{y}_2 - c_2 = 4 - 2 = 2 > 0.$$

Recall that for vectors in the basis the $z_j - c_j = 0$. It follows from our discussion that the basic feasible solution with $\mathbf{a}_1$, $\mathbf{a}_3$ in the basis is an optimal solution. Note that $\mathbf{a}_1 + (1/2)\mathbf{a}_2 + 2\mathbf{a}_3 = \mathbf{b}$ is a feasible non-basic solution. The value of the objective function for this solution is

$$z = \mathbf{c}\mathbf{x} = 1(3) + \tfrac{1}{2}(2) + 2(1) = 6,$$

and this is indeed less than the optimal value $z = 7$.

We must now point out the difficulties that the problem of degeneracy introduces into the above arguments. First of all, when degeneracy is present, we are not sure that the insertion of a vector will produce a new value of z which will be greater than the previous one. The value of the objective function may remain unchanged, and for this reason, a basis may be repeated. This means that we are not sure that condition (1) or (2) can be reached in a finite number of steps. We may possibly enter a loop and cycle, forever repeating the same sequence of bases, without changing the value of z; this would imply that an optimal solution (or an indication of an unbounded solution) would never be achieved. Hence, the foregoing argument does not ensure that if degeneracy appears, there is an optimal basic feasible solution with all $z_j - c_j \geq 0$. In fact, even if there is an optimal solution, we cannot be sure that one of the basic solutions will be optimal.

If it could be demonstrated that a basis never needed to be repeated, then, since the number of bases is finite, the above process would terminate in one of two ways: (1) $z_j - c_j \geq 0$ for all j; or (2) for all $z_j - c_j < 0$, $y_{ij} \leq 0$ for all i. Condition (1) would imply that an optimal basic solution had been found, and (2) would indicate the presence of an unbounded solution. Therefore the resolution of the degeneracy problem centers about the task of proving that a basis never needs to be repeated. Once this is done, it follows that at least one of the basic feasible solutions will be optimal, and at least one of the optimal basic solutions will have all $z_j - c_j \geq 0$. Later we shall resolve the degeneracy problem by showing that a basis never needs to be repeated.

For the present time, we shall assume that even when degeneracy appears, one of the basic feasible solutions will be optimal, and that one of the optimal solutions will have all $z_j - c_j \geq 0$. Incidentally, when degeneracy is present, there can be optimal basic solutions with one or more $z_j - c_j < 0$. An example of this will be presented later. It also is of interest to note that one of the basic feasible solutions can be shown to be optimal in a way that is completely independent of any degeneracy arguments. This will be done when the correspondence between basic feasible solutions and extreme points is discussed, since we know from Chapter 2 that if there is an optimal solution, at least one of the extreme points of the convex set of feasible solutions is optimal.

3–9 Alternative optima. The optimal value of the objective function for any linear programming problem is unique. However, the set of variables which yield the optimal value of the objective function does not need to be unique. Such a case was illustrated in Chapter 1, Fig. 1–2. We saw that if the line representing the optimal value of z lay on one side of the convex set and if two extreme points yielded optimal solutions, then any convex combination of the extreme points was also an optimal solution. Now we wish to develop the generalization of this case.

Suppose that a given linear programming problem has k different basic feasible solutions, $\mathbf{x}_1, \ldots, \mathbf{x}_k$, which are optimal. We assume that each $\mathbf{x}_i$ is an n-component vector and therefore contains the values of all variables (not only the basic ones). Consider any convex combination of these solutions:

$$\mathbf{x} = \sum_{i=1}^{k} \mu_i \mathbf{x}_i, \qquad \mu_i \geq 0 \qquad (i = 1, \ldots, k), \qquad \sum \mu_i = 1. \quad (3\text{–}61)$$

Since each $\mathbf{x}_i \geq \mathbf{0}$, and $\mu_i \geq 0$, it follows that $\mathbf{x} \geq \mathbf{0}$. Furthermore $\mathbf{A}\mathbf{x}_i = \mathbf{b}$, and hence $\mathbf{A}\mathbf{x} = \mathbf{b}$. Consequently, $\mathbf{x}$ is a feasible (but perhaps nonbasic) solution. If $z_0 = \max z = \mathbf{c}\mathbf{x}_i$ $(i = 1, \ldots, k)$, the value of the objective function for $\mathbf{x}$ is

$$\mathbf{c}\mathbf{x} = \sum_{i=1}^{k} \mu_i \mathbf{c}\mathbf{x}_i = \sum_{i=1}^{k} \mu_i z_0 = z_0. \quad (3\text{–}62)$$

Hence $\mathbf{x}$ is an optimal solution. *We have proved that if $\mathbf{x}_1, \ldots, \mathbf{x}_k$ are k different optimal basic feasible solutions to a linear programming problem, then any convex combination of $\mathbf{x}_1, \ldots, \mathbf{x}_k$ is also an optimal solution.*

This shows that if there are two or more different optimal basic feasible solutions, there will be an infinite number of optimal solutions. However, in this case, not all optimal solutions will be basic.

We do not need two or more optimal basic feasible solutions to a linear programming problem in order to have an infinite number of optimal solutions. The other possibility is illustrated in Chapter 1, Fig. 1–7. In this case, the objective function in its optimal position lies on a side of the convex set which extends to infinity. The optimal value of z is finite, but there are optimal solutions with arbitrarily large variables. This situation can also be generalized.

Assume that we have an optimal basic solution to a linear programming problem and that for some vector $\mathbf{a}_j$ not in the basis, $z_j - c_j = 0$, and all $y_{ij} \leq 0$, $i = 1, \ldots, m$. We can then form a new feasible solution

$$\sum_{i=1}^{m} (x_{Bi} - \theta y_{ij})\mathbf{b}_i + \theta \mathbf{a}_j = \mathbf{b}, \qquad \theta > 0, \qquad (3\text{–}63)$$

which can have $m + 1$ nonzero variables. The value of z for this solution is the same as that for the optimal basic feasible solution; hence the solution (3–63) is optimal. However, this holds true for arbitrarily large θ. Moreover, at least one $y_{ij} < 0$ because $\mathbf{a}_j \neq \mathbf{0}$. Consequently, there are optimal solutions for which at least two of the variables can be made arbitrarily large.* Thus we have shown that *if there is an optimal basic feasible solution to a linear programming problem and, for some $\mathbf{a}_j$ not in the basis, $z_j - c_j = 0$, $y_{ij} \leq 0$ for all i, then (3–63) is also an optimal solution for any $\theta > 0$.*

If the set of variables yielding the optimal value of the objective function is not unique, we say that there are alternative optima (see Chapter 1).

3–10 Extreme points and basic feasible solutions. Now we shall finally return to the geometric interpretation of linear programming. Recall that in Chapter 2 it was proved that the set of feasible solutions to $\mathbf{Ax} = \mathbf{b}$ is a convex set. Here we wish to make the connection between basic feasible solutions and the extreme points of the convex set of feasible solutions to $\mathbf{Ax} = \mathbf{b}$. It will be shown that every basic feasible solution is an extreme point of the convex set of feasible solutions, and that every extreme point is a basic feasible solution to the set of constraints.

---

* The reader may feel that this statement is contradicted by an example whose feasible solutions lie in the region shown in Fig. 1–6 and whose objective function is $z = 10x_1$. In the figure, only x_2 can be made arbitrarily large. However, recall that here slack and surplus variables are included in the discussion. As x_2 increases (Fig. 1–6), the slack variable for $x_1 - x_2 \leq 0$ also increases.

Imagine that we have a basic feasible solution $\mathbf{x}$ to the set of constraints $\mathbf{Ax} = \mathbf{b}$. The vector $\mathbf{x}$ will be taken to be an n-component vector; hence it includes both zero and nonzero variables. Let us assume that the variables have been numbered so that $\mathbf{x}$ has the form

$$\mathbf{x} = [\mathbf{x}_B, \mathbf{0}], \qquad \mathbf{x}_B = \mathbf{B}^{-1}\mathbf{b}. \tag{3–64}$$

To demonstrate that $\mathbf{x}$ is an extreme point, we must show that there do not exist feasible solutions $\mathbf{x}_1$, $\mathbf{x}_2$ different from $\mathbf{x}$ such that $\mathbf{x} = \lambda\mathbf{x}_1 + (1 - \lambda)\mathbf{x}_2$, $0 < \lambda < 1$. Suppose that there existed feasible solutions $\mathbf{x}_1$ and $\mathbf{x}_2$ such that

$$\mathbf{x} = \lambda\mathbf{x}_1 + (1 - \lambda)\mathbf{x}_2, \qquad 0 < \lambda < 1. \tag{3–65}$$

Write $\mathbf{x}_1$, $\mathbf{x}_2$ as follows:

$$\mathbf{x}_1 = [\mathbf{u}_1, \mathbf{v}_1], \qquad \mathbf{x}_2 = [\mathbf{u}_2, \mathbf{v}_2], \tag{3–66}$$

where $\mathbf{u}_1$, $\mathbf{u}_2$ are m-component vectors and $\mathbf{v}_1$, $\mathbf{v}_2$ are $(n - m)$-component vectors. Recall that $\mathbf{x}$ is given by (3–64), and use (3–66) in (3–65). Then for the last $n - m$ components of (3–65), we have

$$\mathbf{0} = \lambda\mathbf{v}_1 + (1 - \lambda)\mathbf{v}_2. \tag{3–67}$$

But λ, $(1 - \lambda) > 0$ and $\mathbf{v}_1$, $\mathbf{v}_2 \geq 0$; (3–67) can hold only if

$$\mathbf{v}_1 = \mathbf{v}_2 = \mathbf{0}. \tag{3–68}$$

Therefore we must have

$$\mathbf{Ax}_1 = \mathbf{Bu}_1 = \mathbf{b}; \qquad \mathbf{Ax}_2 = \mathbf{Bu}_2 = \mathbf{b}. \tag{3–69}$$

However, the expression of the vector $\mathbf{b}$ in terms of the basis vectors is unique, and we must conclude that

$$\mathbf{x}_B = \mathbf{u}_1 = \mathbf{u}_2; \qquad \mathbf{x} = \mathbf{x}_1 = \mathbf{x}_2. \tag{3–70}$$

The above arguments show that there do not exist feasible solutions different from $\mathbf{x}$ such that (3–65) holds. Consequently, $\mathbf{x}$ is an extreme point, that is, any basic feasible solution is an extreme point of the convex set of feasible solutions.

Next let us demonstrate that any extreme point $\mathbf{x}^* = [x_1, \ldots, x_n]$ of the set of feasible solutions is a basic solution. To do this, we shall prove that the vectors associated with the positive components of $\mathbf{x}^*$ are linearly independent. Assume that k components of $\mathbf{x}^*$ are nonzero; number the variables so that the first k components are nonzero. Then

$$\sum_{i=1}^{k} x_i\mathbf{a}_i = \mathbf{b}, \qquad x_i > 0, \qquad i = 1, \ldots, k. \tag{3–71}$$

If the columns corresponding to the nonzero components of $\mathbf{x}^*$ are linearly dependent, then there exist λ_i not all zero such that

$$\sum_{i=1}^{k} \lambda_i \mathbf{a}_i = \mathbf{0}. \tag{3-72}$$

Now consider

$$\eta = \min_i \frac{x_i}{|\lambda_i|}, \qquad \lambda_i \neq 0, \qquad i = 1, \ldots, k. \tag{3-73}$$

Note that η is a positive number. If we select an ϵ, $0 < \epsilon < \eta$, then

$$x_i + \epsilon \lambda_i > 0 \qquad \text{and} \qquad x_i - \epsilon \lambda_i > 0, \qquad i = 1, \ldots, k. \tag{3-74}$$

Define an n-component column vector $\boldsymbol{\lambda} \neq \mathbf{0}$ which has the λ_i in the first k positions and zero for the last $n - k$ components. Write

$$\mathbf{x}_1 = \mathbf{x}^* + \epsilon \boldsymbol{\lambda}; \qquad \mathbf{x}_2 = \mathbf{x}^* - \epsilon \boldsymbol{\lambda}. \tag{3-75}$$

Because of (3–74), $\mathbf{x}_1 \geq \mathbf{0}$, $\mathbf{x}_2 \geq \mathbf{0}$. Furthermore by (3–72),

$$\mathbf{A}\boldsymbol{\lambda} = \mathbf{0}, \tag{3-76}$$

so that

$$\mathbf{A}\mathbf{x}_1 = \mathbf{b}; \qquad \mathbf{A}\mathbf{x}_2 = \mathbf{b}. \tag{3-77}$$

If follows that $\mathbf{x}_1$, $\mathbf{x}_2$ are feasible solutions different from $\mathbf{x}^*$, and

$$\mathbf{x}^* = \tfrac{1}{2}\mathbf{x}_1 + \tfrac{1}{2}\mathbf{x}_2. \tag{3-78}$$

This contradicts the fact that $\mathbf{x}^*$ is an extreme point. Hence the columns of $\mathbf{A}$ associated with the nonzero components of any extreme point of the convex set of feasible solutions must be linearly independent. There cannot be more than m linearly independent columns of $\mathbf{A}$, and therefore an extreme point cannot have more than m positive components. If an extreme point has less than m positive components, it can be interpreted as a degenerate basic solution, since we can imagine that some $m - k$ columns of $\mathbf{A}$ are added at a zero level to yield a degenerate basic solution.

We have shown that every basic feasible solution to $\mathbf{A}\mathbf{x} = \mathbf{b}$ is an extreme point of the convex set of feasible solutions, and that every extreme point is a basic feasible solution. In the absence of degeneracy, it must be true that there is a one-to-one correspondence between the extreme points and the basic feasible solutions, i.e., there is only one extreme point for a given basic feasible solution, and only one basic feasible solution corresponds to any one extreme point. It is important to note, however, that when degeneracy occurs, this is not the case. If less than m variables are positive, the vector or vectors from $\mathbf{A}$ which are added at a zero level to yield a degenerate basic feasible solution need not be unique. For this reason, a number of different degenerate basic feasible solutions can correspond to the same extreme point.

This observation allows us to interpret geometrically what happens in the presence of degeneracy. If some vector with $z_j - c_j < 0$ is inserted into the basis and the θ of (3–40) is zero so that it enters at a zero level, we obtain a new degenerate basic feasible solution which is the same extreme point. We have not moved away from the initial extreme point; we have simply changed the vectors appearing at a zero level in the basis. The geometric interpretation also indicates how cycling could develop. Although the basis would be changed by inserting and removing vectors at a zero level, we would never move away from the extreme point; finally we might obtain a new basis which, however, would prove to be our starting basis. The geometric interpretation also gives an intuitive suggestion as to why we should be able to avoid the cycling problem. If we are at an extreme point where degeneracy is present, and if there is another extreme point with an improved value of the objective function, then we expect that there will be an edge of the convex set leading from the given extreme point to an adjacent extreme point with an improved value of the objective function. This intuitive notion is correct and will be discussed in greater detail later.

In this section, we have shown that every extreme point of the convex set of feasible solutions is a basic feasible solution. We have proved in Chapter 2 that if there is an optimal solution, then one or more of the extreme points are optimal. Hence if there is an optimal solution, one or more of the basic feasible solutions will be optimal (this result is completely independent of any nondegeneracy assumptions). *Thus we have obtained the general and very important result that an optimal solution to a linear programming problem never needs to have more than m variables different from zero (m is, of course, the number of constraint equations).* To emphasize the importance of this result, we note that to maximize the profit in the example of Section 1–3, it is never necessary to make more than three of the four products.

The set of constraints (3–15) was obtained from the constraints (3–1) by addition of slack and surplus variables. It is very easy to show that there is a one-to-one correspondence between the extreme points of the convex set of feasible solutions to (3–15) and the extreme points of the convex set of feasible solutions to (3–1). Problem 3–18 will ask the reader to show how to obtain an extreme-point solution to (3–1) from any basic feasible solution to (3–15), and to prove that there is a one-to-one correspondence between the extreme points.

The results of this section also prove that the convex set of feasible solutions has a finite number of extreme points. The number of extreme points is equal to the number of different basic feasible solutions (degenerate basic feasible solutions with the same values of positive variables are not considered to be different). This number cannot be greater than $n!/m!(n-m)!$.

REFERENCES

1. R. G. D. ALLEN, *Mathematical Economics*. London: Macmillan, 1956.
2. A. CHARNES, W. W. COOPER, and A. HENDERSON, *An Introduction to Linear Programming*. New York: Wiley, 1953.
3. S. I. GASS, *Linear Programming*. New York: McGraw-Hill, 1958.
4. S. KARLIN, *Mathematical Methods and Theory in Games, Programming, and Economics*. Reading, Mass.: Addison-Wesley, 1959.
5. T. C. KOOPMANS, ed., *Activity Analysis of Production and Allocation*. New York: Wiley, 1951.
6. S. VAJDA, *The Theory of Games and Linear Programming*. London: Methuen, 1956.

PROBLEMS

3–1. We have noted in Chapter 2 that any point in a convex polyhedron can be written as a convex combination of its extreme points. Let $\mathbf{a}_1 \ldots, \mathbf{a}_k$ be the k extreme points of a convex polyhedron in E^m. Any point $\mathbf{b}$ in the convex polyhedron can be written $\mathbf{b} = \sum_{j=1}^{k} \mu_j \mathbf{a}_j$, all $\mu_j \geq 0$, $\sum \mu_j = 1$. Show that when any point $\mathbf{b}$ of the polyhedron is written as a convex combination of the extreme points, there exist μ_j such that no more than $m+1$ of the μ_j need be different from zero.

3–2. Study the problem of reducing any solution $\mathbf{x}$, which may contain both positive and negative variables, of $\mathbf{Ax} = \mathbf{b}$ to a basic feasible solution (provided there is one). What problems are involved which do not appear in the reduction of any feasible solution to a basic feasible solution?

3–3. Show that, in the absence of degeneracy, every optimal basic solution has $z_j - c_j \geq 0$ for every j.

3–4. If an optimal basic solution is nondegenerate and $z_j - c_j > 0$ for every vector not in the basis, show that the optimal solution is unique.

3–5. Prove that if an optimal nonbasic solution to a linear programming problem exists, we obtain either two or more optimal basic feasible solutions or at least one optimal basic solution which has an edge extending to infinity.

3–6. How many edges can emanate from any given extreme point of the convex set of feasible solutions?

3–7. Prove that the statement, "if there is a feasible solution to $\mathbf{Ax} = \mathbf{b}$, $r(\mathbf{A}) = m$, then there is a basic feasible solution" has its geometrical equivalent in the statement, "if the convex set of feasible solutions is not null, then the convex set has at least one extreme point."

3–8. Show that if the convex set of feasible solutions to $\mathbf{Ax} = \mathbf{b}$ is a convex polyhedron, then at least one of the extreme points must be optimal. Use the fact that any feasible solution is a convex combination of the extreme points. This is one of the theorems in Charnes' development [2].

3–9. Study the problem of devising a method for inserting two vectors instead of a single vector into the basis at the same time. What problems are involved?

3–10. Show that, with the proper interpretation, we can write $z_j - c_j = \partial z/\partial x_j$. Indicate clearly which variables vary and which variables remain constant.

3–11. Show that, with the proper interpretation, we can write $\partial x_{Bi}/\partial x_k = -y_{ik}$. Indicate clearly which variables are held constant and which vary *mutatis mutandis* (as they must).

3–12. Consider the linear programming problem $\mathbf{Ax} = \mathbf{b}$, $\mathbf{x} \geq \mathbf{0}$, max $z = \mathbf{cx}$. If $\mathbf{x}^*$ is an optimal basic solution to this problem, will $\mathbf{x}^*$ be an optimal basic solution to a problem whose price vector is $\lambda \mathbf{c}$, $\lambda > 0$? Will $\mathbf{x}^*$ be an optimal solution to a problem whose price vector is $\mathbf{c} + \lambda \mathbf{1}$, for all $\lambda \neq 0$? Why or why not? Is there any special case for which this last statement will always be true?

3–13. Is it meaningful to have a linear programming problem for which the requirements vector $\mathbf{b} = \mathbf{0}$?

3–14. In finding the minimum in Eq. (3–73), we did not consider only $\lambda_i > 0$. Why?

3–15. Let $\mathbf{x} \geq \mathbf{0}$ be any feasible solution to $\mathbf{Ax} = \mathbf{b}$. Show that if any variable $x_j > 0$ is selected, then as x_j is increased, $z = \mathbf{cx}$ will either remain unchanged, increase monotonically, or decrease monotonically, i.e., show that z will never go through a maximum or minimum as a function of x_j (naturally, we suppose that when x_j is changed, the other variables are changed in such a way that $\mathbf{Ax} = \mathbf{b}$). Assume that we wish to maximize z, and that z increases as x_j is increased. Show that if z is not unbounded, then for x_j sufficiently large, at least one of the other variables must be negative. The largest possible value of x_j which will still maintain a feasible solution is reached when any further increase in x_j would cause one of the other variables to become negative. Using this type of analysis, prove that if a linear programming problem has an optimal solution, at least one basic feasible solution will be optimal.

3–16. Let $\mathbf{x}_B = \mathbf{B}^{-1}\mathbf{b}$ be a basic feasible solution to $\mathbf{Ax} = \mathbf{b}$, and $\mathbf{a}_j$ a vector from $\mathbf{A}$ not in $\mathbf{b}$. Then if $\mathbf{y}_j = \mathbf{B}^{-1}\mathbf{a}_j$, show that $\mathbf{B}(\mathbf{x}_B - \theta\mathbf{y}_j) + \theta\mathbf{a}_j = \mathbf{b}$ is a feasible solution to $\mathbf{Ax} = \mathbf{b}$ for any θ, $0 \leq \theta \leq \theta_{\max}$, where

$$\theta_{\max} = \min_i \left\{ \frac{x_{Bi}}{y_{ij}}, y_{ij} > 0 \right\}.$$

For which values of θ is the new solution basic? Use this result to derive the criterion (3–40) for determining the vector $\mathbf{b}_r$ to be removed from the basis when $\mathbf{a}_j$ is inserted.

3–17. Reduce $2\mathbf{a}_1 + 4\mathbf{a}_2 + \mathbf{a}_3 = \mathbf{b}$ to a basic feasible solution if $\mathbf{a}_1 = [2, 1]$, $\mathbf{a}_2 = [-1, 4]$, $\mathbf{a}_3 = [2, 0]$.

3–18. Denote by X_1 the convex set of feasible solutions to Eq. (3–1) and by X_2 the convex set of feasible solutions to Eq. (3–15). Show that there is a one-to-one correspondence between the extreme points of X_1 and X_2. Also show how to determine the extreme points of X_1 from the extreme points of X_2.

3–19. Suppose that the value of θ in Eq. (3–40) is positive and that the vector to be removed is uniquely determined by Eq. (3–40). Under what conditions will the new basic feasible solution be degenerate? Suppose that the current basic feasible solution is not degenerate. Then, with the above assumptions, prove that the new basic solution will also be nondegenerate.

3–20. Find an optimal solution to the following linear programming problem by computing all basic solutions and then finding one that maximizes the objective function.

$$2x_1 + 3x_2 - x_3 + 4x_4 = 8,$$

$$x_1 - 2x_2 + 6x_3 - 7x_4 = -3,$$

$$\text{all } x_j \geq 0,$$

$$\max z = 2x_1 + 3x_2 + 4x_3 + 7x_4.$$

3–21. For the linear programming problem solved in Problem 3–20, compute the $\mathbf{y}_j$ and z_j for each $\mathbf{a}_j$ not in the optimal basis. Show that the optimality condition is satisfied for the optimal solution.

3–22. Consider the set of constraints $\mathbf{Ax} = \mathbf{b}$ [$\mathbf{A}$ being $m \times n$, $n > m$, $r(\mathbf{A}) = m$] for some linear programming problem. Suppose that we have a feasible, but not basic, solution to the constraints. Discuss in detail the numerical procedure for reducing this feasible solution to a basic feasible solution. Give special attention to the way in which one can obtain a relation such as Eq. (3–21) which expresses the linear dependence of the columns of $\mathbf{A}$, i.e., discuss how numerical values for the α_j may be found. Hint: Review the material in Chapter 2 on solving simultaneous linear equations.

3–23. Consider the set of equations

$$2x_1 - 3x_2 + 4x_3 + 6x_4 = 25,$$

$$x_1 + 2x_2 + 3x_3 - 3x_4 + 5x_5 = 12.$$

Note that $x_1 = 2$, $x_2 = 1$, $x_3 = 3$, $x_4 = 2$, $x_5 = 1$ is a feasible solution. Reduce this feasible solution to two different basic feasible solutions.

3–24. Consider the set of equations

$$5x_1 - 4x_2 + 3x_3 + x_4 = 3,$$

$$2x_1 + x_2 + 5x_3 - 3x_4 = 0,$$

$$x_1 + 6x_2 - 4x_3 + 2x_4 = 15.$$

A feasible solution is $x_1 = 1$, $x_2 = 2$, $x_3 = 1$, $x_4 = 3$. Reduce this solution to a basic feasible solution.

3–25. Consider the linear programming problem described by Eq. (1–16). Solve the problem by obtaining all basic solutions and selecting the one that maximizes the objective function. Show the relation between the basic feasible solutions and the extreme points of the region shown in Fig. 1–1. For the optimal basic feasible solution, compute the $\mathbf{y}_j$, z_j for the vectors not in the basis and demonstrate that the optimality condition is satisfied.

3–26. Make use of the basic solutions obtained in Problem 3–25 to show that for the linear programming problem described by Eq. (1–17), there are precisely two basic feasible solutions which maximize the objective function. Show that any convex combination of these two basic feasible solutions is also an optimal solution.

3–27. Consider the linear programming problem described by Eq. (1–19). Solve the problem by determining all basic solutions and find the one that maximizes the objective function. Relate the basic feasible solutions to the extreme points of the polyhedron shown in Fig. 1–4. Show that adjacent extreme points correspond to basic feasible solutions that differ only in one basis vector, i.e., in moving from one extreme point to an adjacent one just a single vector in the basis is changed.

3–28. Consider the linear programming problem presented in Problem 3–20. Show that a solution which involves only the variables x_1, x_2 at a nonzero level is feasible and basic. For this solution, compute the $\mathbf{y}_j$, z_j for each vector not in the basis. Which of the $\mathbf{a}_j$ not in the basis can be inserted to obtain a new basic feasible solution by removing one of the vectors in the basis? Find all such feasible solutions which can be obtained by changing a single vector in the basis. For which of these solutions is the value of the objective function increased?

CHAPTER 4

DETAILED DEVELOPMENT AND
COMPUTATIONAL ASPECTS OF THE SIMPLEX METHOD

"If you can look into the seeds of time,
And say which grain will grow and which will not,
Speak then to me. . . ."

Shakespeare—Macbeth.

4–1 The simplex method. The time has now come to put together what we have learned and to develop the details of the simplex method for solving the general linear programming problem. After the last few sections of the previous chapter, it should be fairly clear to the reader how a linear programming problem might be solved.

We wish to solve the linear programming problem

$$\mathbf{Ax} = \mathbf{b}, \qquad \mathbf{x} \geq \mathbf{0}, \qquad \max z = \mathbf{cx}, \tag{4–1}$$

where $\mathbf{A}$ is an $m \times n$ matrix. For convenience, the discussion will be centered on a maximization problem. Whenever significant conclusions are obtained, the corresponding adaptation to a minimization problem will also be made.

The results of the preceding chapter have shown: (1) If there is a feasible solution to a linear programming problem, there is a basic feasible solution. (2) If an optimal solution exists, one of the basic feasible solutions will be optimal. (3) If we have a basic feasible solution which is not optimal, then, provided that degeneracy never occurs, it is possible, by changing a single vector in the basis at a time (i.e., by driving one variable in the basic solution to zero and allowing another one, not in the basic solution, to become positive), to reach in a finite number of steps an optimal basic solution, or to show that the objective function can be made arbitrarily large. Here we have the essence of a computational procedure for solving a linear programming problem.

Given any basic feasible, but not optimal, solution, the theory developed indicated how to obtain a new basic solution, with the new value of the objective function at least as good as the old one; or it pointed out that, by adding one vector to the solution, an unbounded solution involving as many as $m + 1$ positive variables existed. In addition to the basic feasible solution $\mathbf{x}_B$, we used the $\mathbf{y}_j$ and $z_j - c_j$ for the vectors not in the basis in order to determine the new basic feasible solution. To find the new basic feasible solution, we first select the vectors for which $z_j - c_j < 0$. If any one of these vectors has all $y_{ij} \leq 0$, $i = 1, \ldots, m$, there is an unbounded solution. Suppose that this is not the case. Then we can insert any vector $\mathbf{a}_j$ with $z_j - c_j < 0$ and obtain a new basic feasible solution, with the new value of the objective function at least as good as the original one. We are not free to remove an arbitrary vector from the basis. If the new basic solution is to be feasible, the vector to be removed must be chosen by means of (3–40). When we make the assumption that degeneracy does not occur, the minimum in (3–40) will be unique (for if it is not, the new basic solution will be degenerate). Furthermore, if degeneracy does not occur, the new value of the objective function will be greater than the old one. The new values of the basic variables are given by (3–42), and the new value of the objective function is given by (3–45).

We now wish to know whether the new basic feasible solution so obtained is optimal. This requires that we find the new $z_j - c_j$, which we shall denote by $\hat{z}_j - c_j$. If it is not optimal, we shall repeat the process and compute another basic feasible solution with a further improvement in the value of the objective function. To do this, we need new $\mathbf{y}_j$'s, which we shall denote by $\hat{\mathbf{y}}_j$. (Note that all new values will be distinguished from the old ones by a caret.) Let us then compute the $\hat{z}_j - c_j$, $\hat{\mathbf{y}}_j$ in terms of the $z_j - c_j$ and $\mathbf{y}_j$. Assume that we inserted $\mathbf{a}_k$ into the basis and removed $\mathbf{b}_r$. In terms of the original basis, we have for any $\mathbf{a}_j$,

$$\mathbf{a}_j = \sum_{i=1}^{m} y_{ij}\mathbf{b}_i. \tag{4–2}$$

However, we replace $\mathbf{b}_r$ by $\mathbf{a}_k$, and hence

$$\mathbf{b}_r = -\sum_{\substack{i=1 \\ i \neq r}}^{m} \frac{y_{ik}}{y_{rk}}\mathbf{b}_i + \frac{1}{y_{rk}}\mathbf{a}_k. \tag{4–3}$$

When (4–3) is substituted into (4–2), we find

$$\mathbf{a}_j = \sum_{\substack{i=1 \\ i \neq r}}^{m} \left(y_{ij} - y_{rj}\frac{y_{ik}}{y_{rk}} \right)\mathbf{b}_i + \frac{y_{rj}}{y_{rk}}\mathbf{a}_k = \sum_{i=1}^{m} \hat{y}_{ij}\hat{\mathbf{b}}_i, \tag{4–4}$$

where $\hat{\mathbf{b}}_i = \mathbf{b}_i$, $i \neq r$; $\hat{\mathbf{b}}_r = \mathbf{a}_k$. Comparison shows that

$$\hat{y}_{ij} = y_{ij} - y_{rj}\frac{y_{ik}}{y_{rk}}, \qquad i \neq r, \tag{4–5a}$$

$$\hat{y}_{rj} = \frac{y_{rj}}{y_{rk}}. \tag{4–5b}$$

Equations (4–5a) and (4–5b) indicate how to compute the $\hat{y}_{ij}$ from the y_{ij}.

These formulas are quite similar to those of (3–42) for the new values of the basic variables.

To compute $\hat{z}_j - c_j$, we use the definition

$$\hat{z}_j - c_j = \hat{\mathbf{c}}_B \hat{\mathbf{y}}_j - c_j = \sum_{i=1}^{m} \hat{c}_{Bi} \hat{y}_{ij} - c_j. \tag{4-6}$$

However, $\hat{c}_{Bi} = c_{Bi},\ i \neq r;\ \hat{c}_{Br} = c_k$. Using (4–5), we obtain

$$\hat{z}_j - c_j = \sum_{\substack{i=1 \\ i \neq r}}^{m} c_{Bi}\left(y_{ij} - y_{rj}\frac{y_{ik}}{y_{rk}}\right) + \frac{y_{rj}}{y_{rk}}c_k - c_j. \tag{4-7}$$

In (4–7) it is convenient to include in the summation the term

$$c_{Br}\left(y_{rj} - y_{rj}\frac{y_{rk}}{y_{rk}}\right) = 0.$$

Expansion of (4–7) then yields

$$\hat{z}_j - c_j = \sum_{i=1}^{m} c_{Bi}y_{ij} - c_j - \frac{y_{rj}}{y_{rk}}\left(\sum_{i=1}^{m} c_{Bi}y_{ik} - c_k\right),$$

or

$$\hat{z}_j - c_j = z_j - c_j - \frac{y_{rj}}{y_{rk}}(z_k - c_k). \tag{4-8}$$

Equation (4–8) shows how to compute $\hat{z}_j - c_j$ from $z_j - c_j,\ z_k - c_k$, and y_{rj}, y_{rk}.

The above paragraphs contain the essence of the simplex method. It is an iterative procedure, and the steps can be briefly described, as follows:

Assume that we have a basic feasible solution $\mathbf{x}_B$ to the linear programming problem, with z the value of the objective function, and that, for all $\mathbf{a}_j$, the $\mathbf{y}_j$ and $z_j - c_j$ corresponding to this given basic feasible solution are known.

(1) Examine the $z_j - c_j$. There are three cases to be distinguished:

(a) All $z_j - c_j \geq 0$. In this case, the given basic feasible solution is optimal.

(b) One or more $z_j - c_j < 0$, and for at least one $\mathbf{a}_k$ for which $z_k - c_k < 0$, all $y_{ik} \leq 0$. Then there is an unbounded solution.

(c) One or more $z_j - c_j < 0$, and each of these has $y_{ij} > 0$ for at least one i. Select any one of these vectors, say $\mathbf{a}_k$, to insert into the basis.

(2) When case (1c) holds, compute the vector to be removed from the basis matrix $\mathbf{B}$, using

$$\frac{x_{Br}}{y_{rk}} = \min_{i}\left\{\frac{x_{Bi}}{y_{ik}},\ y_{ik} > 0\right\}. \tag{4-9}$$

Column r is then removed and replaced by $\mathbf{a}_k$.

(3) Using formulas (3–42), (3–45), (4–5), and (4–8), with the subscript k replacing j in (3–42) and (3–45), compute $\hat{\mathbf{x}}_B$, $\hat{z}$, and $\hat{\mathbf{y}}_j$, $\hat{z}_j - c_j$ for all j. This yields the quantities of interest for the new basic feasible solution. Return to step 1.

In the absence of degeneracy, this iterative procedure leads to an optimal basic feasible solution in a finite number of steps; it is the simplex method for solving linear programming problems.

4–2 Selection of the vector to enter the basis. Several points remain to be clarified. Note first of all that step (1c) does not represent a procedure which uniquely determines the vector to enter the basis. In (1c) we simply suggested that any vector with $z_j - c_j < 0$ would do. If we insert $\mathbf{a}_j$, the increase in the objective function is $\theta(c_j - z_j) = (x_{Br}/y_{rj})(c_j - z_j)$. Hence it seems logical to select the vector to enter the basis which will give the greatest increase in z. According to this criterion, $\mathbf{a}_k$ is selected by means of

$$\frac{x_{Br}}{y_{rk}}(c_k - z_k) = \max_j \left\{ \frac{x_{Br}}{y_{rj}}(c_j - z_j) \right\}, \qquad z_j - c_j < 0. \quad (4\text{--}10)$$

This is a perfectly sound approach, and without further investigation it would appear to be the best criterion for selecting the vector to enter the basis.

In order to apply (4–10), we must compute x_{Br}/y_{rj} from (4–9) for each $\mathbf{a}_j$ having $z_j - c_j < 0$. Such computations can become quite cumbersome if there is a large number of $\mathbf{a}_j$ with $z_j - c_j < 0$. Let us note that the change in the objective function depends on x_{Br}/y_{rj} and $z_j - c_j$. Another procedure for choosing the vector to enter the basis consists of selecting the largest $c_j - z_j$ while neglecting the value of x_{Br}/y_{rj}. This is equivalent to choosing the vector by means of

$$z_k - c_k = \min_j (z_j - c_j), \qquad z_j - c_j < 0. \quad (4\text{--}11)$$

We select the vector with the smallest algebraic value (largest absolute value) of $z_j - c_j$ for those $z_j - c_j < 0$. Both (4–10) and (4–11) have been applied to actual problems, with the interesting result that (4–11) leads to an optimal solution in about the same number of steps as (4–10). In other words, from the computational point of view, there seems to be little or no advantage in using the more complicated criterion (4–10) to determine the vector to enter the basis. No computation is needed to apply (4–11); we simply choose the smallest $z_j - c_j$. For this reason, (4–11) is usually used in preference to (4–10). In particular, almost all computer codes for solving linear programming problems employ (4–11).

The method (4–10) is referred to as the method of steepest ascents, since it gives the greatest possible increase in z at each iteration. The method (4–11) is an approximation to the method of steepest ascents. It will not, in general, give the greatest increase in z at each step, but on the average it seems to be about as efficient as the method of steepest ascents.

The use of (4–11) in determining the vector to be inserted may yield two or more vectors with the same minimum $z_j - c_j$. In this case, the vector to be inserted into the basis is still not uniquely determined. When the computations are performed by hand, one can simply choose any one of the tied vectors or use a chance device, such as flipping a coin, to make the selection. Of course, we could compute x_{Br}/y_{rj} for each tied vector and apply (4–10), but this would not necessarily break the tie; moreover, this technique requires additional calculations, and hence it is not often used. When the computations are performed on a digital computer, a tie is often resolved by selecting the vector with the lowest j-index.

The decisions which finally determine how many iterations there will be in solving a problem by the simplex method are those which, at each iteration, determine the vector to enter the basis. This is, in general, the only degree of freedom when one starts with a given basic feasible solution. The vector to leave the basis cannot be chosen arbitrarily, but must be determined by (4–9). In the above paragraphs, we suggested what seems to be a reasonable procedure for determining the vector to enter the basis. It is by no means true that our criterion for selecting this vector yields a procedure which reaches an optimal solution in the smallest number of steps. The ideal criterion would be one which assured us that once a vector had been inserted into the basis, it would never have to be removed again, i.e., a minimum of basis changes would lead to the optimal basis; in fact, no more than m iterations would ever be needed. Unfortunately, no criteria have been developed which will guarantee that once a vector has been inserted into the basis, it will never be removed. In the simplex method [which uses (4–11) or (4–10) to determine which vector should enter the basis], a vector may enter the basis and leave again. In fact, this can happen several times.

If the linear programming problem is a minimization problem, the selection criteria equivalent to (4–10) and (4–11) are, respectively,

$$\frac{x_{Br}}{y_{rk}}(c_k - z_k) = \min_j \left\{ \frac{x_{Br}}{y_{rj}}(c_j - z_j) \right\}, \qquad z_j - c_j > 0, \qquad (4\text{–}12)$$

and

$$z_k - c_k = \max_j (z_j - c_j), \qquad z_j - c_j > 0. \qquad (4\text{–}13)$$

Another simplification dealing with the vector to be inserted is usually introduced into the simplex method. This involves unbounded solutions. Instead of inspecting all vectors with $z_j - c_j < 0$ to see whether any one has $y_{ij} \leq 0$ for all i, the standard procedure is to examine only the y_{ik} for the vector a_k chosen to enter the basis. The saving in time and effort is particularly great when digital computers are used, because it is quite time-consuming to examine all components of each of a large number of vectors. Since we examine only the vector chosen to enter the basis, it may turn out that if there is an unbounded solution, more iterations will be required before we discover this fact. Of course, if there is an unbounded solution, we shall ultimately find it. However, although we run the risk of more iterations, the simplification discussed here does save time on the average because unbounded solutions caused by an incorrect formulation of the problem occur only rarely.

4–3 Degeneracy and breaking ties. The degeneracy problem has been plaguing us for some time. By now the reader may feel that it presents a formidable problem, even though we have indicated that there are ways to avoid it (these will be discussed later). Fortunately, in practice, degeneracy is really no problem at all. If we use (4–11) to determine the vector to be inserted into the basis and (4–9) to determine the vector to be removed, the simplex method seems to solve any real-world problem without any difficulty, although a large number of the basic variables vanishes. No practical problem has ever cycled, and therefore degeneracy has never made it impossible to reach an optimal solution by means of the simplex method in the form discussed above.

It has been noted earlier that in the absence of degeneracy, the vector to be removed is uniquely determined by (4–9). When degeneracy is present, the minimum in (4–9) may not be unique. We have already seen that any one of the vectors corresponding to the minimum value may be removed, and the new basic solution will be feasible (and degenerate). When performing the computations by hand, we usually make an arbitrary choice among the tied vectors or use a chance device to determine the one to be removed. When the computations are performed on a digital computer, specific rules must be followed, such as choosing the vector with the largest y_{ik}, or if this does not break the tie, selecting the vector with the smallest i-index. In this way, the vector to be removed is uniquely determined. All the rules suggested here have proved quite satisfactory in practical applications of the simplex method. We shall later develop a method for uniquely determining the vector to be removed when degeneracy is present, which will also ensure that cycling will never occur. However, this procedure is time-consuming, especially on a digital computer, and rarely used in practice, because the simple rules discussed above are satisfactory, and cycling never seems to occur.

In the preceding paragraphs, we have described the rudiments of the simplex method. Its essential feature is the change of only one vector in the basis at a time. The reader may have wondered throughout the past discussion why we have restricted our attention to changing only a single vector in the basis at each iteration. The answer is very simple: No way has been found to change more than one vector at a time that is less time consuming than changing only a single vector. (See Problem 3–9.)

4–4 Further development of the transformation formulas. It may be recalled that in Chapter 2 we presented a technique for computing the inverse of a matrix which differs by only one column from another matrix whose inverse is known. In the simplex method, only a single vector in the basis matrix is changed at each iteration. It is instructive and interesting to look at the problem of developing the transformation formulas in the light of the theory discussed in Chapter 2.

We begin with a basic feasible solution characterized by the basis matrix $\mathbf{B} = (\mathbf{b}_1, \ldots, \mathbf{b}_m)$. Now we remove column r, that is $\mathbf{b}_r$, and replace it by column $\mathbf{a}_k$. Let us assume that we know $\mathbf{B}^{-1}$. Then for the original basic feasible solution $\mathbf{x}_B = \mathbf{B}^{-1}\mathbf{b}$, $\mathbf{y}_j = \mathbf{B}^{-1}\mathbf{a}_j$, $j = 1, \ldots, n$. If the new basis matrix is $\hat{\mathbf{B}}$, it follows that $\hat{\mathbf{x}}_B = \hat{\mathbf{B}}^{-1}\mathbf{b}$, $\hat{\mathbf{y}}_j = \hat{\mathbf{B}}^{-1}\mathbf{a}_j$ are the new values of $\mathbf{x}_B$, $\mathbf{y}_j$. Chapter 2 has shown us how to compute $\hat{\mathbf{B}}^{-1}$ from $\mathbf{B}^{-1}$. We know that

$$\hat{\mathbf{B}}^{-1} = \mathbf{E}\mathbf{B}^{-1}, \tag{4–14}$$

where $\mathbf{E}$ is an $m \times m$ matrix which differs from the identity matrix only in that the rth column of $\mathbf{E}$ contains the vector

$$\boldsymbol{\eta} = \left[-\frac{y_{1k}}{y_{rk}}, \ldots, -\frac{y_{r-1,k}}{y_{rk}}, \frac{1}{y_{rk}}, -\frac{y_{r+1,k}}{y_{rk}}, \ldots, -\frac{y_{mk}}{y_{rk}} \right]. \tag{4–15}$$

Hence we can write

$$\hat{\mathbf{x}}_B = \mathbf{E}\mathbf{B}^{-1}\mathbf{b} = \mathbf{E}\mathbf{x}_B; \qquad \hat{\mathbf{y}}_j = \mathbf{E}\mathbf{B}^{-1}\mathbf{a}_j = \mathbf{E}\mathbf{y}_j. \tag{4–16}$$

If (4–16) is reduced to component form, we simply obtain the transformation formulas (3–42) and (4–5).

It is sometimes convenient to derive another form of the transformation formulas for $\mathbf{x}_B$, $\mathbf{y}_j$ by means of (4–16). Note that we can write

$$\mathbf{E} = \mathbf{I} + \mathbf{F}, \tag{4–17}$$

and $\mathbf{F}$ is a matrix which differs only in its rth column from a null matrix. The rth column of $\mathbf{F}$ is the vector $\boldsymbol{\phi} = \boldsymbol{\eta} - \mathbf{e}_r$. Thus,

$$\mathbf{F} = (0, \ldots, 0, \boldsymbol{\phi}, 0, \ldots, 0), \qquad \boldsymbol{\phi} \text{ in column } r, \tag{4–18}$$

and

$$\boldsymbol{\phi} = \boldsymbol{\eta} - \mathbf{e}_r = \left[-\frac{y_{1k}}{y_{rk}}, \ldots, -\frac{y_{r-1,k}}{y_{rk}}, \frac{1}{y_{rk}} - 1, -\frac{y_{r+1,k}}{y_{rk}}, \ldots, -\frac{y_{mk}}{y_{rk}} \right].$$

$$\tag{4–19}$$

With this notation, (4–16) becomes

$$\hat{\mathbf{x}}_B = (\mathbf{I} + \mathbf{F})\mathbf{x}_B = \mathbf{x}_B + \mathbf{Fx}_B. \tag{4-20}$$

But $\mathbf{F}$ has zeros everywhere except in the rth column; thus

$$\mathbf{Fx}_B = x_{Br}\boldsymbol{\phi}. \tag{4-21}$$

Substitution of (4–21) into (4–20) gives

$$\hat{\mathbf{x}}_B = \mathbf{x}_B + x_{Br}\boldsymbol{\phi}. \tag{4-22}$$

In the same way, we find

$$\hat{\mathbf{y}}_j = \mathbf{y}_j + y_{rj}\boldsymbol{\phi}. \tag{4-23}$$

Equations (4–22) and (4–23) are particularly simple to use. Note that the transformation of $\mathbf{x}_B$ and of all the $\mathbf{y}_j$ depends only on their original values and on the vector $\boldsymbol{\phi}$ which in turn depends only on $\mathbf{y}_k$. Once $\boldsymbol{\phi}$ is computed, the $\hat{\mathbf{x}}_B$, $\hat{\mathbf{y}}_j$ follow immediately from (4–22) and (4–23).

Another very interesting observation can now be made. Suppose that we write

$$x_{Bi} = y_{i0} \quad (i = 1, \ldots, m); \qquad z = y_{m+1,0}; \qquad z_j - c_j = y_{m+1,j}. \tag{4-24}$$

The transformation equation for z, that is (3–45), can then be written

$$\hat{y}_{m+1,0} = y_{m+1,0} + y_{r0}\left[-\frac{y_{m+1,k}}{y_{rk}}\right], \tag{4-25}$$

and the transformation equation (4–8) for the $z_j - c_j$ becomes

$$\hat{y}_{m+1,j} = y_{m+1,j} + y_{rj}\left[-\frac{y_{m+1,k}}{y_{rk}}\right]. \tag{4-26}$$

Now if we define $\mathbf{Y}_j = [y_{1j}, \ldots, y_{m+1,j}], j = 0, \ldots, n$, the transformation of every quantity of interest can be expressed in terms of the single transformation formula:

$$\hat{\mathbf{Y}}_j = \mathbf{Y}_j + y_{rj}\boldsymbol{\Phi}, \qquad j = 0, 1, \ldots, n, \tag{4-27}$$

where

$$\mathbf{Y}_j = [\mathbf{y}_j, y_{m+1,j}], \qquad j = 0, \ldots, n; \qquad \boldsymbol{\Phi} = \left[\boldsymbol{\phi}, -\frac{y_{m+1,k}}{y_{rk}}\right].$$

The $\mathbf{Y}_j$, $\boldsymbol{\Phi}$ are $(m + 1)$-component vectors. The single vector equation (4–27) yields the transformation relation for all quantities of interest. For clarity, let us restate the meaning of the $\mathbf{Y}_j$ and $\boldsymbol{\Phi}$ in terms of the more familiar variables. We have

$$\mathbf{Y}_0 = [x_{B1}, \ldots, x_{Bm}, z] = [y_{10}, \ldots, y_{m+1,0}], \tag{4-28}$$

$$\mathbf{Y}_j = [y_{1j}, \ldots, y_{mj}, z_j - c_j] = [y_{1j}, \ldots, y_{mj}, y_{m+1,j}], \qquad j = 1, \ldots, n, \tag{4-29}$$

$$\mathbf{\Phi} = \left[-\frac{y_{1k}}{y_{rk}}, \ldots, -\frac{y_{r-1,k}}{y_{rk}}, \frac{1}{y_{rk}} - 1, -\frac{y_{r+1,k}}{y_{rk}}, \ldots, -\frac{y_{mk}}{y_{rk}}, -\frac{z_k - c_k}{y_{rk}} \right]. \tag{4-30}$$

The transformation formula (4–27) is useful for both manual and machine computations.

The above definitions can also be used to simplify the transformation formulas (3–42), (3–45), (4–5), (4–8), so that all these results can be written in the compact form

$$\hat{y}_{ij} = y_{ij} - y_{ik} \frac{y_{rj}}{y_{rk}}, \qquad j = 0, \ldots, n, \qquad i = 1, \ldots, m + 1, \qquad i \neq r, \tag{4-31a}$$

$$\hat{y}_{rj} = \frac{y_{rj}}{y_{rk}}, \qquad j = 0, \ldots, n. \tag{4-31b}$$

Equations (4–31a) and (4–31b) are merely a rearrangement of the component form of (4–27). They can also be obtained directly by substituting the new definitions into the defining equations. Incidentally, it might be noted that we have encountered transformation formulas of this type in Chapter 2 in the discussion of the gaussian reduction technique for solving simultaneous linear equations.

In this section, we have shown that all quantities of interest in the simplex method transform in the same way in moving from one basic solution to the next. The general transformation equation can be written in vector form as (4–27) and in component form as (4–31).

4–5 The initial basic feasible solution—artificial variables. Up to the present time, all of our discussions have been based on the assumption that we had an initial basic feasible solution to the linear programming problem. We have yet to treat the problem of finding an initial basic feasible solution. Once this has been done, we shall have a computational procedure which will in theory solve any linear programming problem. Now it may turn out that, because of improper formulation, our linear programming problem does not have any solution. In this section, we wish to develop a general procedure which either leads to a basic feasible solution or shows that the problem has no feasible solution.

We shall begin by considering a case where a basic feasible solution can be immediately determined. Suppose that in the original formulation of the problem each of the inequalities was of the form $\leq$, so that a slack variable was added to each constraint to convert it to an equality. The matrix $\mathbf{A}$ for the set of constraints $\mathbf{Ax} = \mathbf{b}$ then has the form

$$\mathbf{A} = (\mathbf{R}, \mathbf{I}), \qquad (4\text{–}32)$$

where $\mathbf{I}$ is an mth-order identity matrix. This follows because the column corresponding to the slack variable x_{r+i} is $\mathbf{e}_i$. If we write $\mathbf{x} = [\mathbf{x}_r, \mathbf{x}_s]$, where $\mathbf{x}_s$ contains the m slack variables and $\mathbf{x}_r$ contains the original r variables, then, setting $\mathbf{x}_r = \mathbf{0}$, we have

$$\mathbf{Ix}_s = \mathbf{b}. \qquad (4\text{–}33)$$

Here we have a basic solution involving only the slack variables. Furthermore, it is feasible because $\mathbf{x}_s = \mathbf{b}$, and $\mathbf{b} \geq \mathbf{0}$ by virtue of the manner originally chosen to set up the problem. This basic solution is especially easy to work with since the basis matrix $\mathbf{B} = \mathbf{I}$, and $\mathbf{B}^{-1} = \mathbf{I}$. Therefore,

$$\mathbf{y}_j = \mathbf{B}^{-1}\mathbf{a}_j = \mathbf{Ia}_j = \mathbf{a}_j, \qquad j = 1, \ldots, n, \qquad (4\text{–}34)$$

and

$$\mathbf{c}_B = \mathbf{0} \qquad (4\text{–}35)$$

because the prices associated with slack variables are zero. Consequently,

$$z_j - c_j = \mathbf{c}_B\mathbf{y}_j - c_j = -c_j, \qquad (4\text{–}36)$$

$$z = \mathbf{c}_B\mathbf{x}_B = 0. \qquad (4\text{–}37)$$

For this basic feasible solution, no computations are needed to obtain the quantities of interest, namely, $\mathbf{x}_B$, z, $\mathbf{y}_j$, $z_j - c_j$. The iterative procedure of the simplex method can now be initiated without any difficulty.

In the above paragraphs we have shown that when a slack variable appears in every constraint, it is a trivial task to find an initial basic feasible solution together with the other quantities of interest, z, $\mathbf{y}_j$, $z_j - c_j$. However, this really did not depend on the addition of a slack variable to every constraint. In fact, the above procedure can be used whenever an $m \times m$ identity matrix appears in $\mathbf{A}$. Of course, if the columns of the identity matrix do not correspond to slack variables, then (4–35) may not hold. However, the $z_j - c_j$ can still be easily computed from

$$\mathbf{c}_B\mathbf{y}_j - c_j = \mathbf{c}_B\mathbf{a}_j - c_j.$$

In many cases no identity matrix will appear in $\mathbf{A}$. This will almost always be the case when some constraints do not require the addition of a slack or surplus variable. Under such conditions, there is usually no easy way of finding an initial basic feasible solution. Let us concentrate our efforts on attempting to construct such a solution if one exists. We have noted that it is desirable to have an identity matrix as the initial basis matrix. Suppose that we begin *always* with an identity matrix for the initial basis matrix. Instead of the original set of constraint equations $\mathbf{Ax} = \mathbf{b}$, let us consider a new set of constraint equations

$$\mathbf{Ax} + \mathbf{Ix}_a = (\mathbf{A}, \mathbf{I}) \begin{bmatrix} \mathbf{x} \\ \mathbf{x}_a \end{bmatrix} = \mathbf{b}. \tag{4–38}$$

We have augmented the given constraint equations by m additional variables x_{ai}, with the columns corresponding to these variables being $\mathbf{e}_i$. These new variables are called artificial variables (artificial because they have no meaning for the original set of constraints). The column $\mathbf{e}_i$, which we shall sometimes designate by $\mathbf{q}_i$, corresponding to the artificial variable x_{ai} is called an artificial vector.

What have we gained by pulling this trick? We have gained what we were looking for, since an identity matrix appears in (4–38). We then immediately have a basic feasible solution to the set of constraints (4–38), namely $\mathbf{x}_a = \mathbf{b}$, $\mathbf{x} = \mathbf{0}$. Note that this is *not*, however, a feasible solution to the original set of constraints. Any solution to (4–38) which is also a solution to the original set of constraints must have $\mathbf{x}_a = \mathbf{0}$, that is, all artificial variables must vanish. Then (4–38) reduces to the original set of constraints $\mathbf{Ax} = \mathbf{b}$. The basic feasible solution $\mathbf{x}_a = \mathbf{b}$ to (4–38) will be of little use unless we can find a way to move from it to a basic feasible solution to the original problem.

An interesting idea now suggests itself: Why not use the simplex method itself to insert legitimate columns $\mathbf{a}_j$ from $\mathbf{A}$ (we use the term "legitimate" to distinguish the columns of $\mathbf{A}$ from the artificial vectors $\mathbf{q}_i$) into the identity matrix in the usual step-by-step fashion and thus, by removing the artificial vectors from the basis, drive all the artificial variables to zero? In this way, we should end up with a basis containing only vectors from $\mathbf{A}$, that is, with a basic feasible solution to the original set of constraints. The simplex method can then be continued to yield an optimal basic feasible solution to the original set of constraints. This is precisely what we shall do.

In the simplex method, the $z_j - c_j$ determine which vector is to be inserted into the basis. Thus far we have said nothing about the prices to be associated with the artificial variables. What we must do is assign prices to the artificial variables which are so unfavorable that the objective function can be improved so long as any artificial variable remains in the basic feasible solution at a positive level. If z is to be maximized and we assign an extremely large negative price to each artificial variable, then we would expect that z could be improved so long as any artificial vector remains in the basis at a positive level. Similarly, if z is to be minimized, a very large positive price should be assigned to each artificial variable.

Let c_{ai} be the price corresponding to the artificial variable x_{ai}. Then we write

$$c_{ai} = -M, \qquad M > 0, \qquad \text{if } z \text{ is to be maximized,} \qquad (4\text{–}39a)$$

$$c_{ai} = M, \qquad M > 0, \qquad \text{if } z \text{ is to be minimized.} \qquad (4\text{–}39b)$$

For hand computations, M is usually not specified as a particular number. It is merely entered into the computations as M, and it is assumed to be large enough so that any price corresponding to a legitimate variable is completely negligible with respect to M. For machine computations, the value of M is often taken to be about 1000 times the largest price corresponding to any legitimate variable.

If for some reason (such as the addition of slack variables to certain constraints) part of an identity matrix is present in $\mathbf{A}$, then it is only necessary to add the artificial vectors $\mathbf{e}_i$ which are needed to give a complete identity matrix. For example, if $\mathbf{e}_1$ appeared in $\mathbf{A}$, then an artificial vector $\mathbf{e}_1$ would not be added to the system.

The introduction of artificial variables provides an easy starting point for solving any linear programming problem. By applying the simplex method to the augmented problem, we ultimately obtain a basic feasible solution to the actual problem if there is one, and then, by continued application of the simplex method, an optimal basic feasible solution to the original problem is found. Initially, the artificial variables are non-negative; because of the way the simplex method works, no artificial variable will ever become negative. Thus $x_{ai} \geq 0$ always. Finally, we must have $x_{ai} = 0$ for all i if we are to obtain a feasible solution to the actual set of constraints.

Given any linear programming problem

$$\mathbf{Ax} = \mathbf{b}, \qquad \mathbf{x} \geq \mathbf{0}, \qquad \max z = \mathbf{cx}, \qquad (4\text{–}40)$$

we can always start our computation with the augmented problem (recall that $\mathbf{1}$ is the sum vector),

$$\mathbf{Ax} + \mathbf{Ix}_a = \mathbf{b}, \qquad \mathbf{x} \geq \mathbf{0}, \qquad \mathbf{x}_a \geq \mathbf{0}, \qquad \max z = \mathbf{cx} - M\mathbf{1x}_a, \qquad (4\text{–}41)$$

and arrive immediately at the basic feasible solution $\mathbf{x}_a = \mathbf{b}$ to (4–41). Application of the simplex method to (4–41) ultimately leads to an optimal basic feasible solution to (4–40) if such a solution exists.

Once an artificial vector has left the basis, it has served its purpose, and we can forget about it. An artificial vector is never considered for re-entry into the basis. The reader is asked to prove in Problem 4–6 that this procedure is legitimate.

The method of assigning a large negative price to an artificial vector in order to drive it out of the basis was first suggested by Charnes. Later we shall discuss another procedure for handling artificial variables known as the "two-phase" method.

EXAMPLE: We shall illustrate the introduction of artificial variables in the following linear programming problem:

$$3x_1 + 4x_2 + 5x_3 + 6x_4 \leq 5,$$

$$2x_1 + 6x_2 + x_3 + 5x_4 \geq 6,$$

$$x_1 + x_2 + 5x_3 + x_4 = 7,$$

$$x_1, x_2, x_3, x_4 \geq 0,$$

$$\max z = 3x_1 + 2x_2 + x_3 + 5x_4.$$

After adding slack and surplus variables, we obtain the constraint equations

$$\begin{bmatrix} 3 & 4 & 5 & 6 & 1 & 0 \\ 2 & 6 & 1 & 5 & 0 & -1 \\ 1 & 1 & 5 & 1 & 0 & 0 \end{bmatrix} [x_1, x_2, x_3, x_4, x_5, x_6] = \begin{bmatrix} 5 \\ 6 \\ 7 \end{bmatrix}.$$

There is present in $\mathbf{A}$ the vector $\mathbf{e}_1$, i.e., the first column of an identity matrix. We must then add two artificial vectors $\mathbf{q}_1 = \mathbf{e}_2$, $\mathbf{q}_2 = \mathbf{e}_3$ whose corresponding variables are x_{a1}, x_{a2}. The price associated with each artificial variable is $-M$. Thus the augmented linear programming problem becomes

$$\begin{bmatrix} 3 & 4 & 5 & 6 & 0 & 1 & 0 & 0 \\ 2 & 6 & 1 & 5 & -1 & 0 & 1 & 0 \\ 1 & 1 & 5 & 1 & 0 & 0 & 0 & 1 \end{bmatrix} [x_1, x_2, x_3, x_4, x_6, x_5, x_{a1}, x_{a2}] = \begin{bmatrix} 5 \\ 6 \\ 7 \end{bmatrix},$$

$$\mathbf{x} \geq \mathbf{0}, \qquad \mathbf{x}_a \geq \mathbf{0},$$

$$\max z = 3x_1 + 2x_2 + x_3 + 5x_4 - Mx_{a1} - Mx_{a2}.$$

An immediate basic feasible solution to the augmented system is

$$\mathbf{x}_B = [x_5, x_{a1}, x_{a2}] = [5, 6, 7],$$

with

$$\mathbf{B} = \mathbf{B}^{-1} = \mathbf{I}, \qquad \mathbf{B} = (\mathbf{a}_5, \mathbf{q}_1, \mathbf{q}_2).$$

Then for all j, $\mathbf{y}_j = \mathbf{a}_j$. Two artificial vectors with prices $-M$ are in columns 2, 3 of the basis. Therefore $\mathbf{c}_B = (0, -M, -M)$. Since

$z_j - c_j = \mathbf{c}_B \mathbf{y}_j - c_j$, we find

$$z_1 - c_1 = -3M - 3; \qquad z_2 - c_2 = -7M - 2;$$

$$z_3 - c_3 = -6M - 1; \qquad z_4 - c_4 = -6M - 5;$$

$$z_6 - c_6 = M.$$

We assume that M is much larger than any other price. Consequently, only terms containing M count. The vector to be inserted into the basis is the one with the smallest $z_j - c_j < 0$. This is $\mathbf{a}_2$. The vector to be removed is determined from

$$\min_i \left\{ \frac{x_{Bi}}{y_{i2}}, y_{i2} > 0 \right\} = \min \left(\frac{5}{4}, \frac{6}{6}, \frac{7}{1} \right) = 1.$$

The minimum is taken on for $i = 2$; this implies that column 2 of $\mathbf{B}$ or $\mathbf{q}_1$ is removed and replaced by $\mathbf{a}_2$. Hence we see that, in the first iteration, one of the artificial vectors is removed from the basis and is replaced by a legitimate vector.

It is by no means true that the artificial vectors will always be removed from the basis before a legitimate vector is removed. If, in the first constraint, b_1 had been 2 instead of 5, the vector to be removed would have been found from min $(2/4, 6/6, 7/1) = 1/2$. The minimum is taken on for $i = 1$, and it follows that $\mathbf{a}_5$ would have been removed and replaced by $\mathbf{a}_2$. Both artificial vectors would have remained in the basis.

4–6 Inconsistency and redundancy. The addition of artificial variables allows us to eliminate another problem which concerned us at the outset. It will be remembered that we assumed $r(\mathbf{A}) = r(\mathbf{A}_b) = m$, so that we knew there was a basic (although not necessarily feasible) solution to the set of constraints. Whenever we begin with an identity matrix in the set of constraints, it is immediately clear that a basic feasible solution exists. When a slack variable is added to every constraint equation of the original problem, then it is at once obvious that $r(\mathbf{A}) = r(\mathbf{A}_b) = m$ and, in addition, it is clear that there is a feasible solution. If artificial variables are added to the problem, it is also true that there is a basic feasible solution to the augmented system. Hence the assumption made in the initial discussion of the theory of the simplex method will always hold when we begin to solve a linear programming problem. We wish to show that if we start with the augmented system whose initial basic feasible solution consists entirely or in part of artificial variables, we shall ultimately determine by means of the simplex method whether the original constraint equations are consistent, and whether any one of the original constraint equations is redundant.

It suffices to consider the possibilities when the optimality criterion is satisfied, i.e., when all $z_j - c_j \geq 0$, since, if no basis is ever repeated, we shall ultimately reach a state in which the optimality criterion is satisfied, provided there is no unbounded solution. We make this assumption here. There are then three cases to be distinguished:

(1) There are no artificial vectors in the basis.

(2) One or more artificial vectors are in the basis at a zero level.

(3) One or more artificial vectors are in the basis at a positive level.

Each of these cases will be considered in turn.

If there are no artificial vectors in the basis and the optimality criterion is satisfied, it is clear that an optimal basic feasible solution to the actual linear programming problem has been found. Hence we know that the original constraint equations are consistent and none of the equations is redundant.

Let us next study what happens when one or more artificial vectors appear in the basis at a zero level and the optimality criterion is satisfied. Since all artificial variables are zero, we have a feasible solution to the original set of constraints, and it follows that the original constraint equations are consistent. There still remains the question of redundancy in the original constraints. Two alternatives may arise: Either $y_{ij} = 0$ for all $\mathbf{a}_j$ and for those i corresponding to the columns of the basis containing artificial vectors at a zero level, or $y_{ij} \neq 0$ for one or more $\mathbf{a}_j$ and for one or more i corresponding to the columns of $\mathbf{B}$ containing artificial vectors.

Assume that for some j, $y_{ij} \neq 0$ (i corresponds to a column of $\mathbf{B}$ containing an artificial vector). We allow y_{ij} to be either positive or negative. Then we know that the artificial vector can be removed from the basis and replaced by $\mathbf{a}_j$, and a basis will still be maintained. Furthermore, since the artificial variable was at a zero level, $\mathbf{a}_j$ will enter the basis at a zero level, and the new basic solution will be feasible. The value of the objective function will be unchanged. If this process can be continued until all artificial vectors are removed, we have obtained a degenerate basic feasible solution (which is also optimal) involving only the columns of $\mathbf{A}$. Consequently, none of the original constraint equations is redundant.

If the above procedure does not remove all artificial vectors, we must ultimately reach a state where $y_{ij} = 0$ for all $\mathbf{a}_j$ and all i corresponding to the columns of $\mathbf{B}$ containing artificial vectors at a zero level. Then we are sure that we cannot remove any artificial vector and replace it by some $\mathbf{a}_j$ while still maintaining a basis. It is also evident that under such circumstances every column in $\mathbf{A}$ can be written as a linear combination of the columns of $\mathbf{A}$ in the basis. The artificial vectors are not needed to express any column of $\mathbf{A}$ in terms of the basis vectors. Suppose that there are k artificial vectors in the basis at a zero level. It follows that every column of $\mathbf{A}$ can be written as a linear combination of the $m - k$ linearly independent columns of $\mathbf{A}$ in the basis. Hence $r(\mathbf{A}) = m - k$, and k of the original constraints were redundant.

We can also determine which of the constraints are redundant. Suppose that a single artificial vector $\mathbf{e}_h$ appears in column s of the basis at a zero level, and for all legitimate vectors, $y_{sj} = 0$. We know that $r(\mathbf{A}, \mathbf{e}_h) = m$ and $r(\mathbf{A}) = m - 1$. Denote the rows of $\mathbf{A}$ by $\mathbf{a}^i$ and the rows of $(\mathbf{A}, \mathbf{e}_h)$ by $(\mathbf{a}^i, 0)$, $i \neq h$, and $(\mathbf{a}^h, 1)$ for the hth row. Since $r(\mathbf{A}) = m - 1$, there exist α_i not all zero such that

$$\sum_{i=1}^{m} \alpha_i \mathbf{a}^i = \mathbf{0}.$$

We now claim that $\alpha_h \neq 0$, and therefore $\mathbf{a}^h$ can be written as a linear combination of the other rows of $\mathbf{A}$. Assume on the contrary that $\alpha_h = 0$. Because $r(\mathbf{A}, \mathbf{e}_h) = m$, the only λ_i satisfying

$$\sum_{\substack{i=1 \\ i \neq h}}^{m} \lambda_i(\mathbf{a}^i, 0) + \lambda_h(\mathbf{a}^h, 1) = \mathbf{0}$$

are $\lambda_i = 0$ $(i = 1, \ldots, m)$. However, if we set $\lambda_i = \alpha_i$, a contradiction is obtained. Applying this reasoning step by step, we see that if a number of artificial vectors $\mathbf{e}_i$ appear in the basis at a zero level and the corresponding $y_{sj} = 0$ for all j, then for each i the ith constraint in the original system of equations is redundant and can be dropped. The solution in case (2) is of course an optimal solution regardless of whether the artificial vectors can be removed from the basis.

We still have to discuss the case where one or more artificial vectors are in the basis at a positive level and the optimality condition is satisfied. It is immediately evident that, in this instance, there is no feasible solution to the original problem; for if a feasible solution existed the artificial variables could be driven to zero, thus yielding an improved value of z. This would contradict the fact that the optimality criterion is satisfied. The absence of a feasible solution may arise because the constraint equations are inconsistent or because there are solutions, but no feasible solutions. It is interesting to note that the simplex procedure allows us to differentiate between these two possibilities.

If for some j there is a $y_{ij} > 0$ for i corresponding to a column of $\mathbf{B}$ which contains an artificial vector, let us insert $\mathbf{a}_j$ into the basis and remove the artificial vector. The new solution may or may not be feasible. Such a situation could not occur if there were only a single artificial vector in the basis at a positive level, since then $z_j - c_j = -My_{ij} +$ small terms < 0, and the optimality criterion would not be satisfied. After this insertion is made, the $z_j - c_j$ for the new basic solution can have any sign. We proceed to insert vectors $\mathbf{a}_j$ and remove artificial vectors so long as there is a $y_{ij} > 0$ in a position i corresponding to an artificial vector in the basis.

The above procedure can end in only one of two ways. Either we remove all the artificial vectors and therefore obtain a basic but not feasible solution to the original set of constraints, or we reach a point where $y_{ij} \leq 0$ for all j and for i corresponding to the columns of $\mathbf{B}$ which contain artificial vectors. Suppose that for some j, $y_{ij} < 0$, and i corresponds to a column of $\mathbf{B}$ containing an artificial vector. We can insert $\mathbf{a}_j$ and remove the artificial vector while maintaining a basis. The new basic solution will not be feasible, because $\mathbf{a}_j$ enters at a negative level. If this process can be continued until all artificial vectors have been removed, we have obtained a basic, but not feasible, solution to the set of constraints.

In the last case to be studied $y_{ij} = 0$ for all j and for i corresponding to the columns of $\mathbf{B}$ which contain artificial vectors. Assume that there are k legitimate vectors from $\mathbf{A}$ in the basis. Then every column of $\mathbf{A}$ can be written as a linear combination of the k columns of $\mathbf{A}$ in the basis, and $r(\mathbf{A}) = k$. On the other hand, $\mathbf{b}$ cannot be written as a linear combination of the k legitimate vectors from $\mathbf{A}$ in the basis. One or more of the artificial vectors are also needed. This implies $r(\mathbf{A}_b) = k + 1$, and the original constraint equations are inconsistent.

Let us summarize the results of the preceding paragraphs:

(1) *If no artificial vectors appear in the basis and the optimality criterion is satisfied, then the solution is an optimal basic feasible solution to the given problem. The constraint equations are consistent, and there is no redundancy in the constraint equations.*

(2) *If one or more artificial vectors appear in the basis at a zero level and the optimality criterion is satisfied, then the solution is an optimal solution to the given problem. The constraint equations are consistent, but in this case redundancy may exist in the constraints.*

(3) *If one or more artificial vectors appear in the basis at a positive level and the optimality criterion is satisfied, the original problem has no feasible solution. There may be no feasible solution either because the constraint equations are inconsistent, or because there are solutions, but none is feasible.*

We have not discussed the meaning of having artificial vectors in the basis and an unbounded solution. This case is not of great interest, and the details of the analysis are left for Problem 4–23.

4–7 Tableau format for simplex computations. When simplex calculations are to be done by hand, it is very desirable to follow a well-organized procedure. A very useful tabular form displaying all the quantities of interest has been developed by Orden, Dantzig, and Hoffman. Its schematic arrangement is shown in Table 4–1. Such a format is called a tableau, and a new tableau is constructed at each iteration, i.e., each time a new vector is introduced into the basis.

The first column of the tableau gives c_B, the prices corresponding to the vectors in the basis. The second column tells which vectors are in the basis. Thus b_1 is the vector from A (or the artificial vector) which is in the first column of B, etc. If a_{12} is in the second column of B, then we would write a_{12} where b_2 appears in Table 4–1. The third column of the tableau, under the heading "b," gives the current value of x_B, together with the value of the objective function for the basic feasible solution described by the given tableau. The remaining columns list the values of y_j for all vectors in A and any artificial vectors which may have been added. We write $B^{-1}q_i = y_{n+i}$. The last entry in each of these columns gives $z_j - c_j$. The first row of the tableau gives the prices associated with the vectors.

This tableau form allows us to keep track of all necessary data. It is also very useful in the actual performance of computations by means of the simplex method. Recall that we must know which column of A is in column i of the basis in order to determine the variable x_j corresponding to x_{Bi}. Column 2 allows us to do this. To find the variable x_j corresponding to x_{Bi}, we look at the row in column 2 where x_{Bi} appears, and see which vector this variable corresponds to. In the same way, the c_j corresponding to c_{Bi} is found. For example, if some particular problem has a three-dimensional basis, and if at some iteration a_6 is in column 1 of B, a_2 in column 2, and a_8 in column 3, then, in the column "vectors in basis," we write a_6 in the first row, a_2 in the second row, and a_8 in the third row. The number appearing in row 1 under the column headed "b" will be $x_6 = x_{B1}$, in row 2, $x_2 = x_{B2}$, and in row 3, $x_8 = x_{B3}$. Now imagine that in the next iteration a_2 is removed and a_7 inserted into column 2 of the basis. In the new tableau, under "vectors in basis," we shall then have a_6, a_7, a_8, in that order, and the numbers in the first three rows under column "b" will be the values of x_6, x_7, x_8.

Since artificial vectors are never considered for re-entry into the basis once they have been removed, columns for these vectors need not be included in the tableaux. Their inclusion would only lead to unnecessary computational efforts in the process of transforming the vectors. However, if it is desired at each stage to have available B^{-1} for the current basis B (see Problem 4–11 and Chapter 11), or if the techniques described in Chapter 6 are being used to resolve the degeneracy problem, then it is necessary to include columns for the artificial vectors and to transform them at each iteration. Columns for these vectors are shown in Table 4–1.

TABLE 4–1

TABLEAU FORM FOR SIMPLEX METHOD

c_B	Vectors in Basis		c_1	c_2	$\cdots$	c_j	$\cdots$	c_n	$\pm M$	$\cdots$	$\pm M$
		b	a_1	a_2	$\cdots$	a_j	$\cdots$	a_n	q_1	$\cdots$	q_s
c_{B1}	b_1	$x_{B1}=y_{10}$	y_{11}	y_{12}	$\cdots$	y_{1j}	$\cdots$	y_{1n}	$y_{1,n+1}$	$\cdots$	$y_{1,n+s}$
c_{B2}	b_2	$x_{B2}=y_{20}$	y_{21}	y_{22}	$\cdots$	y_{2j}	$\cdots$	y_{2n}	$y_{2,n+1}$	$\cdots$	$y_{2,n+s}$
$\cdots$	$\cdots$	$\cdots$	$\cdots$	$\cdots$		$\cdots$		$\cdots$			
c_{Bm}	b_m	$x_{Bm}=y_{m0}$	y_{m1}	y_{m2}	$\cdots$	y_{mj}	$\cdots$	y_{mn}	$y_{m,n+1}$	$\cdots$	$y_{m,n+s}$
		$z=y_{m+1,0}$	$z_1-c_1=$ $y_{m+1,1}$	$z_2-c_2=$ $y_{m+1,2}$	$\cdots$	$z_j-c_j=$ $y_{m+1,j}$	$\cdots$	$z_n-c_n=$ $y_{m+1,n}$	$\cdots$	$\cdots$	$\cdots$

4–8 Use of the tableau format. Let us next see how the tableau is used in solving a linear programming problem. Assume that we are given a basic feasible solution for the problem and the tableau in the form of Table 4–1 for that solution. First of all, we examine the last row. If all $z_j - c_j \geq 0$, the basic feasible solution is optimal. When this is not the case, we select the column having the smallest $z_j - c_j$ (smallest algebraic value—largest absolute value). Call this column k. In the event of a tie, use any one of the methods discussed previously to resolve the tie. If $y_{ik} \leq 0$ for all i, there is an unbounded solution. Assuming that at least one $y_{ik} > 0$, we shall insert $\mathbf{a}_k$ into the basis. The vector to be removed is computed from

$$\frac{x_{Br}}{y_{rk}} = \min_j \left\{ \frac{x_{Bi}}{y_{ik}}, \, y_{ik} > 0 \right\}. \tag{4–42}$$

Column r of the basis is then removed. This means that the vector in the rth row of the column "vector in basis" is removed and replaced by $\mathbf{a}_k$. It is interesting to note that the values used in the computations of (4–42) are easily found. All y_{ik} are found in the column headed "$\mathbf{a}_k$." The x_{Bi} associated with y_{ik} is found in the same row as y_{ik} in the column headed "$\mathbf{b}$." If there is a tie for the vector to be removed, it can be broken in one of the ways discussed earlier. We have now found the vector to enter and leave the basis.

Next it is necessary to compute a new tableau. Practically every quantity in the tableau will change in moving from one iteration to the next. It is the calculation of the new tableau that requires the major amount of computational work. For a large tableau, it can be an extremely laborious job. In Section 4–4 we presented two different forms of the same transformation formulas which can be used to carry out the computation. First let us discuss (4–31), which is the usual form of the transformation formulas. Repeating (4–31), we have

$$\hat{y}_{ij} = y_{ij} - y_{ik} \frac{y_{rj}}{y_{rk}};$$

$$j = 0, \ldots, n, \qquad i = 1, \ldots, m+1, \qquad i \neq r; \tag{4–43a}$$

$$\hat{y}_{rj} = \frac{y_{rj}}{y_{rk}}. \tag{4–43b}$$

Recall that $y_{i0} = x_{Bi}$, $y_{m+1,0} = z$, $y_{m+1,j} = z_j - c_j$. Every number in the tableau can be transformed by means of (4–43). Also, all the information needed to obtain the new tableau is included in the current tableau.

The subscript i in (4–43) refers to a row in the tableau. Row i is the ith row below the headings. Every row except row r transforms according to (4–43a). Row r is a special case and transforms according to (4–43b); for this reason, it is a good idea to begin computing the new tableau by

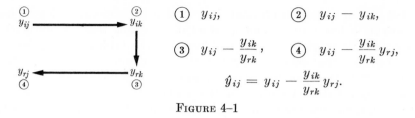

FIGURE 4–1

first computing row r. Note that to compute the new row r we need only the elements of the old row r. Each element in the new row r is found by dividing the corresponding element in the old row r by y_{rk}, the element in row r of the vector to enter the basis. The reader may find it helpful to encircle in the current tableau the column k of the vector to enter the basis and the row r of the vector to leave the basis. We have now filled in the rth row of the new tableau, using only elements in the encircled row r of the current tableau.

Every other row in the new tableau is found by (4–43a). At first glance, this looks like a complicated equation because so many subscripts appear. In actuality, it is easy to use and to remember if one keeps in mind the graphic illustration of Fig. 4–1. To compute $\hat{y}_{ij}$, we start out in the current tableau at column j and row i. We write down y_{ij}; then we move along row i to column k (the encircled column of the vector to enter the basis) and write $y_{ij} - y_{ik}$. Next move along column k to the encircled row r (row of vector to be removed) and write $y_{ij} - y_{ik}/y_{rk}$. Finally, in the encircled row r move back to column j and write $\hat{y}_{ij} = y_{ij} - (y_{ik}/y_{rk})y_{rj}$. This represents an easy method of writing down the numbers which are used in computing $\hat{y}_{ij}$. Because of the circular path transversed in obtaining these numbers, we shall refer to the use of the transformation formulas (4–43) as the "ring around the rosy" method.

The above procedure for filling in rows $i \neq r$ can be simplified further by filling in the entire row i before moving on to the next row. Note that $y_{ik}/y_{rk} = \alpha$ is constant for a given row i. Thus to find $\hat{y}_{ij}$, we first subtract αy_{rj} from y_{ij}, and y_{rj} is in the encircled row r and column j. Once α is determined for row i, we need deal only with two elements in column j to find $\hat{y}_{ij}$.

An alternative technique of transferring the tableau is the use of the vector transformation formula (4–27). Repeating it along with the appropriate definitions, we have

$$\hat{Y}_j = Y_j + y_{rj}\Phi, \qquad j = 0, \ldots, n, \tag{4–44}$$

$$Y_j = [y_{1j}, \ldots, y_{mj}, y_{m+1,j}],$$

$$\Phi = \left[-\frac{y_{1k}}{y_{rk}}, \ldots, -\frac{y_{r-1,k}}{y_{rk}}, \frac{1}{y_{rk}} - 1, -\frac{y_{r+1,k}}{y_{rk}}, \ldots, -\frac{y_{m+1,k}}{y_{rk}} \right].$$

To use this form of the transformation formula, we first determine Φ from column k. Then any new column is found by adding to the corresponding current column $y_{rj}\Phi$, and y_{rj} is the rth element of the old jth column (the element in the encircled row). Whether one prefers the "ring around the rosy" method or the vector transformation formula is largely a matter of taste. With the simplified method of filling in all of row i, the "ring around the rosy" method and the vector transformation method require precisely the same number of mathematical operations.

When computing a new tableau, we shall find it helpful to recall that if $\mathbf{a}_j$ is in column i of the new basis, then $\hat{\mathbf{y}}_j = \mathbf{e}_i$, and $\hat{z}_j - c_j = 0$. For this reason we can, without any computations at all, fill in m of the columns in the new tableau.

The final step in the computation of the new tableau consists in changing the "$\mathbf{c}_B$" and "vectors in basis" columns. Only the rth entry in each of these columns is changed. The number c_{Br} is replaced by c_k, and the vector in the rth position under "vectors in basis" is replaced by $\mathbf{a}_k$. Instead of doing this last, the reader may prefer to perform these two changes first.

Once the new tableau is obtained, we check to see whether the new solution is optimal. If it is not, we repeat the whole procedure all over again. When an optimal solution is obtained, it will be observed that the final tableau provides us with all the necessary information about this optimal solution. Under "vectors in basis," we see which vectors and variables are in the optimal basic feasible solution. Under the column headed "$\mathbf{b}$," we find the values of the optimal basic variables in the first m positions. In the $(m + 1)$-position, we find the optimal value of z, the objective function.

Since we almost always start out with an identity matrix, it is very easy to obtain the initial tableau. For this tableau $\mathbf{x}_B = \mathbf{b}$, $\mathbf{y}_j = \mathbf{a}_j$. Usually, only slack or artificial variables will be in the basis, so that the price c_{Bi} will be either 0 or $\pm M$. If there are only slack variables in the basis, $z = 0$, $z_j - c_j = -c_j$. When some artificial vectors appear in the basis, z, $z_j - c_j$ must be computed from $z = \mathbf{c}_B\mathbf{x}_B = \mathbf{c}_B\mathbf{b}$; $z_j - c_j = \mathbf{c}_B\mathbf{y}_j - c_j = \mathbf{c}_B\mathbf{a}_j - c_j$. This can be done by multiplying the elements in the same row and columns $\mathbf{c}_B$, $\mathbf{b}$, or $\mathbf{a}_j$.

When simplex computations are presented in tableau form, zeros are often not written in explicitly. The matrix $\mathbf{A}$ will quite frequently contain a large proportion of zeros, and their omission saves a considerable amount of writing. For the tableaux presented in this book, all the zeros are written in explicitly in order to avoid confusion.

After having presented the tableau form convenient for manual computations, the reader may have several questions in mind about the rationale of our method. As a trivial point, he may wonder why z is computed for each tableau, although we are interested only in the optimal value of z; could we not compute z from $z = \mathbf{c}_B\mathbf{x}_B$ after obtaining the final tableau?

It is quite true that we do not have to compute z for each tableau. However, sometimes it is interesting to see how much better the optimal z is than the z found in some of the other tableaux. For this reason, if for no other, it is convenient to determine z at each iteration.

A much more profound question concerns the rationale of transferring all the $\mathbf{y}_j$ at each iteration. If one thinks about it, only $\mathbf{x}_B$, all the $z_j - c_j$, and $\mathbf{y}_k$ are needed at each iteration. Note that only $\mathbf{y}_k$ is required to compute the vector to leave the basis. The reader may feel that the new $z_j - c_j$ cannot be computed without a knowledge of all the $\mathbf{y}_j$. However, this is not true since $z_j - c_j = \mathbf{c}_B\mathbf{y}_j - c_j = \mathbf{c}_B\mathbf{B}^{-1}\mathbf{a}_j - c_j$. Consequently, if the new inverse matrix $\hat{\mathbf{B}}^{-1}$ is known, one can find all the $z_j - c_j$ without knowing the $\mathbf{y}_j$. Hence it would appear that instead of transforming all the $\mathbf{y}_j$, we could transform the basis matrix only and compute everything else from it. This is indeed precisely what the revised simplex method does. We shall later discuss this alternative procedure and compare it with the version of the simplex method developed here. Historically, the simplex method, as presented here, evolved first. It also seems true that for hand computations most people still prefer to use this form of the simplex method rather than the revised simplex method which we shall present later.

4–9 Conversion of a minimization problem to a maximization problem.

Through all the discussion of the simplex method, we have treated maximization and minimization problems as if they were completely distinct. This was done only for the purpose of showing all the pertinent relations for both types of problems. In actuality, any minimization problem can be converted by a trivial transformation into a maximization problem, and vice versa.

Suppose that we have any function of n variables, $f(x_1, \ldots, x_n)$, and let f^* be the minimum value of this function for points in some closed region of E^n. Let $\mathbf{x}^*$ be the point (or one of the points) where f takes on its minimum value. By definition of an absolute minimum, we have for every point $\mathbf{x}$ in the region

$$f^* - f \leq 0. \tag{4–45}$$

Multiply (4–45) by (-1). This gives

$$(-f^*) - (-f) \geq 0 \tag{4–46}$$

for every $\mathbf{x}$ in the set. Therefore by definition of an absolute maximum,

$$(-f^*) = \max [-f] \tag{4–47}$$

for points in the region. Then $-f$ takes on its maximum value at $\mathbf{x}^*$.

Consequently, we conclude that

$$\min f = f^* = -(-f^*) = -\max (-f). \qquad (4\text{-}48)$$

The minimum of a function f for some set of points is the negative of the maximum of the function $-f$. The minimum of f and the maximum of $-f$ are taken on at the same points.

As an example suppose that f can take on the integral values $(5, 4, 3, 2, 1)$. The minimum of f is 1. But $-f$ can take on the values

$$(-5, -4, -3, -2, -1),$$

and the maximum of $-f$ is -1 or $-\max (-f) = 1 = \min f$.

We now see how to convert a linear programming problem in which z is to be minimized into a maximization problem. It is only necessary to change the sign of every price. Thus

$$\min z = -\max (-\mathbf{c}\mathbf{x}) = -\max (-\mathbf{c})\mathbf{x}. \qquad (4\text{-}49)$$

The function to be maximized is $z^* = (-\mathbf{c})\mathbf{x}$. Finally, $\min z = -\max z^*$. Suppose that we wanted to minimize $z = 3x_1 + 2x_2 + x_3$. The corresponding maximization problem would maximize $z^* = -3x_1 - 2x_2 - x_3$.

Let us show that the simple change in sign of the prices does reverse the criteria for selecting the vector to enter the basis and the optimality criteria. It will be recalled that in the simplex method a minimum has been reached if

$$z_j - c_j = \mathbf{c}_B\mathbf{y}_j - c_j \le 0, \qquad \text{all } j.$$

The conversion to a maximization problem replaces c_j by $-c_j$, so the above optimality condition becomes on multiplication by -1

$$(-\mathbf{c}_B)\mathbf{y}_j - (-c_j) \ge 0, \qquad \text{all } j;$$

this is precisely the optimality criterion for a maximization problem. Similarly, in a minimization problem, the vector chosen to enter the basis is

$$z_k - c_k = \max_j (z_j - c_j), \qquad z_j - c_j > 0.$$

When c_j is replaced by $-c_j$, we have

$$-z_k - (-c_k) = \min_j [-z - (-c_j)], \qquad -z_j - (-c_j) < 0,$$

which is the criterion for choosing the vector to enter the basis in a maximization problem. This shows us that the same sequence of vectors will enter the basis whether the problem is treated as a maximization problem or a minimization problem.

Since a minimization problem can be converted to a maximization problem by merely changing the sign of the prices, one can, without loss of generality, study only maximization problems. It can be assumed that any minimization problem has been converted to a maximization problem.

4–10 Review of the simplex method. We have presented a rather long discussion of the simplex method for solving the general linear programming problem. It may now be worth while to give a brief review of the method and outline a step-by-step procedure for finding a solution.

(1) We are interested in maximizing the linear objective function $z = \sum_{j=1}^{r} c_j x_j$ subject to m linear inequalities (or equalities) of the form

$$\sum_{j=1}^{r} a_{ij} x_j \{\leq \; = \; \geq\} b_i, \qquad i = 1, \ldots, m, \qquad (4\text{--}50)$$

and the non-negativity restrictions $x_j \geq 0 \; (j = 1, \ldots, r)$.

First we make sure that all b_i are non-negative. If necessary, we multiply an inequality by -1 to obtain $b_i \geq 0$. Next, slack or surplus variables are added to convert each inequality to an equality. Then

$$\sum_{j=1}^{r} a_{ij} x_j \leq b_i \qquad (4\text{--}51)$$

becomes

$$\sum_{j=1}^{r} a_{ij} x_j + x_{r+i} = b_i, \qquad x_{r+i} \geq 0, \qquad (4\text{--}52)$$

and

$$\sum_{j=1}^{r} a_{ij} x_j \geq b_i \qquad (4\text{--}53)$$

becomes

$$\sum_{j=1}^{r} a_{ij} x_j - x_{r+i} = b_i, \qquad x_{r+i} \geq 0. \qquad (4\text{--}54)$$

Each slack or surplus variable is assigned a price of zero.

The problem can then be reformulated to read

$$\max z = \mathbf{c}\mathbf{x}, \qquad \mathbf{A}\mathbf{x} = \mathbf{b}, \qquad \mathbf{x} \geq \mathbf{0}, \qquad \mathbf{A} = (\mathbf{a}_1, \ldots, \mathbf{a}_n). \qquad (4\text{--}55)$$

If a slack variable is added to the inequality i, the column of $\mathbf{A}$ corresponding to x_{r+i} is $\mathbf{e}_i$; if a surplus variable is added to the inequality i, the column of $\mathbf{A}$ corresponding to x_{r+i} is $-\mathbf{e}_i$.

(2) The matrix $\mathbf{A}$ is examined to see whether it contains an $m \times m$ identity matrix (i.e., whether the columns can be interchanged to yield an $\mathbf{I}_m$ in $\mathbf{A}$). If there is not an identity matrix, we add a sufficient number of artificial

vectors q_i and artificial variables x_{ai} in order to obtain an identity matrix. We choose a very large negative value $-M$ as the price of an artificial variable (we can use the same price for each artificial variable). To begin the simplex method, we always use an identity matrix as the basis matrix because, in general, it is very difficult to obtain any other basic feasible solution. The initial basic feasible solution is then $\mathbf{x}_B = \mathbf{b} \geq \mathbf{0}$.

(3) Construct an initial tableau of the form given in Table 4–1. This tableau is easily constructed since $\mathbf{x}_B = \mathbf{b}$, $\mathbf{y}_j = \mathbf{a}_j$. The last row giving z, $z_j - c_j$ must be computed from

$$z = \mathbf{c}_B\mathbf{b}, \qquad z_j - c_j = \mathbf{c}_B\mathbf{a}_j - c_j. \qquad (4\text{--}56)$$

(4) The optimality criterion is then applied.

Optimality criterion: If all $z_j - c_j \geq 0$, the basic feasible solution is optimal.

When one or more $z_j - c_j < 0$, we apply Simplex Criterion I to choose the vector to enter the basis.

Simplex Criterion I: Compute

$$z_k - c_k = \min_j (z_j - c_j), \qquad z_j - c_j < 0. \qquad (4\text{--}57)$$

The vector $\mathbf{a}_k$ enters the basis. If there is a tie for the minimum value, any one of the tied vectors can be chosen to enter the basis. A simple rule to break the tie is to choose from among the tied vectors the one with the smallest j-index. Once $\mathbf{a}_k$ is selected, two possibilities present themselves:

(a) $y_{ik} \leq 0$ for all i: This means that there is an unbounded solution involving the vectors in the basis and $\mathbf{a}_k$. In general, an unbounded solution will not be basic, but there exist unbounded solutions with not more than $m + 1$ variables different from zero.

(b) $y_{ik} > 0$ for at least one i: In this case, a new basic feasible solution can be found having $\hat{z} \geq z$.

(5) If at least one $y_{ik} > 0$, apply Simplex Criterion II to determine the vector to leave the basis (the column of $\mathbf{B}$ to be replaced by $\mathbf{a}_k$).

Simplex Criterion II: Compute

$$\frac{x_{Br}}{y_{rk}} = \min_i \left\{ \frac{x_{Bi}}{y_{ik}}, \, y_{ik} > 0 \right\}. \qquad (4\text{--}58)$$

The vector in column r of the basis is removed and replaced by $\mathbf{a}_k$. If there is a tie, any one of the tied columns can be removed and replaced by $\mathbf{a}_k$. A convenient way to break the tie is to choose the column with the largest y_{ik}. If this does not break the tie, select from this last group of columns the one with the smallest index i.

(6) Compute the new tableau using either the "ring around the rosy" method:

$$\hat{y}_{ij} = y_{ij} - \frac{y_{ik}}{y_{rk}} y_{rj}; \qquad \text{all } j, \quad i = 1, \ldots, m+1, \quad i \neq r, \qquad \text{(4--59a)}$$

$$\hat{y}_{rj} = \frac{y_{rj}}{y_{rk}}, \qquad \text{all } j, \qquad \qquad \qquad \qquad \text{(4--59b)}$$

$$\mathbf{x}_B = \mathbf{y}_0, \qquad z = y_{m+1,0}, \qquad z_j - c_j = y_{m+1,j}, \qquad j = 1, \ldots, n,$$

or the vector transformation formula:

$$\hat{\mathbf{Y}}_j = \mathbf{Y}_j + y_{rj}\mathbf{\Phi},$$

$$\mathbf{Y}_j = [\mathbf{y}_j, y_{m+1,j}], \qquad \text{all } j, \qquad \qquad \qquad \text{(4--60)}$$

$$\mathbf{\Phi} = \left[-\frac{y_{1k}}{y_{rk}}, \ldots, -\frac{y_{r-1,k}}{y_{rk}}, \frac{1}{y_{rk}} - 1, -\frac{y_{r+1,k}}{y_{rk}}, \ldots, -\frac{y_{m+1,k}}{y_{rk}} \right].$$

The price in the rth position of the column headed "$\mathbf{c}_B$" should be replaced by c_j, and the vector in the rth position under "vectors in basis" should be replaced by $\mathbf{a}_k$.

(7) Return to step 4. The simplex method is a finite iterative process and leads in a finite number of steps to an optimal (or unbounded) solution. There is the exceedingly rare possibility that if degeneracy appears, cycling may occur and an optimal solution will never be reached. This has never happened in any practical problem. Later we shall show how to ensure that cycling will not take place. However, since this procedure involves additional computations, it is almost never used.

In the simplex method, we know at each iteration whether the solution is optimal, and if not, whether we can form a new basic solution or whether there is an unbounded solution. In general, the number of iterations (changes of basis) required to reach an optimal solution lies between m and $2m$, where m is the number of constraints.

As indicated in Chapter 1, the term "simplex" method has nothing to do with the technique as it is now used. The name "simplex" was coined in the early days when a geometric interpretation of the method was evolved, with one of the m constraints $\sum_{j=1}^{n} x_j = 1$. We shall briefly discuss this in the next chapter.

4–11 Illustrative examples. In order to gain more familiarity with the actual process of solving a linear programming problem by the simplex method, it is desirable to work out some numerical examples. Two simple examples will be presented in this section. It will soon become evident that even fairly simple problems require considerable computational effort. For this reason, a great deal of energy has been and is being expended in the development of digital computer codes for the solution of linear programming problems.

Consider first the simple maximization problem solved graphically in Chapter 1:

$$3x_1 + 5x_2 \leq 15,$$
$$5x_1 + 2x_2 \leq 10,$$
$$x_1, x_2 \geq 0, \tag{4-61}$$
$$\max z = 5x_1 + 3x_2.$$

After slack variables have been added, the constraints become

$$3x_1 + 5x_2 + x_3 = 15,$$
$$5x_1 + 2x_2 + x_4 = 10. \tag{4-62}$$

Then

$$\mathbf{a}_1 = [3, 5], \qquad \mathbf{a}_2 = [5, 2], \qquad \mathbf{a}_3 = [1, 0],$$
$$\mathbf{a}_4 = [0, 1], \qquad \mathbf{b} = [15, 10].$$

Since we added a slack variable to each constraint, an identity matrix appears in (4–62). Thus we immediately have an initial basic feasible solution with $\mathbf{a}_3, \mathbf{a}_4$ in the basis. The slack variables have zero prices, and hence for this basic solution $\mathbf{c}_B = (0, 0)$. Furthermore, $\mathbf{x}_B = [15, 10]$, $z = 0$, $z_j - c_j = -c_j$. We can at once set up the first tableau, given in Table 4–2. (For clarity, we write $z_j - c_j$ in the last position of the "vectors in basis" column; this indicates that the last row is the $(z_j - c_j)$-row. Of course, the first element in the $(z_j - c_j)$-row, in the column headed "$\mathbf{b}$," is z.)

TABLE 4–2 — TABLEAU 1

c_j			5	3	0	0
c_B	Vectors in Basis	$\mathbf{b}$	$\mathbf{a}_1$	$\mathbf{a}_2$	$\mathbf{a}_3$	$\mathbf{a}_4$
0	$\mathbf{a}_3$	15	3	5	1	0
0	$\mathbf{a}_4$	10	5	2	0	1
	$z_j - c_j$	0	−5	−3	0	0

Obviously, this initial solution is not optimal; two of the $(z_j - c_j)$-values are negative. The minimum value is $z_1 - c_1 = -5$. Therefore, $\mathbf{a}_1$ will enter the basis at the next iteration. In actually carrying out the work, it is helpful to encircle the $\mathbf{a}_1$-column of Tableau 1, as shown. Now we must determine the column of the basis which will be replaced by $\mathbf{a}_1$. Equation (4–58) is used for this purpose. Both y_{11} and y_{21} are positive. The column to be removed is determined from the minimum of the following two numbers:

$$\frac{x_{B1}}{y_{11}} = \frac{15}{3} = 5; \qquad \frac{x_{B2}}{y_{21}} = \frac{10}{5} = 2.$$

The second column of the basis, $\mathbf{a}_4$, is to be replaced by $\mathbf{a}_1$. We encircle the rth row, i.e., the second row, as shown. Note that x_{B1} is found in the column headed "$\mathbf{b}$" in the same row as y_{11} and x_{B2} in the same row as y_{21}.

Now it is necessary to compute the tableau for the new basic feasible solution. Suppose that we use the "ring around the rosy" method. In this case, the rth row, i.e., the second row beneath the headings, is the special row; we wish to find it first. According to (4–59b), the new rth row is obtained by dividing each element of the old rth row by $y_{rk} = y_{21} = 5$. For example,

$$\hat{y}_{20} = \hat{x}_{B2} = \frac{y_{20}}{y_{21}} = \frac{10}{5} = 2, \qquad \hat{y}_{22} = \frac{2}{5} = 0.4, \qquad \hat{y}_{24} = \frac{1}{5} = 0.2.$$

The remaining two rows are filled by means of (4–59a). For row 1,

$$\frac{y_{1k}}{y_{rk}} = \frac{y_{11}}{y_{21}} = \frac{3}{5} = 0.6.$$

Therefore,

$$\hat{y}_{1j} = y_{1j} - 0.6 y_{2j}.$$

In particular,

$$\hat{y}_{10} = 15 - (0.6)(10) = 9, \qquad \hat{y}_{12} = 5 - (0.6)(2) = 3.8,$$

$$\hat{y}_{14} = 0 - (0.6)(1) = -0.6.$$

For row 3 [the $(z_j - c_j)$-row],

$$\frac{y_{3k}}{y_{2k}} = -1, \qquad \text{so} \qquad \hat{y}_{3j} = y_{3j} + y_{2j};$$

hence

$$\hat{y}_{30} = 0 + 10 = 10, \qquad \hat{y}_{32} = 2 - 3 = -1, \qquad \hat{y}_{34} = 0 + 1 = 1.$$

Tableau 2 is presented in Table 4–3.

The new basic solution is still not optimal since $z_2 - c_2 = -1$. This is the only negative $z_j - c_j$. Therefore, $\mathbf{a}_2$ will be inserted at the next

TABLE 4–3 — TABLEAU 2

c_B	Vectors in Basis	c_j	5	3	0	0
		b	$\mathbf{a}_1$	$\mathbf{a}_2$	$\mathbf{a}_3$	$\mathbf{a}_4$
0	$\mathbf{a}_3$	9	0	3.8	1	−0.6
5	$\mathbf{a}_1$	2	1	0.4	0	0.2
	$z_j - c_j$	10	0	−1	0	1

step.   The column of the basis to be removed is determined from the minimum of

$$\frac{x_{B1}}{y_{12}} = \frac{9}{3.8}; \qquad \frac{x_{B2}}{y_{22}} = \frac{2}{0.4}.$$

(The values are, of course, read from Tableau 2 since it contains the current basic feasible solution.)   Thus column 1 of the basis, $\mathbf{a}_3$, is replaced by $\mathbf{a}_2$.

Another tableau is now computed.   This time the rth row is row 1, and we compute it first.   The new row 1 is found from row 1 of Tableau 2 by dividing each element of Tableau 2, row 1, by $y_{rk} = y_{12} = 3.8$.   Hence

$$\hat{y}_{10} = \frac{9}{3.8} = 2.368; \qquad \hat{y}_{13} = \frac{1}{3.8} = 0.2632;$$

$$\hat{y}_{14} = -\frac{0.6}{3.8} = -0.1579.$$

Rows 2 and 3 are found by means of (4–59a).   For row 2,

$$\frac{y_{2k}}{y_{rk}} = \frac{y_{22}}{y_{12}} = \frac{0.4}{3.8} = 0.1053 \qquad \text{and} \qquad \hat{y}_{2j} = y_{2j} - 0.1053 y_{1j}.$$

In particular,

$$\hat{y}_{20} = 2 - 0.1053(9) = 1.053; \quad \hat{y}_{23} = 0 - 0.1053(1) = -0.1053;$$

$$\hat{y}_{24} = 0.2000 + 0.1053(0.6) = 0.2632.$$

For row 3,

$$\frac{y_{32}}{y_{12}} = -\frac{1}{3.8} = -0.2632; \qquad \hat{y}_{3j} = y_{3j} + 0.2632 y_{1j};$$

TABLE 4–4 — TABLEAU 3

c_B	c_j Vectors in Basis	b	5 a_1	3 a_2	0 a_3	0 a_4
3	a_2	2.368	0	1	0.2632	−0.1579
5	a_1	1.053	1	0	−0.1053	0.2632
	$z_j - c_j$	12.37	0	0	0.2632	0.8421

hence

$$\hat{y}_{30} = 10 + 0.2632(9) = 12.37; \qquad \hat{y}_{33} = 0 + 0.2632(1) = 0.2632;$$

$$\hat{y}_{34} = 1 + 0.2632(-0.6) = 0.8421.$$

Tableau 3 is given in Table 4–4.

In Tableau 3, $z_j - c_j \geq 0$ for each a_j. Consequently, we have obtained an optimal solution. The optimal basic solution has a_1, a_2 in the basis. From column b, we see that $x_1 = 1.053$, $x_2 = 2.368$, $z = 12.37$. This is precisely the answer that was obtained in Chapter 1. We can actually follow each iteration on the diagram of Fig. 1–1. For Tableau 1, $x_1 = x_2 = 0$, and we are at the origin of Fig. 1–1. In Tableau 2, $x_1 = 2$, $x_2 = 0$, and we have moved to the extreme point on the x_1-axis. Finally, in Tableau 3, we move to the optimal extreme point.

As a second example, let us solve the problem

$$x_1 + 3x_2 + 2x_3 + 5x_4 \leq 20,$$

$$2x_1 + 16x_2 + x_3 + x_4 \geq 4,$$

$$3x_1 - x_2 - 5x_3 + 10x_4 \leq -10, \tag{4–63}$$

$$x_1, x_2, x_3, x_4 \geq 0,$$

$$\min z = -2x_1 - x_2 - 4x_3 - 5x_4.$$

To illustrate the procedure, we shall convert this to a maximization problem by changing the signs of the prices, i.e., we want to maximize

$$\bar{z} = 2x_1 + x_2 + 4x_3 + 5x_4, \qquad \text{with} \quad \min z = -\max \bar{z}.$$

The constraints must now be considered. We wish to have $\mathbf{b} \geq \mathbf{0}$ in order to obtain an initial basic feasible solution. Hence the third inequality must be multiplied by -1. This gives

$$-3x_1 + x_2 + 5x_3 - 10x_4 \geq 10.$$

After adding slack and surplus variables, we obtain

$$x_1 + 3x_2 + 2x_3 + 5x_4 + x_5 = 20,$$

$$2x_1 + 16x_2 + x_3 + x_4 - x_6 = 4,$$

$$-3x_1 + x_2 + 5x_3 - 10x_4 - x_7 = 10.$$

Clearly, an identity matrix is not present. We do have one column $\mathbf{e}_1$ (for slack variable x_5) of an identity matrix. We then add two columns, $\mathbf{q}_1 = \mathbf{e}_2$, $\mathbf{q}_2 = \mathbf{e}_3$, and two artificial variables x_{a1}, x_{a2}. Prices $-M$ are assigned to x_{a1}, x_{a2}.

We can now construct the first tableau, shown in Table 4–5. The initial basis matrix is $\mathbf{B} = \mathbf{I} = (\mathbf{a}_5, \mathbf{q}_1, \mathbf{q}_2)$, so that $\mathbf{c}_B = (0, -M, -M)$. For this tableau,

$$z_j - c_j = \mathbf{c}_B \mathbf{a}_j - c_j, \qquad \bar{z} = \mathbf{c}_B \mathbf{b};$$

thus, for example,

$$z_3 - c_3 = -M - 5M - 4 = -6M - 4,$$

$$\bar{z} = -4M - 10M = -14M.$$

It will be noted that the expressions for $\bar{z}$, $z_j - c_j$ contain two terms of widely different magnitudes, that is, $\bar{z}$, $z_j - c_j$ are of the form $\alpha M + \beta$. Since M is a very large number, β can be neglected with respect to αM. However, if the β-terms are dropped completely, we shall run into difficulty when the last artificial vector is removed from the basis. Then the αM-terms go to zero (because there are no more artificial vectors in the basis), and only the β-terms will be left. If the β-terms are dropped, the transformation formulas cannot be used to compute the new $\bar{z}$, $z_j - c_j$ at the iteration at which the last artificial vector is removed. Instead we must apply the defining equations $\bar{z} = \mathbf{c}_B \mathbf{x}_B$, $z_j - c_j = \mathbf{c}_B \mathbf{y}_j - c_j$. If the β-terms are retained, as in this example, the transformation formulas can always be used. Furthermore, if there are tied vectors, it is possible to use the β-terms to determine the vector to enter the basis. When the αM-terms are the same for two or more vectors, one can attempt to break the tie by examining the β-terms.

Two vectors $\mathbf{a}_2$, $\mathbf{a}_3$ have $z_j - c_j < 0$. The smallest is $z_2 - c_2 = -17M - 1$. Therefore $\mathbf{a}_2$ enters the basis. All $y_{i2} > 0$; hence the column of the basis to be replaced by $\mathbf{a}_2$ is the minimum of

$$\frac{x_{B1}}{y_{12}} = \frac{20}{3}; \qquad \frac{x_{B2}}{y_{22}} = \frac{4}{16}; \qquad \frac{x_{B3}}{y_{32}} = \frac{10}{1}.$$

The smallest value is x_{B2}/y_{22}, and column 2 of the basis is replaced by $\mathbf{a}_2$, that is, $\mathbf{q}_1$ is removed. We then encircle the column of the vector to be inserted and the row corresponding to the column to be removed, as shown.

Now the new tableau must be found. In the present example, we shall illustrate the use of the vector transformation formula (4–60). First we compute $\boldsymbol{\Phi}$. Since $k = 2$, $r = 2$, $y_{rk} = y_{22} = 16$, and

$$\boldsymbol{\Phi} = \left[-\frac{3}{16}, \frac{1}{16} - 1, -\frac{1}{16}, \frac{17M + 1}{16} \right]$$

$$= [-0.1875, -0.9375, -0.0625, 1.0625M + 0.0625].$$

After finding $\boldsymbol{\Phi}$, it is easy to determine all the new columns. For example, for $\mathbf{Y}_0$, we have $y_{r0} = y_{20} = x_{B2} = 4$, and

$$\hat{\mathbf{Y}}_0 = [20, 4, 10, -14M]$$

$$+ 4[-0.1875, -0.9375, -0.0625, 1.0625M + 0.0625]$$

$$= [19.25, 0.2500, 9.750, -9.750M + 0.2500].$$

This is indeed the "b"-column of the new tableau (Table 4–6). The other columns are found in precisely the same way. Note that the same $\boldsymbol{\Phi}$ is used in the determination of each new column.

At the next iteration, we see from Tableau 2 that $\mathbf{a}_3$ will enter the basis, and column 3, that is $\mathbf{q}_2$, will be removed. In this step, we remove the last artificial vector, and hence in Tableau 3, the M-terms disappear in $\bar{z}$ and $z_j - c_j$. For this iteration $k = 3$ and $r = 3$, so that $y_{rk} = y_{33} = 4.938$, and

$$\boldsymbol{\Phi} = \left[-\frac{1.813}{4.938}, -\frac{0.06250}{4.938}, \frac{1}{4.938} - 1, \frac{4.938M + 3.938}{4.938} \right],$$

$$= [-0.3671, -0.01266, -0.7975, M + 0.7974].$$

To see how the M drop out, suppose that we compute $\hat{\mathbf{Y}}_4$. Since $y_{r4} = y_{34} = -10.06$,

$$\hat{\mathbf{Y}}_4 = [4.812, 0.06250, -10.06, 10.06M - 4.938] -$$

$$10.06[-0.3671, -0.01266, -0.7975, M + 0.7974]$$

$$= [8.506, 0.1899, -2.038, -12.96],$$

which is the column given in Tableau 3.

TABLE 4-5 — TABLEAU 1

c_j			2	1	4	5	0	0	0	$-M$	$-M$
c_B	Vectors in Basis	b	a_1	a_2	a_3	a_4	a_5	a_6	a_7	q_1	q_2
0	a_5	20	1	3	2	5	1	0	0	0	0
$-M$	q_1	4	2	16	1	1	0	-1	0	1	0
$-M$	q_2	10	-3	1	5	-10	0	0	-1	0	1
	$z_j - c_j$	$-14M$	$M-2$	$-17M-1$	$-6M-4$	$9M-5$	0	M	M	0	0

TABLE 4-6 — TABLEAU 2

c_j			2	1	4	5	0	0	0	$-M$	$-M$
c_B	Vectors in Basis	b	a_1	a_2	a_3	a_4	a_5	a_6	a_7	q_1	q_2
0	a_5	19.25	0.6250	0	1.813	4.812	1	0.1875	0	-0.1875	0
1	a_2	0.2500	0.1250	1	0.06250	0.06250	0	-0.06250	0	0.06250	0
$-M$	q_2	9.750	-3.125	0	4.938	-10.06	0	0.06250	-1	-0.06250	1
	$z_j - c_j$	$-9.750M$ $+0.2500$	$3.125M$ -1.875	0	$-4.938M$ -3.938	$10.061M$ -4.938	0	$-0.0625M$ -0.06250	M	$1.0625M$ $+0.06250$	0

TABLE 4-7 — TABLEAU 3

c_j			2	1	4	5	0	0	0	$-M$	$-M$
c_B	Vectors in Basis	b	a_1	a_2	a_3	a_4	a_5	a_6	a_7	q_1	q_2
0	a_5	15.67	1.772	0	0	8.506	1	0.1646	0.3671	-0.1646	-0.3671
1	a_2	0.1266	0.1646	1	0	0.1899	0	-0.06329	0.01266	0.06329	-0.01266
4	a_3	1.975	-0.6329	0	1	-2.038	0	0.01266	-0.2025	-0.01266	0.2025
	$z_j - c_j$	8.025	-4.367	0	0	-12.96	0	-0.01266	-0.7974	—	—

TABLE 4-8 — TABLEAU 4

c_j			2	1	4	5	0	0	0	$-M$	$-M$
c_B	Vectors in Basis	b	a_1	a_2	a_3	a_4	a_5	a_6	a_7	q_1	q_2
0	a_5	10.00	-5.600	-44.80	0	0	1	3.000	-0.2000	-3.000	0.2000
5	a_4	0.6667	0.8667	5.267	0	1	0	-0.3333	0.06667	0.3333	-0.06667
4	a_3	3.333	1.133	10.73	1	0	0	-0.6667	-0.06667	0.6667	0.06667
	$z_j - c_j$	16.67	6.867	68.27	0	0	0	-4.333	0.06667	—	—

TABLE 4-9 — TABLEAU 5

c_B	c_j Vectors in Basis	b	2 a_1	1 a_2	4 a_3	5 a_4	0 a_5	0 a_6	0 a_7	$-M$ q_1	$-M$ q_2
0	a_6	3.333	-1.867	-14.93	0	0	0.3333	1	-0.06667	-1	0.06667
5	a_4	1.778	0.2444	0.2883	0	1	0.1111	0	0.04444	0	-0.04444
4	a_3	5.556	-0.1111	0.7778	1	0	0.2222	0	-0.1111	0	0.1111
	$z_j - c_j$	31.11	-1.222	3.556	0	0	1.444	0	-0.2222	—	—

TABLE 4-10 — TABLEAU 6

c_B	c_j Vectors in Basis	b	2 a_1	1 a_2	4 a_3	5 a_4	0 a_5	0 a_6	0 a_7	$-M$ q_1	$-M$ q_2
0	a_6	16.91	0	-12.74	0	7.636	1.182	1	0.2727	-1	-0.2727
2	a_1	7.273	1	1.182	0	4.091	0.4545	0	0.1818	0	-0.1818
4	a_3	6.364	0	0.9091	1	0.4545	0.2727	0	-0.09091	0	0.09091
	$z_j - c_j$	40.00	0	5.000	0	5.000	2.000	0	0	—	—

As has been indicated previously, it is in general unnecessary to include columns in the tableaux for the artificial vectors. In the present example, the artificial vectors are transformed at each iteration for later use in the problems.

It is unnecessary to discuss in detail the arithmetic involved in computing the remaining tableaux (Tables 4–8, 4–9, 4–10).

Note that, in this case, the simplex method was not too efficient. To obtain an optimal basis involving only three vectors, five iterations were required—two more than the minimum if all the correct vectors had been inserted in order.

The maximum of $\bar{z}$ is 40.00. Thus the minimum of z is -40.00. The optimal basis contains $\mathbf{a}_1$, $\mathbf{a}_3$, $\mathbf{a}_6$. The values of the basic variables are $x_1 = 7.273$, $x_3 = 6.364$, $x_6 = 16.91$. Note that one of the variables in the basis is a surplus variable.

REFERENCES

The references listed at the end of Chapter 3 apply also to this chapter.

PROBLEMS

4–1. Show that any vector which is removed from the basis at one iteration in the simplex method cannot immediately re-enter the basis at the next iteration.

4–2. Can a vector which is inserted at one iteration in the simplex method be removed immediately at the next iteration? When can this occur and when is it impossible?

4–3. Recall from the discussion of the theory of the simplex method that if $\mathbf{a}_k$ is to enter the basis, we consider for removal only those columns of $\mathbf{B}$ which have $y_{rk} > 0$, so that we are sure $\hat{x}_{Br} = x_{Br}/y_{rk} \geq 0$. This must be done when there is no degeneracy. However, when degeneracy is present, a vector can be inserted at a zero level even if $y_{rk} < 0$. If the simplex method is used, why is it sensible to consider only the $y_{rk} > 0$, even in the presence of degeneracy, and ignore the fact that a vector might be inserted at a zero level with $y_{rk} < 0$?

4–4. In the simplex method, we consider as candidates for insertion into the basis only the vectors with $z_j - c_j < 0$ (for a maximization problem). However, if a vector goes in at a zero level, it does not make any difference whether $z_j - c_j \{ < = > \} 0$. When degeneracy is present, does it make sense to consider only the vectors with $z_j - c_j < 0$?

4–5. Using an example in two dimensions (two variables in the original constraint inequalities), show graphically that the procedure of finding the largest increase in the objective function at each iteration can lead to more iterations than a procedure in which z may actually decrease at some point.

4–6. Show that once an artificial vector has been removed from the basis, it is never necessary to re-insert it.

4–7. If inequalities of the form $\sum_j a_{ij}x_j \geq 0$ appear in a linear programming problem, discuss why it is desirable to convert them to the form $\sum_j (-a_{ij})x_j \leq 0$.

4–8. Show that if some variable appears in only one constraint of $\mathbf{Ax} = \mathbf{b}$, the activity vector corresponding to that variable can be converted to a unit vector. Why is it desirable to do this whenever possible?

4–9. Prove that, by a proper choice of the prices in the objective function, any extreme point of the convex set of feasible solutions can be made optimal. In general, what is the minimum number of prices that would have to be specified in order to make any given extreme point optimal?

4–10. Using the results of Problem 4–9, show that the extreme points of the convex set of feasible solutions are connected, i.e., one can move from any one extreme point to any other extreme point by moving from one extreme point to an adjacent extreme point. When presenting the proof, ignore the problems created by degeneracy.

4–11. Show that if we are given any one tableau for the simplex method, the inverse of the basis matrix for the basic solution can be read from the tableau provided we know which columns formed the initial identity basis matrix. Hint: The initial tableau has the form $(\mathbf{b}, \mathbf{I}, \mathbf{R})$. The tableau for any succeeding basic solution with basis matrix $\mathbf{B}$ is formed by multiplying the initial tableau by $\mathbf{B}^{-1}$.

4–12. Suppose that we are given some tableau for the simplex method. Is it possible to determine uniquely the activity vectors $\mathbf{a}_j$ and the requirements vector $\mathbf{b}$? Assume that the only information available is given in the tableau. Would it make any difference if it were known which vectors were in the original identity matrix?

4–13. Solve the following linear programming problem graphically and by the simplex method. Show in the geometrical presentation the extreme point which corresponds to each tableau of the simplex method.

$$3x_1 + 5x_2 \leq 15, \qquad 6x_1 + 2x_2 \leq 24, \qquad x_1, x_2 \geq 0, \qquad \max z = 2x_1 + x_2.$$

4–14. Solve the following linear programming problem by the simplex method:

$$8x_1 + 3x_2 + 4x_3 + x_4 \leq 7,$$
$$2x_1 + 6x_2 + x_3 + 5x_4 \leq 3,$$
$$x_1 + 4x_2 + 5x_3 + 2x_4 \leq 8,$$
$$\text{all } x_j \geq 0,$$
$$\max z = 3x_1 + 4x_2 + x_3 + 7x_4.$$

4–15. Solve the following linear programming problem by the simplex method:

$$x_1 + 5x_2 + 9x_3 - 6x_4 \geq -2,$$
$$3x_1 - x_2 + x_3 + 3x_4 \leq 10,$$
$$-2x_1 - 3x_2 + 7x_3 - 8x_4 \geq 0,$$
$$\text{all } x_j \geq 0,$$
$$\max z = 2x_1 - 3x_2 + 4x_3 + x_4.$$

4–16. Solve the following problem by the simplex method without adding any artificial variables:

$$3x_1 + 2x_2 + 4x_3 + x_4 + 5x_5 = 15,$$
$$x_1 + 2x_2 + x_3 + 5x_4 + 5x_5 = 13,$$
$$2x_3 + 6x_4 + 3x_5 \geq 6,$$
$$\text{all } x_j \geq 0,$$
$$\max z = x_1 + 3x_2 + 5x_3 + 4x_4 + 9x_5.$$

4–17. Solve the following linear programming problem graphically and by the simplex method, using Charnes' $-M$ technique for the artificial vector. Show the correspondence between the simplex iterations after a feasible solution has been found, and the extreme points of the convex set of feasible solutions.

$$3x_1 + 4x_2 \leq 6, \qquad x_1 + 3x_2 \geq 2, \qquad x_1, x_2 \geq 0, \qquad \max z = x_1 + 5x_2.$$

4–18. Using Charnes' $-M$ technique to handle the artificial variables, solve the following linear programming problem by the simplex method:

$$5x_1 - 2x_2 + x_3 - 3x_4 \geq 2,$$
$$6x_1 + x_2 - 5x_3 - 3x_4 \geq 5,$$
$$-x_1 + 4x_2 + 3x_3 + 7x_4 \geq 6,$$
$$\text{all } x_j \geq 0,$$
$$\min z = 3x_1 + 4x_2 + x_3 + 6x_4.$$

4–19. Using the $-M$ technique to handle the artificial variables, solve the following linear programming problem by the simplex method. What can be said about the optimal solution?

$$2x_1 + 3x_2 - 5x_3 + 4x_4 = 7,$$
$$-3x_1 + 2x_2 + 3x_3 - 9x_4 = 8,$$
$$1.75x_1 - x_2 + 3.25x_3 - 4.25x_4 = -4.75,$$
$$\text{all } x_j \geq 0,$$
$$\max z = 8x_1 + x_2 + 3x_3 + 5x_4.$$

4–20. Using the $-M$ technique for the artificial variables, solve the following linear programming problem by the simplex method. What can be said about the optimal solution?

$$4x_1 + 5x_2 + x_3 - 3x_4 = 5,$$
$$2x_1 - 3x_2 - 4x_3 + 5x_4 = 7,$$
$$x_1 + 4x_2 + 2.5x_3 - 4x_4 = 6,$$
$$\text{all } x_j \geq 0,$$
$$\max z = 3x_1 + 2x_2 + x_3 + 4x_4.$$

4-21. Consider the linear programming problem $\mathbf{Ax} = \mathbf{b}$, $\mathbf{x} \geq \mathbf{0}$, max $z = \mathbf{cx}$. Suppose that $\mathbf{A}$ is a matrix with many rows and columns. However, assume that it can be written in partitioned form as

$$
\mathbf{A} = \begin{bmatrix} \mathbf{A}_1 & \mathbf{0} & \cdots & \mathbf{0} \\ \mathbf{0} & \mathbf{A}_2 & \cdots & \mathbf{0} \\ \vdots & & & \vdots \\ \mathbf{0} & \cdots & \cdots & \mathbf{A}_k \end{bmatrix}.
$$

Show how such a problem can be simplified by breaking it down into a series of smaller problems.

4-22. In the simplex method, the criterion determining the vector to enter the basis selects the vector which gives the greatest unit increase in z (i.e., the greatest increase in z if one unit of x_k was inserted). Consider instead the following criterion: We wish to select the vector which maximizes $\mathbf{c}(\hat{\mathbf{x}} - \mathbf{x})$, where $\hat{\mathbf{x}}$ is the new n-component vector for $\mathbf{Ax} = \mathbf{b}$. What is the geometrical interpretation of this criterion? What does it reduce to analytically? Is this criterion identical with any other criterion considered so far?

4-23. Suppose that in solving some linear programming problem, we reach a stage where one or more artificial vectors are in the basis and an indication of an unbounded solution is obtained (i.e., for the vector $\mathbf{a}_k$ to enter the basis, all $y_{ik} \leq 0$). Discuss the various possible meanings of such a situation. Show that by Charnes' $-M$ method feasibility will be reached before an indication of an unbounded solution appears, if there is a feasible solution.

4-24. In this chapter, preliminary transformations were always made to ensure that $\mathbf{b} \geq \mathbf{0}$ in $\mathbf{Ax} = \mathbf{b}$. Show that these are really unnecessary. Demonstrate that with $b_i < 0$, we can get started if the ith column of the initial basis matrix is $-\mathbf{e}_i$ instead of $\mathbf{e}_i$. Thus if some of the b_i are negative, the original basis matrix can contain columns of the form $-\mathbf{e}_i$ as well as columns of the form $\mathbf{e}_i$. What is the inverse of a matrix which is an identity matrix except for the fact that some of the diagonal elements are -1 instead of 1? How does one obtain the first tableau? Show that the number of artificial vectors needed will not depend on whether or not a transformation is made to make the b_i non-negative.

4-25. When making simplex computations by hand, it is very important to have some means for making numerical checks on the computations at each iteration. Compute the number of operations (multiplications and divisions) required to make the following checks:

(a) Substitute the basic solution into the set of equations $\mathbf{Ax} = \mathbf{b}$ to see whether the solution satisfies the equations.

(b) Compute the $z_j - c_j$ from $z_j - c_j = \mathbf{c}_B \mathbf{y}_j - c_j$, and check to see whether the same result was obtained by the transformation formulas.

(c) Find $\mathbf{B}^{-1}$ in the current tableau and multiply it by $\mathbf{B}$ (found in the initial tableau) to see whether an identity matrix has been obtained.

(d) Compute the $\mathbf{y}_j$ from $\mathbf{y}_j = \mathbf{B}^{-1}\mathbf{a}_j$, and see whether the result is the same as that given by the transformation formulas.

4–26. Find $\mathbf{B}^{-1}$ in Table 4–7. Compute $\mathbf{B}^{-1}\mathbf{B}$. Is the resulting matrix an identity matrix?

4–27. In Table 4–8, substitute the basic solution into the original set of equations. Does this "solution" satisfy the equations?

4–28. A very convenient way of performing a numerical check on the computations at each stage of the simplex method is to use a so-called sum-check column. This is done as follows: Define the vector $\boldsymbol{\sigma}$ as

$$\boldsymbol{\sigma} = \mathbf{b} + \sum_{j=1}^{n} \mathbf{a}_j + \sum_{i=1}^{s} \mathbf{q}_i,$$

and the vector $\boldsymbol{\Omega}$ as

$$\boldsymbol{\Omega} = \mathbf{B}^{-1}\boldsymbol{\sigma} = \mathbf{x}_B + \sum_{j=1}^{n+s} \mathbf{y}_j = [\Omega_1, \ldots, \Omega_m].$$

For a given tableau, Ω_i can be obtained by adding all the elements in row i of the tableau. However, $\boldsymbol{\Omega}$ also obeys the same transformation relations as all other columns of the tableau, i.e.,

$$\hat{\Omega}_i = \Omega_i - \frac{y_{ik}}{y_{rk}}\Omega_r, \quad i \neq r; \quad \hat{\Omega}_r = \frac{\Omega_r}{y_{rk}}.$$

Prove this. Suppose that we annex the vector $\boldsymbol{\Omega} = \boldsymbol{\sigma}$ as an additional column of the initial tableau. When transforming the tableau, we then transform $\boldsymbol{\Omega} = \boldsymbol{\sigma}$, using the usual transformation formulas. In the new tableau we add all elements in row i (except in column $\boldsymbol{\Omega}$). This should yield the element Ω_i in the $\boldsymbol{\Omega}$-column. Add a sum-check column to each of the tableaux in Tables 4–5 through 4–10. Transform this column and then perform the appropriate summations to show that a check has been obtained. Show that the sum check can also be used on the $(z_j - c_j)$-row. Note that the $\mathbf{q}_i$ need not be included in $\boldsymbol{\sigma}$ unless the artificial vectors are included in the tableaux and are transformed at each iteration.

4–29. How many additional operations (multiplications and divisions) are required at each iteration in order to carry along a sum-check column?

4–30. Make a list of the type of errors which can be made during simplex calculations. Are any of these self-correcting? Which errors will lead to an incorrect answer?

CHAPTER 5

FURTHER DISCUSSION OF THE SIMPLEX METHOD

*"Once more unto the breach, dear
friends, once more."*

Shakespeare, Henry V.

5–1 The two-phase method for artificial variables. In the preceding chapter, we have made the following observations: It is frequently necessary to add artificial variables and vectors to the set of constraints in order to find easily an initial basic feasible solution to a linear programming problem. If the original problem is to be solved, the artificial variables must be driven to zero. This can be achieved by assigning a large negative price $(-M)$ to each artificial variable, thus making it unprofitable to have such variables in the basis.

There are several aspects of the $-M$ method which can lead us into difficulty, especially if the problem is to be solved on a digital computer. To use a digital computer, M must be assigned some numerical value which is much larger than any of the other prices appearing in the problem. Since a computer has only a fixed number of digits, the large difference in order of magnitude between M and the other prices can cause problems. We have already noted that the $z_j - c_j$ will be of the form $\alpha M + \beta$ when artificial vectors are in the basis. If the computer, for example, has only four digits, and if $\alpha M = 1014$, $\beta = 1.472$, then to four figures, $\alpha M + \beta = 1015$; this implies that three significant figures in β have been lost. However, when the last artificial vector is driven from the basis, the αM-terms drop out, and only the β-terms remain. If most of the significance in the β-terms has been lost, then $z, z_j - c_j$ will need to be recomputed from their definitions. Consequently, in the computer code a special procedure will often be required for the iteration at which the last artificial vector is removed. Of course, at every iteration, we could compute the $z_j - c_j$ from the definition, but this would again result in more work than is really needed.

There is a further difficulty: If M is not chosen large enough, an incorrect answer may be obtained. For example, if α is very small, it may turn out that β is not negligible with respect to αM. Hence one might conclude that there is no solution when in reality a solution exists.

Another method of treating artificial vectors has been developed by Dantzig, Orden, and others at the RAND Corporation. Although they were searching mainly for a technique that would be suitable for use on

149

digital computers, they developed a method, called the "two-phase technique," which can be used equally well for hand computations. In this chapter we shall present a form of the two-phase technique which is useful for hand computations, while Chapter 7 will discuss a different format which can also be used for hand computations, but which is especially well suited for use with digital computers.

The general idea of the two-phase method is as follows: Suppose that we try to solve the linear programming problem in two parts. First we drive all artificial variables to zero. This is called Phase I. Then we maximize the actual objective function z, starting from a basic feasible solution which either contains no artificial vectors or some artificial vectors at a zero level. This is Phase II.

5–2 Phase I. In Phase I, let us assign to an artificial variable a price of -1 rather than a price of $-M$. To all other variables we assign the price 0 (regardless of what their prices are in the actual problem). Then, instead of considering the actual objective function, we maximize the function

$$z^* = \sum_{i=1}^{s} (-1)x_{ai} = -x_{a1} - \cdots - x_{as} = -\mathbf{1}\mathbf{x}_a, \qquad (5\text{–}1)$$

where $\mathbf{x}_a$ is an s-component column vector containing the artificial variables. It will be recalled that the initial basic feasible solution to the augmented problem has $\mathbf{x}_a \geq \mathbf{0}$. Furthermore, the simplex method prevents any variable from ever becoming negative. Consequently, the artificial variables will always be non-negative. Hence it is always true that $z^* \leq 0$, and the maximum value of z^* is zero; z^* will be zero only if each artificial variable is zero.

If max $z^* = 0$, we drive all the artificial variables to zero by maximizing z^*. If max $z^* < 0$, then the artificial variables cannot be driven to zero, and the original problem has no feasible solution. Thus Phase I consists of the usual simplex calculations except for the fact that we are maximizing z^* rather than z. The price of each legitimate variable is set to 0, and a price of -1 is assigned to each artificial variable.

In Phase I, we stop as soon as z^* becomes zero, because we know that this is the maximum value of z^*. We need not continue until the optimality criterion is satisfied, if z^* becomes zero before this happens.

During Phase I, the sequence of vectors to enter and leave the basis is the same as in Charnes' $-M$ method. It is not hard to see why this is so. With the $-M$ method,

$$z_j - c_j = -M \sum_r y_{rj} + \beta \qquad (5\text{–}2)$$

for any legitimate vector $\mathbf{a}_j$. The sum is taken over those r that correspond to the columns of the basis containing artificial vectors; β contains the terms involving the ordinary prices, and is assumed to be negligible with respect to the $-M$ term. However, in Phase I,

$$z_j - c_j = -\sum_r y_{rj} \qquad (5\text{–}3)$$

for any legitimate vector because the price of an artificial variable is -1 and that of a legitimate variable is 0. Since β is negligible, this expression differs from the $z_j - c_j$ of the $-M$ method only by the factor M. Thus in both cases, the same vector will be chosen to enter the basis.

The only possible exception is the situation where the vectors are tied. In this instance, the β-terms can be used to break the tie in Charnes' method. This β-term does not appear in the two-phase method, and therefore some other procedure must be used to break the tie. In such a case, the vector entering the basis in Charnes' method might be different from that in the two-phase method.

At the end of Phase I (when the optimality condition is satisfied or $z^* = 0$), three possibilities exist:

(1) max $z^* < 0$; one or more artificial vectors appear in the basis at a positive level. The original problem has no feasible solution.

(2) max $z^* = 0$; no artificial vectors appear in the basis. We have found a basic feasible solution to the original problem.

(3) max $z^* = 0$; one or more artificial vectors appear in the basis at a zero level. We have found a feasible solution to the original problem. Because some artificial vectors appear in the basis at a zero level, there may be redundancy in the original constraint equations.

5–3 Phase II. When Phase I results in (2) or (3), we go on to Phase II to find an optimal solution. In Phase II, we assign its actual price c_j to each legitimate variable and a price of 0 to any artificial variables which may appear in the basis at a zero level. The function to be optimized in Phase II is the actual objective function z. The first tableau for Phase II is the last tableau for Phase I, the only difference being that the $(z_j - c_j)$-row for the last tableau of Phase I must be altered to take account of the change in the prices. The new $(z_j - c_j)$-row is found from $z = \mathbf{c}_B \mathbf{x}_B$, $z_j - c_j = \mathbf{c}_B \mathbf{y}_j - c_j$. The last tableau of Phase I can be used as the first tableau of Phase II because it gives a feasible solution to the original set of constraints.

When Phase I ends in (2), no artificial variables appear in the basis. Therefore we start off Phase II with a basic feasible solution to the original constraints, and there are no problems. If, however, Phase I ends in (3), we must give some attention to the artificial variables which appear in the basis at a zero level. We must make sure that the artificial variables never become positive in Phase II. *A priori*, we cannot be certain that the artificial variables will remain zero because they have a price of zero in Phase II. In Charnes' method this problem does not arise: Once the artificial variables go to zero, they will remain zero because of the price $-M$; if they became positive, z would be worsened, and by the nature of the simplex method this cannot happen.

In the section which dealt with redundancy, we saw that if we had a basic feasible solution with artificial vectors in the basis at a zero level, we could either remove these artificial vectors and obtain a degenerate basic feasible solution to the original problem; or if the artificial vectors could not be removed, the redundant equations could be eliminated, and we would obtain a basic feasible solution to the new set of constraints with the redundant equations removed. Hence, if Phase I ended in (3), we could, theoretically, remove all artificial vectors which appear at a zero level. However, the insertion of legitimate vectors into the basis and the removal of the artificial vectors would not necessarily bring us any closer to an optimal solution. This method could therefore involve a great deal of unnecessary work, and for this reason, we do not attempt to use it. If $y_{ij} = 0$ for all j and for those i that correspond to the columns of the basis containing artificial vectors, we shall show below that we can cross off the rows with all $y_{ij} = 0$ and drop the corresponding artificial vectors. This allows us to proceed with a smaller basis and tableau.

Let us now study how to proceed in Phase II when at the beginning one or more artificial variables appear at a zero level and for at least one i corresponding to a column of the basis containing an artificial vector, there exists one or more $y_{ij} \neq 0$. We must make sure the artificial variables remain zero at each iteration in Phase II. Suppose that at some iteration in Phase II we insert the vector $\mathbf{a}_k$ into the basis. If $y_{ik} > 0$ for one or more i corresponding to columns of the basis containing artificial vectors at a zero level, then our criterion determining the vector to be removed indicates that an artificial vector can be removed. Then $\mathbf{a}_k$ enters the basis at a zero level. This means that the values of the variables in the basis remain unchanged, and therefore any artificial variables in the new basis remain zero. No difficulty can arise in this case.

Next imagine that $\mathbf{a}_k$ is to enter the basis, and $y_{ik} = 0$ for all i corresponding to the columns of the basis containing artificial vectors. No artificial vector will be removed. Assume that the legitimate vector in column r of the basis is removed. The values of the artificial variables in the new basic solution are

$$\hat{x}_{Bi} = x_{Bi} - \frac{y_{ik}}{y_{rk}} x_{Br} = 0 \qquad (5\text{–}4)$$

because $x_{Bi} = 0$ and $y_{ik} = 0$. This possibility causes no difficulty either.

At this point, it is instructive to note one more thing. Consider the situation where $y_{ij} = 0$ for all legitimate vectors when i corresponds to a column of **B** containing an artificial vector. The values of $\hat{y}_{ij}$ are given by

$$\hat{y}_{ij} = y_{ij} - \frac{y_{ik}}{y_{rk}} y_{rj} = 0 \qquad \text{(all } j) \tag{5–5}$$

because $y_{ij} = y_{ik} = 0$. The new tableau will again have a row of zeros. This demonstrates that the artificial vector in column i of **B** will never be removed. For this reason, we can cross off the row that will always contain zeros and drop column i of the basis. We then continue the computation with a new tableau (reduced by one row) and an $(m - 1) \times (m - 1)$ basis. The above result shows why, at the end of Phase I, we can cross off rows with $y_{ij} = 0$ for all j when i corresponds to an artificial vector. Incidentally, this applies not only to the two-phase method but also to Charnes' method. It is merely another way of stating the result obtained in Section 4–6 which says that if the above conditions hold, constraint i is redundant and can be dropped.

In the last case to be examined, the $\mathbf{a}_k$ to enter the basis has $y_{ik} \leq 0$ for all i that correspond to the columns of **B** containing artificial vectors, and $y_{ik} < 0$ for at least one i. In this instance, the usual criterion which is used to determine the vector to leave the basis would not consider any artificial vector for removal. A legitimate vector would be removed instead. If a legitimate vector $\mathbf{b}_r$ is removed and $x_{Br} > 0$, the values of the artificial variables with $y_{ik} < 0$ in the new basis are

$$\hat{x}_{Bi} = x_{Bi} - \frac{y_{ik}}{y_{rk}} x_{Br} = - \frac{y_{ik}}{y_{rk}} x_{Br} > 0. \tag{5–6}$$

Here we have encountered the only possible circumstance under which the artificial variables in the basis can become positive; that is, $y_{ik} < 0$ for i corresponding to one or more of the columns of **B** that contain artificial variables. It is now also clear how to avoid this possibility. Instead of removing a legitimate vector, we remove any one of the artificial vectors with $y_{ik} < 0$. Because $y_{ik} \neq 0$, we are sure that the new solution will be basic. It will also be feasible because the artificial vector was at a zero level, and therefore $\mathbf{a}_k$ will enter at a zero level. Furthermore, $\hat{z} = z$.

Let us summarize what we do in Phase II when artificial variables appear at a zero level in the basis at the end of Phase I. First, if at the end of Phase I, $y_{ij} = 0$ for all j and for i corresponding to a column of **B** that contains an artificial vector, this row (or rows) is crossed off the tableau, and we begin Phase II with a basis of smaller size. This can be done because we have shown that the corresponding artificial vector will never be removed, and hence that there is redundancy in the constraints.

In Phase II, we apply the usual criterion to determine the vector to enter the basis. We also apply the usual criterion to determine the vector to leave the basis unless $y_{ik} \leq 0$ when i corresponds to a column of $\mathbf{B}$ containing an artificial vector and $y_{ik} < 0$ for at least one such i. Then, instead of removing some legitimate vector as the usual simplex criterion would require, we remove one of the artificial vectors with $y_{ik} < 0$. In this way, we ensure that the artificial vectors will never become positive.

If, in Phase II, artificial vectors appear in the basis at a zero level, the sequence of vectors entering the basis will, in general, be different from that obtained by the $-M$ method. Because of the $-M$, the artificial vectors would control the vector to enter the basis (except where $y_{ij} = 0$ for all j and for i corresponding to the columns of $\mathbf{B}$ that contain artificial vectors, in which case these rows should be crossed off). In Phase II, the price of an artificial vector is 0 and does not affect the vector to enter the basis. The two-phase method would seem to be preferable in this case, because it selects the vector to enter the basis as if no artificial vectors were present.

5–4 Numerical examples of the two-phase method. It will be helpful to illustrate the two-phase method by considering two simple numerical examples. As the first example, consider the problem worked out by the $-M$ method in Chapter 4 (Tables 4–5 through 4–10). In the two-phase method, we begin by assigning prices of zero to the legitimate variables and of -1 to the artificial variables. For the problem at hand, we desire to maximize $z^* = -x_{a1} - x_{a2}$ in Phase I. We shall denote the $z_j - c_j$ and $\mathbf{c}_B$ of Phase I by $z_j^* - c_j^*$ and $\mathbf{c}_B^*$. The first tableau, constructed in the usual way, is given in Table 5–1. Using the prices appropriate to Phase I, we compute the $z_j^* - c_j^*$. In the first step, $\mathbf{a}_2$ enters the basis. As expected, $\mathbf{a}_2$ and the vector which first entered the basis with the $-M$ method are identical. Tables 5–2 and 5–3 contain the remaining tableaux of Phase I. At the end of Phase I, there are no artificial variables in the basis. We assign to the legitimate vectors their actual prices c_j and recompute the $(z_j - c_j)$-row. This yields Table 4–7. We then proceed with Phase II and obtain Tables 4–8 through 4–10.

As a second example, let us solve the following linear programming problem:

$$3x_1 + 2x_2 + x_3 + 4x_4 \leq 6,$$
$$2x_1 + x_2 + 5x_3 + x_4 \leq 4,$$
$$2x_1 + 6x_2 - 4x_3 + 8x_4 = 0,$$
$$x_1 + 3x_2 - 2x_3 + 4x_4 = 0,$$
$$x_1, x_2, x_3, x_4 \geq 0,$$
$$\max z = x_1 + 1.5x_2 + 5x_3 + 2x_4.$$

TABLE 5–1 — TABLEAU 1: PHASE I

c_B^*	c_j^* Vectors in Basis	b	a_1	a_2	a_3	a_4	a_5	a_6	a_7	q_1	q_2
			0	0	0	0	0	0	0	-1	-1
0	a_5	20	1	3	2	5	1	0	0	0	0
-1	q_1	4	2	16	1	1	0	-1	0	1	0
-1	q_2	10	-3	1	5	-10	0	0	-1	0	1
	$z_j^* - c_j^*$	-14	1	-17	-6	9	0	1	1	0	0

After the addition of slack variables the constraints become:

$$3x_1 + 2x_2 + x_3 + 4x_4 + x_5 = 6,$$
$$2x_1 + x_2 + 5x_3 + x_4 + x_6 = 4,$$
$$2x_1 + 6x_2 - 4x_3 + 8x_4 = 0,$$
$$x_1 + 3x_2 - 2x_3 + 4x_4 = 0.$$

Since the last equation is one-half the third one, there is clearly redundancy in the constraints. Rather than dropping the redundant constraint, we shall retain it to show what happens in the two-phase method.

Two artificial variables are needed to obtain an initial basic feasible solution. Because of the redundancy, we know that one artificial vector will be in the basis at the termination of Phase II. This example then gives us the opportunity of demonstrating how to handle artificial variables in Phase II. Note that in the initial basic feasible solution both artificial variables are equal to zero. Thus, Phase I is not required, and we begin with Phase II. The tableaux for Phase II are given in Tables 5–4 through 5–6.

At the first iteration, the usual rule for determining the vector to leave the basis would yield a_6. However, if this were done, both artificial variables would be positive at the next stage. Hence we must use our alternative rule and remove one of the artificial vectors. It was arbitrarily decided to remove q_1. In the second tableau, the row opposite q_2 contains only zeros. Thus we know that q_2 will always be in the basis. Therefore, we

TABLE 5–2 — TABLEAU 2: PHASE I

c_B^*	c_j^* Vectors in Basis	b	0 a_1	0 a_2	0 a_3	0 a_4	0 a_5	0 a_6	0 a_7	-1 q_1	-1 q_2
0	a_5	19.25	0.6250	0	1.813	4.812	1	0.1875	0	-0.1875	0
0	a_2	0.2500	0.1250	1	0.06250	0.06250	0	-0.06250	0	0.06250	0
-1	q_2	9.750	-3.125	0	4.938	-10.06	0	0.06250	-1	-0.06250	1
	$z_j^* - c_j^*$	-9.750	3.125	0	-4.938	10.06	0	-0.06250	1	1.0625	0

TABLE 5–3 — TABLEAU 3: PHASE I

c_B^*	c_j^* Vectors in Basis	b	0 a_1	0 a_2	0 a_3	0 a_4	0 a_5	0 a_6	0 a_7	-1 q_1	-1 q_2
0	a_5	15.67	1.772	0	0	8.506	1	0.1646	0.3671	-0.1646	-0.3671
0	a_2	0.1266	0.1646	1	0	0.1899	0	-0.06329	0.01266	0.06329	-0.01266
0	a_3	1.975	-0.6329	0	1	-2.038	0	0.01266	-0.2025	-0.01266	0.2025
	$z_j^* - c_j^*$	0	0	0	0	0	0	0	0	1	1

TABLE 5–4 — TABLEAU 1

c_B	c_j Vectors in Basis	b	1 a_1	1.5 a_2	5 a_3	2 a_4	0 a_5	0 a_6
0	a_5	6	3	2	1	4	1	0
0	a_6	4	2	1	5	1	0	1
0	q_1	0	2	6	−4	8	0	0
0	q_2	0	1	3	−2	4	0	0
	$z_j - c_j$	0	−1	−1.5	−5	−2	0	0

TABLE 5–5 — TABLEAU 2

c_B	c_j Vectors in Basis	b	1 a_1	1.5 a_2	5 a_3	2 a_4	0 a_5	0 a_6
0	a_5	6	3.5	3.5	0	6	1	0
0	a_6	4	4.5	8.5	0	11	0	1
5	a_3	0	−0.5	−1.5	1	−2	0	0
0	q_2	0	0	0	0	0	0	0
	$z_j - c_j$	0	−3.5	−9	0	−12	0	0

TABLE 5–6 — TABLEAU 3

c_B	Vectors in Basis	b	c_j 1 a_1	1.5 a_2	5 a_3	2 a_4	0 a_5	0 a_6
0	a_5	3.8	1.05	−1.13	0	0	1	−0.54
2	a_4	0.36	0.41	0.77	0	1	0	0.09
5	a_3	0.73	0.32	0.05	1	0	0	0.18
	$z_j - c_j$	4.4	1.4	0.27	0	0	0	1.09

cross off this row and proceed with a tableau containing one row less than the preceding one. The next tableau gives the optimal solution. The appearance of q_2 in the optimal solution verifies that the last constraint equation is not linearly independent of the others. If it had been dropped at the start, we would have obtained the same tableau as in Table 5–6. No columns for artificial vectors were included in the tableaux.

5–5 Requirements space. There are two multidimensional euclidean spaces which are important in the solution of a linear programming problem. First, there is the n-dimensional space which contains the solutions $\mathbf{x}$ to $\mathbf{Ax} = \mathbf{b}$. This space is called the "solutions space." Then there is an m-dimensional space, elements of which are the activity vectors $\mathbf{a}_j$ and the requirements vector $\mathbf{b}$. This space is called the "requirements space." In this section, we shall present a discussion of the requirements space.

Let us begin by summarizing the results of Chapter 2. The set of activity vectors $\mathbf{a}_1, \ldots, \mathbf{a}_n$ can be imagined to generate a convex polyhedral cone C in the requirements space. This cone will be m-dimensional since $r(\mathbf{A}) = m$ (or the rank of the matrix including the artificial vectors is m). We saw that a feasible solution to $\mathbf{Ax} = \mathbf{b}$ will exist if and only if $\mathbf{b}$ is an element of the polyhedral cone generated by the $\mathbf{a}_j$.

[A slightly different interpretation can be given to this necessary and sufficient condition for the existence of a feasible solution, i.e., the $\mathbf{a}_j$ can be thought of as generating a convex polyhedron P also. This polyhedron is the set of points $\mathbf{A\mu}$ for all μ such that $\mathbf{1\mu} = 1$, $\mu \geq \mathbf{0}$. Suppose that

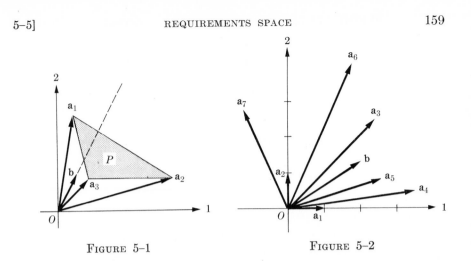

FIGURE 5–1   FIGURE 5–2

there is a feasible solution $\mathbf{x}$ to $\mathbf{Ax} = \mathbf{b}$. Divide by $\mathbf{1x}$ and write $\boldsymbol{\mu} = \mathbf{x}/\mathbf{1x}$. Then $\mathbf{1}\boldsymbol{\mu} = 1$, $\boldsymbol{\mu} \geq \mathbf{0}$, and $\mathbf{A}\boldsymbol{\mu} = \mathbf{b}/\mathbf{1x}$. Now $\mathbf{b}/\mathbf{1x}$ is a point on the half-line generated by $\mathbf{b}$. Therefore we can say that there will be a feasible solution to $\mathbf{Ax} = \mathbf{b}$ if and only if at least one point on the half-line generated by $\mathbf{b}$ is an element of the convex polyhedron generated by the $\mathbf{a}_j$ (see Fig. 5–1).]

Given any set of m linearly independent vectors from $\mathbf{A}$, these vectors also generate a convex polyhedral cone C_B of dimension m. Furthermore, $C_B \subset C$. If the vectors which generate C_B yield a feasible solution to $\mathbf{Ax} = \mathbf{b}$, then $\mathbf{b} \in C_B$. Now consider what is done in the simplex method. The basis vectors span an m-dimensional cone C_B. At the next iteration, one of the vectors is removed and replaced by another vector. This gives a new m-dimensional polyhedral cone $C_{\hat{B}}$. However, $\mathbf{b} \in C_{\hat{B}}$ because the new basic solution is feasible. Thus in the simplex method, we move from one m-dimensional polyhedral cone in the requirements space to another in such a way that $\mathbf{b}$ is an element of each of these cones.

Let us examine a specific example to get a geometric feeling for what happens in the simplex method. Suppose that the constraint equations are

$$\sum_{j=1}^{7} x_j \mathbf{a}_j = \mathbf{b}, \tag{5–7}$$

where the vectors $\mathbf{a}_j$, $\mathbf{b}$ are plotted in Fig. 5–2.

In the simplex method, we always start out with an identity matrix as the basis, and therefore the initial basis of our example will contain $\mathbf{a}_1$, $\mathbf{a}_2$. The convex cone spanned by these vectors is the non-negative orthant. Since $\mathbf{b} \geq \mathbf{0}$, this initial basis will always give a feasible solution, that is, $\mathbf{b}$ will always be an element of the cone spanned by the unit vectors. Assume that, at the first iteration, $\mathbf{a}_6$ is inserted into the basis. We see

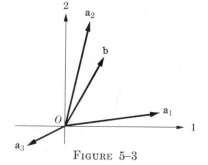

FIGURE 5–3

that we cannot remove $\mathbf{a}_1$ while still maintaining a feasible solution. Thus $\mathbf{a}_2$ must be removed. The polyhedral cone spanned by $\mathbf{a}_1$, $\mathbf{a}_6$ does contain $\mathbf{b}$, and hence the new solution will be feasible. If $\mathbf{a}_5$ is inserted next, $\mathbf{a}_1$ must be removed because the cone spanned by $\mathbf{a}_1$, $\mathbf{a}_5$ does not contain $\mathbf{b}$. However, $\mathbf{b}$ is in the cone spanned by $\mathbf{a}_5$, $\mathbf{a}_6$, etc.

It will be recalled that the solution to a linear programming problem is unbounded if for some vector $\mathbf{a}_j$, $z_j - c_j < 0$, and $y_{ij} \leq 0$ for all i. This can be illustrated geometrically in the requirements space, as shown in Fig. 5–3. Note that $\mathbf{a}_3$ can be written

$$\mathbf{a}_3 = -\alpha_1\mathbf{a}_1 - \alpha_2\mathbf{a}_2, \qquad \alpha_1, \alpha_2 > 0.$$

However, $\mathbf{b}$ can be written

$$x_1\mathbf{a}_1 + x_2\mathbf{a}_2 = \mathbf{b}, \qquad x_1, x_2 > 0.$$

Adding and subtracting $\theta\mathbf{a}_3$, we find

$$(x_1 + \theta\alpha_1)\mathbf{a}_1 + (x_2 + \theta\alpha_2)\mathbf{a}_2 + \theta\mathbf{a}_3 = \mathbf{b},$$

and the solution will be feasible for any $\theta > 0$. If $z_3 - c_3 < 0$, then z can be made arbitrarily large, and an unbounded solution exists.

The idea of the requirements space can be generalized somewhat to yield a more complete geometric interpretation of the simplex method. To each vector $\mathbf{a}_j$ and $\mathbf{b}$, we shall add an $(m + 1)$-component. These new vectors will be denoted by $\mathbf{a}_j^*$ and $\mathbf{b}^*$; they are defined by

$$\mathbf{a}_j^* = [\mathbf{a}_j, c_j]; \qquad \mathbf{b}^* = [\mathbf{b}, z]. \tag{5–8}$$

We note that for any feasible solution to $\mathbf{Ax} = \mathbf{b}$,

$$\sum x_j\mathbf{a}_j^* = \mathbf{b}^*. \tag{5–9}$$

Now we can think of the $\mathbf{a}_j^*$ as generating a convex polyhedral cone in a space of dimension $m + 1$, which we shall call the "extended requirements space." Consider a set of m basis vectors $\mathbf{b}_1, \ldots, \mathbf{b}_m$ which yields a feasible solution to $\mathbf{Ax} = \mathbf{b}$. We can define

$$\mathbf{b}_i^* = [\mathbf{b}_i, c_{Bi}]; \tag{5–10}$$

then

$$\sum_{i=1}^m x_{Bi} \mathbf{b}_i^* = \mathbf{b}^*.$$

Also note that

$$[\mathbf{a}_j, z_j] = \sum y_{ij} \mathbf{b}_i^*. \tag{5–11}$$

It should be observed that $[\mathbf{a}_j, c_j]$ will not be a linear combination of the $\mathbf{b}_i^*$ unless $z_j - c_j = 0$. Thus if $\mathbf{a}_j^*$ is not one of the $\mathbf{b}_i^*$ and $z_j - c_j \neq 0$, $\mathbf{a}_j^*$ will be linearly independent of the $\mathbf{b}_i^*$ in the extended requirements space.

In the simplex method, we are searching for a set of m, $\mathbf{b}_i^*$ which will yield a feasible solution and maximize the value of the last component of $\mathbf{b}^*$. The basis vectors $\mathbf{b}_i^*$ generate a polyhedral cone of dimension m in E^{m+1}, and therefore they lie on a hyperplane passing through the origin. The point $\mathbf{b}^*$ lies on a line through $\mathbf{b}$ which is parallel to the z-axis. The intersection of this line with the hyperplane spanned by the $\mathbf{b}_i^*$ determines the actual $\mathbf{b}^*$ for the given basic feasible solution, that is, it determines z. If we have a set of $\mathbf{b}_i$ such that the $\mathbf{b}_i$ yield a feasible solution, and if there is an $\mathbf{a}_k$ with $z_k - c_k < 0$, then $\mathbf{a}_k^*$ is linearly independent of the $\mathbf{b}_i^*$, and the $m + 1$ vectors, $\mathbf{b}_i^*$ ($i = 1, \ldots, m$) and $\mathbf{a}_k^*$ span an $(m + 1)$-dimensional cone in the extended requirements space. Furthermore, the m-dimensional cone spanned by the $\mathbf{b}_i^*$ is a face of the $(m + 1)$-dimensional cone spanned by the $\mathbf{b}_i^*$ ($i = 1, \ldots, m$) and $\mathbf{a}_k^*$. This follows immediately because if $\mathbf{vb}_i^* = 0$ ($i = 1, \ldots, m$), then the proper choice of $\mathbf{v}$ will yield $\mathbf{va}_k^* > 0$ since $\mathbf{a}_k^*$ is linearly independent of the $\mathbf{b}_i^*$. Any point $\mathbf{w}$ in the cone spanned by the $\mathbf{b}_i^*$ and $\mathbf{a}_k^*$ satisfies $\mathbf{vw} \geq 0$ since $\mathbf{w}$ can be written $\mathbf{w} = \sum_{i=1}^m \lambda_i \mathbf{b}_i^* + \lambda_{m+1} \mathbf{a}_k^*$, $\lambda_i \geq 0$ ($i = 1, \ldots, m + 1$). Thus the hyperplane spanned by the $\mathbf{b}_i^*$ is an extreme supporting hyperplane for the cone spanned by the $\mathbf{b}_i^*$ and $\mathbf{a}_k^*$.

Because of (5–11) the vector $[\mathbf{a}_k, z_k]$ lies in the hyperplane spanned by the $\mathbf{b}_i^*$. Intuitively, it is merely the projection of $\mathbf{a}_k^*$ parallel to the c_k-axis onto this hyperplane. When $\mathbf{a}_k$ replaces $\mathbf{b}_r$ to yield a new basis, then the new set of $\mathbf{b}_i^*$ also generates an m-dimensional polyhedral cone which is a face of the cone spanned by the original set of $\mathbf{b}_i^*$ and $\mathbf{a}_k$. In general, however, the intersection of the line through $\mathbf{b}$ parallel to the z-axis with the new face will be higher up the z-axis than the intersection of the same line with the preceding face.

The above argument is best illustrated by means of an example. Assume $\mathbf{b}_1, \mathbf{b}_2$ compose the current basic feasible solution to some linear program-

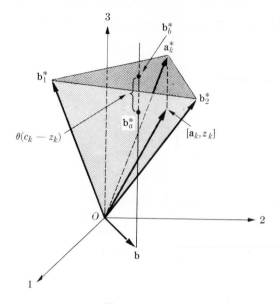

FIGURE 5–4

ming problem and assume that there exists a vector $\mathbf{a}_k$ with $z_k - c_k < 0$. The cone spanned by $\mathbf{b}_1^*$, $\mathbf{b}_2^*$, $\mathbf{a}_k^*$ is shown in Fig. 5–4. The vectors $\mathbf{b}_1^*$, $\mathbf{b}_2^*$ generate one face of this cone. The line through $\mathbf{b}$ intersects this face at $\mathbf{b}_a^*$ and hence determines the value of the objective function z_a for this basic solution. When $\mathbf{a}_k$ is inserted into the basis, $\mathbf{b}_2$ must be removed. The vectors $\mathbf{b}_1^*$, $\mathbf{a}_k^*$ also generate a face of the cone, and the intersection of the line through $\mathbf{b}$ with this face yields $\mathbf{b}_b^*$ with $z_b > z_a$.

The preceding discussion is a generalization of an early geometric interpretation which gave the simplex method its name. If one of the m constraints is $\sum x_j = 1$, and if this constraint is removed and treated separately, then the $\mathbf{a}_j^*$ become m-component vectors. Thus the set of all convex combinations of the $\mathbf{b}_i^*$ $(i = 1, \ldots, m)$ and $\mathbf{a}_k^*$ form a simplex in E^m. One face of the simplex is generated by all convex combinations of the $\mathbf{b}_i^*$. When $z_k - c_k < 0$, all points in the simplex lie on or above this face. The line through $\mathbf{b}$ parallel to the z-axis intersects this face of the simplex in $\mathbf{b}_a^*$, with the objective function given by z_a. When $\mathbf{a}_k$ replaces $\mathbf{b}_r$, the new set of $\mathbf{b}_i^*$ generates a face of the simplex, and the intersection of the line through $\mathbf{b}$ with this face yields $\mathbf{b}_b^*$ with $z_b \geq z_a$. The introduction of convex polyhedral cones instead of polyhedra allows the removal of the restriction $\sum x_j = 1$ from the geometric interpretation.

5–6 Solutions space. The convex set of feasible solutions to the constraints $\mathbf{Ax} = \mathbf{b}$ for the general linear programming problem lies in an

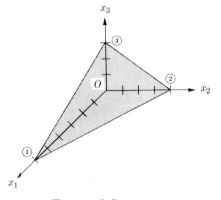

FIGURE 5–5

n-dimensional euclidean space which has been named the solutions space. We have proved that an extreme point of this convex set is a basic feasible solution to $\mathbf{Ax} = \mathbf{b}$, and hence at least $n - m$ of the components of an extreme point are zero. The extreme points of this convex set have the property of lying in the intersection of $n - m$ hyperplanes of the form $\mathbf{e}_j'\mathbf{x} = 0 = x_j$. In Chapter 1, we saw that in E^2 and E^3 it is very easy to represent the intersection of two or more half-spaces as a convex region. However, it is not nearly so simple to provide a geometric representation in E^2 or E^3 of the feasible solutions to the constraints when these are converted to a set of simultaneous equations. For example, if we start out with two inequalities in two variables and add a slack or surplus variable to each, we already have a four-dimensional space. We shall now illustrate the only two cases of interest which can be exhibited in E^3.

(1) The most elementary three-dimensional example is that of a single constraint equation in three variables, e.g.,

$$2x_1 + 3x_2 + 4x_3 = 12, \qquad x_1,\, x_2,\, x_3 \geq 0.$$

This equation is plotted in Fig. 5–5. The convex set of feasible solutions is planar, and the extreme points 1, 2, 3 lie on the coordinate axes and, as expected, have only one variable different from zero.

(2) In the remaining case, the solutions lie on a line (the case of a unique solution is not of any interest). An example of such a case is

$$x_1 + x_2 = 6, \qquad 2x_1 + 3x_2 \leq 30, \qquad x_1,\, x_2 \geq 0.$$

After adding a slack variable, we obtain

$$x_1 + x_2 = 6, \qquad 2x_1 + 3x_2 + x_3 = 30, \qquad x_1,\, x_2,\, x_3 \geq 0.$$

The set of solutions is the set of points lying in the intersection of these

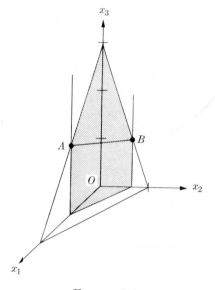

FIGURE 5–6

two planes and in the non-negative orthant. The convex set of feasible solutions is therefore the line AB shown in Fig. 5–6. The extreme points are A, B. They lie in the coordinate planes and have only two nonzero variables.

In the general case, $\mathbf{Ax} = \mathbf{b}$, $\mathbf{x} \geq \mathbf{0}$, $r(\mathbf{A}) = m$, where $\mathbf{A}$ is $m \times n$ and $n > m$. Hence we know (Chapter 2) that the solutions lie in an affine subspace of dimension $n - m$ in E^n. (The convex set of feasible solutions lies in this affine subspace.)

Given a set of basis vectors $\mathbf{b}_1, \ldots, \mathbf{b}_m$ which yield a basic feasible solution, and some other vector $\mathbf{a}_k$ from $\mathbf{A}$, then the set of feasible solutions to $\mathbf{Ax} = \mathbf{b}$ of the form (see Problem 3–16)

$$\sum_{i=1}^{m} (x_{Bi} - \theta y_{ik})\mathbf{b}_i + \theta \mathbf{a}_k = \mathbf{b}, \qquad \theta \geq 0, \qquad (5\text{--}12)$$

forms a one-dimensional space, i.e., a line in E^n. When $\theta = 0$, we are at one extreme point of the convex set of feasible solutions. If one or more $y_{ik} > 0$, then θ cannot be made arbitrarily large if the solution is to remain feasible. The largest value of θ is that which drives one or more $x_{Bi} - \theta y_{ik}$ to zero, that is,

$$\theta_{\max} = \min_{i} \left\{ \frac{x_{Bi}}{y_{ik}}, y_{ik} > 0 \right\} = \frac{x_{Br}}{y_{rk}}. \qquad (5\text{--}13)$$

This criterion for determining $\theta_{\max}$ is, of course, the familiar criterion used in the simplex method to determine the vector to be removed. If $\theta_{\max} > 0$, then (5–12) is not a basic feasible solution unless $\theta = \theta_{max}$ or 0. For $0 < \theta < \theta_{max}$, $m + 1$ variables can be different from zero. Consequently, the set of feasible solutions (5–12) is a line in E^n which begins at the extreme point defined by the basis $\mathbf{b}_1, \ldots, \mathbf{b}_m$ and ends at the extreme point defined by the basis $\hat{\mathbf{b}}_1, \ldots, \hat{\mathbf{b}}_m$; $\hat{\mathbf{b}}_i = \mathbf{b}_i$, $i \neq r$, $\hat{\mathbf{b}}_r = \mathbf{a}_k$.

Let us show that if $\theta_{max} > 0$, the line defined by (5–12) which joins one extreme point to the extreme point corresponding to a new basic feasible solution in which one vector in the basis is changed is an edge of the convex set. This in turn will demonstrate that in moving from one tableau of the simplex method to the next, we move from one extreme point to an *adjacent* extreme point if $\theta_{max} > 0$, since two extreme points are adjacent if the line joining them is an edge of the set (see Chapter 2).

To prove that the set of points in (5–12) is an edge of the convex set, we must show that it is the intersection of the convex set of feasible solutions with a supporting hyperplane. If we assume that $n - m > 1$, then $n - m - 1$ of the x_j will be zero for any feasible solution represented by (5–12). Consider the hyperplane in E^n,

$$\sum_{n-m-1} x_j = 0, \tag{5–14}$$

the summation being taken over the $n - m - 1$ variables x_j mentioned above. Note that the basic feasible solution corresponding to $\mathbf{b}_1, \ldots, \mathbf{b}_m$ lies on this hyperplane as does the feasible solution corresponding to $\hat{\mathbf{b}}_1, \ldots, \hat{\mathbf{b}}_m$. Furthermore, because the variables are non-negative, we must have for any feasible solution

$$\sum_{n-m-1} x_j \geq 0. \tag{5–15}$$

Therefore the hyperplane (5–14) is indeed a supporting hyperplane to the convex set of feasible solutions. If none of the variables whose coefficient is 1 in (5–14) is >0, then the feasible solutions are given by (5–12). Each of these solutions lies on the hyperplane (5–14) because, in (5–14), the coefficient of any nonzero variable is zero. If a feasible solution is not contained in (5–12), then one of the variables whose coefficient is 1 in (5–14) must be >0. However, this solution must lie in the half-space

$$\sum_{n-m-1} x_j > 0, $$

and not on the hyperplane. Thus when θ varies between 0 and θ_{max}, the intersection of the convex set of feasible solutions with the hyperplane (5–14) is the set of points (5–12). Hence, the line joining the two extreme points is an edge of the convex set, and the two extreme points are adjacent.

In the event that $n - m = 1$, there are at most two distinct extreme points, and they are automatically adjacent since the line joining them is the entire convex set of feasible solutions.

The above paragraphs have demonstrated that two basic feasible solutions which differ from each other only in that one basic vector has been changed to convert one solution to the other, are either adjacent extreme points or the two solutions are degenerate and are merely different representations of the same extreme point. Hence, when we move from one tableau of the simplex method to the next, we either remain at the same extreme point ($\theta_{max} = 0$) or move to an adjacent extreme point ($\theta_{max} > 0$).

If in (5–12) $y_{ik} \leq 0$ for all i, then (5–12) is a feasible solution for any $\theta \geq 0$. In this case, we can also show that the set of feasible solutions (5–12) is an edge of the convex set. The proof is merely a reproduction of the above development. However, the edge does not lead to another extreme point, because θ can be made arbitrarily large without driving any variable to a negative value. The edge goes out to infinity instead. Since either all $y_{ik} \leq 0$ or at least one $y_{ik} > 0$, we see that an edge emanating from a given extreme point either leads to another extreme point or extends to infinity.

Finally, we wish to note that the matrix $\mathbf{A} = (\mathbf{a}_1, \ldots, \mathbf{a}_n)$ performs a linear transformation on the n-dimensional solutions space and takes it into the m-dimensional requirements space. In particular, the convex set of feasible solutions in the solutions space is taken into the single point $\mathbf{b}$ in the requirements space.

5–7 Determination of all optimal solutions. We have shown that if k different basic feasible solutions to a linear programming problem are optimal, any convex combination of these basic solutions is also an optimal solution. The simplex procedure, as we have discussed it, stops once an optimal basic feasible solution has been obtained. It is seldom that any effort is made to find alternative optima. In fact, most computer codes supply a single optimum and make no provision for determining other optimal basic feasible solutions (if there are any). Sometimes, useful information can be obtained from the knowledge of all optimal basic feasible solutions. Hence, it is desirable to show how they can be found. However, there should be no economic reason for preferring one optimal basic feasible solution to another since all optimal solutions should be equally good. If this is not the case, then incorrect prices were assigned to the activity vectors during the formulation of the problem.

The final simplex tableau is the starting point for finding all other optimal basic solutions which may exist. If the optimal solution represented by the last tableau is not degenerate, and if $z_j - c_j > 0$ for each $\mathbf{a}_j$ not in the basis, then the optimal basic feasible solution is unique. No vector can be inserted into the basis without decreasing the value of the objective function.

When $z_j - c_j = 0$ for one or more $\mathbf{a}_j$ not in the basis, any such vector $\mathbf{a}_j$ can be inserted to yield a different optimal solution if $y_{ij} > 0$ for at least one i and min (x_{Bi}/y_{ij}), $y_{ij} > 0$, is positive. If $\mathbf{a}_j$ enters at a zero level, we do not obtain a different solution; the result is only a different representation of the same degenerate extreme point. If $y_{ij} \leq 0$ for all i, then $\mathbf{a}_j$ can be inserted to give a set of optimal solutions containing at least two variables which can be made arbitrarily large. It is also true that if the optimal solution is degenerate, then any vector $\mathbf{a}_j$ for which $y_{ij} \neq 0$ for any i corresponding to an $x_{Bi} = 0$ can be inserted into the basis, and a new representation of the same degenerate extreme point will be obtained. This can be done even if $z_j - c_j > 0$ since $\mathbf{a}_j$ enters at a zero level.

The above paragraph suggests the procedure for finding all optimal basic feasible solutions. Starting from the final tableau, which contains an optimal solution to the problem, we construct a new set of tableaux, each new tableau differing from the final tableau only in that one vector in the basis is changed. For insertion into the basis, we consider the vectors $\mathbf{a}_j$ with $z_j - c_j = 0$ or vectors which can enter at a zero level (even if $z_j - c_j > 0$). If $\mathbf{a}_j$ enters at a positive level, we obtain an alternative optimal basic solution. When $\mathbf{a}_j$ enters at a zero level, we do not obtain a different solution. However, we construct these tableaux anyway, because in the subsequent steps they may lead to new optimal basic solutions.

We repeat the same procedure with each of the new tableaux, and obtain some other optimal solutions which may or may not be optimal solutions different from those obtained in the first step. This is continued with each set of new tableaux until it is no longer possible to find any optimal basic solutions different from those already obtained. It is desirable to keep a record of all optimal basic solutions to prevent the computation of new tableaux which only yield an optimal solution that has already been determined. In schematic form, the process is represented by a treelike structure, as shown for a hypothetical case in Fig. 5–7. The basic solutions corresponding to different extreme points have different letters, and different degenerate basic solutions corresponding to the same extreme point have different subscripts on the letters. In our example, there are six

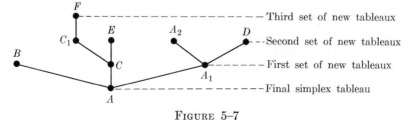

FIGURE 5–7

different optimal basic solutions (different extreme points) A, B, C, D, E, F. After constructing a sufficient number of tableaux, we only repeat solutions already obtained.

Clearly, if a fair number of optimal solutions exists, a good deal of work could be involved in determining all of them, since each change of basis requires the computation of a whole new tableau.

If desired, the second best and third best, etc., solutions to the problem can be found. To find the second best solution, for example, compute

$$\min_{j} \frac{x_{Br}}{y_{rj}} (z_j - c_j), \qquad z_j - c_j > 0, \qquad y_{rj} > 0, \qquad x_{Br} > 0. \quad (5\text{–}16)$$

This minimum is determined for each optimal tableau. Then the minimum of all these minima is found in order to obtain the smallest possible decrease in z.

Let us now consider the problem whose final tableau is given in Table 4–10. To the accuracy of the computations (and this is really all that can ever be said in numerical calculations where only a fixed number of digits is retained) there is a vector $\mathbf{a}_7$ (not in the basis) with $z_7 - c_7 = 0$. Thus the optimal solution is not unique. We know that there is one other basis that will yield the same optimal value of the objective function. Indeed, we can see immediately that there are only two basic optimal solutions. This follows since, after a vector with $z_k - c_k = 0$ has been inserted into the basis, $\hat{z}_j - c_j = z_j - c_j$, and the $(z_j - c_j)$-row in the new tableau with $\mathbf{a}_7$ in the basis will be the same as in Table 4–10. There is no vector other than $\mathbf{a}_7$ with $z_j - c_j = 0$. Furthermore, the optimal solutions are not degenerate, and hence a vector with $z_j - c_j > 0$ cannot be inserted.

We can easily compute the new optimal basic solution. Note that $\mathbf{a}_7$ replaces $\mathbf{a}_1$. Hence

$$x_{B1} = 16.91 - \frac{0.2727}{0.1818} (7.273) = 6.00 = x_6,$$

$$x_{B2} = \frac{7.273}{0.1818} = 40.0 = x_7,$$

$$x_{B3} = 6.364 + \frac{0.09091}{0.1818} (7.273) = 10.0 = x_3.$$

Of course, any convex combination of these two basic optimal solutions will also be an optimal solution.

5–8 Unrestricted variables. Thus far our discussion of linear programming has always been based on the assumption that the variables x_j are restricted to be non-negative. On occasions, one encounters problems of the linear programming type in which some or all of the variables can have any sign. Variables which can be positive, negative, or zero are called unrestricted variables. We wish to solve linear programming problems containing unrestricted variables. This can be done very easily by converting the problem to one having non-negative variables. Then the simplex method can be used without alteration.

Suppose that in a given problem the variable x_j is unrestricted in sign. Let us then write this variable as

$$x_j = x_j' - x_j'', \qquad x_j', x_j'' \geq 0. \tag{5–17}$$

The variable x_j has been written as the difference of two non-negative variables x_j' and x_j''. If $x_j' > x_j''$, then $x_j > 0$, and if $x_j' < x_j''$, it follows that $x_j < 0$. Also, if $x_j' = x_j''$, then $x_j = 0$. Hence, depending on the magnitudes of x_j' and x_j'', x_j can have any sign.

By replacing a single unrestricted variable by two non-negative variables, any linear programming problem involving unrestricted variables can be transformed into another linear programming problem involving only non-negative variables. If $\mathbf{a}_j$ is the activity vector corresponding to x_j in the original problem, the new problem contains

$$\mathbf{a}_j(x_j' - x_j'') = \mathbf{a}_j x_j' + (-\mathbf{a}_j)x_j'',$$

where the activity vector $\mathbf{a}_j$ corresponds to x_j', and the activity vector $-\mathbf{a}_j$ corresponds to x_j''. Similarly, the prices c_j and $-c_j$ correspond to x_j' and x_j'', respectively.

We can now make an important observation. Any basic feasible solution with non-negative variables cannot have x_j' and x_j'' in the basic solution. If both variables could be different from zero, then $\mathbf{a}_j$ and $-\mathbf{a}_j$ would be in the basis. However, $\mathbf{a}_j$, $-\mathbf{a}_j$ are not linearly independent, and no basis can contain both of them. Thus in any optimal basic solution, either $x_j'' = 0$ and $x_j = x_j'$, or $x_j' = 0$ and $x_j = -x_j''$, or $x_j' = x_j'' = 0$ and $x_j = 0$. This demonstrates that the value of x_j uniquely determines the values of x_j', x_j''. If $x_j' > 0$, then $x_j'' = 0$ and vice versa.

EXAMPLE: Consider the following linear programming problem:

$$x_1\mathbf{a}_1 + x_2\mathbf{a}_2 + x_3\mathbf{a}_3 = \mathbf{b}, \qquad \max z = 3x_1 + 2x_2 + x_3;$$

$$\mathbf{a}_1 = [2, 3], \qquad \mathbf{a}_2 = [5, 4], \qquad \mathbf{a}_3 = [1, 0], \qquad \mathbf{b} = [12, 11].$$

Assume that x_1 is unrestricted in sign. We write $x_1 = x_1' - x_1''$. The column vector corresponding to x_1' is $\mathbf{a}_1$, and that corresponding to x_1'' is $-\mathbf{a}_1$; the price of x_1' is 3 and that of x_1'' is -3. In terms of non-negative variables, the new problem is

$$x_1'\mathbf{a}_1 + (-\mathbf{a}_1)x_1'' + x_2\mathbf{a}_2 + x_3\mathbf{a}_3 = \mathbf{b}, \qquad x_1', x_1'', x_2, x_3 \geq 0,$$

$$\max z = 3x_1' - 3x_1'' + 2x_2 + x_3.$$

This is a new linear programming problem in one additional variable. If we write $x_1' = y_1$, $x_1'' = y_2$, $x_2 = y_3$, $x_3 = y_4$, then the linear programming problem to which we apply the simplex method is

$$y_1 \begin{bmatrix} 2 \\ 3 \end{bmatrix} + y_2 \begin{bmatrix} -2 \\ -3 \end{bmatrix} + y_3 \begin{bmatrix} 5 \\ 4 \end{bmatrix} + y_4 \begin{bmatrix} 1 \\ 0 \end{bmatrix} = \begin{bmatrix} 12 \\ 11 \end{bmatrix}, \quad y_j \geq 0, \quad j = 1, \dots, 4,$$

$$\max z = 3y_1 - 3y_2 + 2y_3 + y_4.$$

REFERENCES

The references listed at the end of Chapter 3 apply also to this chapter.

PROBLEMS

5–1. Using the two-phase method, solve the following linear programming problem:

$$3x_1 + 4x_2 + 5x_3 + x_4 + x_5 + x_6 = 8,$$
$$x_1 + 3x_2 + 2x_3 + 5x_4 + 2x_5 + x_6 = 3,$$
$$2.5x_1 + 5x_2 + 4.5x_3 + 5.5x_4 + 2.5x_5 + 4x_6 = 7,$$
$$\text{all } x_j \geq 0,$$
$$\max z = x_1 + 3x_2 + 2x_3 + 5x_4 + x_5 + 6x.$$

5–2. Solve the following problem by the simplex method:

$$4x_1 - 5x_2 - 9x_3 + x_4 - 2x_5 \leq 6,$$
$$2x_1 + 3x_2 + 4x_3 - 5x_4 + x_5 \leq 9,$$
$$x_1 + x_2 - 5x_3 - 7x_4 + 11x_5 \leq 10,$$
$$\min z = 3x_1 + x_2 - 4x_3 + 5x_4 + 9x_5.$$

Assume that the variables x_3, x_5 are unrestricted in sign, while x_1, x_2, x_4 are non-negative.

5–3. We have shown in the text that if at some stage in the simplex computation, $y_{ij} = 0$ for all legitimate vectors $\mathbf{a}_j$ and for an i corresponding to a column of $\mathbf{B}$ that contains an artificial vector, then row i of the tableau can be crossed off, and the artificial vector will never be removed. Show that this is true even if a legitimate vector is in column i of $\mathbf{B}$. Note, however, that in this case redundancy is not implied.

5–4. Using the two-phase method or the $-M$ technique, show that if there is a tie between an artificial vector and a legitimate vector, it is always desirable to remove the artificial vector. Show that this can be done without any fear of cycling.

5–5. Show how to solve a set of n simultaneous linear equations in n unknowns by means of the simplex method. Hint: Note that the variables are unrestricted in sign. Maximize $z = -1x_a$, where x_a is the vector containing artificial variables. How does the simplex method indicate that the matrix of the coefficients is singular? What happens when there is no solution?

5–6. Using the procedure developed in Problem 5–5, solve the following set of simultaneous linear equations by the simplex method:

$$3x_1 + 2x_2 = 5,$$
$$5x_1 + x_2 = 9.$$

5–7. Solve the following set of simultaneous equations by means of the simplex method:

$$5x_1 + 3x_2 + x_3 = 2,$$
$$4x_1 - x_2 + 6x_3 = 0,$$
$$9x_1 + 7x_2 + 4x_3 = 1.$$

5–8. Show how to invert a matrix by means of the simplex method. Hint: One can use any non-null vector for $\mathbf{b}$. Why? What happens if the matrix is singular?

5–9. Using the simplex method, invert the matrix

$$\mathbf{A} = \begin{bmatrix} 4 & 1 \\ 2 & 9 \end{bmatrix}.$$

5–10. Using the simplex method, invert the matrix

$$\mathbf{A} = \begin{bmatrix} 5 & 1 & 7 \\ 3 & 4 & 8 \\ 2 & 6 & 8 \end{bmatrix}.$$

5–11. Consider a linear programming problem of the form $\mathbf{Ax} = \mathbf{b}$, $\mathbf{x} \geq \mathbf{d} \geq 0$, max $z = \mathbf{cx}$. Instead of non-negativity restrictions, we now have lower bounds d_j on each variable that can be positive. Show how to treat these lower bounds without explicitly including them as constraints, i.e., show how to convert the above problem to $\mathbf{Fy} = \mathbf{f}$, $\mathbf{y} \geq 0$, max $\mathbf{gy}$, where $\mathbf{F}$ is $m \times n$ if $\mathbf{A}$ is $m \times n$. Use this procedure to solve the following linear programming problem:

$$2x_1 + 3x_2 - x_3 + 4x_4 \leq 40,$$
$$-2x_1 + 2x_2 + 5x_3 - x_4 \leq 35,$$
$$x_1 + x_2 - 2x_3 + 3x_4 \leq 100,$$
$$x_1 \geq 2, \, x_2 \geq 1, \, x_3 \geq 3, \, x_4 \geq 4,$$
$$\text{max } z = 3x_1 + x_2 + 2x_3 + 7x_4.$$

5–12. Show how the simplex method can be used to solve a problem of the following type:

$$\mathbf{Ax} = \mathbf{b}, \qquad \max z = \sum c_j |x_j|.$$

The variables x_j are unrestricted, and $|x_j|$ is the absolute value of x_j. Show that the same technique can be used if the cost corresponding to a negative x_j is different from that corresponding to a positive x_j. The activity vector for x_j remains, of course, the same, regardless of whether x_j is positive or negative.

5–13. Illustrate degeneracy in the extended requirements space. Show how it is possible to have $z_j - c_j < 0$ with one or more $y_{ij} > 0$, while z remains unchanged when $\mathbf{a}_j$ is inserted into the basis.

5–14. Suppose that we are given the following tableau for some linear programming problem:

c_B	c_j Vectors in Basis	$\mathbf{b}$	1 $\mathbf{a}_1$	4 $\mathbf{a}_2$	2 $\mathbf{a}_3$	5 $\mathbf{a}_4$	19 $\mathbf{a}_5$	1 $\mathbf{a}_6$	5 $\mathbf{a}_7$	3 $\mathbf{a}_8$
1	$\mathbf{a}_1$	2	1	0	0	0	1	0	1	2
4	$\mathbf{a}_2$	3	0	1	0	0	2	−3	1	0
2	$\mathbf{a}_3$	0	0	0	1	0	0	2	0	0
5	$\mathbf{a}_4$	1	0	0	0	1	2	2	0	2
	$z_j - c_j$	19	0	0	0	0	0	1	0	9

Find all alternative optimal basic solutions.

5–15. Find the second best and third best solutions to the problem described in Problem 5–14.

5–16. If the set of constraints $\mathbf{Ax} = \mathbf{b}$, $\mathbf{b} \geq \mathbf{0}$, to a linear programming problem was obtained by adding a surplus variable to each constraint, show that if $b_k = \max b_i$, and if $\hat{\mathbf{A}} = \|\hat{a}_{ij}\|$, $\hat{a}_{ij} = a_{kj} - a_{ij}$, $i \neq k$, $\hat{a}_{kj} = a_{kj}$, $\hat{\mathbf{b}} = [\hat{b}_1, \ldots, \hat{b}_m]$, $\hat{b}_i = b_k - b_i$, $i \neq k$, $\hat{b}_k = b_k$, then $\hat{\mathbf{A}}\mathbf{x} = \hat{\mathbf{b}}$, and only one artificial vector has to be used for the new system of constraints.

Show that the new problem is equivalent to the original one. If the number of surplus variables is large, the simple transformation suggested above can materially reduce the number of artificial variables, and this in turn might be expected to reduce the number of iterations. It is somewhat surprising that such techniques have not been used more frequently to decrease the number of artificial variables.

5–17. Interpret geometrically, in the requirements space, the criterion used in the simplex method to select the vector to leave the basis. In particular, give the interpretation for the example illustrated in Fig. 5–2.

5–18. For the examples presented in Tables 4–2 through 4–4 plot, in the extended requirements space, the convex cones for each change of basis. Also plot the convex cone generated by all four vectors and show how z finally reaches its maximum value.

5–19. Solve Problem 4–19 by means of the two-phase method.

5–20. Solve Problem 4–20 by means of the two-phase method.

CHAPTER 6

RESOLUTION OF THE DEGENERACY PROBLEM

"The strawberry grows underneath the nettle,
And wholesome berries thrive and ripen best
Neighbor'd by fruit of baser quality."

Shakespeare—Henry V.

6–1 Introduction. The general theory of the simplex method has shown that if any basic feasible, but not optimal solution to the set of constraints exists, and if degeneracy never appears, it is possible, by changing a single vector in the basis at a time, to reach an optimal solution (or an indication of an unbounded solution) in a finite number of steps. This follows because there is only a finite number of bases, and since at each step $\hat{z} > z$, no basis can be repeated. The step-by-step procedure terminates either when $y_{ij} \leq 0$, all i, for some $\mathbf{a}_j$ with $z_j - c_j < 0$, or when $z_j - c_j \geq 0$ for all $\mathbf{a}_j$. The first case indicates the existence of an unbounded solution, while the second implies that an optimal solution has been found.

We have seen that degeneracy introduces complications into the above arguments. When degeneracy is present, the objective function may not change when we move from one basic feasible solution to another. Then we can no longer be sure that no basis will be repeated. In fact, we may get into a situation where we cycle forever, repeating the same sequence of bases, and never reach an optimal solution. Furthermore, there may be no way of avoiding this. In the following sections we shall show that it is possible to move from any initial basic feasible solution to an optimal basic solution without repeating any basis, i.e., that cycling need never occur. Indeed, a computational procedure that avoids the possibility of cycling will be presented.

We have noted previously that once we have shown that a basis never need be repeated, it immediately follows that one of the basic solutions will be optimal and that one of the optimal basic solutions will have all $z_j - c_j \geq 0$. In this way, we prove by strictly algebraic means that one of the basic solutions is optimal even if degeneracy is present. Thus the theory is completely divorced from reliance on the geometric theory of convex sets.

As already indicated, cycling never seems to occur in actual practice, although degeneracy is a quite frequent phenomenon. Hence, from a practical point of view, we do not need to worry about degeneracy. Although $\hat{z} = z$ for a number of iterations, an optimal solution will be reached in a finite number of steps. Examples where cycling does take place have been constructed, although in a very artificial way. Conse-quently, it is possible for a problem to cycle, and for this reason, it is desirable to develop a procedure that will ensure that cycling will never occur. Two different approaches to the resolution of the degeneracy prob-lem have been developed. One is the perturbation method of Charnes [1, 2]. The other, developed by Dantzig, Orden, and Wolfe [4], is a scheme involv-ing lexicographically ordered vectors. We shall discuss both methods. On the surface, these techniques appear to be quite different; however, in practice, it turns out that they are operationally equivalent.

6–2 Charnes' perturbation method. We shall first discuss Charnes' perturbation method. All degeneracy problems arise from the nature of **b**. Degeneracy occurs because for some bases formed from the columns of **A** we do not need a positive amount of each basis vector $\mathbf{b}_i$ in order to write **b** as a linear combination of the $\mathbf{b}_i$. Now if **b** were altered very slightly (this is usually referred to as "perturbing" **b**), then, when writing **b** as a linear combination of the basis vectors, we might hope that the perturbed value of **b** would require positive amounts of each basis vector for every feasible basis. This can be done, and it is exactly the technique which will be used to resolve the degeneracy problem.

Instead of considering only the problem to be solved, we shall examine an associated set of problems whose requirements vectors, denoted by $\mathbf{b}(\epsilon)$, will differ slightly from the **b** of the original problem. When the perturba-tion is zero, this associated set of problems will include the original problem to be solved. We shall show that perturbed problems never become de-generate and that therefore no basis is ever repeated. The entire theory which we developed with the assumption that degeneracy does not appear can then be applied to the perturbed problem. Once the solutions to the set of perturbed problems have been found, it will be seen that the solution to the original problem is immediately available. We are therefore im-bedding the problem of interest into a whole set of related problems.

Suppose that we replace the $\mathbf{b} \geq \mathbf{0}$ of our problem by

$$\mathbf{b}(\epsilon) = \mathbf{b} + \sum_{j=1}^{n} \epsilon^j \mathbf{a}_j + \sum_{i=1}^{s} \epsilon^{n+i} \mathbf{q}_i. \qquad (6\text{–}1)$$

We have added to **b** a polynomial in the number ϵ, with vector coefficients involving the other vectors in **A** and any artificial vectors needed in the original problem. The number ϵ will be taken to be positive and usually very small. A certain maximum allowable value of ϵ, denoted by $\epsilon_{\max}$, is determined by the nature of the problem and is positive. It will never be necessary to compute $\epsilon_{\max}$ explicitly. However, the assumption will always be made that $\epsilon < \epsilon_{\max}$. We can then think of ϵ as a variable whose region of variation is $0 \leq \epsilon < \epsilon_{\max}$. When $\epsilon = 0$, $\mathbf{b}(\epsilon) = \mathbf{b}$, and we are reduced to the actual problem of interest. In (6–1) ϵ^j simply means ϵ raised to the jth power. If, for example, $\mathbf{A}$ contained three vectors $\mathbf{a}_1, \mathbf{a}_2, \mathbf{a}_3$ and no artificial vectors were needed, $\mathbf{b}$ would be replaced by

$$\mathbf{b}(\epsilon) = \mathbf{b} + \epsilon \mathbf{a}_1 + \epsilon^2 \mathbf{a}_2 + \epsilon^3 \mathbf{a}_3.$$

It makes no difference which vector from $\mathbf{A}$ is chosen as $\mathbf{a}_1$, the coefficient of ϵ. Later, however, we shall find it quite desirable to have the vectors which make up the initial identity matrix correspond to the lowest powers of ϵ. When $\epsilon > 0$ and very small, then $\mathbf{b}(\epsilon)$ will differ only slightly from $\mathbf{b}$. Any problem with $\mathbf{b}(\epsilon)$ for any ϵ, $0 < \epsilon < \epsilon_{\max}$, as its requirements vector will be referred to as a perturbed problem.

Consider any basic feasible solution to the problem of interest. It can be written

$$\sum_{i=1}^{m} x_{Bi} \mathbf{b}_i = \mathbf{b}. \tag{6–2}$$

Because of the possibility of degeneracy, one or more of the x_{Bi} may be zero. Let us see what the solution will be if the basis is retained and $\mathbf{b}$ is replaced by $\mathbf{b}(\epsilon)$. If this solution is denoted by $\mathbf{x}_B(\epsilon)$, it follows that

$$\mathbf{x}_B(\epsilon) = \mathbf{B}^{-1}\mathbf{b}(\epsilon) = \mathbf{B}^{-1}\mathbf{b} + \sum_{j=1}^{n} \epsilon^j \mathbf{B}^{-1}\mathbf{a}_j + \sum_{i=1}^{s} \epsilon^{n+i}\mathbf{B}^{-1}\mathbf{q}_i,$$

or

$$\mathbf{x}_B(\epsilon) = \mathbf{x}_B + \sum_{j=1}^{n+s} \epsilon^j \mathbf{y}_j. \tag{6–3}$$

If none of the x_{Bi} in (6–2) vanish, ϵ can be chosen small enough (since x_{Bi} is independent of ϵ) so that $\mathbf{x}_B(\epsilon) > \mathbf{0}$. On the other hand, if any x_{Bi} is zero, there may not be any $\epsilon > 0$ such that $\mathbf{x}_B(\epsilon) > \mathbf{0}$. This depends on the signs of the y_{ij}.

For the moment, we shall assume that we have a nondegenerate basic feasible solution to the perturbed problem, i.e., each of the basic variables is strictly positive. Later, we shall show how to find an initial basic feasible solution to the perturbed problem, with $\mathbf{x}_B(\epsilon) > \mathbf{0}$. It follows from (6–3) that the value of the objective function $z(\epsilon)$ for the solution $\mathbf{x}_B(\epsilon) > \mathbf{0}$ to the perturbed problem is

$$z(\epsilon) = \mathbf{c}_B \mathbf{x}_B(\epsilon) = \mathbf{c}_B \mathbf{x}_B + \sum_{j=1}^{n+s} \epsilon^j \mathbf{c}_B \mathbf{y}_j,$$

or

$$z(\epsilon) = z + \sum_{j=1}^{n+s} \epsilon^j z_j. \tag{6–4}$$

Note that only **b** is perturbed; the prices remain unchanged. The ϵ-terms appear only in $\mathbf{x}_B(\epsilon)$, not in the $\mathbf{y}_j$. Hence, the $z_j - c_j$ are the same for the perturbed problem and for the original problem.

Given a nondegenerate basic feasible solution to the perturbed problem, $\mathbf{x}_B(\epsilon) > 0, 0 < \epsilon < \epsilon_{\max}$, we shall show that if this solution is not optimal, then it is possible to apply the simplex method without any risk of degeneracy, so that at each iteration $\hat{z}(\epsilon) > z(\epsilon)$. After an optimal solution to the perturbed problem is obtained, we can set ϵ to zero to find an optimal solution to the actual problem. At this point, the reader may be concerned at the thought of trying to apply the simplex method to the perturbed problem and having to worry about all the powers of ϵ which appear. In practice, it will turn out that the cycling problem can be eliminated without ever using ϵ explicitly. Only the tableaux that are constructed to solve the actual problem are needed. The ϵ's are merely used to prove that the final operational procedure actually prevents cycling.

6–3 Selecting the vector to be removed. We are ready to change bases in the perturbed problem: The vector to enter the basis is computed in the usual way. If $\mathbf{a}_k$ is to enter the basis and all $y_{ik} \leq 0$, then there is an unbounded solution to the perturbed problem and to the actual problem (as we can see by setting $\epsilon = 0$). When one or more $y_{ik} > 0$, we must select the vector to leave the basis. As usual, this is done by finding

$$\frac{x_{Br}(\epsilon)}{y_{rk}} = \min_i \left\{ \frac{x_{Bi}(\epsilon)}{y_{ik}}, y_{ik} > 0 \right\} = \theta(\epsilon). \tag{6–5}$$

If degeneracy is not to appear at the next iteration, this minimum must be unique. We are sure $\theta(\epsilon) \neq 0$ because each $x_{Bi}(\epsilon) > 0$.

Let us show how the minimum in (6–5) is found. We can reformulate (6–5) to read

$$\frac{x_{Br}(\epsilon)}{y_{rk}} = \min_i \left\{ \frac{x_{Bi}}{y_{ik}} + \sum_{j=1}^{n+s} \epsilon^j \frac{y_{ij}}{y_{ik}}, y_{ik} > 0 \right\}. \tag{6–6}$$

It is important to note that when ϵ is small enough ($\epsilon < \epsilon_{\max}$), only the lowest powers of ϵ are important in (6–6). This implies that if $\min_i (x_{Bi}/y_{ik})$ is unique and is taken on at $i = r$, then for $\epsilon < \epsilon_{\max}$, the minimum in (6–6) is taken on at $i = r$. If the $\min_i (x_{Bi}/y_{ik})$ is not unique, the minimum in (6–6) will be taken on at one of the i-values for which x_{Bi}/y_{ik} is minimal; but in order to decide which i-value this is, the coefficients of the higher powers of ϵ must be examined. Thus, if there is a tie for $\min_i (x_{Bi}/y_{ik})$, then for those i for which x_{Bi}/y_{ik} is minimal, we examine the coefficients of ϵ, that is, the y_{i1}/y_{ik}. If for the i under consideration, $\min_i y_{i1}/y_{ik}$ is unique and is taken on at $i = r$, then the minimum in

(6–6) is taken on for $i = r$ if $\epsilon < \epsilon_{\max}$. If again a unique minimum is not obtained, it is necessary to examine the coefficients of ϵ^2, etc. We shall now prove in detail that this procedure for determining the minimum in (6–6) does yield a unique value and that the new basic solution will be feasible and nondegenerate, i.e., that for each $\hat{x}_{Bi}(\epsilon)$ the first non-vanishing power of ϵ has a positive coefficient.

Consider

$$\theta_0 = \min_i \left\{ \frac{x_{Bi}}{y_{ik}}, \; y_{ik} > 0 \right\}. \tag{6–7}$$

If there is a unique minimum x_{Br}/y_{rk}, we remove the vector in column r, and the new basic solution will be feasible and nondegenerate. To see this note that the values of the variables for the new basic solution are

$$\hat{x}_{Bi}(\epsilon) = x_{Bi} + \sum_{j=1}^{n+s} \epsilon^j y_{ij} - \left(x_{Br} + \sum_{j=1}^{n+s} \epsilon^j y_{rj} \right) \left(\frac{y_{ik}}{y_{rk}} \right)$$

$$= \hat{x}_{Bi} + \sum_{j=1}^{n+s} \epsilon^j \hat{y}_{ij}, \quad i \neq r; \tag{6–8}$$

$$\hat{x}_{Br}(\epsilon) = \frac{x_{Br}}{y_{rk}} + \sum_{j=1}^{n+s} \epsilon^j \frac{y_{rj}}{y_{rk}} = \hat{x}_{Br} + \sum_{j=1}^{n+s} \epsilon^j \hat{y}_{rj}. \tag{6–9}$$

There are several cases to be considered. First suppose that $\theta_0 > 0$. Then for those i for which $x_{Bi} > 0$ (this includes x_{Br}), $\hat{x}_{Bi}(\epsilon) > 0$ since $\hat{x}_{Bi} > 0$. For those i (if any) for which $x_{Bi} = 0$ and $y_{ik} < 0$, $\hat{x}_{Bi}(\epsilon) > 0$ since $\hat{x}_{Bi} > 0$. For those i (if any) for which $x_{Bi} = 0$ and $y_{ik} = 0$, $\hat{x}_{Bi}(\epsilon) = x_{Bi}(\epsilon) > 0$. Since $\theta_0 > 0$, there are no i for which $x_{Bi} = 0$ and $y_{ik} > 0$. Thus the new solution is feasible and nondegenerate. Now suppose that $\theta_0 = 0$, that is, $x_{Br} = 0$. Let us first show that $\hat{x}_{Br}(\epsilon) > 0$. This follows immediately from (6–9). By assumption, $x_{Br}(\epsilon) > 0$. Since $x_{Br} = 0$, it follows that the first $y_{rj} \neq 0$ (i.e., with the lowest index j) must be positive. Then y_{rj}/y_{rk} is the first nonzero coefficient in (6–9) and it is positive since $y_{rk} > 0$, and hence for small nonzero ϵ, $\hat{x}_{Br}(\epsilon) > 0$.

When $i \neq r$, we see immediately that for those i for which $x_{Bi} > 0$, we have $\hat{x}_{Bi}(\epsilon) > 0$. For those $i \neq r$ for which $x_{Bi} = 0$ (if any), it must be true that $y_{ik} \leq 0$, for otherwise θ_0 would not be unique. If there exist i with $x_{Bi} = 0$ and $y_{ik} = 0$, then $\hat{x}_{Bi}(\epsilon) = x_{Bi}(\epsilon) > 0$. It remains to consider those i for which $x_{Bi} = 0$ and $y_{ik} < 0$. We must show that the first nonvanishing $\hat{y}_{ij}$ is positive. Recall that

$$\hat{y}_{ij} = y_{ij} - y_{rj} \frac{y_{ik}}{y_{rk}}.$$

Because $x_{Bi}(\epsilon) > 0$ by assumption, we know that the first nonvanishing y_{ij} is positive. Also $-y_{ik}/y_{rk} > 0$ since $y_{ik} < 0$. Denote by j' the lowest index j such that $y_{rj} > 0$, and by j'' the lowest index j such that $y_{ij} > 0$. If $j'' < j'$, then $\hat{y}_{ij} = 0$, $j < j''$, and $\hat{y}_{ij}'' = y_{ij}'' > 0$ so that $x_{Bi}(\epsilon) > 0$. If $j' < j''$, $\hat{y}_{ij} = 0$, $j < j'$, and $\hat{y}_{ij}' = -y_{rj}'y_{ik}/y_{rk} > 0$ so that $x_{Bi}(\epsilon) > 0$. Finally, if $j' = j''$, $\hat{y}_{ij} = 0$, $j < j''$, and $\hat{y}_{ij}'' > 0$ since $y_{ij}'' > 0$, $y_{rj}'' > 0$. Thus $\hat{x}_{Bi}(\epsilon) > 0$ in every case, and the new basic solution is feasible and nondegenerate.

Next let us suppose that θ_0 is not unique. If, in this case, the tie is resolved by an arbitrary choice of the vector to leave the basis, then $\hat{x}_{Bi} = 0$ for all $i \neq r$ where the minimum is taken on in (6–7). We are not sure that for these i-values $\hat{x}_{Bi}(\epsilon) > 0$ since this depends on the sign of the $\hat{y}_{ij}$, the coefficient of the lowest nonvanishing power of ϵ. If we proceed by making an arbitrary selection, this $\hat{y}_{ij}$ can have either sign. Assume, however, that for the i tied in (6–7), we compute

$$\min \left\{ \frac{y_{i1}}{y_{ik}} \right\}. \tag{6–10}$$

The smallest algebraic value is chosen (it may be negative because y_{i1} may be negative). If there is a unique minimum y_{r1}/y_{rk}, we remove the vector in column r; then the new basic solution is feasible and nondegenerate. The new values of the variables are given by (6–8) and (6–9). The discussion of the case where θ_0 is unique shows that all variables are positive except the $i \neq r$ tied in (6–7). We can show that if (6–10) yields a unique result, these $x_{Bi}(\epsilon) > 0$. First of all, for the i under consideration, $\hat{x}_{Bi} = 0$ because of the tie in (6–7). However, for these $i \neq r$,

$$\hat{y}_{i1} = y_{i1} - \frac{y_{ik}}{y_{rk}} y_{r1} > 0, \tag{6–11}$$

since we have $y_{i1}/y_{ik} > y_{r1}/y_{rk}$. The coefficient of the first power of ϵ in $\hat{x}_{Bi}(\epsilon)$ for each such $i \neq r$ is positive, and therefore, for sufficiently small ϵ, $\hat{x}_{Bi}(\epsilon) > 0$.

If there are also ties in (6–10), the $\hat{y}_{i1}$ are zero for the tied $i \neq r$; again we are not sure that the $\hat{x}_{Bi}(\epsilon)$ are positive. To resolve this problem, we move to the ϵ^2-terms and find

$$\min_i \left\{ \frac{y_{i2}}{y_{ik}} \right\} \tag{6–12}$$

for those i where a tie occurred in (6–10). If there is a unique minimum y_{r2}/y_{rk}, column r of the basis is removed, and the problem is solved. The above discussion shows that $\hat{x}_{Bi}(\epsilon) > 0$ for all $i \neq r$ except those tied in (6–10).   Equation (6–11) with the subscript 1 replaced by 2 shows that the variables $x_{Bi}(\epsilon)$ [tied in (6–10)] will be positive if the minimum in (6–12) is unique.   In this case, the variables $x_{Bi}(\epsilon)$ will differ from zero only by terms involving ϵ^2 and higher powers of ϵ.

This process is continually repeated until we find some power of ϵ for which there is no tie.   It is certain that sooner or later we shall obtain a unique minimum.   If we do not, i.e., if for every j a tie occurs for two or more values of i, then two rows in the tableau are proportional, for, if $y_{uj}/y_{uk} = y_{vj}/y_{vk}$, all j, including the artificial vectors, then $y_{uj} = (y_{uk}/y_{vk})y_{vj}$, all j, and rows u, v are proportional.   However, the original tableau contained an identity matrix, and all other tableaux contain $\mathbf{B}^{-1}$ (see Problem 4–11).   Hence there is a matrix of rank m in the tableau, and no two rows can be proportional (i.e., linearly dependent).   We conclude that, ultimately, the tie will be broken for some power of ϵ.   The vector to be removed is uniquely determined, and all the new basic variables are positive.   Furthermore

$$\hat{z}(\epsilon) = z(\epsilon) + \frac{x_{Br}(\epsilon)}{y_{rk}} (z_j - c_j) > z(\epsilon). \qquad (6\text{–}13)$$

The above analysis applies at every iteration.   Hence degeneracy will never occur in the perturbed problem, and at each iteration $\hat{z}(\epsilon) > z(\epsilon)$.

If at each iteration $\hat{z}(\epsilon) > z(\epsilon)$, no basis can be repeated.   Since there is only a finite number of bases, the process must terminate in a finite number of steps.   It can terminate only if (1) all $y_{ij} \leq 0$ for some $\mathbf{a}_j$ with $z_j - c_j < 0$, or (2) $z_j - c_j \geq 0$ for all legitimate vectors $\mathbf{a}_j$.   If the terminal condition is (1), there is an unbounded solution to the perturbed problem and to the original problem.   If the iterative process terminates with condition (2), then we know that an optimal solution to the perturbed problem has been found (Section 3–8).   If we set $\epsilon = 0$, we also have an optimal solution to the original problem since varying ϵ does not change the $z_j - c_j$.

Note that our discussion has proved that if there is an optimal solution to the original problem, at least one basic feasible solution will be optimal.   In addition, there is at least one optimal basic feasible solution with $z_j - c_j \geq 0$ for all legitimate $\mathbf{a}_j$.   This follows because if there is an optimal solution, the perturbed problem must end with all $z_j - c_j \geq 0$.   Setting $\epsilon = 0$ in an optimal solution to the perturbed problem yields an optimal solution to the original problem.   We have also proved that it is possible to move from any basic nondegenerate feasible solution of the perturbed problem to an optimal solution in a finite number of steps.   Using the same sequence of bases, we can also move from the corresponding basic feasible (but possibly degenerate) solution for the unperturbed problem to an optimal solution.

6–4 Order of vectors in b(ϵ). We have yet to show how to find an initial basic feasible and nondegenerate solution to the perturbed problem. Let us number the vectors so that those forming the initial identity matrix come first, i.e., e_1 is the first vector, e_2 the second, $\ldots$, e_m the mth. Thus the basic variables of the perturbed problem for the initial tableau are of the form

$$x_{B1}(\epsilon) = x_{B1} + \epsilon \ + \text{higher order terms,}$$
$$x_{B2}(\epsilon) = x_{B2} + \epsilon^2 + \text{higher order terms,}$$
$$\vdots$$
$$x_{Bm}(\epsilon) = x_{Bm} + \epsilon^m + \text{higher order terms.}$$

This arrangement of the vectors shows that although some of the x_{Bi} are zero, each $x_{Bi}(\epsilon) > 0$ for small enough ϵ. Hence, when we start out with an identity matrix for a basis, we can always obtain an initial basic feasible solution to the perturbed problem with $\mathbf{x}_B(\epsilon) > \mathbf{0}$. It follows that it is always possible to begin the solution to a linear programming problem with an identity matrix for the basis, and reach an optimal solution (or the indication of an unbounded solution) in a finite number of steps, that is, we can always prevent the occurrence of cycling.

We have indicated that the value of ϵ for the perturbed problem has to be in the range $0 < \epsilon < \epsilon_{\max}$. We have not shown how to find $\epsilon_{\max}$. We compute $\epsilon_{\max}$ by determining the largest possible value of ϵ at each step which imposes the condition "for small enough ϵ." Then $\epsilon_{\max}$ will be the smallest of all these values. This procedure could require a great deal of work, but fortunately it does not need to be carried out. However, it is important to know that $\epsilon_{\max} > 0$, and that any ϵ in the range $0 < \epsilon < \epsilon_{\max}$ will work for the perturbed problem. There is no limit on how small ϵ is chosen to be, provided it is > 0; there is only a limit on how large ϵ can be.

Our discussion has shown that degeneracy causes difficulties only in determining the vector to be removed from the basis. If the proper vector is removed, cycling will never occur, regardless of how degenerate the basic feasible solutions become. However, we shall later present an example of cycling and see that if the wrong vector is removed, cycling can occur.

6–5 Use of perturbation technique with simplex tableau format. To apply Charnes' perturbation technique, only the tableau format ordinarily used to solve a linear programming problem is needed. It will be observed that ϵ never really entered the computations at all. In a sense, the powers of ϵ only serve to keep the vectors $\mathbf{a}_j$ ordered. We always consider the lowest powers of ϵ first since, for small enough ϵ, they are the only ones that count. This means that we always consider the ratios y_{ij}/y_{ik} with the smallest j first. To decide which vector is to leave the basis, we start with the entries in the column headed "$\mathbf{b}$" and compute min $\{x_{Bi}/y_{ik}\}, y_{ik} > 0$. If there is no unique minimum, we concentrate on the rows for which x_{Bi}/y_{ik} takes on the minimum value. For these rows, we move to the column headed "$\mathbf{a}_1$" and compute min $\{y_{i1}/y_{ik}\}$. If a unique minimum is not obtained, we turn our attention to those rows where y_{i1}/y_{ik} has taken on its minimum value. For these rows, move to the column headed "$\mathbf{a}_2$" and compute min $\{y_{i2}/y_{ik}\}$, etc. Ultimately, there will be a unique minimum. If it occurs in row r, this means that column r of the basis is removed. The procedure is applied to each tableau as needed. The ϵ's are never used. However, we must take care that the same column ordering is maintained from one tableau to the next. Of course, to use the perturbation technique within the tableau format, it is necessary to include in the tableaux, columns for any artificial vectors which may have been required.

6–6 Geometrical interpretation. A geometrical interpretation of the perturbation method facilitates the intuitive understanding. We have previously seen that several degenerate basic feasible solutions can correspond to the same extreme point in the solutions space. In the perturbed problem, there is no degeneracy, and hence only one basic feasible solution corresponds to each extreme point. This means that, in the perturbed problem, all degenerate solutions corresponding to a single extreme point are broken down so that each solution corresponds to a single extreme point. The degenerate extreme point of the original problem becomes a cluster of extreme points in the perturbed problem, with all the extreme points in the cluster lying very close to the point which was the original degenerate extreme point. The distance between these perturbed extreme points and the original extreme point depends on the size of ϵ. As ϵ approaches 0, all the perturbed extreme points corresponding to a given degenerate point move closer and closer to this point until they all merge into the single degenerate extreme point. Note that the perturbation is such that the extreme points remain in the non-negative orthant.

Note: Perturbation techniques similar to the types discussed here find applications in many other fields. For example, the removal of degeneracy in the energy levels of an atom by applying some perturbation such as an electric or magnetic field (Stark or Zeeman effects) is an illustration which arises in quantum mechanics.

In the requirements space, any set of basis vectors generates an m-dimensional convex polyhedral cone. The cone generated by any $k < m$ of these vectors lies on a face of the m-dimensional cone. When there is degeneracy, $\mathbf{b}$ can be expressed in terms of $k < m$ of the basis vectors, and thus $\mathbf{b}$ also lies on a face of the m-dimensional cone. The perturbation method moves $\mathbf{b}$ inside the cone generated by the basis vectors, and hence all the basis vectors are needed to express $\mathbf{b}(\epsilon)$ in terms of the basis vectors.

In fact, $\mathbf{b}(\epsilon)$ is inside every cone that yields a basic feasible solution to the problem.

6–7 The generalized linear programming problem. The other technique for eliminating degeneracy is called the generalized simplex method. It uses lexicographically ordered vectors. We shall begin by defining a lexicographically positive vector. *A vector* $\mathbf{x}$ *is lexicographically positive* (*written* $\mathbf{x} > \mathbf{0}$) *if its first nonzero component is positive.* In other words, if we examine the components of the vector in dictionary order (from left to right), then the first nonzero component is positive. For example, $(0, 2, -1, 4)$ is lexicographically positive since 2, the first nonzero component in dictionary order, is positive. On the other hand, $(0, 0, -1, 7, 6, 3)$ is not lexicographically positive. Note that the symbol "$\mathbf{x} > \mathbf{0}$" has a completely different meaning from "$\mathbf{x} > \mathbf{0}$" which implies that each component of $\mathbf{x}$ is positive. By $\mathbf{x}_1 > \mathbf{x}_2$ we mean $\mathbf{x}_1 - \mathbf{x}_2 > \mathbf{0}$. A vector is lexicographically non-negative (written $\mathbf{x} \geqslant \mathbf{0}$) if it is either lexicographically positive or if all its components vanish.

To resolve the degeneracy problem, Dantzig, Orden and Wolfe [4] replace each variable x_j of the original problem by a row vector $\mathbf{x}_j$ with $m + 1$ components, the first component being x_j. Then the requirements vector $\mathbf{b}$ is replaced by an $m \times (m + 1)$ matrix $\mathbf{P}$ given by

$$\mathbf{P} = (\mathbf{b}, \mathbf{I}_m). \tag{6–14}$$

The matrix $\mathbf{P}$ contains $\mathbf{b}$ in the first column, and the m, $\mathbf{e}_i$ in the last m columns. Since $\mathbf{P}$ contains an identity matrix, $r(\mathbf{P}) = m$. If the rows of $\mathbf{P}$ are denoted by $\mathbf{p}^i$, it follows from (6–14) that $\mathbf{p}^i > \mathbf{0}$ ($i = 1, \ldots, m$), i.e., the rows of $\mathbf{P}$ are lexicographically positive. The matrix $\mathbf{P}$ can be thought of as having for its columns $2, \ldots, (m + 1)$, the vectors from $\mathbf{A}$ or the artificial vectors which make up the initial identity matrix that would have been obtained if the problem had been solved in the usual way.

The set of constraints $\mathbf{Ax} = \mathbf{b}$ to the original problem now becomes

$$\begin{aligned}
a_{11}\mathbf{x}_1 + \cdots + a_{1n}\mathbf{x}_n &= \mathbf{p}^1 = (b_1, 1, 0, \cdots, 0), \\
a_{21}\mathbf{x}_1 + \cdots + a_{2n}\mathbf{x}_n &= \mathbf{p}^2 = (b_2, 0, 1, \ldots, 0), \\
&\vdots \\
a_{m1}\mathbf{x}_1 + \cdots + a_{mn}\mathbf{x}_n &= \mathbf{p}^m = (b_m, 0, 0, \ldots, 1).
\end{aligned} \tag{6–15}$$

If $\mathbf{X}$ is the matrix whose rows are the $\mathbf{x}_j$, then

$$\mathbf{AX} = \mathbf{P} \tag{6–16}$$

is the set of constraints for the generalized problem. The matrix $\mathbf{X}$ is an $n \times (m + 1)$ matrix.

Next, the objective function of the original problem is replaced by the vector function

$$\mathbf{z} = \sum_{j=1}^{n} c_j \mathbf{x}_j. \tag{6-17}$$

Note that $\mathbf{z}$ is an $(m + 1)$-component row vector, and the first component of $\mathbf{z}$ is the z of the original problem. It will be observed that the prices have not been converted to vectors; they remain scalars. However, the price c_j is now associated with the vector variable $\mathbf{x}_j$.

6–8 The generalized simplex method. Using the ideas suggested above, we can propose the following generalized linear programming problem involving vector variables: Find a set of lexicographically non-negative variables $\mathbf{x}_j \geqslant \mathbf{0}$ which maximize the $\mathbf{z}$ of (6–17) in a lexicographic sense and satisfy the constraints (6–16). By maximizing $\mathbf{z}$ in a lexicographic sense we mean that if $\mathbf{z}^*$ is the optimal $\mathbf{z}$, then $\mathbf{z}^* \geqslant \mathbf{z}$ for $\mathbf{z}$ corresponding to any other feasible solution of (6–16), i.e., any other solution of (6–16) with $\mathbf{x}_j \geqslant \mathbf{0}$ for all j.

We shall now present the generalized simplex method, which is merely the simplex method as applied to the generalized linear programming problem outlined above. For the generalized problem, we shall show that degeneracy never occurs, and therefore all the related problems are eliminated. Note that when an optimal solution to the generalized problem is found, an optimal solution to the original problem will be contained in the first components of the $\mathbf{z}$, $\mathbf{x}_j$.

As usual, we shall denote by $\mathbf{B}$ a nonsingular matrix containing m columns from $\mathbf{A}$. A basic feasible solution to (6–16) is one with no more than m of the $\mathbf{x}_j$ lexicographically positive. The remaining $n - m$ of the $\mathbf{x}_j$ are null vectors. To be perfectly rigorous at this point, we should repeat the derivation of the basic theory of the simplex method for this generalized problem. We shall not do this since the arguments are identical with those developed for the ordinary problem. The details of some of these derivations are left for Problems 6–2 and 6–3. We shall proceed heuristically, i.e., the theory for the ordinary simplex method will be directly applied to the generalized problem.

Any basic feasible solution to (6–16) can be written

$$\mathbf{X}_B = \mathbf{B}^{-1}\mathbf{P} = (\mathbf{B}^{-1}\mathbf{b}, \mathbf{B}^{-1}\mathbf{e}_1, \ldots, \mathbf{B}^{-1}\mathbf{e}_m) = (\mathbf{x}_B, \mathbf{y}_1, \ldots, \mathbf{y}_m). \tag{6-18}$$

We have assumed that the vectors in the original problem have been numbered in such a way that the unit vectors $\mathbf{e}_1, \ldots, \mathbf{e}_m$ come first. Hence $\mathbf{y}_1 = \mathbf{B}^{-1}\mathbf{e}_1$, etc. We find an initial basic feasible solution to the vector problem by setting $\mathbf{X}_B = \mathbf{P}$. Recall that the rows of $\mathbf{P}$ are lexicographically positive. It is assumed that any artificial variables which must be added to the original problem are also added as vector variables to the generalized problem.

The $z_j - c_j$ corresponding to any $\mathbf{a}_j$ in the generalized problem are the same as those for the basic feasible solution corresponding to $\mathbf{B}$ in the original problem. The vector to enter the basis at any one iteration is determined in the same way as in the ordinary simplex method and is, in fact, the same vector that would enter if we were dealing with the basic feasible solution $\mathbf{x}_B$ to the original problem.

Let us now consider how to determine the vector to be removed. We use a straightforward generalization of the usual formula, that is,

$$\frac{\mathbf{x}_{Br}}{y_{rk}} = \min_i \left\{ \frac{\mathbf{x}_{Bi}}{y_{ik}}, y_{ik} > 0 \right\}. \tag{6–19}$$

The difference appears in the computation of the minimum. Let us suppose that the vector variables $\mathbf{x}_{Bi}$ of the basic feasible solution (6–18) are lexicographically positive. We shall show that it is possible to obtain a minimum to (6–19) which is unique in the lexicographic sense. It then follows that all the new basic vector variables will be lexicographically positive. To determine the minimum in (6–19), we first compute min x_{Bi}/y_{ik}. If a unique minimum x_{Br}/y_{rk} is obtained, we remove column r from the basis. When a unique minimum is not found, we compute min y_{i1}/y_{ik} for those i for which the x_{Bi}/y_{ik} assumed the minimum value. If there is still a tie, we move on and determine min y_{i2}/y_{ik} for those i for which y_{i1}/y_{ik} took on the minimum value. However, there cannot always be a tie since this would imply that two rows of $\mathbf{X}_B$ are proportional. However, $r(\mathbf{B}^{-1}) = m$, $r(\mathbf{P}) = m$ whence $r(\mathbf{X}_B) = m$, and two rows cannot be proportional. Thus the vector to be removed will be uniquely determined.

Next, we must show that the new basic vector variables are lexicographically positive. Clearly, $\hat{\mathbf{x}}_{Br} = \mathbf{x}_{Br}/y_{rk} \succ \mathbf{0}$. For the others,

$$\hat{\mathbf{x}}_{Bi} = \mathbf{x}_{Bi} - \frac{y_{ik}}{y_{rk}} \mathbf{x}_{Br}, \qquad i \neq r. \tag{6–20}$$

Here again we must go through the type of analysis used in the discussion of Charnes' perturbation method to show that each $\hat{\mathbf{x}}_{Bi}(\epsilon) \succ \mathbf{0}$, $i \neq r$. In fact, precisely the same analysis shows that each $\hat{\mathbf{x}}_{Bi} \succ \mathbf{0}$, $i \neq r$. We shall not repeat this material.

The new value of the objective function $\hat{\mathbf{z}}$ is given by

$$\hat{\mathbf{z}} = \mathbf{z} + \frac{\mathbf{x}_{Br}}{y_{rk}} (c_k - z_k). \tag{6–21}$$

But $(\mathbf{x}_{Br}/y_{rk})(c_k - z_k) \succ \mathbf{0}$, so that $\hat{\mathbf{z}} \succ \mathbf{z}$. In the lexicographic sense, there has been an increase in the objective function. At each iteration, the objective function increases lexicographically. Hence we conclude that no basis can ever be repeated. The $\mathbf{x}_{Bi} = (x_{Bi}, y_{i1}, \ldots, y_{im})$ are uniquely determined by the basis. If we have two bases with the same vectors from $\mathbf{A}$, and these vectors are in different column positions in $\mathbf{B}$, then the rows in $\mathbf{B}^{-1}$ and the rows of $\mathbf{X}_B$ are changed around, but the $\mathbf{x}_{Bi}$ are not affected. Consequently, the $\mathbf{z}$ for any basic feasible solution is unique.

Thus we conclude that the process can terminate only if (1) $y_{ij} \leq 0$, all i, for some $\mathbf{a}_j$ with $z_j - c_j < 0$, or (2) $z_j - c_j \geq 0$ for all legitimate vectors $\mathbf{a}_j$; in the latter case, the basic feasible solution is optimal. Since any basic feasible solution to the generalized problem contains within it (in the first components of $\mathbf{x}_{Bi}$, $\mathbf{z}$) a basic feasible solution to the original problem, we have proved that it is possible to move from any basic feasible solution of the original problem to an optimal basic feasible solution by changing a single vector at a time. We have also proved that there is at least one optimal basic feasible solution to the original problem, with all $z_j - c_j \geq 0$.

The reader may be disturbed at the suggestion of carrying out a computation involving $(m + 1)$-component vectors by means of the generalized simplex method. A little thought, however, shows that the impressive notation was necessary only to prove that a certain way of selecting a vector to be removed really does prevent cycling. We do not need to use the generalized simplex method to prevent cycling when degeneracy occurs. We only have to arrange the columns of the usual simplex tableau so that the columns associated with the original identity matrix come first and in the proper order. Then, if at any stage in the ordinary simplex method min x_{Bi}/y_{ik} is not unique, we move to the next column and compute min y_{i1}/y_{ik} for those i for which x_{Bi}/y_{ik} assumed the minimum value, etc. In this way, the vector to be removed will be uniquely determined, and cycling will never occur. An optimal solution will be reached in a finite number of steps.

We have already mentioned that although Charnes' perturbation method and the generalized simplex method appear to be quite different, they are operationally equivalent. That is, the rule for determining the vector to be removed in the ordinary simplex tableau is identical for both methods, provided the vectors forming the original identity matrix come first in the tableau. Recall that the ϵ^j's in Charnes' method only served to introduce a certain order. Dantzig, Orden, and Wolfe took advantage of this observation and developed an arrangement using lexicographically ordered vectors rather than powers of ϵ. At this point, we also wish to note that Charnes, in replacing $\mathbf{b}$ by $\mathbf{b}(\epsilon)$, did not really have to include all the vectors in the tableau. He needed only those vectors that make up the original identity matrix.

6–9 Examples pertaining to degeneracy. The preceding discussions may
have led the reader to believe that at any stage in the solution of a linear
programming problem, there is always a vector which, if the optimality
criterion is not satisfied, can be inserted such that $\hat{z} > z$. This is not true.
There may not be any vector to be inserted that will actually increase z.
To be able to jump to an adjacent extreme point which increases z, it
may be necessary to change several vectors in the basis.

EXAMPLE: Consider the problem given in Table 6–1. No vector can be
inserted such that $\hat{z} > z$. Only $\mathbf{a}_1$, $\mathbf{a}_2$ are not in the basis. Both can be
inserted, but each enters at a zero level. It will be noted that

$$\theta \mathbf{a}_1 + \frac{\theta}{2}\mathbf{a}_2 + 2\theta \mathbf{a}_4 + \mathbf{a}_5 = \mathbf{b}, \qquad \text{any } \theta > 0,$$

and therefore z can be made arbitrarily large. Thus it is possible to increase z, but at the first iteration z cannot be improved.

TABLE 6–1 — INITIAL TABLEAU

	c_j		2	3	0	0	0
c_B	Vectors in Basis	$\mathbf{b}$	$\mathbf{a}_1$	$\mathbf{a}_2$	$\mathbf{a}_3$	$\mathbf{a}_4$	$\mathbf{a}_5$
0	$\mathbf{a}_3$	0	2	−4	1	0	0
0	$\mathbf{a}_4$	0	−3	2	0	1	0
0	$\mathbf{a}_5$	1	0	0	0	0	1
	$z_j - c_j$	0	−2	−3	0	0	0

It might also be thought that if the optimality criterion is not satisfied,
then there must be an increase in z before it will be satisfied. This is not
true. It is possible to insert a vector at a zero level, with z remaining
unchanged, and move from a solution where the optimality criterion is
not satisfied to one where it is.

EXAMPLE: Consider

$$x_1\mathbf{a}_1 + x_2\mathbf{a}_2 + x_3\mathbf{a}_3 = \mathbf{b}, \qquad \text{all } x_j \geq 0, \qquad \max z = c_1 x_1 + c_2 x_2 + c_3 x_3,$$
$$\mathbf{a}_1 = [1, 0], \qquad \mathbf{a}_2 = [0, 1], \qquad \mathbf{a}_3 = [2, 1], \qquad \mathbf{b} = [0, 1],$$
$$c_1 = 2, \qquad c_2 = 3, \qquad c_3 = 10.$$

If the initial basis is $\mathbf{B} = (\mathbf{a}_1, \mathbf{a}_2) = \mathbf{I}$, then $z_3 - c_3 = -3$, and at the next iteration $\mathbf{a}_3$ enters the basis, and $\mathbf{a}_1$ is removed. The original basic solution is $\mathbf{x}_B = [0, 1]$, and the new basic solution is $\hat{\mathbf{x}}_B = [0, 1]$ since $\mathbf{a}_3$ enters at a zero level. Hence $\hat{z} = z$. The new basis matrix is $\hat{\mathbf{B}} = (\mathbf{a}_3, \mathbf{a}_2)$, and

$$\hat{\mathbf{B}}^{-1} = \tfrac{1}{2} \begin{bmatrix} 1 & 0 \\ -1 & 2 \end{bmatrix};$$

thus

$$\hat{\mathbf{y}}_1 = \hat{\mathbf{B}}^{-1}\mathbf{a}_1 = \tfrac{1}{2} \begin{bmatrix} 1 & 0 \\ -1 & 2 \end{bmatrix} \begin{bmatrix} 1 \\ 0 \end{bmatrix} = \tfrac{1}{2} \begin{bmatrix} 1 \\ -1 \end{bmatrix},$$

and

$$\hat{z}_1 - c_1 = \tfrac{1}{2}(10 - 3) - 2 = 1.5.$$

Hence for the new basic solution the optimality criterion is satisfied, although this was not the case for the original solution. However, the solution $\mathbf{x}$ and z did not change.

It will be helpful to give an example illustrating the procedure for uniquely determining the vector to be removed, which assures us that cycling will not occur. At the same time, we might note that the simplex tableaux constructed to solve the original problem essentially contain the solutions to Charnes' perturbed problem and the solution of the generalized simplex method. Recall that for Charnes' perturbation method,

$$x_{Bi}(\epsilon) = x_{Bi} + \sum_{j=1}^{n+s} \epsilon^j y_{ij}; \qquad z(\epsilon) = z + \sum_{j=1}^{n+s} \epsilon^j z_j.$$

The tableau provides us with the x_{Bi}, y_{ij}, z and, from $z_j = (z_j - c_j) + c_j$, the z_j. Thus the tableau yields all coefficients of the polynomials appearing in the perturbation method. However, we are not supplied with the value of ϵ_{max}.

For the generalized simplex method, the vector variables and the vector objective function are given by

$$\mathbf{x}_{Bi} = (x_{Bi}, y_{i1}, \ldots, y_{im}),$$

$$\mathbf{z} = \mathbf{c}_B \mathbf{X}_B = \mathbf{c}_B(\mathbf{x}_B, \mathbf{y}_1, \ldots, \mathbf{y}_m) = (z, z_1, \ldots, z_m).$$

Thus, at any stage, the usual tableau supplies the complete corresponding basic feasible solution to the generalized simplex method.

EXAMPLE: Consider the linear programming problem whose initial tableau is Table 6–2. On the first iteration, $\mathbf{a}_4$ will enter the basis. When min x_{Bi}/y_{i4} is computed, a value 0 is obtained for x_{B2}/y_{24}, x_{B3}/y_{34}.

TABLE 6–2 — TABLEAU 1

c_B	c_j Vectors in Basis	b	0 a_1	0 a_2	0 a_3	4 a_4	3 a_5
0	a_1	2	1	0	0	2	4
0	a_2	0	0	1	0	3	1
0	a_3	0	0	0	1	4	2
	$z_j - c_j$	0	0	0	0	−4	−3

The vector to be removed is not uniquely determined from this computation. We then move to the a_1-column and determine y_{21}/y_{24}, y_{31}/y_{34}. Both of these are 0 also. Next we move to the a_2-column and find $y_{22}/y_{24} = \frac{1}{3}$, $y_{32}/y_{34} = 0$. Here a unique minimum is obtained, and column 3 of the basis is removed. The new tableau is given in Table 6–3.

From the information given in the tableaux, let us write down the corresponding solutions for Charnes' perturbation method and the gen-

TABLE 6–3 — TABLEAU 2

c_B	c_j Vectors in Basis	b	0 a_1	0 a_2	0 a_3	4 a_4	3 a_5
0	a_1	2	1	0	$-\frac{1}{2}$	0	3
0	a_2	0	0	1	$-\frac{3}{4}$	0	$-\frac{1}{2}$
4	a_4	0	0	0	$\frac{1}{4}$	1	$\frac{1}{2}$
	$z_j - c_j$	0	0	0	1	0	−1

eralized simplex method. For the first tableau, we find that for Charnes' scheme

$$x_{B1}(\epsilon) = 2 + \epsilon + 2\epsilon^4 + 4\epsilon^5, \qquad x_{B2}(\epsilon) = \epsilon^2 + 3\epsilon^4 + \epsilon^5,$$
$$x_{B3}(\epsilon) = \epsilon^3 + 4\epsilon^4 + 2\epsilon^5,$$

and since $z_j = z_j - c_j + c_j$, $z(\epsilon) = 0$. The new values obtained on inserting $\mathbf{a}_4$ are simply read off the second tableau. They are

$$\hat{x}_{B1}(\epsilon) = 2 + \epsilon - \tfrac{1}{2}\epsilon^3 + 3\epsilon^5, \qquad \hat{x}_{B2}(\epsilon) = \epsilon^2 - \tfrac{3}{4}\epsilon^3 - \tfrac{1}{2}\epsilon^5,$$
$$\hat{x}_{B3}(\epsilon) = \tfrac{1}{4}\epsilon^3 + \epsilon^4 + \tfrac{1}{2}\epsilon^5.$$

For small enough ϵ, the $x_{Bi}(\epsilon)$ are indeed positive. Note that $x_{B2}(\epsilon)$, $x_{B3}(\epsilon)$ differ from zero only by terms involving $\epsilon^j, j > 1$. Also, $\hat{z}(\epsilon) = \epsilon^3 + 4\epsilon^4 + 2\epsilon^5$, and $\hat{z}(\epsilon) > z(\epsilon)$.

The generalized simplex method yields for the initial solution

$$\mathbf{x}_{B1} = (2, 1, 0, 0); \qquad \mathbf{x}_{B2} = (0, 0, 1, 0); \qquad \mathbf{x}_{B3} = (0, 0, 0, 1);$$
$$\mathbf{z} = (0, 0, 0, 0).$$

The basic vector variables are lexicographically positive. For the second tableau,

$$\hat{\mathbf{x}}_{B1} = (2, 1, 0, -\tfrac{1}{2}), \qquad \hat{\mathbf{x}}_{B2} = (0, 0, 1, -\tfrac{3}{4}),$$
$$\hat{\mathbf{x}}_{B3} = (0, 0, 0, \tfrac{1}{4}), \qquad \hat{\mathbf{z}} = (0, 0, 0, 1).$$

The new basic vector variables are also lexicographically positive and $\hat{\mathbf{z}} > \mathbf{z}$.

6–10 An example of cycling.

Examples have been constructed for which cycling will occur if the wrong vectors are removed from the basis. These examples are quite artificial and were constructed solely for the purpose of demonstrating that cycling can take place. Specifically, there exist at least two examples: One was developed by Hoffman [5] and the other by Beale [1]. The example used here is one suggested by Beale.* The reader should keep in mind that the example was constructed solely to demonstrate cycling, and that no actual problem has ever cycled.

Consider the linear programming problem

$$0.25x_1 - 8x_2 - x_3 + 9x_4 \leq 0,$$
$$0.5x_1 - 12x_2 - 0.5x_3 + 3x_4 \leq 0,$$
$$x_3 \leq 1, \quad x_1, x_2, x_3, x_4 \geq 0,$$
$$\max z = 0.75x_1 - 20x_2 + 0.5x_3 - 6x_4. \tag{6-22}$$

_____

* In actuality, this example is the dual of one suggested by Beale.

The first tableau is given in Table 6–4. We have arranged the vectors so that those forming the initial identity matrix come first. This will allow us to use the procedure which we have developed for the purpose of uniquely determining the vector to be removed. At the first iteration $\mathbf{a}_1$ is inserted, and either $\mathbf{a}_5$ or $\mathbf{a}_6$ can be removed. If we move to the $\mathbf{a}_5$-column and compute $y_{15}/y_{11} = 4$, $y_{25}/y_{21} = 0$, we find that $\mathbf{a}_6$ should be removed if we wish to ensure that cycling will not occur.

Suppose that instead of $\mathbf{a}_6$, $\mathbf{a}_5$ is removed. By properly choosing the vectors to be removed from the tied values, we can obtain the sequence of tableaux given in Tables 6–4 through 6–10. Note that tableau 7 is precisely the same as tableau 1. Hence we have cycled and come back to our starting point. If we continue to remove the same vectors, we shall cycle forever, and an optimal solution will never be reached.

Beginning with Table 6–10, which is the same as Table 6–4, let us remove $\mathbf{a}_6$ instead of $\mathbf{a}_5$; $\mathbf{a}_6$ is the only other vector which can be removed. We then obtain Tables 6–11 and 6–12. Observe that in tableau 8, there is no tie for the vector to be removed. An optimal basic feasible solution is obtained in tableau 9.

It is interesting to note that if we had not resolved the ties by the method which ensures that cycling will not occur, but had instead used the simple rule prescribing that we remove the vector for which y_{ik} is the largest among the i corresponding to the tied vectors, we would have removed $\mathbf{a}_6$, and cycling would not have occurred.

TABLE 6–4 — TABLEAU 1

c_B	Vectors in Basis	c_j	0	0	0	0.75	−20	0.5	−6
		b	$\mathbf{a}_5$	$\mathbf{a}_6$	$\mathbf{a}_7$	$\mathbf{a}_1$	$\mathbf{a}_2$	$\mathbf{a}_3$	$\mathbf{a}_4$
0	$\mathbf{a}_5$	0	1	0	0	0.25	−8	−1	9
0	$\mathbf{a}_6$	0	0	1	0	0.50	−12	−0.50	3
0	$\mathbf{a}_7$	1	0	0	1	0	0	1	0
	$z_j - c_j$	0	0	0	0	−0.75	20	−0.5	6

TABLE 6–5 — TABLEAU 2

c_B	c_j		0	0	0	0.75	−20	0.5	−6
	Vectors in Basis	b	a_5	a_6	a_7	a_1	a_2	a_3	a_4
0.75	a_1	0	4	0	0	1	−32	−4	36
0	a_6	0	−2	1	0	0	4	1.5	−15
0	a_7	1	0	0	1	0	0	1	0
	$z_j - c_j$	0	3	0	0	0	−4	−3.5	33

TABLE 6–6 — TABLEAU 3

c_B	c_j		0	0	0	0.75	−20	0.5	−6
	Vectors in Basis	b	a_5	a_6	a_7	a_1	a_2	a_3	a_4
0.75	a_1	0	−12	8	0	1	0	8	−84
−20	a_2	0	−0.5	0.25	0	0	1	0.375	−3.75
0	a_7	1	0	0	1	0	0	1	0
	$z_j - c_j$	0	1	1	0	0	0	−2	18

TABLE 6–7 — TABLEAU 4

	c_j		0	0	0	0.75	−20	0.5	−6
c_B	Vectors in Basis	b	a_5	a_6	a_7	a_1	a_2	a_3	a_4
0.5	a_3	0	−1.5	1	0	0.125	0	1	−10.5
−20	a_2	0	0.0625	−0.125	0	−0.0469	1	0	0.1875
0	a_7	1	1.5	−1	1	−0.125	0	0	10.5
	$z_j - c_j$	0	−2	3	0	0.250	0	0	−3

TABLE 6–8 — TABLEAU 5

	c_j		0	0	0	0.75	−20	0.5	−6
c_B	Vectors in Basis	b	a_5	a_6	a_7	a_1	a_2	a_3	a_4
0.5	a_3	0	2	−6	0	−2.5	56	1	0
−6	a_4	0	0.333	−0.667	0	−0.25	5.33	0	1
0	a_7	1	−2	6	1	2.5	−56	0	0
	$z_j - c_j$	0	−1	1	0	−0.5	16	0	0

TABLE 6-9 — TABLEAU 6

c_B	Vectors in Basis	b	0 a_5	0 a_6	0 a_7	0.75 a_1	-20 a_2	0.5 a_3	-6 a_4
0	a_5	0	1	-3	0	-1.25	28	0.5	0
-6	a_4	0	0	0.333	0	0.167	-4.0	-0.167	1
0	a_7	1	0	0	1	0	0	1	0
	$z_j - c_j$	0	0	-2	0	-1.75	44	0.5	0

TABLE 6-10 — TABLEAU 7

c_B	Vectors in Basis	b	0 a_5	0 a_6	0 a_7	0.75 a_1	-20 a_2	0.5 a_3	-6 a_4
0	a_5	0	1	0	0	0.25	-8	-1	9
0	a_6	0	0	1	0	0.50	-12	-0.50	3
0	a_7	1	0	0	1	0	0	1	0
	$z_j - c_j$	0	0	0	0	-0.75	20	-0.5	6

Table 6-11 — Tableau 8

c_B	Vectors in Basis	b	0	0	0	0.75	-20	0.5	-6
			a_5	a_6	a_7	a_1	a_2	a_3	a_4
0	a_5	0	1	-0.50	0	0	-2	-0.75	7.5
0.75	a_1	0	0	2	0	1	-24	-1	6
0	a_7	1	0	0	1	0	0	1	0
	$z_j - c_j$	0	0	1.50	0	0	2	-1.25	10.5

Table 6-12 — Tableau 9

c_B	Vectors in Basis	b	0	0	0	0.75	-20	0.5	-6
			a_5	a_6	a_7	a_1	a_2	a_3	a_4
0	a_5	0.75	1	-0.50	0.75	0	-2	0	7.5
0.75	a_1	1	0	2	1	1	-24	0	6
0.5	a_3	1	0	0	1	0	0	1	0
	$z_j - c_j$	1.25	0	1.50	1.25	0	2	0	10.5

References

1. E. M. L. Beale, "Cycling in the Dual Simplex Algorithm," *Naval Research Logistics Quarterly*, **2**, pp. 269–75, 1955.
2. A. Charnes, W. W. Cooper, and A. Henderson, *An Introduction to Linear Programming*. New York: Wiley, 1953.
3. A. Charnes, "Optimality and Degeneracy in Linear Programming," *Econometrica*, **20**, pp. 160–70, 1952.
4. G. B. Dantzig, A. Orden, and P. Wolfe, "The Generalized Simplex Method for Minimizing a Linear Form under Linear Inequality Restraints," *Pacific Journal of Mathematics*, **5**, 2, 1955, and *RM–1264*, The RAND Corporation, April, 1954.
5. A. J. Hoffman, "Cycling in the Simplex Algorithm," *National Bureau of Standards Report*, No. 2974, Dec., 1953.

Problems

6-1. Solve the following linear programming problem by the simplex method. Determine the vector to leave the basis in such a way that degeneracy will not occur. Does this method yield an answer different from that obtained by selecting the vector for which y_{ij} is the greatest of the tied values? If there is a difference, compute the sequence of tableaux for both methods.

$$1.5x_1 + 0.5x_2 + 3x_3 + x_4 + 4x_5 + 2x_6 \geq 0,$$
$$2x_1 + 3x_2 + 0.5x_3 + 4x_4 + x_5 + 7x_6 \geq 0,$$
$$x_1 - 4x_2 - x_3 - 8x_4 + 6x_5 - x_6 \leq 0,$$
$$-0.5x_1 - 2x_2 - 1.5x_3 + 4x_4 + 3x_5 - 5x_6 \leq 1,$$
$$\text{all } x_j \geq 0,$$
$$\max z = 5x_1 + 6x_2 + 3x_3 + x_4 - 2x_5 + 7x_6.$$

6-2. For the generalized simplex method involving vector variables, prove that if there is a feasible solution, there is a basic feasible solution.

6-3. For the generalized simplex method, prove that if for some $\mathbf{a}_j$ not in the basis $z_j - c_j < 0$, then if all $y_{ij} \leq 0$, there is an unbounded solution (what is the meaning of an unbounded solution?), and if one or more $y_{ij} > 0$, there is another basic feasible solution with $\hat{z} > z$. Thus show that if there is an optimal solution, one can move by changing a single vector in the basis at a time from any basic feasible solution to an optimal basic feasible solution in a finite number of steps. Also show that any optimal basic feasible solution has all $z_j - c_j \geq 0$.

6-4. Show that cycling can never occur so long as a unique minimum is obtained in the computation of $\min_i x_{Bi}/y_{ik} > 0$. Show that this is true even if $x_{Br}/y_{rk} = 0$ and degeneracy occurs.

6-5. After having studied this chapter, can you provide a better answer to Problems 4-3 and 4-4?

6-6. Give a general proof for Problem 4-10 which does not require the nondegeneracy assumption.

CHAPTER 7

THE REVISED SIMPLEX METHOD

"Though this be madness, yet there is method in't."
Shakespeare—Hamlet.

7–1 Introduction. The revised simplex method was developed by Dantzig, Orchard-Hays and others at the RAND Corporation as an efficient computational procedure for solving linear programming problems on digital computers. The revised simplex method solves a linear programming problem in the same way as the simplex method. Given any basic feasible solution, we move from that solution to an optimal basic feasible solution by changing a single vector in the basis at a time. For the revised simplex method, the criteria used to determine the vector to enter and leave the basis are precisely the same as those used in the simplex method. The "revised" aspect concerns the procedure of changing tableaux. In discussing the tableau format for the simplex method in Chapter 4, we noted that it was unnecessary to transform all the y_j, x_B, $z_j - c_j$, z at each iteration. In fact, all new quantities can be computed directly from their definitions if B^{-1} is known, i.e., if only the basis inverse is transformed. The revised simplex method makes use of this observation. At each iteration, only B^{-1}, x_B, $c_B B^{-1}$, and z are transformed (z, x_B, $c_B B^{-1}$ are also transformed since this requires less computational effort than their computation from definitions). None of the y_j is transformed. In fact, the only y_j that is ever determined at each iteration is the one for the vector which is going to enter the basis. As we shall see later, this type of transformation scheme has several advantages over that used in the simplex method.

There are two standard forms for the revised simplex method, depending on whether it is necessary to add artificial vectors to obtain an initial identity matrix. For Standard Form I, it is assumed that an identity matrix is present after slack and surplus variables have been added, and hence artificial variables are not needed. If artificial vectors must be added, then Standard Form II is used. As might be expected, the revised simplex method uses the two-phase technique to handle artificial variables. However, it does so in a way slightly different from that discussed in Chapter 5.

7–2 Revised simplex method: Standard Form I. In the revised simplex method, the objective function is essentially treated as if it were another constraint. Where we dealt with an m-dimensional basis in the simplex method, we deal with an $(m + 1)$-dimensional basis when using Standard Form I of the revised simplex method. There is a good reason for doing this, which we shall point out later.

Our usual formulation of the linear programming problem would be $\mathbf{Ax} = \mathbf{b}, \mathbf{x} \geq \mathbf{0}$, max $z = \mathbf{cx}$. Instead of writing $z = \mathbf{cx}$, let us write

$$z - \mathbf{cx} = z - c_1 x_1 - \cdots - c_n x_n = 0. \tag{7-1}$$

This can be considered as another constraint equation for which z is to be made as large as possible. If we now write

$$\begin{aligned} z - c_1 x_1 - \cdots - c_n x_n &= 0, \\ a_{11} x_1 + \cdots + a_{1n} x_n &= b_1, \\ &\ \vdots \\ a_{m1} x_1 + \cdots + a_{mn} x_n &= b_m, \end{aligned} \tag{7-2}$$

then (7-2) can be considered to be a system of $m + 1$ simultaneous linear equations in $n + 1$ variables $z, x_1, \ldots, x_n$. We wish to find a solution to (7-2) such that z is as large as possible (and unrestricted in sign), subject to the non-negativity restrictions $x_j \geq 0$ $(j = 1, \ldots, n)$.

Equation (7-2) can be rewritten in a more symmetric notation, as follows:

$$\begin{aligned} x_0 + a_{01} x_1 + \cdots + a_{0n} x_n &= 0, \\ a_{11} x_1 + \cdots + a_{1n} x_n &= b_1, \\ &\ \vdots \\ a_{m1} x_1 + \cdots + a_{mn} x_n &= b_m, \end{aligned} \tag{7-3}$$

where $z = x_0$, $-c_j = a_{0j}$. In partitioned matrix form, this can be written

$$\begin{bmatrix} 1 & \mathbf{a}^0 \\ 0 & \mathbf{A} \end{bmatrix} \begin{bmatrix} x_0 \\ \mathbf{x} \end{bmatrix} = \begin{bmatrix} 0 \\ \mathbf{b} \end{bmatrix}, \tag{7-4}$$

where $\mathbf{a}^0 = (a_{01}, \ldots, a_{0n})$ and $\mathbf{A}$ is the $\mathbf{A}$ of $\mathbf{Ax} = \mathbf{b}$. In terms of our original notation, (7-4) would be written

$$\begin{bmatrix} 1 & -\mathbf{c} \\ 0 & \mathbf{A} \end{bmatrix} \begin{bmatrix} z \\ \mathbf{x} \end{bmatrix} = \begin{bmatrix} 0 \\ \mathbf{b} \end{bmatrix}. \tag{7-5}$$

Equation (7-2) or (7-3) is referred to as Standard Form I for the revised simplex method. A linear programming problem with an identity matrix in $\mathbf{A}$ is cast into this form when it is to be solved by the revised simplex method.

Corresponding to each activity vector $\mathbf{a}_j$ of $\mathbf{A}$, we can define a new $(m + 1)$-component vector*

$$\mathbf{a}_j^{(1)} = [-c_j, \mathbf{a}_j] = [a_{0j}, \mathbf{a}_j], \qquad j = 1, \ldots, n, \qquad (7\text{--}6)$$

and corresponding to $\mathbf{b}$, we can define the $(m + 1)$-component vector

$$\mathbf{b}^{(1)} = [0, \mathbf{b}]. \qquad (7\text{--}7)$$

The column corresponding to $z = x_0$ is the $(m + 1)$-component unit vector $\mathbf{e}_1$.

A basis matrix for the set of equations (7–4) or (7–5) will be of order $m + 1$. We are seeking a basic solution to (7–4) or (7–5), with one of the basic variables being $z = x_0$ and the other m basic variables $x_{Bi} \geq 0$, such that, subject to the non-negativity restrictions, x_0 is as large as possible. Since we are trying to maximize x_0, this variable must be in every basic solution, i.e., the vector $\mathbf{e}_1$ corresponding to x_0 must be in every basis matrix. We shall assume that it is always in the first column. An $(m + 1) \times (m + 1)$ basis matrix containing $\mathbf{e}_1$ and m linearly independent vectors $\mathbf{a}_j^{(1)}$ will be denoted by $\mathbf{B}_1$, where

$$\mathbf{B}_1 = (\mathbf{e}_1, \mathbf{b}_1^{(1)}, \ldots, \mathbf{b}_m^{(1)}) = (\mathbf{b}_0^{(1)}, \mathbf{b}_1^{(1)}, \ldots, \mathbf{b}_m^{(1)}). \qquad (7\text{--}8)$$

As in the simplex method, the $\mathbf{b}_i^{(1)}$ refer to the columns of $\mathbf{B}_1$, and we must know by other means which $\mathbf{a}_j^{(1)}$ is in column i of $\mathbf{B}_1$. Clearly, $\mathbf{e}_1$ and any m vectors $\mathbf{a}_j^{(1)} = [a_{0j}, \mathbf{a}_j]$ such that the corresponding $\mathbf{a}_j$ are linearly independent will form a basis for E^{m+1} since there is no linear combination of the $\mathbf{a}_j^{(1)}$ which will yield a vector whose last m components are zero unless the scalar coefficient of each $\mathbf{a}_j^{(1)}$ is zero.

There is a one-to-one correspondence between the basis matrices $\mathbf{B}_1$ for the set of constraints (7–4) and the basis matrices $\mathbf{B}$ for the set of constraints $\mathbf{Ax} = \mathbf{b}$. In fact, it is very useful to write any $\mathbf{B}_1$ in the partitioned form

$$\mathbf{B}_1 = \begin{bmatrix} 1 & -\mathbf{c}_B \\ 0 & \mathbf{B} \end{bmatrix}, \qquad (7\text{--}9)$$

---

* Some notational difficulties are encountered in the discussion of the revised simplex method. For Standard Form I, all vectors have $m + 1$ components rather than m components, as was customary in the simplex method. Similarly, the basis matrix in Standard Form I is of order $m + 1$. For Standard Form II, all vectors have $m + 2$ components, and the basis matrix is of order $m + 2$. A superscript $^{(1)}$ on vectors will indicate that they have $m + 1$ components, and that they are the vectors for Standard Form I of the revised simplex method. A subscript $_1$ on a basis matrix will indicate that it is of order $m + 1$. A superscript $^{(2)}$ on vectors and a subscript $_2$ on the basis matrix will indicate the quantities appropriate to Standard Form II of the revised simplex method.

where $\mathbf{B}$ is the basis matrix for $\mathbf{Ax} = \mathbf{b}$ containing those columns $\mathbf{a}_j$ from $\mathbf{A}$ which are in the columns $\mathbf{a}_j^{(1)}$ that appear in $\mathbf{B}_1$. Equation (7–9) shows how to move from any basis matrix for $\mathbf{Ax} = \mathbf{b}$ to the corresponding basis matrix for (7–4) or (7–5), and vice versa.

The results of Chapter 2 on the partitioned form of the inverse allow us to write down immediately the inverse of (7–9). We see that

$$\mathbf{B}_1^{-1} = \begin{bmatrix} 1 & \mathbf{c}_B \mathbf{B}^{-1} \\ 0 & \mathbf{B}^{-1} \end{bmatrix}. \tag{7–10}$$

We can write any $\mathbf{a}_j^{(1)}$ as

$$\mathbf{a}_j^{(1)} = y_{0j}\mathbf{b}_0^{(1)} + y_{1j}\mathbf{b}_1^{(1)} + \cdots + y_{mj}\mathbf{b}_m^{(1)}, \tag{7–11}$$

or if

$$\mathbf{y}_j^{(1)} = [y_{0j}, \ldots, y_{mj}], \tag{7–12}$$

then

$$\mathbf{y}_j^{(1)} = \mathbf{B}_1^{-1}\mathbf{a}_j^{(1)}. \tag{7–13}$$

However, suppose that we use (7–10) for $\mathbf{B}_1^{-1}$ and (7–6) for $\mathbf{a}_j^{(1)}$. This yields

$$\mathbf{y}_j^{(1)} = \begin{bmatrix} 1 & \mathbf{c}_B \mathbf{B}^{-1} \\ 0 & \mathbf{B}^{-1} \end{bmatrix} \begin{bmatrix} -c_j \\ \mathbf{a}_j \end{bmatrix} = \begin{bmatrix} -c_j + \mathbf{c}_B \mathbf{B}^{-1}\mathbf{a}_j \\ \mathbf{B}^{-1}\mathbf{a}_j \end{bmatrix} = \begin{bmatrix} z_j - c_j \\ \mathbf{y}_j \end{bmatrix}. \tag{7–14}$$

We have obtained the interesting result that the first component of $\mathbf{y}_j^{(1)}$ is $z_j - c_j$, and the last m components make up $\mathbf{y}_j$. Here we have the reason for treating the objective function as one of the constraints. To find $z_j - c_j$ for any $\mathbf{a}_j$, we simply form the scalar product of the first row of $\mathbf{B}_1^{-1}$ with $\mathbf{a}_j^{(1)}$. This requires only m multiplications. We shall see that, in moving from one iteration to the next, we have to perform only $m + 1$ multiplications to obtain the first row of $\mathbf{B}_1^{-1}$. Thus, in order to compute $n - m$ of the $z_j - c_j$, only $nm - m^2 + m + 1$ multiplications are required. However, if we transformed only $\mathbf{B}^{-1}$, we would have to compute $\mathbf{c}_B \mathbf{B}^{-1}$ at each stage, and this would require m^2 multiplications, so that nm multiplications would be necessary to determine $n - m$ of the $z_j - c_j$. Unless m is negligible with respect to n, we avoid a considerable amount of computation by using the larger basis. In reality, all that is accomplished by using the larger basis is that $\mathbf{c}_B \mathbf{B}^{-1}$ as well as $\mathbf{B}^{-1}$ are transformed at each stage [see (7–10)].

Note: When discussing the number of arithmetic operations involved in any computation, we shall usually count only multiplications and divisions, because, by hand and on a digital computer, multiplication and division take considerably more time than addition or subtraction.

If we define the $(m + 1)$-component vector $\mathbf{x}_B^{(1)}$ by

$$\mathbf{x}_B^{(1)} = \mathbf{B}_1^{-1}\mathbf{b}^{(1)}, \tag{7-15}$$

then $\mathbf{x}_B^{(1)}$ is a basic solution for (7-4) corresponding to the basis matrix $\mathbf{B}_1$. From (7-7) and (7-10), we see that

$$\mathbf{x}_B^{(1)} = \begin{bmatrix} 1 & \mathbf{c}_B\mathbf{B}^{-1} \\ 0 & \mathbf{B}^{-1} \end{bmatrix} \begin{bmatrix} 0 \\ \mathbf{b} \end{bmatrix} = \begin{bmatrix} \mathbf{c}_B\mathbf{B}^{-1}\mathbf{b} \\ \mathbf{B}^{-1}\mathbf{b} \end{bmatrix} = \begin{bmatrix} z \\ \mathbf{x}_B \end{bmatrix}. \tag{7-16}$$

As expected, $\mathbf{x}_B^{(1)}$ contains as its first component z and as the remaining m components the x_{Bi} of the basic solution for $\mathbf{Ax} = \mathbf{b}$ corresponding to the basis matrix $\mathbf{B}$.

7-3 Computational procedure for Standard Form I. It should now be fairly clear how the above definitions are used in solving a linear programming problem. To apply Standard Form I we must assume that an identity matrix appears in $\mathbf{A}$. For the initial basis matrix for the system of constraints (7-4), we use the columns $\mathbf{a}_j^{(1)}$ for which the $\mathbf{a}_j$ yield the initial identity matrix in $\mathbf{A}$. The inverse of the first basis can then be written

$$\mathbf{B}_1^{-1} = \begin{bmatrix} 1 & \mathbf{c}_B \\ 0 & \mathbf{I}_m \end{bmatrix}, \tag{7-17}$$

and if the columns from $\mathbf{A}$ making up $\mathbf{I}_m$ correspond to slack variables, $\mathbf{c}_B = \mathbf{0}$. The initial basic solution to (7-4) is $\mathbf{x}_B^{(1)} = [\mathbf{c}_B\mathbf{b}, \mathbf{b}]$; it is feasible, since a feasible solution to (7-4) is one for which the last m components of $\mathbf{x}_B^{(1)}$ are non-negative; the first component z can have any sign. We now have a basic feasible solution to (7-4) and the inverse of the basis matrix.

To initiate the revised simplex method, we compute the $z_j - c_j$ for each $\mathbf{a}_j^{(1)}$ not in the basis by forming the scalar product of the first row of $\mathbf{B}_1^{-1}$ with each $\mathbf{a}_j^{(1)}$. The vector $\mathbf{a}_k^{(1)}$ to enter the basis is determined from

$$z_k - c_k = \min_j (z_j - c_j), \qquad z_j - c_j < 0. \tag{7-18}$$

If there is a tie, we can choose the smallest index j. Next we must determine the vector to be removed. Recall that we always wish to have $x_0 = z$ in the basis. Therefore, the first column of $\mathbf{B}_1$ is never a candidate for removal. Let us number the columns of $\mathbf{B}_1$ by $0, 1, \ldots, m$ so that the first column has the index 0. At the present time we do not have $\mathbf{y}_k^{(1)}$. We now compute $\mathbf{y}_k^{(1)}$ from $\mathbf{y}_k^{(1)} = \mathbf{B}_1^{-1}\mathbf{a}_k^{(1)} = [z_k - c_k, \mathbf{y}_k]$.

The vector to be removed is then determined in the usual way. We compute

$$\frac{x_{Br}}{y_{rk}} = \min_{i} \left\{ \frac{x_{Bi}}{y_{ik}}, \, y_{ik} > 0 \right\}, \qquad (7\text{--}19)$$

and remove column r of $\mathbf{B}_1$ (if the physical columns were counted, this would be column $r + 1$, but by our numbering it is column r). A tie can be broken in any of the ways discussed previously.

At this point, it might be noted that $\mathbf{B}_1^{-1}$ provides all the information necessary to ensure that cycling will not occur. The identity matrix from $\mathbf{A}$ appeared in the first $\mathbf{B}_1$ in columns $1, \ldots, m$. Therefore columns $1, \ldots, m$ of $\mathbf{B}_1^{-1}$ are equivalent to the first m columns in the usual simplex tableau, provided the columns making up the initial identity matrix come first in the tableau. Consequently, columns $1, \ldots, m$ of $\mathbf{B}_1^{-1}$ can be used to determine uniquely the vector to leave the basis.

Having obtained the vector to enter the basis and the vector to leave the basis, we are now ready to perform the transformation to the new basic feasible solution of (7–4), where the first component of $\mathbf{x}_B^{(1)}$ is at least as large as the preceding one. In the revised simplex method, only the quantities $\mathbf{x}_B^{(1)}$ and $\mathbf{B}_1^{-1}$ are transformed. We transform $\mathbf{x}_B^{(1)}$ as well as $\mathbf{B}_1^{-1}$, since only $m + 1$ multiplications are required to transform $\mathbf{x}_B^{(1)}$, while its computation from the definition $\mathbf{x}_B^{(1)} = \mathbf{B}_1^{-1}\mathbf{b}_1$ requires $m(m + 1)$ multiplications.

If the new inverse is denoted by $\hat{\mathbf{B}}_1^{-1}$ and the new basic solution by $\hat{\mathbf{x}}_B^{(1)}$, then, using the theory developed in Chapter 2, we see that

$$\hat{\mathbf{B}}_1^{-1} = \mathbf{E}_1\mathbf{B}_1^{-1},$$
$$\hat{\mathbf{x}}_B^{(1)} = \mathbf{E}_1\mathbf{B}_1^{-1}\mathbf{b}^{(1)} = \mathbf{E}_1\mathbf{x}_B^{(1)}. \qquad (7\text{--}20)$$

Matrix $\mathbf{E}_1$ has the form

$$\mathbf{E}_1 = (\mathbf{e}_1, \ldots, \mathbf{e}_r, \boldsymbol{\eta}^{(1)}, \mathbf{e}_{r+2}, \ldots, \mathbf{e}_{m+1}). \qquad (7\text{--}21)$$

We must be careful to notice that $\boldsymbol{\eta}^{(1)}$ appears in column $r + 1$ of $\mathbf{E}_1$. This is the case because the actual physical column of $\mathbf{B}_1$ which is being removed is $r + 1$. We called it column r of $\mathbf{B}_1$, since we numbered the columns $0, 1, \ldots, m$. Then

$$\boldsymbol{\eta}^{(1)} = \left[-\frac{z_k - c_k}{y_{rk}}, \, -\frac{y_{1k}}{y_{rk}}, \ldots, \frac{1}{y_{rk}}, \ldots, -\frac{y_{mk}}{y_{rk}} \right]. \qquad (7\text{--}22)$$

It is a little more convenient to apply a transformation formula of vector type (like that developed for the simplex method) than use multiplication by $\mathbf{E}_1$. Suppose that we denote the last m columns of $\mathbf{B}_1^{-1}$ by $\boldsymbol{\beta}_1^{(1)}, \ldots,$ $\boldsymbol{\beta}_m^{(1)}$ and $\boldsymbol{\beta}_j^{(1)} = [\beta_{0j}, \beta_{1j}, \ldots, \beta_{mj}]$. Then

$$\hat{\mathbf{B}}_1^{-1} = (\mathbf{e}_1, \hat{\boldsymbol{\beta}}_1^{(1)}, \ldots, \hat{\boldsymbol{\beta}}_m^{(1)}) = \mathbf{E}_1 \mathbf{B}_1^{-1} = (\mathbf{e}_1, \mathbf{E}_1 \boldsymbol{\beta}_1^{(1)}, \ldots, \mathbf{E}_1 \boldsymbol{\beta}_m^{(1)}), \quad (7\text{-}23)$$

and hence

$$\hat{\boldsymbol{\beta}}_j^{(1)} = \mathbf{E}_1 \boldsymbol{\beta}_j^{(1)}, \qquad j = 1, \ldots, m; \qquad \hat{\mathbf{x}}_B^{(1)} = \mathbf{E}_1 \mathbf{x}_B^{(1)}. \qquad (7\text{-}24)$$

Let us write $\boldsymbol{\Phi}^{(1)} = \boldsymbol{\eta}^{(1)} - \mathbf{e}_{r+1}$; then

$$\hat{\boldsymbol{\beta}}_j^{(1)} = \boldsymbol{\beta}_j^{(1)} + \beta_{rj} \boldsymbol{\Phi}^{(1)}, \qquad \hat{\mathbf{x}}_B^{(1)} = \mathbf{x}_B^{(1)} + x_{Br} \boldsymbol{\Phi}^{(1)}, \qquad (7\text{-}25)$$

where

$$\boldsymbol{\Phi}^{(1)} = \left[-\frac{z_k - c_k}{y_{rk}}, \; -\frac{y_{1k}}{y_{rk}}, \ldots, \frac{1}{y_{rk}} - 1, \ldots, \; -\frac{y_{mk}}{y_{rk}} \right]. \qquad (7\text{-}26)$$

The "ring around the rosy" method of transformation can also be used here for the following reason: If we write

$$\beta_{00} = z, \qquad \beta_{i0} = x_{Bi}, \qquad i = 1, \ldots, m; \qquad y_{0k} = z_k - c_k, \qquad (7\text{-}27)$$

then the transformation formulas (7–25) can be written

$$\hat{\beta}_{ij} = \beta_{ij} - \frac{y_{ik}}{y_{rk}} \beta_{rj}, \qquad i = 0, \ldots, m, \qquad i \neq r, \qquad j = 0, \ldots, m,$$

$$(7\text{-}28)$$

$$\hat{\beta}_{rj} = \frac{\beta_{rj}}{y_{rk}}. \qquad (7\text{-}29)$$

We have shown how to transform $\mathbf{B}_1^{-1}$ and $\mathbf{x}_B^{(1)}$ when we move from one basic feasible solution to the next. Using the new $\mathbf{B}_1^{-1}$, we find the new $z_j - c_j$ by forming the scalar product of the first row of $\mathbf{B}_1^{-1}$ with the $\mathbf{a}_j^{(1)}$ not in the basis. If all $\hat{z}_j - c_j$ are not ≥ 0, the whole process is repeated.

The computations for the revised simplex method can also be arranged into a convenient tableau form (see Table 7–1). Note that the first column of $\mathbf{B}_1^{-1}$ is always $\mathbf{e}_1$. Therefore, we never need this column in the tableau and we never need to transform it. We only need columns $\boldsymbol{\beta}_1^{(1)}, \ldots, \boldsymbol{\beta}_m^{(1)}$ of $\mathbf{B}_1^{-1}$, $\mathbf{x}_B^{(1)}$, and $\mathbf{y}_k^{(1)}$. It is somewhat more complicated to use this tableau form than that for the simplex method because the given tableau does not contain all necessary information. In addition to constructing a tableau like Table 7–1 at each step, we must have a tableau containing the vectors $\mathbf{a}_j^{(1)}$.

In moving from one iteration to the next, we first fill in the columns $\boldsymbol{\beta}_1^{(1)}, \ldots, \boldsymbol{\beta}_m^{(1)}, \mathbf{x}_B^{(1)}$ of the new tableau, using the transformation formulas

(7–25) or (7–28) and (7–29), together with the pertinent information in the preceding tableau. The $y_k^{(1)}$-column is not filled in at this point. We next use the first row of the new tableau and the vectors $\mathbf{a}_j^{(1)}$ in the additional tableau and perform some side computations on "scratch paper" to find the $z_j - c_j$. This determines the vector to enter the basis at the next step. We can now fill in the $y_k^{(1)}$-column, since $\mathbf{a}_k^{(1)}$ has been determined. To find $\mathbf{y}_k^{(1)}$, we use $\mathbf{y}_k^{(1)} = \mathbf{B}_1^{-1}\mathbf{a}_k^{(1)}$; this computation is also made on scratch paper. Then, the vector to be removed can be obtained from the numbers in the last two columns (if one wishes to use the rigorous method to ensure that cycling will not occur, the first m columns in the tableau may also be needed).

The above procedure is the revised simplex method for Standard Form I. This form can be used when no artificial vectors are needed. It should be noted that if a problem is solved by the revised simplex method, it is not easy to find the corresponding tableaux for the standard simplex method. The revised simplex method does not compute all the $\mathbf{y}_j$, which, if needed, must be computed from $\mathbf{B}_1^{-1}\mathbf{a}_j^{(1)}$. It is easy to move from a tableau for the standard simplex method to one for the revised simplex method because $\mathbf{B}^{-1}$ is available, and we need to compute only the first row $\mathbf{c}_B\mathbf{B}^{-1}$ of the revised simplex tableau.

TABLE 7–1

TABLEAU FORM OF THE REVISED SIMPLEX METHOD

STANDARD FORM I

Variables in Basis	$\boldsymbol{\beta}_1^{(1)}$	$\cdots\cdots\cdots\cdots$	$\boldsymbol{\beta}_m^{(1)}$	$\mathbf{x}_B^{(1)}$	$\mathbf{y}_k^{(1)}$
x_0	β_{01}		β_{0m}	$z = x_0$	$z_k - c_k$
x_{B1}	$\cdot$		$\cdot$	x_{B1}	y_{1k}
$\cdot$	$\cdot$		$\cdot$	$\cdot$	$\cdot$
$\cdot$	$\cdot$		$\cdot$	$\cdot$	$\cdot$
$\cdot$	$\cdot$		$\cdot$	$\cdot$	$\cdot$
x_{Bm}	β_{m1}		β_{mm}	x_{Bm}	y_{mk}

7-4 Revised simplex method : Standard Form II.   Standard Form II is used when artificial vectors must be added to obtain an identity matrix for the initial basis matrix.   The two-phase method is used to handle the artificial variables: In Phase I, the artificial variables are driven to zero, and in Phase II, an optimal solution to the original problem is found.

We have noted previously that if some artificial variables appear in the basis at a zero level upon termination of Phase I, special precautions must be taken to make sure that these variables do not become positive in Phase II.   In Chapter 5 we have outlined one procedure for keeping the artificial variables at a zero level in Phase II.

Dantzig and Orchard-Hays do not use that procedure in the revised simplex method.   Instead, at the beginning of Phase II, they annex the additional constraint equation

$$\sum_{i=1}^{s} x_{ai} = 0. \qquad (7\text{-}30)$$

Since the simplex method always maintains each $x_{ai} \geq 0$, Eq. (7-30) requires that all artificial variables be zero.

In the discussion of Standard Form I, we have seen that it is very convenient to treat the function to be optimized as one of the constraints.   Let us use this approach in setting up the two-phase method.   To be specific, it will be assumed that an artificial variable was added to each constraint equation.

In Phase I, we have the following set of equations:

$$
\begin{aligned}
z^* + x_{a1} + \cdots + x_{am} &= 0, \\
x_{a1} \qquad\qquad\quad + a_{11}x_1 + \cdots + a_{1n}x_n &= b_1, \\
&\ \ \vdots \\
x_{am} + a_{m1}x_1 + \cdots + a_{mn}x_n &= b_m.
\end{aligned}
\qquad (7\text{-}31)
$$

We wish to find a basic feasible solution to (7-31) with z^* in the basis, which maximizes z^* (recall that a basic feasible solution to (7-31) does not require that z^* be non-negative).   If we write $z^* = x_{n+1}$, $x_{a1} = x_{n+2}$, $\ldots, x_{am} = x_{n+m+1}$, then (7-31) can be written in the more symmetrical form

$$
\begin{aligned}
x_{n+1} + x_{n+2} + \cdots + x_{n+m+1} &= 0, \\
a_{11}x_1 + \cdots + a_{1n}x_n \qquad + x_{n+2} \qquad\qquad &= b_1, \\
\vdots \qquad\qquad\qquad\qquad\qquad\quad & \\
a_{m1}x_1 + \cdots + a_{mn}x_n \qquad\qquad\qquad + x_{n+m+1} &= b_m,
\end{aligned}
\qquad (7\text{-}32)
$$

and x_{n+1} is to be maximized.

If max $x_{n+1} = 0$, we go on to Phase II. When max $x_{n+1} < 0$, there is no feasible solution to the problem. Let us assume that max $x_{n+1} = 0$, and that one or more artificial vectors may be in the basis at a zero level when Phase I terminates. Then in Phase II, we deal with the following set of equations:

$$
\begin{aligned}
z - c_1 x_1 - \cdots - c_n x_n &= 0, \\
x_{n+2} + \cdots + x_{n+m+1} &= 0, \\
a_{11} x_1 + \cdots + a_{1n} x_n + x_{n+2} &= b_1, \quad (7\text{--}33) \\
\vdots \qquad\qquad \ddots \qquad\qquad & \\
a_{m1} x_1 + \cdots + a_{mn} x_n \qquad\qquad + x_{n+m+1} &= b_m.
\end{aligned}
$$

The second constraint equation is the one added to ensure that the artificial vectors remain zero. It is convenient to increase the row index by one and to rewrite the original constraint matrix $\mathbf{A}$ and the requirements vector $\mathbf{b}$ as follows:

$$
\mathbf{A} = \begin{bmatrix} a_{21} & \cdots & a_{2n} \\ \vdots & & \vdots \\ a_{m+1,1} & \cdots & a_{m+1,n} \end{bmatrix}, \qquad \mathbf{b} = [b_2, \ldots, b_{m+1}].
$$

This permits us to write (7–33) in the more symmetrical form

$$
\begin{aligned}
x_0 + a_{01} x_1 \quad + \cdots + a_{0n} x_n &= 0, \\
x_{n+2} + \cdots + x_{n+m+1} &= 0, \\
a_{21} x_1 \quad + \cdots + a_{2n} x_n \quad + x_{n+2} &= b_2, \quad (7\text{--}34) \\
\vdots \qquad\qquad \ddots \qquad\qquad & \\
a_{m+1,1} x_1 + \cdots + a_{m+1,n} x_n \qquad\qquad + x_{n+m+1} &= b_{m+1}.
\end{aligned}
$$

We can now note that, aside from the variable x_{n+1}, (7–34) is merely (7–32) plus an additional equation. However, at the end of Phase I, $x_{n+1} = 0$; hence, we could include it in (7–34) without changing anything, since the simplex method will always maintain it at a zero level. This leads to the interesting conclusion that the function to be optimized in Phase I serves as a constraint for the purpose of keeping the artificial variables at a zero level in Phase II. When x_{n+1} is included in (7–34), we have

$$
\begin{aligned}
x_0 + a_{01} x_1 + \cdots + a_{0n} x_n &= 0, \\
x_{n+1} + x_{n+2} + \cdots + x_{n+m+1} &= 0, \quad (7\text{--}35) \\
a_{21} x_1 + \cdots + a_{2n} x_n \quad + x_{n+2} &= b_2, \\
\vdots \qquad\qquad \ddots \qquad\qquad & \\
a_{m+1,1} x_1 + \cdots + a_{m+1,n} x_n \qquad\qquad + x_{n+m+1} &= b_{m+1}.
\end{aligned}
$$

At this point, the following question may be asked: "Why not use the single set of equations (7–35) in both Phase I and Phase II?" In Phase I, we maximize x_{n+1} (and ignore x_0), and in Phase II, we maximize x_0. During Phase I, all variables except x_0, x_{n+1} are required to be non-negative. During Phase II, x_0 is the only variable which does not need to be non-negative. This means that, in Phase I, the first equation involving the actual function to be optimized is merely carried along, and if no artificial vectors appear in the basis at the end of Phase I, then in Phase II, the same is true for the constraint which maintains the artificial vectors at a zero level. This is precisely what is done. The set of equations (7–35) is referred to as Standard Form II for the revised simplex method.

7–5 Computational procedure for Standard Form II. We are now ready to examine the details of the computation by means of Standard Form II. Let us denote the column vector corresponding to any variable x_j in (7–35) by

$$\mathbf{a}_j^{(2)} = [a_{0j}, a_{1j}, \ldots, a_{m+1,j}]. \tag{7–36}$$

For legitimate vectors,

$$\mathbf{a}_j^{(2)} = [-c_j, 0, \mathbf{a}_j], \qquad j = 1, \ldots, n, \tag{7–37}$$

and for artificial vectors,

$$\mathbf{a}_{n+1+i}^{(2)} = \mathbf{q}_i^{(2)} = [0, 1, \mathbf{e}_i]. \tag{7–38}$$

The vector corresponding to x_0 is $\mathbf{e}_1$, and the vector corresponding to x_{n+1} is $\mathbf{e}_2$. The rank of the matrix of the coefficients in (7–35) is $m + 2$ so that any basis matrix will be of order $m + 2$ and will be denoted by

$$\mathbf{B}_2 = (\mathbf{e}_1, \mathbf{b}_1^{(2)}, \ldots, \mathbf{b}_{m+1}^{(2)}) = (\mathbf{b}_0^{(2)}, \mathbf{b}_1^{(2)}, \ldots, \mathbf{b}_{m+1}^{(2)}). \tag{7–39}$$

It will be assumed that the first column of $\mathbf{B}_2$ always contains $\mathbf{e}_1$. In Phase I, the second column of $\mathbf{B}_2$ will always contain $\mathbf{e}_2$. A basic solution to (7–35) is feasible if all variables except x_0, x_{n+1} are non-negative in Phase I and all variables except x_0 are non-negative in Phase II.

A basic feasible solution to (7–35) can be obtained by setting all variables to zero, except x_0, x_{n+1} and the artificial variables. The basis matrix is

$$\mathbf{B}_2 = \begin{bmatrix} 1 & 0 & 0 \cdots 0 \\ 0 & 1 & 1 \cdots 1 \\ 0 & 0 & 1 \cdots 0 \\ \vdots & & \vdots \\ 0 & 0 & 0 \cdots 1 \end{bmatrix}, \tag{7–40}$$

and it is not an identity matrix. However, if we apply in two steps the procedure of Chapter 2 for computing the inverse by partitioning, we immediately see that the inverse is

$$
\mathbf{B}_2^{-1} = \begin{bmatrix} 1 & 0 & 0 \cdots & 0 \\ 0 & 1 & -1 \cdots & -1 \\ 0 & 0 & 1 \cdots & 0 \\ \vdots & & & \vdots \\ 0 & 0 & 0 \cdots & 1 \end{bmatrix} = \left[\begin{array}{cc|c} 1 & 0 & 0 \\ \hline 0 & 1 & -\mathbf{1}_m \\ \hline 0 & & \mathbf{I}_m \end{array} \right]. \tag{7-41}
$$

This is easily checked by showing that $\mathbf{B}_2^{-1}\mathbf{B}_2 = \mathbf{I}_{m+2}$.

If the right-hand side of (7–35) is denoted by $\mathbf{b}^{(2)}$, then the basic feasible solution $\mathbf{x}_B^{(2)}$ whose corresponding basis matrix is $\mathbf{B}_2$ can be written

$$
\mathbf{x}_B^{(2)} = \mathbf{B}_2^{-1}\mathbf{b}^{(2)} = [x_0, x_{B1}, \ldots, x_{B,m+1}], \tag{7-42}
$$

and when $\mathbf{B}_2$ is given by (7–40), then

$$
\mathbf{x}_B^{(2)} = \left[0, \ -\sum_{i=2}^{m+1} b_i, b_2, \ldots, b_{m+1} \right]. \tag{7-43}
$$

Equations (7–41) and (7–43) yield the $\mathbf{x}_B^{(2)}$ and the $\mathbf{B}_2^{-1}$ needed to get started.

In Phase I, we can partition any $\mathbf{B}_2$ containing $\mathbf{e}_1$ in the first column, $\mathbf{e}_2$ in the second column, and m vectors $\mathbf{a}_j^{(2)}$ as follows:

$$
\mathbf{B}_2 = \left[\begin{array}{cc|c} 1 & 0 & -\mathbf{c}_B \\ \hline 0 & 1 & -\mathbf{c}_B^* \\ \hline 0 & & \mathbf{B} \end{array} \right],
$$

where $\mathbf{B}$ is the corresponding basis for $\mathbf{Ax} = \mathbf{b}$ containing the $\mathbf{a}_j$, $\mathbf{c}_B^*$ contains the prices appropriate to Phase I, and $\mathbf{c}_B$ the prices appropriate to Phase II. On computing the inverse by partitioning, we see that the second row of $\mathbf{B}_2^{-1}$ is $(0, 1, \mathbf{c}_B^*\mathbf{B}^{-1})$. It is immediately evident that the scalar product of the second row of $\mathbf{B}_2^{-1}$ with any legitimate $\mathbf{a}_j^{(2)}$ is the $z_j - c_j$ for Phase I, that is, $z_j^* - c_j^*$.

To determine the vector to enter the basis in Phase I, we form the scalar product of the second row of $\mathbf{B}_2^{-1}$ with each legitimate $\mathbf{a}_j^{(2)}$ not in the basis. The $\mathbf{a}_k^{(2)}$ yielding the smallest such number is the vector to enter the basis provided the smallest number is negative. If we define

$$\mathbf{y}_j^{(2)} = \mathbf{B}_2^{-1}\mathbf{a}_j^{(2)} = [y_{0j}, y_{1j}, \ldots, y_{m+1,j}], \tag{7–44}$$

it is clear that since $\mathbf{B}^{-1}$ appears in the lower right-hand corner of $\mathbf{B}_2^{-1}$, the last m components of $\mathbf{y}_j^{(2)}$ are the $\mathbf{y}_j$ for the corresponding basic solution to $\mathbf{Ax} = \mathbf{b}$. Similarly, the last m components of $\mathbf{x}_B^{(2)}$ are the x_{Bi}. Because of our previous change in the subscripts of the a_{ij}, the quantities $x_{B,i+1}$, $y_{i+1,j}$ in (7–42) and (7–44) correspond to x_{Bi}, y_{ij} for the corresponding solution to $\mathbf{Ax} = \mathbf{b}$.

In Phase I, the first two columns never leave the basis. Hence the vector to be removed is determined from

$$\frac{x_{Br}}{y_{rk}} = \min_i \left\{ \frac{x_{Bi}}{y_{ik}}, y_{ik} > 0 \right\}, \qquad i = 2, \ldots, m+1, \tag{7–45}$$

where the x_{Bi}, y_{ik} are those defined by (7–42) and (7–44).

We are now ready to perform the transformation to the new basic solution. This can be done exactly as in Standard Form I, and hence we shall not repeat it. Phase I terminates when $x_{n+1} = 0$ or when all the $z_j - c_j$ for Phase I are non-negative.

For Phase II, we can imagine $\mathbf{B}_2$ partitioned as

$$\mathbf{B}_2 = \begin{bmatrix} 1 & -\mathbf{c}_B^{(1)\prime} \\ 0 & \mathbf{B}_1 \end{bmatrix}, \tag{7–46}$$

where $\mathbf{B}_1$ is a basis matrix of order $m+1$ for the set of constraints which includes the constraint maintaining the artificial vectors at a zero level. From this it immediately follows that the first row of $\mathbf{B}_2^{-1}$ is $(1, \mathbf{c}_B^{(1)\prime}\mathbf{B}_1^{-1})$, and $\mathbf{c}_B^{(1)}$ contains the $m+1$ prices of the vectors in $\mathbf{B}_1$. Therefore, the scalar product of the first row of $\mathbf{B}_2^{-1}$ with any legitimate vector $\mathbf{a}_j^{(2)}$ gives $z_j - c_j$ for Phase II. Hence the scalar product of the first row of $\mathbf{B}_2^{-1}$ with the $\mathbf{a}_j^{(2)}$ yields the set of numbers which determines the vector to enter the basis.

In Phase II, x_{n+1} is treated like any other artificial variable; it can be removed from the basic solution. Only x_0 must always remain in the basic solution. However, we are sure that there will always be at least one artificial vector in $\mathbf{B}_2$ because it is not possible to have an $(m+2)$-dimensional basis without one. Having decided that $\mathbf{a}_k^{(2)}$ will enter the basis, we compute

$$\mathbf{y}_k^{(2)} = \mathbf{B}_2^{-1}\mathbf{a}_k^{(2)} = [y_{0k}, y_{1k}, \ldots, y_{m+1,k}].$$

The vector to leave the basis is then found from

$$\frac{x_{Br}}{y_{rk}} = \min_i \left\{ \frac{x_{Bi}}{y_{ik}}, y_{ik} > 0 \right\}, \qquad i = 1, \ldots, m+1. \tag{7–47}$$

The tableau for Standard Form II is the same as for Standard Form I except that there are an additional row and column. Although the second column of $\mathbf{B}_2^{-1}$ is always $\mathbf{e}_2$ in Phase I, it is included in the tableau since it may change in Phase II. It should always be remembered in Phase II that there is a 1 which is the first component of the first row of $\mathbf{B}_2^{-1}$ that does not appear in the tableau since the first column of $\mathbf{B}_2^{-1}$ is not included.

It may appear at first glance that more computations are required if Standard Form II of the revised simplex method is used than if (7–32) were used for Phase I, and (7–33) for Phase II only when one or more artificial vectors appear in the basis at a zero level at the end of Phase I; i.e., it seems unnecessary to carry along the extra equation in Phase I and to use the additional constraint in Phase II unless it is required. However, this is not correct. If the basis of order $m + 2$ were not used in Phase I, then, at the end of Phase I, computations would have to be performed to find the first row $(0, \mathbf{c}_B^{(1)'}\mathbf{B}_1^{-1})$ for the basis inverse to be used in the initial iteration of Phase II; m or more iterations would be necessary in Phase I before the computations would equal those required to make the conversion. If no artificial vectors appear in the basis at the end of Phase I, no computations are required to transform the second row of $\mathbf{B}_2^{-1}$ in Phase II, since x_{n+1} will never leave the basis and the second row will remain $\mathbf{e}_2'$. Finally, using the same format in both phases simplifies the coding of the problem for a digital computer.

7–6 Initial identity matrix for Phase I. The line of 1's in the second row of the initial basis (7–40) did not bother us since it was very easy to invert the matrix by partitioning. Dantzig *et al.* found it of advantage to begin the solution on a digital computer, using an exact identity matrix as a basis matrix for a reason to be explained in Section 7–9. Hence the row of 1's in (7–40) had to be removed. This can be easily done: Suppose that in (7–35) we subtract from the second row the sum of rows 3 through $m + 2$, i.e., we consider

$$x_{n+1} + \sum_{i=2}^{m+1} x_{n+i} - \sum_{i=2}^{m+1} a_{i1}x_1 - \cdots$$

$$- \sum_{i=2}^{m+1} a_{in}x_n - \sum_{i=2}^{m+1} x_{n+i} = - \sum_{i=2}^{m+1} b_i.$$

This yields a new equation,

$$x_{n+1} - \sum_{i=2}^{m+1} a_{i1}x_1 - \cdots - \sum_{i=2}^{m+1} a_{in}x_n = - \sum_{i=2}^{m+1} b_i. \qquad (7\text{–}48)$$

Let us use (7–48) for the second equation. The new system can be written

$$
\begin{aligned}
x_0 + a_{01}x_1 &\quad + \cdots + a_{0n}x_n &&&& = 0, \\
a_{11}x_1 &\quad + \cdots + a_{1n}x_n &\quad + x_{n+1} &&& = b_1, \\
a_{21}x_1 &\quad + \cdots + a_{2n}x_n &&\quad + x_{n+2} && = b_2, \qquad (7\text{–}49) \\
&\vdots &&&\ddots \\
a_{m+1,1}x_1 &+ \cdots + a_{m+1,n}x_n &&&\quad + x_{n+m+1} &= b_{m+1},
\end{aligned}
$$

where

$$
a_{1j} = - \sum_{i=2}^{m+1} a_{ij}, \qquad j = 1, \ldots, n, \qquad b_1 = - \sum_{i=2}^{m+1} b_i.
$$

We now apply the revised simplex method to the system (7–49). It will be noted that the initial basis matrix $\mathbf{B}_2$ is a strict identity matrix $\mathbf{I}_{m+2}$. To convince ourselves that (7–49) is equivalent to (7–35), it is only necessary to show that maximizing x_{n+1} [given by the second row of (7–49)] drives all artificial variables to zero, provided they can be driven to zero. First note that when each artificial variable is zero, then $\sum_{j=1}^{n} a_{ij}x_j = b_i$ $(i = 2, \ldots, m + 1)$, and hence,

$$
- \sum_{i=2}^{m+1} a_{i1}x_1 - \cdots - \sum_{i=2}^{m+1} a_{in}x_n = - \sum_{i=2}^{m+1} b_i,
$$

or $x_{n+1} = 0$. Furthermore, since each artificial variable is positive,

$$
- \sum_{j=1}^{n} \sum_{i=2}^{m+1} a_{ij}x_j \geq - \sum_{i=2}^{m+1} b_i,
$$

and $x_{n+1} \leq 0$ always. Finally, if any artificial variable is positive, $x_{n+1} < 0$. Therefore, if $\max x_{n+1} = 0$, maximizing x_{n+1} in (7–49) drives all artificial variables to zero.

The details of applying the revised simplex method to (7–49) are precisely what has been already described, provided we make the following definitions:

$$
\mathbf{a}_j^{(2)} = [-c_j, -\mathbf{1}a_j, \mathbf{a}_j]; \qquad \mathbf{b}^{(2)} = [0, -\mathbf{1}b, \mathbf{b}]. \qquad (7\text{–}50)
$$

7–7 An example. Using the revised simplex method, let us solve the following linear programming problem:

$$
\begin{aligned}
2x_1 + 5x_2 &\geq 6, \\
x_1 + x_2 &\geq 2, \\
x_1, x_2 &\geq 0, \qquad\qquad (7\text{–}51) \\
\min z = x_1 + 2x_2.
\end{aligned}
$$

This problem can be converted to

$$2x_1 + 5x_2 - x_3 + x_{a1} = 6,$$
$$x_1 + x_2 - x_4 + x_{a2} = 2,$$
$$x_1, x_2, x_3, x_4, x_{a1}, x_{a2} \geq 0,$$
$$\max x_0 = -x_1 - 2x_2.$$

Since we had to add artificial variables, we must use Standard Form II of the revised simplex method. In this form, the problem becomes (if we write $x_{a1} = x_6$, $x_{a2} = x_7$)

$$x_0 + x_1 + 2x_2 = 0,$$
$$x_5 + x_6 + x_7 = 0,$$
$$2x_1 + 5x_2 - x_3 + x_6 = 6,$$
$$x_1 + x_2 - x_4 + x_7 = 2.$$

In Phase I, we maximize x_5 and in Phase II, we maximize x_0. The vectors are

$$\mathbf{a}_1^{(2)} = [1, 0, 2, 1], \qquad \mathbf{a}_2^{(2)} = [2, 0, 5, 1], \qquad \mathbf{a}_3^{(2)} = [0, 0, -1, 0],$$
$$\mathbf{a}_4^{(2)} = [0, 0, 0, -1], \qquad \mathbf{a}_5^{(2)} = \mathbf{e}_2, \qquad \mathbf{a}_6^{(2)} = [0, 1, 1, 0],$$
$$\mathbf{a}_7^{(2)} = [0, 1, 0, 1], \qquad \mathbf{b}^{(2)} = [0, 0, 6, 2].$$

The inverse of the initial basis is

$$\mathbf{B}_2^{-1} = \begin{bmatrix} 1 & 0 & 0 & 0 \\ 0 & 1 & -1 & -1 \\ 0 & 0 & 1 & 0 \\ 0 & 0 & 0 & 1 \end{bmatrix},$$

and the initial basic feasible solution is

$$\mathbf{x}_B^{(2)} = [x_0, x_5, x_6, x_7] = [0, -8, 6, 2].$$

The initial tableau is shown in Table (7–2). The first column of $\mathbf{B}_2^{-1}$ is not included because it is always $\mathbf{e}_1$. The $\mathbf{y}_k^{(2)}$-column is not filled in until the vector to enter the basis is determined.

In Phase I, we determine the vector to enter the basis by finding the smallest $z_j^* - c_j^* < 0$, where $z_j^* - c_j^*$ is the scalar product of the second row of $\mathbf{B}_2^{-1}$ with $\mathbf{a}_j^{(2)}$. At the first iteration, we have $z_1^* - c_1^* = -2 - 1 = -3$, $z_2^* - c_2^* = -5 - 1 = -6$, $z_3^* - c_3^* = 1$, $z_4^* - c_4^* = 1$. Hence $\mathbf{a}_2^{(2)}$ enters the basis. Now we compute $\mathbf{y}_2^{(2)} = \mathbf{B}_2^{-1} \mathbf{a}_2^{(2)}$. This

TABLE 7–2 — TABLEAU 1

Variables in Basis	$\boldsymbol{\beta}_1^{(2)}$	$\boldsymbol{\beta}_2^{(2)}$	$\boldsymbol{\beta}_3^{(2)}$	$\mathbf{x}_B^{(2)}$	$\mathbf{y}_k^{(2)}$
x_0	0	0	0	0	2
x_5	1	−1	−1	−8	−6
x_6	0	1	0	6	5
x_7	0	0	1	2	1

result appears in the $\mathbf{y}_k^{(2)}$-column of Table 7–2. The vector to leave the basis is determined from

$$\min \left(\tfrac{6}{5}, \tfrac{2}{1}\right) = \tfrac{6}{5}.$$

Thus $\mathbf{b}_2^{(2)}$, the third column of $\mathbf{B}_2$, is replaced by $\mathbf{a}_2^{(2)}$.

A new tableau for the new basic feasible solution must be found. If we use the vector transformation formula, then

$$\boldsymbol{\Phi}^{(2)} = [-\tfrac{2}{5}, \tfrac{6}{5}, \tfrac{1}{5} - 1, -\tfrac{1}{5}] = [-0.40, 1.20, -0.80, -0.20],$$

and

$$\hat{\boldsymbol{\beta}}_j^{(2)} = \boldsymbol{\beta}_j^{(2)} + \beta_{2j}\boldsymbol{\Phi}^{(2)}; \qquad \hat{\mathbf{x}}_B^{(2)} = \mathbf{x}_B^{(2)} + x_{B2}\boldsymbol{\Phi}^{(2)}.$$

For example,

$$\hat{\boldsymbol{\beta}}_2^{(2)} = [0, -1, 1, 0] + 1[-0.40, 1.20, -0.80, -0.20]$$
$$= [-0.40, 0.20, 0.20, -0.20],$$

and

$$\hat{\mathbf{x}}_B^{(2)} = [0, -8, 6, 2] + 6[-0.40, 1.20, -0.80, -0.20]$$
$$= [-2.40, -0.80, 1.20, 0.80].$$

The new tableau is presented in Table 7–3.

At this stage, x_5 is still not zero; hence the end of Phase I has not been reached. Forming the scalar product of the second row of $\mathbf{B}_2^{-1}$ in Table 7–3 with each $\mathbf{a}_j^{(2)}$ not in the basis, we find

$$z_1^* - c_1^* = -0.6, \qquad z_3^* - c_3^* = -0.20, \qquad z_4^* - c_4^* = 1.$$

TABLE 7–3 — TABLEAU 2

Variables in Basis	$\boldsymbol{\beta}_1^{(2)}$	$\boldsymbol{\beta}_2^{(2)}$	$\boldsymbol{\beta}_3^{(2)}$	$\mathbf{x}_B^{(2)}$	$\mathbf{y}_k^{(2)}$
x_0	0	-0.40	0	-2.40	0.20
x_5	1	0.20	-1	-0.80	-0.60
x_2	0	0.20	0	1.20	0.40
x_7	0	-0.20	1	0.80	0.60

Therefore $\mathbf{a}_1^{(2)}$ enters at the next iteration. Then $\mathbf{y}_1^{(2)}$ is computed. The vector to be removed is the last column of the basis. The new tableau is given in Table 7–4. Here $x_0 = 0$; hence all artificial variables are zero, and Phase I is ended.

To initiate Phase II, we take the scalar product of the first row of $\mathbf{B}_2^{-1}$ in Table 7–4 with each $\mathbf{a}_j^{(2)}$ not in the basis. This gives

$$z_3 - c_3 = 0.333, \qquad z_4 - c_4 = 0.333.$$

Both of these values are positive, and consequently the solution is optimal. No iterations need to be made in Phase II. We see that min $z = -\max x_0 = 2.667$. The $\mathbf{y}_k^{(2)}$-column in the last tableau is not filled in since no more iterations are to be made. In this example, we did not replace the second row $\sum_{i=1}^{m+1} x_{n+i} = 0$ by (7–48). We could have done this, but for hand

TABLE 7–4 — TABLEAU 3

Variables in Basis	$\boldsymbol{\beta}_1^{(2)}$	$\boldsymbol{\beta}_2^{(2)}$	$\boldsymbol{\beta}_3^{(2)}$	$\mathbf{x}_B^{(2)}$	$\mathbf{y}_k^{(2)}$
x_0	0	-0.333	-0.333	-2.667	
x_5	1	0	0	0	
x_2	0	0.333	-0.667	0.667	
x_1	0	-0.333	1.667	1.333	

computations it is not necessary. The reader may easily check the correctness of the solution by solving the problem graphically.

7–8 Comparison of the simplex and revised simplex methods. The revised simplex method has not met with wide acceptance for hand computations, although the computational effort is normally not much greater, and can even be less, than that required by the standard simplex method. Probably one of the reasons is the fact that side computations must always be made on scratch paper, while a tableau of the original vectors has to be available at the same time. These requirements can lead to more computational mistakes than might be made with the simplex method.

If a digital computer is used, the above objections are of no importance. In this case, the revised simplex method has some real advantages over the simplex method. Let us first make a rough estimate of the total number of computations required to move from one iteration to the next, using (1) the simplex method and (2) the revised simplex method.* For the simplex method, $n - m + 1$ columns must be transformed. The m columns in the new basis form an identity matrix in the tableau, and no arithmetic operations are necessary to obtain them. The extra column is the column $\mathbf{y}_0 = \mathbf{x}_B$. We have to transform $m + 1$ elements in each column ($\mathbf{y}_j$ and $y_{m+1,j} = z_j - c_j$). A total of $(m + 1)(n - m + 1)$ elements undergo transformation. Once we have y_{ik}/y_{rk}, the only multiplication is $y_{rj}(y_{ik}/y_{rk})$. Thus, in changing tableaux, we essentially need $(m + 1)(n - m + 1) \doteq nm - m^2 + n$ multiplications. Furthermore, m divisions are needed to obtain the y_{ik}/y_{rk}. The total number of operations is about $nm - m^2 + n + m$. For $n = 20$, $m = 5$, this would amount to 100 operations.

Consider now the revised simplex method. There are $m + 1$ columns with $m + 1$ elements in each column, which must be transformed. Again, one multiplication is required for each. This results in about $m^2 + 2m$ operations. Computation of the $n - m$ values of $z_j - c_j$ requires $(n - m)m$ operations since m multiplications are needed to find each $z_j - c_j$. Also, m^2 multiplications are required to compute the last m components of $\mathbf{y}_k^{(1)}$, and m divisions to determine y_{ik}/y_{rk}. Thus, the total number of operations for the revised simplex method is approximately $nm + m^2 + 3m$. For $n = 20$, $m = 5$, this amounts to 140 operations—considerably more than for the simplex method.

While on *a priori* grounds the revised simplex method might seem to require more computations for changing bases than the simplex method,

---

* This estimate will be made for Standard Form I of the revised simplex method. Standard Form II requires slightly more computational effort than Standard Form I, but normally the additional amount is not significant.

it can turn out that it will actually require less. Suppose that we start out with a matrix which has a large number of zeros. This situation occurs rather frequently. In the simplex method, as changes are made from one tableau to the next, the zeros are soon replaced by y_{ij} which are different from zero. Hence, in moving from one tableau to the next, we soon find it necessary to carry out all $nm - m^2 + n + m$ operations. With the revised simplex method, however, all the $z_j - c_j$, $\mathbf{y}_k^{(1)}$ are computed by means of the original $\mathbf{a}_j^{(1)}$. Thus the zeros are preserved, and the total number of operations required can be considerably less than $nm + m^2 + 3m$.

Another advantage of the revised simplex method is that fewer entries need to be made in each tableau. This aspect is not too important for hand computations, but may be important when the problem is solved on a digital computer. For the simplex method, essentially $(m + 1)(n + 1)$ elements must be written in each tableau. With the revised simplex method, only $(m + 1)(m + 2)$ elements need be recorded. If n is considerably larger than m, a great deal less writing is required in the revised simplex method. A computer would normally record the tableaux for a large problem on magnetic tape. This form of writing is relatively time-consuming, and consequently, it is important to reduce (whenever possible) the amount of writing required.

A final advantage of the revised simplex method lies in the control of rounding-off errors which occur when a digital computer is used. Since a digital computer has only a fixed number of digits, every multiplication or division requires a rounding-off operation. After thousands of operations, the errors due to rounding off can become quite significant. Rounding-off errors are one of the factors that limit the size of a problem which can be solved on a digital computer. For a problem with a large percentage of zeros, the revised simplex method requires, at each iteration, considerably fewer multiplications involving nonzero elements than does the simplex method where zeros soon disappear. This reduction in the number of operations implies a corresponding reduction in the rounding-off errors.

The revised simplex method allows rounding-off errors to be controlled in another way. The basis is transformed at each iteration by the usual transformation formula for the simplex method. This means that the new basis inverse is found by multiplying the current inverse by an $\mathbf{E}$-matrix. After m iterations, more operations will have been performed to transform the inverse than if the matrix had been inverted directly. Thus, if the code for solving a linear programming problem has a built-in provision for directly inverting the basis matrix at any point, rounding-off errors can be kept within bounds. It is theoretically possible to prevent rounding-off errors from growing much above those that would result after m iterations. If m is large, it is quite time-consuming to invert the basis matrix, and one would never do this unless the problem required considerably more than m iterations. Some judgment is required by the person solving the problem to know whether it is advisable to re-invert the basis. It might be noted that a basis-inversion routine could be used with the simplex method, but it would not be nearly so useful as it is with the revised simplex method because, after re-inversion, a new tableau would have to be computed by means of the new basis.

In addition to its practical value for machine computations, the revised simplex method is also of theoretical interest. It will be of help in the discussion of duality in Chapter 8.

7–9 The product form of the inverse. When the revised simplex method is used for hand computations, the following transformations are made at each iteration:*

$$\hat{\mathbf{B}}^{-1} = \mathbf{E}\mathbf{B}^{-1}, \qquad \hat{\mathbf{x}}_B = \mathbf{E}\mathbf{x}_B. \tag{7–52}$$

The new inverse and new basic solution are computed by means of (7–52). When problems are solved on digital computers, the inverse is usually stored on tape. Then there are advantages to be gained if one never specifically computes the inverse at all, but instead represents it in its product form, i.e., as the product of $\mathbf{E}$-matrices. After p iterations the inverse will be represented as the product of p, $\mathbf{E}$-matrices. It is really unnecessary to record the entire $\mathbf{E}$-matrix in computer storage. Only the column $\boldsymbol{\eta}$ and an index telling which column of $\mathbf{E}$ is $\boldsymbol{\eta}$ need be recorded since $\mathbf{E}$ differs from the identity matrix only because of the column containing $\boldsymbol{\eta}$. Thus recording the $\boldsymbol{\eta}$-vectors, along with an index indicating the proper column of the respective $\mathbf{E}$-matrices which contain $\boldsymbol{\eta}$, is equivalent to having the inverse of the basis. Using the product form of the inverse will reduce the time required to write the new inverse on tape since only a single column has to be recorded at each iteration.

After p iterations, $\mathbf{B}^{-1}$ will have the form

$$\mathbf{B}^{-1} = \mathbf{E}_p\mathbf{E}_{p-1} \ldots \mathbf{E}_1. \tag{7–53}$$

Assume that $\boldsymbol{\eta}^s$ appears in column r of $\mathbf{E}_s$. Since $\mathbf{B}^{-1}$ is never computed explicitly, we must show how to determine $\mathbf{y}_k$ and the $z_j - c_j$, using only the $\boldsymbol{\eta}^s$-vectors. Consider first $\mathbf{y}_k$. Now

$$\mathbf{y}_k = \mathbf{B}^{-1}\mathbf{a}_k = \mathbf{E}_p\mathbf{E}_{p-1} \cdots \mathbf{E}_1\mathbf{a}_k. \tag{7–54}$$

Let

$$\boldsymbol{\alpha}^s = \mathbf{E}_s\mathbf{E}_{s-1} \cdots \mathbf{E}_1\mathbf{a}_k, \qquad s = 1, \ldots, p. \tag{7–55}$$

---

* We here drop the subscripts and superscripts 1, 2 since the discussion applies both to Standard Form I and Standard Form II.

Then $\mathbf{y}_k = \boldsymbol{\alpha}^p$ and $\boldsymbol{\alpha}^s = \mathbf{E}_s \boldsymbol{\alpha}^{s-1}$ or, in component form,

$$\alpha_i^s = \alpha_i^{s-1} + \eta_i^s \alpha_r^{s-1}, \qquad i \neq r, \qquad s = 1, \ldots, p,$$

$$\alpha_r^s = \eta_r^s \alpha_r^{s-1}, \tag{7-56}$$

where $\boldsymbol{\alpha}^0 = \mathbf{a}_k$.

We have seen how to compute $\mathbf{y}_k$ by means of the $\boldsymbol{\eta}^s$-vectors. It remains to show how the $z_j - c_j$ can be computed when the inverse is kept in the product form. Let us suppose that we are in Phase II so that $z_j - c_j$ is obtained by taking the scalar product of the first row of the inverse with activity vector $\mathbf{a}_j$. Denote the first row of $\mathbf{B}^{-1}$ by $\boldsymbol{\beta}^0$. Therefore,

$$\boldsymbol{\beta}^0 = \mathbf{e}_1' \mathbf{B}^{-1} = \mathbf{e}_1' \mathbf{E}_p \mathbf{E}_{p-1} \cdots \mathbf{E}_1 \tag{7-57}$$

and if $\boldsymbol{\gamma}^t = \mathbf{e}_1' \mathbf{E}_p \mathbf{E}_{p-1} \cdots \mathbf{E}_{p-t+1}$, $t = 1, \ldots, p$, then $\boldsymbol{\gamma}^t = \boldsymbol{\gamma}^{t-1} \mathbf{E}_{p-t+1}$

and

$$\gamma_i^t = \gamma_i^{t-1}, \qquad i \neq r, \qquad \gamma_r^t = \boldsymbol{\gamma}^{t-1} \boldsymbol{\eta}^{p-t+1}, \qquad t = 1, \ldots, p, \tag{7-58}$$

where $\boldsymbol{\gamma}^0 = \mathbf{e}_1'$, $\boldsymbol{\gamma}^p = \boldsymbol{\beta}^0$. Finally $z_j - c_j = \boldsymbol{\beta}^0 \mathbf{a}_j$. Precisely the same transformation formulas can be used in Phase I, except that $\boldsymbol{\gamma}^0 = \mathbf{e}_2'$. It will be observed that to use the product form of the inverse, it is necessary that the initial basis matrix be an identity matrix. This is why it is necessary in Standard Form II to make the transformation discussed in Section 7-6 in order to obtain an identity matrix if the inverse of the matrix is used in its product form. It is also true that to use Standard Form I, along with the product of the inverse, Eq. (7-17) must be an identity matrix, i.e., $\mathbf{c}_B = \mathbf{0}$. No transformation like that discussed in Section 7-6 can be used here to convert $\mathbf{c}_B$ to zero (why?). Unless there is an identity matrix of order $m + 1$ in (7-5), Standard Form II must be used.

REFERENCES

1. G. B. DANTZIG, "Computational Algorithm of the Revised Simplex Method," *RM*–**1266,** The RAND Corp., Oct., 1953.

2. G. B. DANTZIG, A. ORDEN, and P. WOLFE, "The Generalized Simplex Method for Minimizing a Linear Form under Linear Inequality Restraints," *Pacific Journal of Mathematics*, **5,** 2, 1955, and *RM*–**1264,** The RAND Corp., April, 1954.

3. S. I. GASS, *Linear Programming*. New York: McGraw-Hill, 1958.

4. W. ORCHARD-HAYS, "Background, Development, and Extensions of the Revised Simplex Method," *RM*–**1433,** The RAND Corp., April, 1954.

5. H. M. WAGNER, "A Comparison of the Original and Revised Simplex Methods," *Operations Research*, **5,** 3, 1957.

Problems

7–1 Solve the following linear programming problem by the revised simplex method:

$$3x_1 + 4x_2 \leq 6,$$
$$6x_1 + x_2 \leq 3,$$
$$x_1, x_2 \geq 0,$$
$$\max z = 2x_1 + x_2.$$

7–2. Solve the following linear programming problem by the revised simplex method:

$$x_1 + 2x_2 \geq 7,$$
$$4x_1 + x_2 \geq 6,$$
$$x_1, x_2 \geq 0,$$
$$\min z = x_1 + x_2.$$

7–3. Solve the following linear programming problem by the revised simplex method:

$$2x_1 - 3x_2 + x_3 + 4x_4 + 5x_5 \geq 10,$$
$$-3x_1 + 4x_2 + 5x_3 + x_4 + 9x_5 \geq 5,$$
$$x_1 + 2x_2 - 7x_3 + 8x_4 - 5x_5 \geq 8,$$
$$\text{all } x_j \geq 0,$$
$$\max z = 2x_1 + 5x_2 + 6x_3 + x_4 + 3x_5.$$

7–4. Solve the following linear programming problem graphically and by the revised simplex method:

$$x_1 \leq 4,$$
$$x_2 - x_1 \geq 0,$$
$$x_1, x_2 \geq 0,$$
$$\max z = 2x_1 + 3x_2.$$

7–5. Solve the following problem graphically and by the revised simplex method:

$$x_1 - x_2 \geq 0,$$
$$2x_1 + 3x_2 \leq -6,$$
$$\max z = 8x_2.$$

Assume that the variables x_1, x_2 are unrestricted in sign.

7–6. For the revised simplex method, discuss the types of computational errors that are self-correcting and the types that are not. Is it possible to use a sum-check column?

7–7. Solve Problem 4–16 by the revised simplex method.

7–8. Show how the tableau format of the revised simplex method can be used at each iteration to select the vector to be removed from the basis in such a way that cycling will never occur.

7–9. Discuss Standard Form II of the revised simplex method when it is not necessary to add an artificial variable to every constraint. Write the initial basis inverse corresponding to (7–41).

7–10. In an article "A Two-Phase Method for the Simplex Tableau," *Operations Research*, **4,** 4, pp. 443–47, 1956, Wagner suggests a version of the two-phase method for hand computations which is similar to the revised simplex method. If at the end of Phase I, there are some artificial vectors in the basis at a zero level, he leaves the $(z_j - c_j)$-row for Phase I in the tableau for Phase II, so that at the beginning of Phase II we have a basis of dimension $m + 1$ with x_{n+1} in the basis at a zero level. A column for x_{n+1}, $\mathbf{q}_0 = \mathbf{e}_{m+1}$, is added to the tableau. However, in Phase II, Wagner does not allow x_{n+1} to be removed from the basis. He points out that if x_{n+1} can be removed, i.e., if $y_{m+1,k} > 0$, then there is another artificial vector with $y_{ik} \neq 0$ that can be removed. Show that $y_{m+1,k} = -\sum_i y_{ik}$, where i corresponds to the columns of the basis which contains an artificial vector at a zero level. Hence show that Wagner really does what we suggested for the two-phase method in Section 5–3, and that it is therefore unnecessary to introduce an additional row which only serves to point out an instance where, when i corresponds to some artificial vector, we have a $y_{ik} < 0$.

7–11. From Section 7–8 it will be observed that most of the computational effort in the revised simplex method is devoted to computing the $z_j - c_j$. Suppose that instead of using Eq. (7–18) to determine the vector to enter the basis, we simply choose the first vector for which $z_j - c_j < 0$. This could eliminate the computation of a large number of the $z_j - c_j$. Discuss the advantages and disadvantages of such a rule.

7–12. Compare the number of arithmetic operations required when Eqs. (7–56) and (7–58) are used with that required when Eq. (7–52) is applied.

7–13. Discuss in detail the difficulties that would be encountered if one attempted to use Eq. (7–41) for the initial basis inverse while at the same time using transformation equations of the form given in Eqs. (7–56), (7–58).

7–14. Consider the $\mathbf{B}_2$ given by Eq. (7–46). Assume that no artificial vectors appear in the last m columns of $\mathbf{B}_2$. Also assume that $\mathbf{e}_2$ is in column two. Then write $\mathbf{B}_2^{-1}$ in terms of $\mathbf{B}$ and $\mathbf{c}_B$, where $\mathbf{B}$ is the basis matrix for the corresponding basic solution to $\mathbf{Ax} = \mathbf{b}$.

CHAPTER 8

DUALITY THEORY AND ITS RAMIFICATIONS

*"All of this of Pot and Potter—Tell me then
who is the Potter, pray, and who the Pot?"*

Edward Fitzgerald—The Rubayiat.

8–1 Alternative formulations of linear programming problems. To solve a linear programming problem by the simplex method it was found convenient to convert the original set of constraint inequalities or equalities,

$$\sum_{j=1}^{r} a_{ij}x_j \{\leq \; = \; \geq\} b_i, \qquad i = 1, \ldots, m, \tag{8–1}$$

to a set of simultaneous linear equations $\mathbf{Ax} = \mathbf{b}$, $\mathbf{b} \geq \mathbf{0}$. A slightly different formulation of the constraints will be found quite useful in treating the material discussed in this chapter. Instead of converting (8–1) to a set of equalities, we shall now convert (8–1) to a form such that each constraint has an inequality sign (no strict equalities), with the additional property that the inequality sign is in the same direction for each constraint.

First let us observe that any equation

$$\sum_{j=1}^{r} a_{ij}x_j = b_i \tag{8–2}$$

in the original set of constraints (8–1) is equivalent to two inequalities:

$$\sum_{j=1}^{r} a_{ij}x_j \leq b_i,$$
$$\sum_{j=1}^{r} a_{ij}x_j \geq b_i. \tag{8–3}$$

The set of points lying on the hyperplane (8–2) is precisely the intersection of the two closed half-spaces (8–3). By use of (8–3) for (8–2) all constraints in (8–1) can be expressed as inequalities (no equations). If there were any equations in the original set of constraints (8–1), the new set of constraints containing only inequalities will have more constraints than (8–1) since two inequalities replace a single equation.

221

If, after converting all the equation constraints to inequality form, we multiply all those with a $\geq$ sign by -1, all inequalities will have a $\leq$ sign and can be written

$$\sum_{j=1}^{r} d_{ij}x_j \leq d_i, \qquad i = 1, \ldots, m + p, \tag{8-4}$$

where p is the number of the original constraint equations. In matrix form, (8-4) can be written

$$\mathbf{Dx}_r \leq \mathbf{d}, \qquad \mathbf{D} = ||d_{ij}||. \tag{8-5}$$

Here it is not necessarily true that $\mathbf{d} \geq \mathbf{0}$. The matrix $\mathbf{D}$ is $(m + p) \times r$. We use the subscript r on $\mathbf{x}_r$ (an r-component vector) to distinguish it from the $\mathbf{x}$ of $\mathbf{Ax} = \mathbf{b}$.

In a similar way, we can multiply all the constraints with a $\leq$ sign by -1 to obtain a $\geq$ sign. Then the constraints become

$$\mathbf{Gx}_r \geq \mathbf{g}, \tag{8-6}$$

where $\mathbf{G} = -\mathbf{D}$ and $\mathbf{g} = -\mathbf{d}$.

We can now formulate the general linear programming problem in either of the two following forms:

(a) Find an $\mathbf{x}_r \geq \mathbf{0}$ satisfying $\mathbf{Dx}_r \leq \mathbf{d}$ such that $z = \mathbf{c}_r\mathbf{x}_r$ is maximized or minimized.

(b) Find an $\mathbf{x}_r \geq \mathbf{0}$ satisfying $\mathbf{Gx}_r \geq \mathbf{g}$ such that $z = \mathbf{c}_r\mathbf{x}_r$ is maximized or minimized.

It should be noted that when the constraints are written in the form $\mathbf{Ax} = \mathbf{b}$, the matrix $\mathbf{A}$ will be of different dimensions than the matrices $\mathbf{D}$, $\mathbf{G}$. The matrix $\mathbf{A}$ is $m \times n$, while the two matrices $\mathbf{D}$, $\mathbf{G}$ are $(m + p) \times r$. Also, $\mathbf{x}$ will usually contain some slack and/or surplus variables and will have more components than $\mathbf{x}_r$.

In general, it will be clear from the context which formulation of the constraints we are considering, and hence the subscript r on $\mathbf{x}_r$ will seldom be used. We shall simply abbreviate (a) and (b) by $\mathbf{Dx} \leq \mathbf{d}$, $\mathbf{x} \geq \mathbf{0}$, max or min $z = \mathbf{cx}$, and $\mathbf{Gx} \geq \mathbf{g}$, $\mathbf{x} \geq \mathbf{0}$, max or min $z = \mathbf{cx}$, respectively.

8–2 Dual linear programming problems. Given any linear programming problem:

$$\mathbf{Dx} \leq \mathbf{d}, \qquad \mathbf{x} \geq \mathbf{0}, \qquad \max z = \mathbf{cx}, \tag{8-7}$$

there is another linear programming problem:

$$\mathbf{D'w} \geq \mathbf{c'}, \qquad \mathbf{w} \geq \mathbf{0}, \qquad \min Z = \mathbf{d'w}, \tag{8-8}$$

which is called the dual of (8–7). We shall spend a considerable amount of time studying the relationship between problems (8–7) and (8–8) which, at first glance, may seem to be essentially unrelated.

Note first of all that the dual of (8–7) contains the same constants d_{ij}, d_i, c_j as (8–7), but in a rearranged order. The variables for (8–8) are, of course, different from those of (8–7). The primes in (8–8) denote, as usual, the transpose. If D is $s \times r$ so that x is an r-component vector, then D' is $r \times s$, and w is an s-component vector.

There is a good reason for formulating the constraints to the given linear programming problem (8–7) as a set of inequalities instead of as a set of equations. If the constraints to the given problem are written $Ax = b$, we shall later see that the variables of the dual problem are unrestricted in sign. If the variables for both problems are to be non-negative, the constraints must be written in the above form.

On taking the transpose of the appropriate relations in (8–8), the dual of (8–7) can be written as

$$w'D \geq c, \qquad w' \geq 0, \qquad \min Z = w'd. \tag{8–9}$$

It is helpful to attach a name to the given linear programming problem (8–7). We shall call it the primal problem. Both the primal and the dual problems can be conveniently represented at the same time in the following tableau format:

$$
\begin{array}{c}
x_1, \ldots , x_r \\
\begin{array}{c} w_1 \\ \vdots \\ w_s \end{array}
\begin{bmatrix} d_{11} \ldots d_{1r} \\ \vdots \quad \vdots \\ d_{s1} \ldots d_{sr} \end{bmatrix}
\leq
\begin{bmatrix} d_1 \\ \vdots \\ d_s \end{bmatrix} . \\
\text{IV} \\
(c_1, \ldots , c_r)
\end{array}
\tag{8–10}
$$

The columns of D are the activity vectors for the primal, while the rows of D are the activity vectors for the dual problem. An abbreviated notation for (8–10) is

$$
\begin{array}{c}
x' \\
w \ (D) \leq d. \\
\text{IV} \\
c
\end{array}
\tag{8–11}
$$

In (8–10), the variable x_j or w_i is written above or to the left of its corresponding column or row, respectively.

Equation (8–8) can be written

$$(-\mathbf{D}')\mathbf{w} \leq -\mathbf{c}', \qquad \mathbf{w} \geq \mathbf{0}, \qquad \max (Z^*) = (-\mathbf{d}')\mathbf{w}, \qquad (8\text{–}12)$$

and

$$\min Z = -\max Z^*.$$

Now the dual problem "looks like" the primal problem. A very important observation can be made at this point. If we consider (8–12) [or equivalently (8–8)] to be the given (primal) problem and write down its dual, we have from (8–12) and (8–7), (8–8),

$$-\mathbf{Dx} \geq -\mathbf{d}, \qquad \mathbf{x} \geq \mathbf{0}, \qquad \min z^* = -\mathbf{cx},$$

or

$$\mathbf{Dx} \leq \mathbf{d}, \qquad \mathbf{x} \geq \mathbf{0}, \qquad \max z = \mathbf{cx},$$

where

$$\min z^* = -\max z.$$

This is precisely the original primal problem (8–7). For this reason we shall also define (8–7) to be the dual of (8–8). With this definition we see that *the dual of the dual is the primal.*

From this it immediately follows that instead of writing the primal problem in the form (8–7), we could have equally well used the formulation

$$\mathbf{Gx} \geq \mathbf{g}, \qquad \mathbf{x} \geq \mathbf{0}, \qquad \min z = \mathbf{cx}; \qquad (8\text{–}13)$$

its dual is then

$$\mathbf{G}'\mathbf{w} \leq \mathbf{c}', \qquad \mathbf{w} \geq \mathbf{0}, \qquad \max Z = \mathbf{g}'\mathbf{w}. \qquad (8\text{–}14)$$

An examination of the pairs of problems (8–7), (8–8) and (8–13), (8–14) shows that there is complete symmetry between the primal and dual problems. If either problem in the set (8–7), (8–8) or (8–13), (8–14) is considered to be the primal, the other is its dual.

As yet we have not indicated why one should be interested in the dual of a given linear programming problem. In the following sections, we shall present some of the mathematical reasons for the significance of duality. In Chapters 11 and 13, it will be shown that the dual problem has some interesting economic interpretations. We shall begin the mathematical discussion by demonstrating that if the primal problem has an optimal solution, then the dual has also an optimal solution. In addition, we shall prove the even more amazing result that in such a case $\max z = \min Z$ for (8–7) and (8–8). Furthermore, it will be demonstrated that solving the primal problem by the simplex method also provides an optimal solution to the dual. Using this result, we shall find that, under certain circumstances, the duality theory can be of considerable help in solving linear programming problems.

EXAMPLES: 1. Give the dual of the following linear programming problem:

$$\begin{bmatrix} 2 & -3 \\ 4 & 1 \end{bmatrix} \begin{bmatrix} x_1 \\ x_2 \end{bmatrix} \leq \begin{bmatrix} 3 \\ -4 \end{bmatrix}, \qquad x_1, x_2 \geq 0,$$

$$\max z = x_1 + 2x_2.$$

This problem is given in the form of (8–7). The dual can be written down immediately; it is

$$\begin{bmatrix} 2 & 4 \\ -3 & 1 \end{bmatrix} \begin{bmatrix} w_1 \\ w_2 \end{bmatrix} \geq \begin{bmatrix} 1 \\ 2 \end{bmatrix}, \qquad w_1, w_2 \geq 0,$$

$$\min Z = 3w_1 - 4w_2.$$

2. Give the dual of the following linear programming problem (with non-negative dual variables):

$$\begin{aligned} 4x_1 + 3x_2 + x_3 &= 6, \\ x_1 + 2x_2 + 5x_3 &= 4, \\ x_1, x_2, x_3 &\geq 0, \\ \max z = 2x_1 + 3x_2 + x_3. \end{aligned} \qquad (8\text{–}15)$$

We must first convert the problem either to the form of (8–7) or to that of (8–13). Let us write it in the form of (8–7). Then

$$\begin{aligned} 4x_1 + 3x_2 + x_3 &\leq 6, \\ -4x_1 - 3x_2 - x_3 &\leq -6, \\ x_1 + 2x_2 + 5x_3 &\leq 4, \\ - x_1 - 2x_2 - 5x_3 &\leq -4, \end{aligned} \quad \text{or} \quad \begin{bmatrix} 4 & 3 & 1 \\ -4 & -3 & -1 \\ 1 & 2 & 5 \\ -1 & -2 & -5 \end{bmatrix} \begin{bmatrix} x_1 \\ x_2 \\ x_3 \end{bmatrix} \leq \begin{bmatrix} 6 \\ -6 \\ 4 \\ -4 \end{bmatrix};$$

$$\max z = 2x_1 + 3x_2 + x_3.$$

The dual problem can now be written down. It is:

$$\begin{bmatrix} 4 & -4 & 1 & -1 \\ 3 & -3 & 2 & -2 \\ 1 & -1 & 5 & -5 \end{bmatrix} [w_1, w_2, w_3, w_4] \geq \begin{bmatrix} 2 \\ 3 \\ 1 \end{bmatrix}, \qquad w_1, w_2, w_3, w_4 \geq 0,$$

$$\min Z = 6w_1 - 6w_2 + 4w_3 - 4w_4.$$

If we had converted the primal problem to the form (8–13), we would have nonetheless obtained the same dual problem; however, all signs would have been reversed.

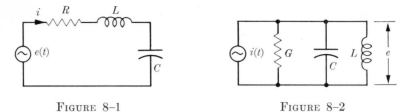

FIGURE 8–1   FIGURE 8–2

According to its dictionary definition, dual means double. As applied to linear programming, duality implies that a double meaning can be attached to every linear programming problem. It can be thought of as a primal problem or as the dual of some other problem. Unless we are told, it is not possible to determine which interpretation someone is placing on a given problem.

Note: Duality is by no means a concept restricted to linear programming. It occurs frequently in mathematics, economics, engineering, physics, and many other fields.

As an example from electrical engineering, consider the following series *RCL*-network (Fig. 8–1). We assume that e is the voltage applied to the circuit, i is the current, and R, L, C are the resistance, inductance, and capacitance, respectively. The equation relating the current to the applied voltage at any given time is

$$L\frac{di}{dt} + Ri + \frac{1}{C}\int i\,dt = e(t). \tag{8–16}$$

If we interchange (e, i), and (L, C), and replace R by $G = 1/R$, we obtain

$$C\frac{de}{dt} + Ge + \frac{1}{L}\int e\,dt = i(t). \tag{8–17}$$

This is the equation representing the voltage in terms of the current for the parallel network of Fig. 8–2. Instead of a voltage generator we have here a current generator.

An equation of the form

$$a\frac{dx}{dt} + bx + c\int x\,dt = y(t) \tag{8–18}$$

can be considered to describe a network of the type shown in Fig. 8–1 or of the type shown in Fig. 8–2. Unless someone tells us, we do not know which type of circuit it represents. Thus equation (8–18) has a dual interpretation. The network of Fig. 8–2 can be considered to be the dual of the network of Fig. 8–1 or, conversely, the network of Fig. 8–1 can be considered to be the dual of the network of Fig. 8–2.

Thus in electric circuit theory, duality exists between series and parallel circuits. The conversions necessary to go from one circuit to its dual are listed below:

Series	Parallel
e	i
R	G
L	C
C	L

An example of duality which arises in economics appears in the Leontief input-output system; it will be discussed in Chapter 13. This example is much closer to linear programming. If we imagine an economy to consist of n activities (n industries producing a single good), the Leontief input-output model determines how much each industry should produce to meet a specified exogenous demand (consumer demand, foreign trade, etc.). Inter-industry transfers are automatically taken care of. With appropriate assumptions about the nature of the production process, the problem reduces to solving the following set of n simultaneous linear equations in n unknowns:

$$(\mathbf{I} - \mathbf{A})\mathbf{x} = \mathbf{b}, \qquad (8\text{–}19)$$

where $\mathbf{b}$ is a vector of the net demands and $\mathbf{A}$ is a "technology matrix." The components of $\mathbf{x}$ are the quantities of each good that must be produced.

Another problem deals with determining the price of each good in terms of the value added in production. The prices p_j are found as solutions to

$$(\mathbf{I} - \mathbf{A})'\mathbf{p} = \mathbf{r} \qquad \text{or} \qquad (\mathbf{I} - \mathbf{A}')\mathbf{p} = \mathbf{r}, \qquad (8\text{–}20)$$

where $\mathbf{r}$ is a vector of the values added and $\mathbf{A}'$ is the transpose of $\mathbf{A}$.

A system of equations

$$(\mathbf{I} - \mathbf{B})\mathbf{y} = \mathbf{h} \qquad (8\text{–}21)$$

can be given a dual interpretation. It may be thought of as determining the quantities to be manufactured in one economy or the prices in another economy. Unless we are told, we do not know which interpretation someone has in mind.

The problem of determining the prices can be considered to be the dual of that of determining the quantities to be produced, or vice versa. Note that here, just as in linear programming, the dual problem involves the transposed matrix.

In the above examples, duality had a very important physical or economic interpretation. In certain cases, an interesting economic interpretation can also be given to dual linear programming problems. The duality, as in the Leontief models, exists between quantities and prices. This is discussed in Chapter 13. In Chapter 11, we shall also show that if the primal linear programming problem is one player's problem in a zero-sum, two-person game, then the dual is the other player's problem.

8–3 Fundamental properties of dual problems. In this section, we wish to show that if one of the pair of dual problems (8–7), (8–8) has an optimal solution, then the other also has an optimal solution. We shall also demonstrate how to find an optimal solution to the dual once we have determined an optimal solution to the primal by use of the simplex method. We begin by proving the following statement:

If $\mathbf{x}$ *is any feasible solution to problem* (8–7) *and* $\mathbf{w}$ *is any feasible solution to problem* (8–8), *then*

$$\mathbf{cx} \leq \mathbf{d'w}, \quad \text{that is,} \quad z \leq Z. \tag{8–22}$$

To see this, observe that for any feasible solution to (8–7) we can write

$$(\mathbf{Dx})_i \leq d_i, \quad i = 1, \ldots, s,$$

and since $w_i \geq 0$, $i = 1, \ldots, s$, for any feasible solution to (8–8),

$$w_i(\mathbf{Dx})_i \leq w_i d_i.$$

Summing over i, we have

$$\sum w_i(\mathbf{Dx})_i \leq \sum w_i d_i \quad \text{or} \quad \mathbf{w'Dx} \leq \mathbf{d'w}. \tag{8–23}$$

Similarly, since $\mathbf{x} \geq \mathbf{0}$, it follows from (8–8), or equivalently from (8–9), that

$$\mathbf{w'Dx} \geq \mathbf{cx}. \tag{8–24}$$

Combining (8–23) and (8–24), we obtain the result $\mathbf{cx} \leq \mathbf{d'w}$ or $z \leq Z$.

Next let us show that *if* $\hat{\mathbf{x}}$ *is a feasible solution to* (8–7) *and* $\hat{\mathbf{w}}$ *is a feasible solution to* (8–8) *such that* $\mathbf{c\hat{x}} = \mathbf{d'\hat{w}}$, *then* $\hat{\mathbf{x}}$ *is an optimal solution to* (8–7), *and* $\hat{\mathbf{w}}$ *is an optimal solution to* (8–8). By assumption,

$$\mathbf{c\hat{x}} = \mathbf{d'\hat{w}}. \tag{8–25}$$

But for any feasible solution $\mathbf{x}$, (8–22) holds or

$$\mathbf{cx} \leq \mathbf{d'\hat{w}} = \mathbf{c\hat{x}}, \tag{8–26}$$

and $\hat{\mathbf{x}}$ is optimal. Similarly, for any feasible $\mathbf{w}$,

$$\mathbf{d'\hat{w}} = \mathbf{c\hat{x}} \leq \mathbf{d'w}, \tag{8–27}$$

and therefore $\hat{\mathbf{w}}$ is optimal also.

Finally, let us show that *if one of the set of problems* (8–7), (8–8) *has an optimal solution, then the other also has an optimal solution.* (Recall that unbounded solutions are not called optimal.) We shall prove this by actually constructing an optimal solution to the dual from a given optimal solution to the primal. It suffices to show that if (8–7) has an optimal solution, then so does its dual (8–8). The fact that (8–7) has an optimal solution if (8–8) does, follows because, as we have seen, (8–8) can be converted to the form (8–7), and (8–7) can be converted to the form (8–8).

To solve (8–7) by the simplex method, we first transform the constraint inequalities into a set of equations. Equation (8–7) can then be written

$$\mathbf{Dx} + \mathbf{Ix}_s = \mathbf{d}, \qquad \mathbf{x} \geq \mathbf{0}, \qquad \mathbf{x}_s \geq \mathbf{0}, \qquad \max z = \mathbf{cx}, \quad (8\text{–}28)$$

where $\mathbf{x}_s$ contains the slack variables. Assume that $\mathbf{x}_B$ is an optimal basic feasible solution to (8–28); let $\mathbf{B}$ be the corresponding basis matrix and $\mathbf{c}_B$ contain the prices of the basic variables. Note that $\mathbf{d}$ is the same as in (8–7); hence it is not necessarily true that $\mathbf{d} \geq \mathbf{0}$. Imagine that an optimal solution has been found without making each component of the requirements vector non-negative (the reader who has worked Problem 4–24 will have seen that it is very easy to get started on the simplex method even if some components of $\mathbf{d}$ are negative).

Because $\mathbf{x}_B$ is optimal, we have $z_j - c_j \geq 0$ for all j and, in particular, for the vectors $\mathbf{d}_j$ of $\mathbf{D}$. Thus,

$$\mathbf{c}_B\mathbf{B}^{-1}\mathbf{d}_j \geq c_j \qquad (j = 1, \ldots, r),$$

or

$$\mathbf{c}_B\mathbf{B}^{-1} (\mathbf{d}_1, \ldots, \mathbf{d}_r) \geq (c_1, \ldots, c_r),$$

or

$$\mathbf{c}_B\mathbf{B}^{-1}\mathbf{D} \geq \mathbf{c}. \tag{8–29}$$

If we write $\mathbf{w}' = \mathbf{c}_B\mathbf{B}^{-1}$, Eq. (8–9) shows that $\mathbf{c}_B\mathbf{B}^{-1}$ is a solution to the dual problem (8–8).

When we consider the $z_j - c_j$ for the slack vectors of (8–28), we can immediately see that $\mathbf{w}' = \mathbf{c}_B\mathbf{B}^{-1}$ is feasible. Since the price associated with a slack variable is zero, the $z_j - c_j$ for the slack vectors are

$$\mathbf{c}_B\mathbf{B}^{-1}\mathbf{e}_i - 0 \geq 0$$

or

$$\mathbf{c}_B\mathbf{B}^{-1}(\mathbf{e}_1, \ldots, \mathbf{e}_s) \geq \mathbf{0};$$

hence

$$\mathbf{c}_B\mathbf{B}^{-1}\mathbf{I} \geq \mathbf{0} \qquad \text{and} \qquad \mathbf{c}_B\mathbf{B}^{-1} \geq \mathbf{0}. \tag{8–30}$$

We have yet to show that $\mathbf{w}' = \mathbf{c}_B \mathbf{B}^{-1}$ is an optimal solution to the dual (8–8). Consider

$$Z = \mathbf{w}'\mathbf{d} = \mathbf{c}_B \mathbf{B}^{-1}\mathbf{d} = \mathbf{c}_B \mathbf{x}_B = \max z. \qquad (8\text{--}31)$$

Here we have shown that $\mathbf{w}'$, $\mathbf{x}_B$ are feasible solutions to (8–8), (8–7), respectively, for which $z = Z$; thus $\mathbf{w}'$ is an optimal solution to (8–8).

We have just obtained a very interesting result: If there is an optimal solution to (8–7), we have proved by construction that there is an optimal solution to its dual (8–8). Indeed, if $\mathbf{B}$ is the basis matrix for the primal problem corresponding to an optimal solution and $\mathbf{c}_B$ contains the prices in the basis, then an optimal solution to the dual is $\mathbf{w}' = \mathbf{c}_B \mathbf{B}^{-1}$. In addition, we have proved that $\max z = \min Z$, i.e., the optimal values of the objective functions for the two problems are equal.

There is something familiar about the solution to the dual. Recall that if the revised simplex method is used to solve the primal, the first row of the optimal tableau is $(\mathbf{c}_B \mathbf{B}^{-1}, z)$. Hence, when the revised simplex method is used, the solution to the dual problem is contained in the first row of the optimal tableau for the primal. For simplicity, we gave above the first row for Standard Form I. In the event Standard Form II is used, the last $s + 1$ elements of the first row yield $\mathbf{w}' = \mathbf{c}_B \mathbf{B}^{-1}$, $Z = z$.

If the primal problem is solved by the simplex method, it is also easy to find an optimal solution to the dual problem in an optimal tableau for the primal. From (8–30) we see that $\mathbf{w} = \mathbf{c}_B \mathbf{B}^{-1}$ is found in the $(z_j - c_j)$-row under the columns corresponding to the slack vectors, that is, since for the slack vectors, $z_j - c_j = z_j = \mathbf{c}_B \mathbf{B}^{-1}\mathbf{e}_i$, w_1 is found in the $(z_j - c_j)$-position under the slack vector $\mathbf{e}_1$, etc.

Thus far we have been assuming that, prior to application of the simplex method, the primal problem has been cast into the form (8–7). It would be annoying if this procedure were always necessary in order to find the solution to the dual. Fortunately this is not the case. In the following section, we shall show that it is easy to obtain the solution to the dual when the primal problem is solved in the manner described in Chapter 4. It is immediately clear from the above arguments, however, that if $\mathbf{x}_B = \mathbf{B}^{-1}\mathbf{g}$ is an optimal solution to (8–13), an optimal solution to the dual (8–14) is $\mathbf{w}' = \mathbf{c}_B \mathbf{B}^{-1}$.

Without any additional explanations, we can see how the duality theory may, at times, be of assistance in actually solving a linear programming problem. If some given linear programming problem contains many constraints and only few variables, then the large number of constraints yields a large basis. When there are only few variables in the original set of constraint inequalities, most of the variables in this large basis will be slack or surplus variables. Let us consider the dual problem: The size of its basis is that of the number of variables in the primal problem. Thus solving the dual provides all primal variables, and we need not solve a problem involving a very large basis. An example will further clarify this point.

EXAMPLE: Solve

$$
\begin{aligned}
x_1 &\leq 6, \\
x_2 &\leq 8, \\
x_1 + x_2 &\leq 7, \quad \text{or} \\
3x_1 + x_2 &\leq 15, \\
- x_2 &\leq 1,
\end{aligned}
\qquad
\begin{bmatrix}
1 & 0 \\
0 & 1 \\
1 & 1 \\
3 & 1 \\
0 & -1
\end{bmatrix}
\begin{bmatrix} x_1 \\ x_2 \end{bmatrix}
\leq
\begin{bmatrix}
6 \\
8 \\
7 \\
15 \\
1
\end{bmatrix}
\qquad (8\text{--}32)
$$

$$x_1, x_2 \geq 0,$$

$$\max z = 4x_1 + 3x_2.$$

If we solved this problem directly, the basis matrix would be of order 5, while in reality there are only two variables, x_1, x_2, in which we are interested.

The dual problem is

$$
\begin{bmatrix}
1 & 0 & 1 & 3 & 0 \\
0 & 1 & 1 & 1 & -1
\end{bmatrix}
[w_1, w_2, w_3, w_4, w_5] \geq
\begin{bmatrix} 4 \\ 3 \end{bmatrix},
$$

$$w_j \geq 0, \qquad j = 1, \ldots, 5,$$

$$\min Z = 6w_1 + 8w_2 + 7w_3 + 15w_4 + w_5.$$

We shall solve the dual problem by the revised simplex method. An optimal solution to the primal can then be read off immediately from the optimal tableau for the dual. Since an identity matrix appears in the above constraints, we can use Standard Form I. When the dual problem is cast into this form, we have

$$
\begin{bmatrix}
1 & -6 & -8 & -7 & -15 & -1 & 0 & 0 \\
0 & 1 & 0 & 1 & 3 & 0 & -1 & 0 \\
0 & 0 & 1 & 1 & 1 & -1 & 0 & -1
\end{bmatrix}
\begin{bmatrix} w_0 \\ w_1 \\ \vdots \\ w_7 \end{bmatrix}
=
\begin{bmatrix} 0 \\ 4 \\ 3 \end{bmatrix}.
$$

The vectors corresponding to the w_j will be denoted by $\mathbf{a}_j^{(1)}$ and are numbered in order of their appearance. The tableaux for the solution to the dual problem are shown in Tables 8–1 through 8–3. The solution to the original problem is contained in the first row of Tableau 3. We read $x_1 = 4$, $x_2 = 3$, $\max z = 25$. It should be noted that we did not convert the dual to a maximization problem; it was solved as a minimization

TABLE 8–1 — TABLEAU 1

Variables in Basis	$\boldsymbol{\beta}_1^{(1)}$	$\boldsymbol{\beta}_2^{(1)}$	$\mathbf{w}_B^{(1)}$	$\mathbf{y}_k^{(1)}$
w_0	6	8	48	11
w_1	1	0	4	3
w_2	0	1	3	1

TABLE 8–2 — TABLEAU 2

Variables in Basis	$\boldsymbol{\beta}_1^{(1)}$	$\boldsymbol{\beta}_2^{(1)}$	$\mathbf{w}_B^{(1)}$	$\mathbf{y}_k^{(1)}$
w_0	2.333	8	33.33	3.333
w_4	0.3333	0	1.333	0.3333
w_2	−0.3333	1	1.667	0.6667

TABLE 8–3 — TABLEAU 3

Variables in Basis	$\boldsymbol{\beta}_1^{(1)}$	$\boldsymbol{\beta}_2^{(1)}$	$\mathbf{w}_B^{(1)}$	$\mathbf{y}_k^{(1)}$
w_0	4	3	25.00	
w_4	0.5000	− 0.5000	0.5000	
w_3	−0.5000	1.500	2.500	

problem. If x_1, x_2 are substituted into (8–32), it is seen that they do indeed yield a feasible solution with $z = 25$. It is optimal since $z = Z$. If we had solved the original problem directly, there would have been three slack vectors in the optimal basis at a nonzero level. The dual solution did not give us the values of these slack variables, but they can readily be computed once x_1, x_2 are known. The correctness of the solution may be easily checked by solving the primal problem graphically.

8–4 Other formulations of dual problems. Suppose that we have decided to solve some linear programming problem by means of the dual. After the dual has been obtained, it is not necessarily true that each component of the requirements vector is non-negative. Although we can get started on the simplex method even if some components of the requirements vector are negative (by means of the procedure developed in Problem 4–24), the usual procedure is to convert first the inequalities to a form such that the requirements vector is non-negative. One reason for doing this might be that the computer program to be used requires that the requirements vector be non-negative. We now wish to investigate what influence the transformation to a non-negative requirements vector for the dual has on obtaining an optimal solution to the primal.

If we have the linear programming problem $\mathbf{Dx} \leq \mathbf{d}$, $\mathbf{x} \geq \mathbf{0}$, max $z = \mathbf{cx}$, and if one or more of the $d_i < 0$, let us multiply the constraints with $d_i < 0$ by -1. This gives a new set of constraints which has a non-negative requirements vector, but some constraints now have a $\geq$ sign. After adding slack and surplus variables, we obtain the linear programming problem $\mathbf{A}[\mathbf{x}, \mathbf{x}_s] = \mathbf{b}$, $\mathbf{b} \geq \mathbf{0}$, $[\mathbf{x}, \mathbf{x}_s] \geq \mathbf{0}$, max $z = \mathbf{cx}$, where $\mathbf{x}_s$ is a vector containing the slack and surplus variables. Corresponding to any basis matrix $\mathbf{B}$ for this problem, there is a basis matrix $\overline{\mathbf{B}}$ for $\mathbf{Dx} + \mathbf{Ix}_s = \mathbf{d}$. Indeed $\overline{\mathbf{B}}$ differs from $\mathbf{B}$ only in that the rows i of $\overline{\mathbf{B}}$ for which $d_i < 0$, are the negatives of the corresponding rows of $\mathbf{B}$. When the basic feasible solution of the given problem corresponding to $\overline{\mathbf{B}}$ is optimal, then an optimal solution to the dual of the given problem will be $\mathbf{c}_B \overline{\mathbf{B}}^{-1}$. Since we solve the problem with the non-negative requirements vector, $\mathbf{c}_B \mathbf{B}^{-1}$ is obtained. We now wish to determine $\mathbf{c}_B \overline{\mathbf{B}}^{-1}$ from $\mathbf{c}_B \mathbf{B}^{-1}$.

If any row i of a matrix is multiplied by -1, then column i of the inverse is multiplied by -1. This follows immediately from the fact that $\mathbf{B}^{-1}\mathbf{B} = \mathbf{I}$. Therefore $\mathbf{B}^{-1}$ differs from $\overline{\mathbf{B}}^{-1}$ only in that the columns i of $\mathbf{B}^{-1}$ for which $d_i < 0$ are the negatives of the corresponding columns of $\overline{\mathbf{B}}^{-1}$. Hence we see that the solution to the dual problem can be found from $\mathbf{c}_B \mathbf{B}^{-1}$ by multiplying by -1 those components i of this vector for which $d_i < 0$.

The above discussion shows that if we are solving some linear programming problem by means of the dual, and if we convert the requirements vector of the dual into a non-negative one by multiplying the ith dual constraint by -1, then the ith primal variable computed from $\mathbf{c}_B\mathbf{B}^{-1}$ of the dual problem will be nonpositive, and we must multiply it by -1 to obtain the correct answer.

EXAMPLES: 1. Let us show by an example that changing the signs of row i in $\mathbf{B}$ changes the signs of column i in $\mathbf{B}^{-1}$. Let

$$\mathbf{B} = \begin{bmatrix} 2 & 3 \\ 1 & 2 \end{bmatrix}, \qquad \mathbf{B}^{-1} = \begin{bmatrix} 2 & -3 \\ -1 & 2 \end{bmatrix}.$$

Suppose that we change the signs of the second row of $\mathbf{B}$ to yield a new matrix $\mathbf{B}_1$. Then

$$\mathbf{B}_1 = \begin{bmatrix} 2 & 3 \\ -1 & -2 \end{bmatrix}, \qquad \mathbf{B}_1^{-1} = \begin{bmatrix} 2 & 3 \\ -1 & -2 \end{bmatrix},$$

and the signs of the second column of $\mathbf{B}^{-1}$ have been changed.

2. Using the dual, solve the following linear programming problem:

$$
\begin{aligned}
x_1 \quad\quad &\leq 4, \\
x_2 &\leq 6, \\
x_1 + x_2 &\leq 5, \\
- x_2 &\leq -1, \\
x_1, x_2 &\geq 0, \\
\max z = 3x_1 &- 2x_2.
\end{aligned}
$$

The dual is

$$
\begin{aligned}
w_1 + w_3 \quad\quad &\geq 3, \\
w_2 + w_3 - w_4 &\geq -2, \\
w_j \geq 0, \qquad j &= 1, \dots, 4, \\
\min Z = 4w_1 + 6w_2 + 5w_3 &- w_4.
\end{aligned}
$$

To solve this problem by the simplex method in the usual way we first multiply the second constraint by -1. After doing this and adding slack and surplus, we have:

$$
\begin{aligned}
w_1 + w_3 - w_5 &= 3, \\
-w_2 - w_3 + w_4 + w_6 &= 2, \\
w_j \geq 0, \qquad j &= 1, \dots, 6, \\
\min Z = 4w_1 + 6w_2 + 5w_3 &- w_4.
\end{aligned}
$$

This dual problem can be solved by inspection. The optimal revised simplex tableau is given in Table 8–4. To obtain the solution to the primal

TABLE 8–4 — TABLEAU 1

Variables in Basis	$\boldsymbol{\beta}_1^{(1)}$	$\boldsymbol{\beta}_2^{(1)}$	$\mathbf{w}_B^{(1)}$	$\mathbf{y}_k^{(1)}$
w_0	4	−1	10	
w_1	1	0	3	
w_4	0	1	2	

we look at the first row of the tableau. Since we multiplied the second dual constraint by -1, we must multiply the second element of the first row by -1. This second element is indeed negative. Thus an optimal solution to the primal is $x_1 = 4$, $x_2 = 1$, max $z = 10$. The correctness of this result can be easily checked by solving the primal problem graphically.

We may cast the above results into a slightly different form. Essentially, what we have shown above is that multiplying a primal constraint by -1 changes the sign of the corresponding dual variable. Suppose that we are given a linear programming problem of the following type:

$$\sum_{j=1}^{r} d_{ij}x_j \leq d_i, \qquad i = 1, \ldots, k,$$

$$\sum_{j=1}^{r} d_{ij}x_j \geq d_i, \qquad i = k+1, \ldots, s, \qquad (8\text{–}33)$$

$$x_j \geq 0, \qquad \text{all } j,$$

$$\max z = \mathbf{cx}.$$

It follows that if $\mathbf{D} = \|d_{ij}\|$ and $\mathbf{d} = [d_1, \ldots, d_s]$, then the dual of this problem has the form

$$\mathbf{D'w} \geq \mathbf{c'}, \qquad (8\text{–}34)$$

$$\min Z = \mathbf{d'w},$$

where the dual variables satisfy

$$w_i \geq 0 \quad (i = 1, \ldots, k)$$

and

$$w_i \leq 0 \quad (i = k+1, \ldots, s).$$

To see this, multiply constraints $k + 1, \ldots, s$ of (8–33) by -1, form the dual, and obtain

$$\sum_{i=1}^{k} w'_i\, \mathbf{d}^i - \sum_{i=k+1}^{s} w'_i\, \mathbf{d}^i \geq \mathbf{c},$$

$$w'_i \geq 0, \qquad i = 1, \ldots, s,$$

$$\min Z = \sum_{i=1}^{k} d_i w'_i - \sum_{i=k+1}^{s} d_i w'_i,$$

where, of course, $\mathbf{d}^i = (d_{i1}, \ldots, d_{ir})$. Introduce new variables $w_i = w'_i$, $i = 1, \ldots, k$; $w_i = -w'_i$, $i = k + 1, \ldots, s$, and (8–34) results.

Quite frequently computer codes for solving linear programming problems make provisions only for maximizing the objective function. If we are solving some linear problem by means of the dual, let us see what happens if we have to convert a minimization problem to a maximization problem by changing the prices of the dual problem. Assume that $\overline{\mathbf{B}}$ is a basis matrix for the dual corresponding to an optimal basic solution to the dual. Then the solution to the primal is $\mathbf{x}' = \mathbf{d}_B \overline{\mathbf{B}}^{-1}$, where $\mathbf{d}_B$ contains the actual prices of the dual problem. To solve the dual problem the price of each variable is changed, and therefore the first row of an optimal revised simplex tableau would contain $-\mathbf{d}_B \overline{\mathbf{B}}^{-1}$, and we would need to multiply each component by -1 to find the correct solution to the primal.

If a primal problem with an equality for one of its constraints is to be cast into the form of (8–7), the equation must be replaced by two inequalities. This one constraint equation then yields two variables in the dual. The dual column corresponding to one of the dual variables is the negative of the other. Similarly, the price of one of these dual variables is just the negative of the other. If we think back to the subject of unrestricted variables, we see that the two dual variables can be replaced by a single unrestricted variable. The column corresponding to this unrestricted variable would be that obtained if the original equation in the primal had not been converted to two inequalities. Thus we have the interesting result that *if the ith constraint in the primal is an equality, then the ith dual variable is unrestricted in sign.*

The above paragraph has shown that if we write the primal problem in the form

$$\sum_{j=1}^{r} d_{ij} x_j \leq d_i, \qquad i = 1, \ldots, k,$$

$$\sum_{j=1}^{r} d_{ij} x_j = d_i, \qquad i = k + 1, \ldots, s, \tag{8–35}$$

$$x_j \geq 0, \qquad j = 1, \ldots, r, \qquad \max z = \mathbf{cx},$$

then the dual problem is

$$\mathbf{D'w} \geq \mathbf{c'}, \qquad \min Z = \mathbf{d'w}, \qquad\qquad (8\text{--}36)$$

$$w_i \geq 0, \qquad i = 1, \ldots, k; \qquad w_i \ \text{unrestricted}, \qquad i = k + 1, \ldots, s.$$

The first k variables of the dual are non-negative, and the remaining variables are unrestricted in sign.

A special case of (8–35) is presented by the primal problem

$$\mathbf{Ax} = \mathbf{b}, \qquad \mathbf{x} \geq \mathbf{0}, \qquad \max z = \mathbf{cx}. \qquad\qquad (8\text{--}37)$$

The dual must be

$$\mathbf{A'w} \geq \mathbf{c'}, \qquad \min Z = \mathbf{b'w}, \qquad\qquad (8\text{--}38)$$

and all the dual variables are unrestricted in sign. Here we have found the dual of the standard formulation of the linear programming problem developed in Chapter 4. The dual variables are all unrestricted. This is the reason why, at the beginning, we did not use (8–37) as the formulation of the primal.

It is important to note that the presence of equality signs in some of the primal constraints in no way affects the inequality signs which appear in the dual. A change from inequalities to equalities in the primal affects the nature of the dual variables, not the nature of the inequalities signs in the dual constraints.

EXAMPLE: Suppose that the primal problem is

$$3x_1 + 2x_2 \leq 6,$$
$$3x_1 + \ x_2 = 4,$$
$$x_1, x_2 \geq 0,$$
$$\max z = x_1 + 3x_2.$$

If the dual of this problem is written down directly from (8–36), we obtain

$$3w_1 + 3w_2 \geq 1,$$
$$2w_1 + \ w_2 \geq 3,$$
$$w_1 \geq 0,$$
$$\min Z = 6w_1 + 4w_2.$$

According to our discussion, w_2 should be an unrestricted variable. To demonstrate this, the equation in the original problem will be converted to two inequalities. We find

$$3x_1 + 2x_2 \leq 6,$$
$$3x_1 + x_2 \leq 4,$$
$$-3x_1 - x_2 \leq -4.$$

The dual problem is

$$3w_1' + 3w_2' - 3w_3' \geq 1,$$
$$2w_1' + w_2' - w_3' \geq 3,$$
$$w_1', w_2', w_3' \geq 0,$$
$$\min Z = 6w_1' + 4w_2' - 4w_3'.$$

If we write $w_2 = w_2' - w_3'$, $w_1 = w_1'$, we see that the result is identical with the result obtained above without replacing the equation by two inequalities. As expected, w_2 is unrestricted.

The reader can probably guess at this point that *if some variable x_j in the primal is unrestricted in sign, then the jth constraint of the dual problem will be a strict equality.* This is correct and can be easily proved. Note that in order to convert a primal problem with unrestricted variables into the form of (8–7), we replace x_j by $x_j' - x_j''$. If $\mathbf{d}_j$ is the vector corresponding to x_j', then $-\mathbf{d}_j$ is the vector corresponding to x_j''. Similarly, the prices corresponding to x_j' and x_j'' are c_j and $-c_j$, respectively. The columns corresponding to x_j' and x_j'' in the primal give the constraints $\mathbf{d}_j'\mathbf{w} \geq c_j$, $-\mathbf{d}_j'\mathbf{w} \geq -c_j$; these are equivalent to the single constraint $\mathbf{d}_j'\mathbf{w} = c_j$. This single constraint corresponds to the single column $\mathbf{d}_j$ in the primal, which must be associated with the unrestricted variable x_j. Thus the following expressions are dual problems:

$$\mathbf{D}\mathbf{x} \leq \mathbf{d}, \qquad \max z = \mathbf{c}\mathbf{x}, \tag{8–39}$$

with $x_j \geq 0, j = 1, \ldots, k$, x_j unrestricted for $j = k + 1, \ldots, r$, and

$$\sum_{i=1}^{s} d_{ij}w_i \geq c_j, \qquad j = 1, \ldots, k,$$
$$\sum_{i=1}^{s} d_{ij}w_i = c_j, \qquad j = k + 1, \ldots, r, \tag{8–40}$$
$$\mathbf{w} \geq \mathbf{0},$$
$$\min Z = \mathbf{d}'\mathbf{w}.$$

It should be recognized that none of the dual formulations given in this section is more general than the pair (8–7), (8–8). In fact, these new formulations were obtained from (8–7), (8–8). Furthermore, if $\mathbf{x}_B = \mathbf{B}^{-1}\mathbf{d}$, $z = \mathbf{c}_B\mathbf{x}_B$ is an optimal solution to any one of the formulations of the primal considered in this section, then $\mathbf{w}' = \mathbf{c}_B\mathbf{B}^{-1}$ is an optimal solution to the dual. Now, of course, it may not be true that all $w_i \geq 0$. This depends on the nature of the primal. In Problem 8–9 the reader will be asked to show this in detail.

8–5 Complementary slackness. Given a linear programming problem in the form of (8–7), we know from Chapter 3 that if $\mathbf{D}$ is $s \times r$, an optimal solution need not have more than s variables different from zero. If the problem (8–7) is solved by means of the dual, then an optimal solution to (8–7) is $\mathbf{x}' = \mathbf{d}_B'\overline{\mathbf{B}}^{-1}$, where $\overline{\mathbf{B}}$ is an optimal basis for the dual, and $\mathbf{d}_B$ contains the dual prices in the optimal solution to the dual. Now $\overline{\mathbf{B}}$ is an rth-order matrix, and therefore $\mathbf{x}' = \mathbf{d}_B'\overline{\mathbf{B}}^{-1}$ can apparently have r components different from zero. Normally, we would use the dual formulation only when $r < s$. In this case, the fact that we only find $r < s$ values of x_j merely means that the solution by the dual does not yield the values of any of the slack variables that would be added to (8–7) to obtain a set of equations. These slack variables may, of course, be easily computed from their defining equations. However, the solution to the dual does give some information about the slack variables. We shall prove below that if w_i is in the optimal basic feasible solution to the dual, then for the corresponding optimal solution to the primal, $\mathbf{x}' = \mathbf{d}_B'\overline{\mathbf{B}}^{-1}$, the ith primal constraint is satisfied as a strict equality, i.e., the ith primal slack variable is zero.

Suppose now that we solved (8–7) by using the dual and $r > s$. In this case, it would seem that more than s values of $\mathbf{x}$ could differ from zero. However, this is not true. The dual solution gives all values of the x_j, those which are positive and those which are zero. Thus no more than s components of $\mathbf{x}' = \mathbf{d}_B'\overline{\mathbf{B}}^{-1}$ will differ from zero. If $r > s$, the dual basis $\overline{\mathbf{B}}$ must contain at least $r - s$ surplus vectors. We shall prove the interesting result that if a surplus variable appears in column i of $\overline{\mathbf{B}}$, then x_i of $\mathbf{x}' = \mathbf{d}_B'\overline{\mathbf{B}}^{-1}$ is zero.

Let us now restate and prove the two theorems referred to in the above paragraphs. As usual we give the formulation in terms of the primal. The theorems are:

(a) *If a slack or surplus variable x_{r+i} which has been added to the ith primal constraint appears in an optimal basic solution (with the basis matrix being* $\mathbf{B}$), *then for the corresponding optimal solution to the dual* $\mathbf{w}' = \mathbf{c}_B\mathbf{B}^{-1}$, *the ith dual variable is zero, that is,* $w_i = 0$.

(b) *If the variable x_j appears in an optimal basic solution to the primal problem, then in the corresponding optimal solution to the dual,* $\mathbf{w}' = \mathbf{c}_B\mathbf{B}^{-1}$, *the jth dual constraint holds as a strict equality, that is, the dual slack or surplus variable* $w_{s+j} = 0$.

To prove (a) note that since x_{r+i} is in the optimal basic solution, and since the activity vector for x_{r+i} is $\pm \mathbf{e}_i$ and its price is zero,

$$z_{r+i} - c_{r+i} = \mathbf{c}_B \mathbf{B}^{-1}(\pm \mathbf{e}_i) = \pm (\mathbf{c}_B \mathbf{B}^{-1})_i = w_i = 0. \quad (8\text{--}41)$$

If we let $\mathbf{d}_j$ be the column vector corresponding to the x_j, then the proof of (b) follows from the fact that $z_j - c_j = 0$ since x_j is in the optimal solution. It is only necessary to note that

$$z_j - c_j = \mathbf{c}_B \mathbf{B}^{-1} \mathbf{d}_j - c_j = \mathbf{w}' \mathbf{d}_j - c_j = 0, \quad (8\text{--}42)$$

so that $\mathbf{w}$ does satisfy the jth dual constraint as a strict equality. Observe that the proofs used hold for all formulations of the primal and are not restricted to the form (8–7).

The results (a) and (b) are usually presented in a slightly different form. Consider (a) first. The modified form reads:

(a) *If a slack variable x_{r+i} which has been added to the ith constraint of (8–7) is different from zero in any optimal solution to (8–7), then in (8–8) the ith variable w_i is zero in every optimal solution. Conversely, if w_i is different from zero in any optimal solution to (8–8), $x_{r+i} = 0$ in every optimal solution to (8–7). This can be summarized by saying that for any pair of optimal solutions to (8–7), (8–8), $w_i x_{r+i} = 0$, $i = 1, \ldots, s$. Note that this holds for any optimal solutions to (8–7), (8–8), not merely for basic solutions.*

To prove this modified form of (a), we first convert the constraints to equations; this yields

$$\mathbf{D}\mathbf{x} + \mathbf{I}\mathbf{x}_s = \mathbf{d}.$$

Multiplying on the left by $\mathbf{w}' \geq \mathbf{0}$, we obtain

$$\mathbf{w}' \mathbf{D}\mathbf{x} + \mathbf{w}' \mathbf{x}_s = \mathbf{w}' \mathbf{d}. \quad (8\text{--}43)$$

However, if $[\mathbf{x}, \mathbf{x}_s]$ is an optimal solution to the primal and $\mathbf{w}$ is an optimal solution to the dual, then according to (8–25)

$$\max z = \mathbf{w}' \mathbf{D}\mathbf{x} = \min Z = \mathbf{w}' \mathbf{d};$$

hence it follows from (8–43) that

$$\mathbf{w}' \mathbf{x}_s = \sum_{i=1}^{s} w_i x_{r+i} = 0, \quad \text{or} \quad w_i x_{r+i} = 0, \quad i = 1, \ldots, s, \quad (8\text{--}44)$$

since $w_i \geq 0$, $x_{r+i} \geq 0$. Therefore, if $x_{r+i} \neq 0$, $w_i = 0$. Conversely, if $w_i \neq 0$, $x_{r+i} = 0$. This result is less general than (8–41) in that we must assume that $x_{r+i} \neq 0$ for at least one optimal solution to the primal, to show that $w_i = 0$ for any optimal solution to the dual. However, it is more general than (8–41) in the sense that it does not require the optimal solutions to be basic, and it holds for any form of optimal solutions rather than only for corresponding optimal solutions of the form $\mathbf{x}_B = \mathbf{B}^{-1}\mathbf{d}$, $\mathbf{w}' = \mathbf{c}_B\mathbf{B}^{-1}$. The modified version of (b) reads:

(b) *If* $\mathbf{x}$ *is any optimal solution to* (8–7) *and if* $\mathbf{w}_s$ *contains the surplus variables for any optimal solution to* (8–8), *then*

$$\mathbf{x}'\mathbf{w}_s = 0, \quad \text{or} \quad x_j w_{s+j} = 0, \quad j = 1, \dots, r. \quad (8\text{–}45)$$

The proof is precisely the same as that presented above if one begins with (8–8) instead of (8–7).

The properties (a), (b) are sometimes referred to as complementary slackness. To see why this name is used, let us include the non-negativity restrictions as constraints and write the primal and dual constraints as

$$\begin{matrix} \mathbf{x} \geq \mathbf{0}, & \mathbf{D}'\mathbf{w} \geq \mathbf{c}', \\ \mathbf{D}\mathbf{x} \leq \mathbf{d}, & \mathbf{w} \geq \mathbf{0}. \end{matrix} \quad (8\text{–}46)$$

If the constraints are numbered in this order, and if for any pair of optimal solutions to (8–46), the kth constraint of the primal is a strict inequality, then the kth constraint of the dual is a strict equality. Therefore, the constraints which can be inequalities in the dual are complementary to those which are strict inequalities in the primal. However, this does not imply that the kth dual constraint will be a strict inequality if the kth primal constraint is a strict equality (see Problem 8–11). Both the kth primal and the kth dual constraints may hold as equalities.

The remarks made in the preceding paragraph apply to any optimal solutions of the primal and dual problems. It is an interesting fact that one can prove that if the primal has an optimal solution, then there is one optimal solution to the primal and one optimal solution to the dual such that if $x_{r+i} = 0$, then $w_i > 0$, and if $x_j = 0$, then $w_{s+j} > 0$; furthermore, if $w_i = 0$, $x_{r+i} > 0$, and if $w_{s+j} = 0$, $x_j > 0$. This statement is stronger than the results obtained above. However, these latter results do not necessarily hold for all optimal solutions. The proof of the result given in this paragraph is left for Problem 8–13.

8–6 Unbounded solution in the primal. We have shown that if the primal problem has an optimal solution, then so does the dual. If the primal problem has an unbounded solution, then the dual has either no solution or an unbounded solution. This follows because if the dual had an optimal solution, then the primal would also have an optimal solution since it is the dual of the dual. We shall now show that *if the primal has an unbounded solution, the dual has no feasible solution.*

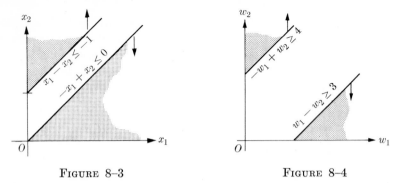

FIGURE 8–3   FIGURE 8–4

Let us assume that the primal problem has been cast into the form (8–7). We have shown previously that for any feasible solution $\mathbf{w}$ to the dual (8–8),

$$\max z = \max \mathbf{cx} \leq \mathbf{d'w}. \qquad (8\text{–}47)$$

But, by assumption, $\max z = \infty$, which means that there is no feasible $\mathbf{w}$ whose components are all finite. Hence there is no feasible solution to the dual.

One must be careful not to conclude that if the primal has no solution, then the dual has an unbounded solution. It may be true that neither problem has a solution. The following example illustrates this point.

EXAMPLE: The linear programming problem,

$$x_1 - x_2 \leq -1,$$
$$-x_1 + x_2 \leq 0,$$
$$x_1, x_2 \geq 0,$$
$$\max z = 3x_1 + 4x_2,$$

has no solution since the constraints are inconsistent (see Fig. 8–3). Similarly, the dual problem below has no solution (see Fig. 8–4):

$$w_1 - w_2 \geq 3,$$
$$-w_1 + w_2 \geq 4,$$
$$w_1, w_2 \geq 0,$$
$$\min Z = -w_1.$$

8–7 Dual simplex algorithm.* The reader may have already noticed that for any linear programming problem, the $z_j - c_j$ are completely independent of the requirements vector. Consequently, the set of basic

---

* This is the first time that we have used the word algorithm, although it appears frequently in linear programming. All numerical techniques for solving

solutions to $\mathbf{Ax} = \mathbf{b}$ with $z_j - c_j \geq 0$ for all j depends only on the $\mathbf{a}_j$ and the c_j, but not on $\mathbf{b}$. In general, not every basic solution with all $z_j - c_j \geq 0$ will be feasible. However, any basic feasible solution with all $z_j - c_j \geq 0$ will be an optimal solution.

The above observation presents an interesting possibility. If we could start with some basic, but not feasible, solution to a given linear programming problem which had all $z_j - c_j \geq 0$ and move from this basic solution to another by changing one vector at a time in such a way that we kept all $z_j - c_j \geq 0$, then, provided no basis had to be repeated, an optimal solution to the linear programming problem would be obtained in a finite number of steps. This is precisely what the dual simplex algorithm does. The fact that we maintain all the $z_j - c_j \geq 0$ at each step and are not concerned about the feasibility of the basic solutions (i.e., about the requirements vector) suggests that the duality theory should be of help in developing such an algorithm.

By examining the application of the simplex method to the dual of a linear programming problem, C. E. Lemke, a student of Charnes, discovered a new algorithm for solving the primal problem which meets the suggestions made in the above paragraph. Because it is not always easy to get started by means of this new algorithm, it does not have the general applicability of the usual simplex method. However, it can be used in certain cases to eliminate the necessity for a Phase I and the consequent introduction of artificial variables. It will also prove very helpful in treating some of the problems to be discussed in Chapter 11. Lemke's algorithm has been called the dual simplex algorithm since the criteria for inserting and removing a vector are those for the dual rather than the primal problem.

Let us assume that we have cast the given (primal) linear programming problem into the standard form for the application of the simplex method, i.e.,

$$\mathbf{Ax} = \mathbf{b}, \qquad \mathbf{x} \geq \mathbf{0}, \qquad \max z = \mathbf{cx}. \tag{8–48}$$

The dual of this problem is

$$\mathbf{w'A} \geq \mathbf{c}, \tag{8–49}$$
$$\min Z = \mathbf{w'b},$$

and Section 8–4 has shown that the dual variables are unrestricted in sign.

---

linear programming problems are called algorithms; thus, e.g., the simplex method is called the simplex algorithm. Roughly speaking, an algorithm is just a prescription or specific routine for solving a given problem. A precise mathematical definition of an algorithm has been formulated only recently (1933) by Alonzo Church. He also showed that some problems are so complex that they have no algorithmic solutions. In 1936, Post and Turing independently formulated a very general theory of algorithms or routine processes.

For any feasible solution $\mathbf{x}$ to (8–48) and any solution $\mathbf{w}$ to (8–49), we have, by (8–48),

$$\mathbf{w}'\mathbf{A}\mathbf{x} = \mathbf{w}'\mathbf{b},$$

and by (8–49),

$$\mathbf{w}'\mathbf{A}\mathbf{x} \geq \mathbf{c}\mathbf{x}.$$

Consequently, for any feasible solution $\mathbf{x}$ to (8–48) and any solution $\mathbf{w}$ to (8–49),

$$\mathbf{c}\mathbf{x} \leq \mathbf{w}'\mathbf{b}. \tag{8–50}$$

The derivation of the dual simplex algorithm will be first presented in the form of Lemke's treatment, which is very neat and simple. Since his development does not indicate too well the intuitive motivation for the procedure, we shall, in addition, present a more straightforward and detailed treatment.

As usual, $\mathbf{A}$ will be taken to be an $m \times n$ matrix. Note that the constraints of (8–49) can be written

$$\mathbf{w}'\mathbf{a}_j \geq c_j, \qquad j = 1, \ldots, n. \tag{8–51}$$

Suppose that we have obtained from $\mathbf{A}$ a basis matrix $\mathbf{B} = (\mathbf{b}_1, \ldots, \mathbf{b}_m)$ such that the solution $\mathbf{w}$ to the set of m simultaneous linear equations in m unknowns

$$\mathbf{w}'\mathbf{b}_i = c_{Bi}, \qquad i = 1, \ldots, m, \qquad \text{or} \qquad \mathbf{w}' = \mathbf{c}_B \mathbf{B}^{-1}$$

is a solution to the dual, i.e.,

$$\mathbf{w}'\mathbf{b}_i = c_{Bi}, \qquad i = 1, \ldots, m, \tag{8–52a}$$

$$\mathbf{w}'\mathbf{a}_j \geq c_j, \tag{8–52b}$$

for every $\mathbf{a}_j$ not in the basis. Since $\mathbf{w}' = \mathbf{c}_B \mathbf{B}^{-1}$, we can write

$$\mathbf{c}_B \mathbf{B}^{-1}\mathbf{a}_j - c_j \geq 0 \qquad \text{all } j, \tag{8–53}$$

or $z_j - c_j \geq 0$ for all j, which implies that the optimality criterion is satisfied for the primal problem. Then if

$$\mathbf{x}_B = \mathbf{B}^{-1}\mathbf{b} \geq \mathbf{0}, \tag{8–54}$$

we have an optimal solution to the primal and the dual since

$$\mathbf{c}\mathbf{x} = \mathbf{c}_B \mathbf{x}_B = \mathbf{c}_B \mathbf{B}^{-1}\mathbf{b} = \mathbf{w}'\mathbf{b}. \tag{8–55}$$

When we have a solution to the dual, $\mathbf{w}' = \mathbf{c}_B \mathbf{B}^{-1}$, and it is not optimal, we are forced to conclude that one or more of the x_{Bi} in (8–54) are negative.

Let us study the case where one or more $x_{Bi} < 0$. Denote the rows of $\mathbf{B}^{-1}$ by $\boldsymbol{\beta}^j$. It follows that

$$\boldsymbol{\beta}^j \mathbf{b}_i = \delta_{ij}, \qquad i, j = 1, \ldots, m. \tag{8–56}$$

Consider any $x_{Br} < 0$ which is given by

$$x_{Br} = \boldsymbol{\beta}^r \mathbf{b}. \tag{8–57}$$

We shall investigate the properties of a new vector $\hat{\mathbf{w}}$ given by

$$\hat{\mathbf{w}}' = \mathbf{w}' - \theta \boldsymbol{\beta}^r. \tag{8–58}$$

Then

$$\hat{Z} = \hat{\mathbf{w}}'\mathbf{b} = \mathbf{w}'\mathbf{b} - \theta \boldsymbol{\beta}^r \mathbf{b} = Z - \theta x_{Br}. \tag{8–59}$$

Consequently, if $\theta < 0$, $\hat{Z} < Z$ since $x_{Br} < 0$, and $\hat{\mathbf{w}}$ will yield a smaller value of Z. If $\hat{\mathbf{w}}$ can be made to satisfy the constraints of (8–49), we have a new solution to the dual with $\hat{Z} < Z$.

Now observe that

$$\hat{\mathbf{w}}'\mathbf{b}_i = \mathbf{w}'\mathbf{b}_i - \theta \boldsymbol{\beta}^r \mathbf{b}_i = c_{Bi} - \theta \delta_{ir}. \tag{8–60}$$

Thus,

$$\hat{\mathbf{w}}'\mathbf{b}_i = c_{Bi} \qquad (i \neq r), \tag{8–61a}$$

$$\hat{\mathbf{w}}'\mathbf{b}_r = c_r - \theta \geq c_r \qquad \text{if} \qquad \theta \leq 0. \tag{8–61b}$$

For all $\mathbf{a}_j$ not in the primal basis,

$$\hat{\mathbf{w}}'\mathbf{a}_j = \mathbf{w}'\mathbf{a}_j - \theta \boldsymbol{\beta}^r \mathbf{a}_j. \tag{8–62}$$

If $\boldsymbol{\beta}^r \mathbf{a}_j \geq 0$ for every $\mathbf{a}_j$ not in the basis, then for any $\theta \leq 0$,

$$\hat{\mathbf{w}}'\mathbf{a}_j \geq c_j. \tag{8–63}$$

In such a situation, θ can be made an arbitrarily large negative number, and we still have a solution to the dual. Thus Z can be made arbitrarily small, and the dual has an unbounded solution. From Section 8–6 we know that the primal has no feasible solution.

Let us suppose that there is at least one $\mathbf{a}_j$ such that $\boldsymbol{\beta}^r \mathbf{a}_j < 0$. Note that

$$\boldsymbol{\beta}^r \mathbf{a}_j = y_{rj}, \tag{8–64}$$

where y_{rj} is just the rth component of $\mathbf{B}^{-1} \mathbf{a}_j$. For all $y_{rj} < 0$, we must have

$$\mathbf{w}'\mathbf{a}_j - c_j \geq \theta y_{rj}$$

to obtain $\hat{\mathbf{w}}'\mathbf{a}_j \geq c_j$. Therefore, we require that

$$\theta \geq \frac{\mathbf{w}'\mathbf{a}_j - c_j}{y_{rj}}, \tag{8-65}$$

since $y_{rj} < 0$. To decrease Z to the utmost, θ must (a) be as large in absolute value as possible and (b) satisfy (8–65). The best we can do is to take

$$\theta = \max_j \frac{\mathbf{w}'\mathbf{a}_j - c_j}{y_{rj}}, \qquad y_{rj} < 0.$$

Recall, however, that in terms of the primal notation, $\mathbf{w}'\mathbf{a}_j - c_j = z_j - c_j \geq 0$. Therefore,

$$\theta = \frac{z_k - c_k}{y_{rk}} = \max_j \frac{z_j - c_j}{y_{rj}}, \qquad y_{rj} < 0. \tag{8-66}$$

We have found a new solution to the dual, given by

$$\hat{\mathbf{w}}'\mathbf{b}_i = c_{Bi}, \qquad i \neq r,$$
$$\hat{\mathbf{w}}'\mathbf{b}_r \geq c_{Br},$$
$$\hat{\mathbf{w}}'\mathbf{a}_j \geq c_j \qquad \text{for } \mathbf{a}_j \text{ not in } \mathbf{B} \text{ and } j \neq k, \tag{8-67}$$
$$\hat{\mathbf{w}}'\mathbf{a}_k = \mathbf{w}'\mathbf{a}_k - \theta y_{rk} = c_k, \qquad \theta \leq 0,$$
$$\hat{Z} = Z - \theta x_{Br}.$$

If $\theta < 0$, $\hat{Z} < Z$. Furthermore, note that the strict equality holds for the dual constraint involving $\mathbf{a}_k$. Since $y_{rk} \neq 0$, $\mathbf{a}_k$, together with the $\mathbf{b}_i$ $(i \neq r)$, forms a new primal basis $\hat{\mathbf{B}}$ in which column r of $\mathbf{B}$ has been replaced by $\mathbf{a}_k$.

If $\hat{\mathbf{x}}_B = \hat{\mathbf{B}}^{-1}\mathbf{b}$ still contains one or more negative components, we can repeat the entire process. Observe that the actual computations do not require the dual problem at all. Although the changes to be made were developed from a consideration of the dual problem, we see that they can be expressed solely in terms of the primal.

Hence, the new algorithm for the primal can be described as follows: We begin with a basic solution to the primal with one or more $x_{Bi} < 0$, but with $z_j - c_j \geq 0$ for all j. As in the simplex method, we move from this solution to an optimal solution by changing a single vector in the basis at each step. The criteria for the change of basis are:

I. Vector to be removed: Choose

$$x_{Br} = \min_i x_{Bi}, \qquad x_{Bi} < 0. \tag{8-68}$$

Column $\mathbf{b}_r$ is removed from the basis, and x_{Br} is therefore driven to zero.

II. Vector to enter basis: The vector $\mathbf{a}_k$ to enter the basis is determined from

$$\theta = \frac{z_k - c_k}{y_{rk}} = \max_j \frac{z_j - c_j}{y_{rj}}, \qquad y_{rj} < 0. \qquad (8\text{–}69)$$

Originally, we chose any $x_{Br} < 0$. The greatest decrease in Z will come when θx_{Br} is as large as possible. Instead of computing θ for each $x_{Bi} < 0$, we simply choose the smallest x_{Bi} in (8–68) to determine the vector to leave the basis. This procedure is similar to choosing the smallest $z_j - c_j$ rather than the smallest $(x_{Br}/y_{rj})(z_j - c_j)$ in the simplex method. If there is a tie, any rule can be used to break it.

The value of θ computed from (8–69) need not be negative; it may be zero. Then Z does not change, and we have a case of dual degeneracy. If at any iteration the maximum in Eq. (8–69) is not unique, then the vector to enter is not uniquely determined. At the next step, there will be one or more $z_j - c_j = 0$ for vectors not in the primal basis, and dual degeneracy will appear. This situation is best handled by using some arbitrary rule for determining the vector to enter the basis. Under these circumstances, cycling can theoretically occur in the dual simplex algorithm. Problem 8–25 will ask the reader to show how cycling can rigorously be avoided.

Note that in the dual simplex algorithm one first determines the vector to leave the basis and then the vector to enter. This is the reverse of what is done in the simplex method. Also note that degeneracy and cycling appear in choosing the vector to enter the primal basis, whereas in the simplex method degeneracy causes difficulties in determining the vector to leave the basis. In the following section, we shall show that the appearance of dual degeneracy in the primal implies the vanishing of one or more basic variables in the dual problem.

The reader may be wondering how we determine whether the primal problem has an unbounded solution when the dual simplex algorithm is used. If the primal has an unbounded solution, the dual problem has no solution, and consequently, we can never find a solution to the dual problem. Hence if the primal has an unbounded solution, we can never find a basic solution to the primal with all $z_j - c_j \geq 0$.

We have shown that the dual simplex algorithm can be applied directly to the primal problem. In fact, at each iteration, we construct precisely the same type of tableau as in the simplex method. The formulas used to transform from one tableau to the next are indeed those used for the simplex method. The difference in the algorithms is manifested in the selection of the vectors to enter and leave the basis.

8–8 Alternative derivation of the dual simplex algorithm. It is desirable to derive the dual simplex algorithm in a more straightforward way. We shall do this by applying the simplex method directly to the dual problem. After adding surplus variables to the dual problem,[*] we can write it in the form used in applications of the simplex method, i.e.,

$$\mathbf{A'w} - \mathbf{Iw}_s = \mathbf{c'},$$
$$\mathbf{w}_s \geq \mathbf{0}, \tag{8-70}$$
$$\min Z = \mathbf{b'w}.$$

The w_i of $\mathbf{w}$ are unrestricted in sign.

Consider now any solution $\mathbf{x}$ (not necessarily feasible) to $\mathbf{Ax} = \mathbf{b}$ and any solution $\mathbf{w}$ to the dual. Then

$$\mathbf{x'A'w} - \mathbf{x'w}_s = \mathbf{x'c'}.$$

If it is true that

$$\mathbf{x'w}_s = 0, \tag{8-71}$$

then

$$Z = \mathbf{b'w} = \mathbf{cx} = z. \tag{8-72}$$

Thus for any solution to the primal and any solution to the dual with $\mathbf{x'w}_s = 0$, it follows that the objective functions for both problems are equal. It will be noted that the dual simplex algorithm as described in the previous section does maintain $\mathbf{x'w}_s = 0$ at each stage.

Let us apply the simplex method to (8-70). The constraint matrix $(\mathbf{A'}, -\mathbf{I})$ is $n \times (m + n)$. As usual, it will be assumed that $n > m$. Any basis matrix $\overline{\mathbf{B}}$ for the dual problem will be $n \times n$. The columns of $\mathbf{A'}$, are $\mathbf{a}^i$, the rows of $\mathbf{A}$. We shall consider a basic feasible solution to the dual to be a basic solution with non-negative surplus variables. The variables w_i are unrestricted. Since there are only m columns in $\mathbf{A'}$, there must always be at least $n - m$ surplus variables in any basic solution whose basis matrix $\overline{\mathbf{B}}$ is formed from the columns of $(\mathbf{A'}, -\mathbf{I})$.

Assume that we have found a basic feasible solution to the dual which contains the m vectors of $\mathbf{A'}$. It will be helpful to study the structure of the basis matrix in some detail. Without loss in generality, we can assume that $\mathbf{a}^1, \ldots, \mathbf{a}^m$ are in the first m columns of $\overline{\mathbf{B}}$. The last $n - m$ columns will contain surplus vectors of the form $-\mathbf{e}_j$. To be specific, take the surplus vectors to be $\mathbf{e}_{m+1}, \ldots, \mathbf{e}_n$. The rows of the dual problem can always be rearranged so that this will be true. Then $\overline{\mathbf{B}}$ is

$$\overline{\mathbf{B}} = (\mathbf{a}^{1'}, \ldots, \mathbf{a}^{m'}, -\mathbf{e}_{m+1}, \ldots, -\mathbf{e}_n).$$

---

[*] For clarity, we shall denote the surplus variables in this and the following sections by w_{sj} rather than w_{n+j}.

The first m columns of $\bar{\mathbf{B}}$ are $\mathbf{A}'$. Therefore $\bar{\mathbf{B}}$ can be written in terms of the columns of $\mathbf{A}$ as

$$\bar{\mathbf{B}} = \begin{bmatrix} \mathbf{a}'_1 & 0 & 0 \cdots & 0 \\ \mathbf{a}'_2 & 0 & 0 \cdots & 0 \\ \vdots & & & \vdots \\ \mathbf{a}'_m & 0 & 0 \cdots & 0 \\ \mathbf{a}'_{m+1} & -1 & 0 \cdots & 0 \\ \vdots & & & \vdots \\ \mathbf{a}'_n & 0 & 0 \cdots & -1 \end{bmatrix}. \tag{8-73}$$

Of course, $\mathbf{a}_1, \ldots, \mathbf{a}_m$ in (8-73) may be any m columns of the original $\mathbf{A}$ [since we rearranged the rows of $\mathbf{A}'$ (columns of $\mathbf{A}$) so that the surplus vectors would be those shown], provided that $\bar{\mathbf{B}}$ yields a basic feasible solution to the dual.

Since $r(\bar{\mathbf{B}}) = n$, the first m rows of $\bar{\mathbf{B}}$ are linearly independent. Therefore, $\mathbf{a}_1, \ldots, \mathbf{a}_m$ must be linearly independent. We immediately see that $\mathbf{B} = (\mathbf{a}_1, \ldots, \mathbf{a}_m)$ is a basis for the *primal* system. In terms of $\mathbf{B}$, $\bar{\mathbf{B}}$ can be written

$$\bar{\mathbf{B}} = \begin{bmatrix} \mathbf{B}' & \mathbf{0} \\ \mathbf{R} & -\mathbf{I}_{n-m} \end{bmatrix}; \qquad \mathbf{R} = [\mathbf{a}'_{m+1}, \ldots, \mathbf{a}'_n]. \tag{8-74}$$

We see that $\bar{\mathbf{B}}$, $\mathbf{B}$ yield solutions to the dual and primal, respectively, which have $\mathbf{x}'\mathbf{w}_s = 0$. Whenever we have a basic feasible solution to the dual with $\mathbf{a}^1, \ldots, \mathbf{a}^m$ in $\bar{\mathbf{B}}$, we can immediately find a basic solution to the primal by the method discussed above. The manner in which we obtained the primal from the dual basis clearly shows that when $\mathbf{a}_j$ is in the primal basis, $-\mathbf{e}_j$ is not in the dual basis, and conversely. Consequently, $x_j = 0$ when $w_{sj} \neq 0$, and $w_{sj} = 0$ when $x_j \neq 0$. This means that (8-71) holds, and $z = Z$ for the corresponding solutions to the primal and dual problems.

Having obtained the basic feasible solution to the dual discussed above, we now wish to know whether it is optimal or whether it can be improved. When $\bar{\mathbf{B}}$ is of the form (8-73), the prices of the variables in the dual basis will be the b_i for the first m columns and 0 for the remaining columns. Denote the price vector by $\mathbf{b}_{\bar{B}} = (\mathbf{b}', \mathbf{0})$. Note that the only vectors for the dual problem not in the dual basis are surplus vectors. Write

$$Z_i = \mathbf{b}_{\bar{B}}\bar{\mathbf{B}}^{-1}(-\mathbf{e}_i), \qquad i = 1, \ldots, m. \tag{8-75}$$

The basic feasible solution to the dual will be optimal if $Z_i \leq 0$ for the surplus vectors not in the dual basis. This follows from the optimality criterion of the simplex method applied to a minimization problem (recall that the price of a surplus variable is zero).

Using (8–74), we can write

$$\bar{\mathbf{B}}^{-1} = \begin{bmatrix} (\mathbf{B}')^{-1} & \mathbf{0} \\ \mathbf{R}(\mathbf{B}')^{-1} & -\mathbf{I} \end{bmatrix}. \tag{8–76}$$

Therefore,

$$Z_i = (\mathbf{b}', \mathbf{0}) \begin{bmatrix} (\mathbf{B}')^{-1} & \mathbf{0} \\ \mathbf{R}(\mathbf{B}')^{-1} & -\mathbf{I} \end{bmatrix} (-\mathbf{e}_i) = (\mathbf{x}_B', \mathbf{0})(-\mathbf{e}_i) = -x_{Bi}. \tag{8–77}$$

Thus, if all $x_{Bi} \geq 0$, we have an optimal solution to the dual, and $\mathbf{x}_B$ is an optimal solution to the primal, as expected.

If one or more $Z_i > 0$, we know that Z can be decreased (or that at least a new basis with the same value of Z can be obtained). Using the simplex criterion, we choose the vector to enter the dual basis from

$$Z_r = \max Z_i, \qquad Z_i > 0, \tag{8–78}$$

or, in terms of the x_{Bi}, we determine the vector to be removed from the primal basis, using

$$x_{Br} = \min x_{Bi}, \qquad x_{Bi} < 0. \tag{8–79}$$

This is the result obtained in the previous section in a less straightforward way. According to (8–78) or (8–79), $-\mathbf{e}_r$ enters the dual basis at the next iteration. It follows that the primal variable corresponding to x_{Br} is thereby driven to zero.

Before determining which vector should leave the dual basis, let us compute the basic feasible solution to the dual $\mathbf{w}_{\bar{B}}$; we have

$$\mathbf{w}_{\bar{B}} = \bar{\mathbf{B}}^{-1}\mathbf{c}' = \begin{bmatrix} (\mathbf{B}')^{-1} & \mathbf{0} \\ \mathbf{R}(\mathbf{B}')^{-1} & -\mathbf{I} \end{bmatrix} \begin{bmatrix} \mathbf{c}_B' \\ \mathbf{c}_R' \end{bmatrix}, \tag{8–80}$$

and $\mathbf{c}_R$ contains the prices not in the primal basis $\mathbf{B}$. Also the first m components of $\mathbf{w}_{\bar{B}}$ are $\mathbf{w}$. For these first m components,

$$\mathbf{w} = (\mathbf{B}')^{-1}\mathbf{c}_B' \qquad \text{or} \qquad \mathbf{w}' = \mathbf{c}_B\mathbf{B}^{-1}; \tag{8–81}$$

this is the same result as that obtained in the previous section.

The last $n - m$ components of $\mathbf{w}_{\bar{B}}$ are

$$\mathbf{R}(\mathbf{B}')^{-1}\mathbf{c}_B' - \mathbf{c}_R',$$

or, taking the transpose, we have

$$\mathbf{c}_B \mathbf{B}^{-1} \mathbf{R}' - \mathbf{c}_R.$$

In terms of components, this is

$$w_{sj} = \mathbf{c}_B \mathbf{B}^{-1} \mathbf{a}_j - c_j = z_j - c_j. \qquad (8\text{-}82)$$

Thus the surplus variable w_{sj} in the dual basis has the value $z_j - c_j$ for the primal variable x_j not in the primal basis. Since $z_j - c_j = 0$ for the vectors in the primal basis, and since $-\mathbf{e}_j$ is not in $\overline{\mathbf{B}}$ if $\mathbf{a}_j$ is in $\mathbf{B}$, we can also write $w_{sj} = z_j - c_j$ for the surplus variables not in the dual basis. Hence,

$$w_{sj} = z_j - c_j, \qquad j = 1, \ldots, n. \qquad (8\text{-}83)$$

We can now turn to the subject of deciding which vector should leave the dual basis. We never want to remove $\mathbf{a}^1, \ldots, \mathbf{a}^m$ because if we do, we shall not be able to determine a corresponding basis for the primal problem. We know that if $r(\mathbf{A}) = m$, an optimal solution to the primal will have m of the $\mathbf{a}_j$ in the primal basis, and therefore at least m of the dual constraints will be strict equalities. If we write

$$\mathbf{y}^r = \overline{\mathbf{B}}^{-1}(-\mathbf{e}_r), \qquad (8\text{-}84)$$

then

$$\mathbf{y}^r = \begin{bmatrix} (\mathbf{B}')^{-1} & \mathbf{0} \\ \mathbf{R}(\mathbf{B}')^{-1} & -\mathbf{I} \end{bmatrix} (-\mathbf{e}_r) = - \begin{bmatrix} (\mathbf{B}')^{-1}\mathbf{e}_r^* \\ \mathbf{R}(\mathbf{B}')^{-1}\mathbf{e}_r^* \end{bmatrix}, \qquad (8\text{-}85)$$

where $\mathbf{e}_r^*$ is a vector containing the first m components of $\mathbf{e}_r$. It follows from our previous arrangement that the last $n - m$ components of any $-\mathbf{e}_r$ not in the basis are zero.

The vector to be removed from the surplus vectors in the basis is, as usual, determined from

$$\frac{w_{sk}}{y_k^r} = \min_j \left\{ \frac{w_{sj}}{y_j^r}, y_j^r > 0 \right\}, \qquad j = m + 1, \ldots, n. \qquad (8\text{-}86)$$

We can ignore the first m components of $\mathbf{w}_B$ because they are unrestricted in sign, and we do not want to remove any of the first m columns. Let us evaluate more explicitly the last $n - m$ components of $\mathbf{y}^r$. Recall that $\mathbf{y}_j$ for the corresponding basic solution to the primal is given by $\mathbf{y}_j = \mathbf{B}^{-1}\mathbf{a}_j$ or $\mathbf{y}_j' = \mathbf{a}_j'(\mathbf{B}')^{-1}$. However, $\mathbf{a}_j'$ is one of the rows of $\mathbf{R}$. Thus $\mathbf{R}(\mathbf{B}')^{-1}$ is a matrix of the $\mathbf{y}_j'$ for vectors not in the primal basis. Also $\mathbf{y}_j'\mathbf{e}_r^* = y_{rj}$. Thus we see that the last $n - m$ components of $\mathbf{y}^r$ are the $-y_{rj}$. In particular,

$y_j^r = -y_{rj}$. One must be careful to note the interchange of subscripts; y_j^r is the jth component of $\mathbf{y}^r$ for the dual, and y_{rj} is the rth component of $\mathbf{y}_j$ for the primal.

Thus, in terms of the primal, the criterion for the vector to be removed from the dual basis is, from (8–86),

$$\frac{z_k - c_k}{-y_{rk}} = \min_j \frac{z_j - c_j}{-y_{rj}}, \qquad -y_{rj} > 0.$$

This is equivalent to

$$\frac{z_k - c_k}{y_{rk}} = \max_j \frac{z_j - c_j}{y_{rj}}, \qquad y_{rj} < 0, \qquad (8\text{–}87)$$

which is the result obtained in the preceding section. Of course, if $y_{rj} \geq 0$ for all vectors not in the primal basis, the dual has an unbounded solution, and the primal has no solution.

8–9 Initial solution for dual simplex algorithm. The dual simplex algorithm will be used to solve a linear programming problem only if it reduces the amount of work. If artificial vectors are not needed in the application of the simplex method to a given linear programming problem, there is no reason for using the dual simplex algorithm. However, in addition to the direct solution of linear programming problems, the dual simplex algorithm has other important applications, which will be discussed later. In these cases, we always have an initial solution for the dual simplex algorithm.

In general, it is not an easy task to find an initial basic solution to the primal with all $z_j - c_j \geq 0$. Equivalently, this implies that it can be difficult to find a basic feasible solution to the dual. In the worst case, we may have to add n artificial vectors to the dual problem. Even after determining a feasible solution to the dual in this manner, we may not find $\mathbf{a}^1, \ldots, \mathbf{a}^m$ in the basis, and more work would be required to obtain a basic solution to the primal with all $z_j - c_j \geq 0$. Clearly, such a procedure could be considerably more time-consuming than the direct application of the two-phase method to the primal.

There is one particular case where one can easily find a basic solution to the primal problem with all $z_j - c_j \geq 0$. Suppose that a surplus variable has been added to each constraint. Also assume that $c_j \leq 0$ for every j. If the initial basis matrix is $\mathbf{B} = -\mathbf{I}$, then $\mathbf{x}_B = -\mathbf{b}$, and $z_j - c_j = -c_j \geq 0$. This follows since the columns of $-\mathbf{I}$ are surplus vectors and their price is 0. Here we have a basic solution with all $z_j - c_j \geq 0$, and the dual simplex algorithm can now be applied.

At least two other methods have been suggested, one by Lemke and one by Dantzig, for getting started on the dual simplex algorithm. They require a good deal of work and hence seem to offer no advantage over the addition of artificial variables to the primal. The details of these two methods are studied in Problems 8–23 and 8–24.

8–10 The dual simplex algorithm; an example. Consider the following linear programming problem:

$$x_1 + x_2 \geq 1,$$
$$2x_1 + 3x_2 \geq 2, \qquad (8\text{–}88)$$
$$x_1, x_2 \geq 0,$$
$$\max z = -3x_1 - x_2.$$

After conversion to the standard form for the simplex method, we have

$$x_1 + x_2 - x_3 = 1,$$
$$2x_1 + 3x_2 - x_4 = 2,$$
$$\max z = -3x_1 - x_2.$$

If the problem were to be solved by the standard simplex method, we would need to introduce two artificial vectors. Suppose instead that we consider the basis which contains x_3, x_4, that is,

$$\mathbf{B} = \begin{bmatrix} -1 & 0 \\ 0 & -1 \end{bmatrix}, \qquad \mathbf{B}^{-1} = \begin{bmatrix} -1 & 0 \\ 0 & -1 \end{bmatrix}.$$

For this basis, $\mathbf{x}_B = [-1, -2]$. Furthermore $z_1 - c_1 = -c_1 = 3$, $z_2 - c_2 = 1$. Here we have a basic feasible solution with all $z_j - c_j \geq 0$. Hence the dual simplex method can be used, and artificial vectors are not needed.

The initial tableau is shown in Table 8–5. Note that $\mathbf{y}_j = -\mathbf{a}_j$ since $\mathbf{B} = -\mathbf{I}$. In the dual simplex method we first choose the vector to leave the basis, using (8–68); $x_{B2} = -2$ is the most negative x_{Bi}, and therefore the second column of $\mathbf{B}$ will be removed. It may now be helpful to encircle the second row of tableau 1, as shown.

The vector to enter is determined from (8–69): We select all the $y_{rj} < 0$, that is, all the $y_{2j} < 0$ (the y_{rj} in the encircled row). In our particular case, both y_{21} and $y_{22} < 0$. Then we divide the $z_j - c_j$ with $y_{rj} < 0$ by y_{rj} and select the largest number. Hence,

$$\frac{z_k - c_k}{y_{rk}} = \max\left\{ \frac{z_1 - c_1}{y_{21}} = -\frac{3}{2}; \frac{z_2 - c_2}{y_{22}} = -\frac{1}{3} \right\} = -\frac{1}{3}.$$

Therefore, $\mathbf{a}_2$ enters the basis. We can now encircle column $\mathbf{a}_2$.

TABLE 8–5 — TABLEAU 1

c_B	c_j Vectors in Basis	**b**	-3 $\mathbf{a}_1$	-1 $\mathbf{a}_2$	0 $\mathbf{a}_3$	0 $\mathbf{a}_4$
0	$\mathbf{a}_3$	-1	-1	-1	1	0
0	$\mathbf{a}_4$	-2	-2	-3	0	1
	$z_j - c_j$	0	3	1	0	0

TABLE 8–6 — TABLEAU 2

c_B	c_j Vectors in Basis	**b**	-3 $\mathbf{a}_1$	-1 $\mathbf{a}_2$	0 $\mathbf{a}_3$	0 $\mathbf{a}_4$
0	$\mathbf{a}_3$	$-\frac{1}{3}$	$-\frac{1}{3}$	0	1	$-\frac{1}{3}$
-1	$\mathbf{a}_2$	$\frac{2}{3}$	$\frac{2}{3}$	1	0	$-\frac{1}{3}$
	$z_j - c_j$	$-\frac{2}{3}$	$\frac{7}{3}$	0	0	$\frac{1}{3}$

The transformation to the new tableau is made in the same way as in the simplex method, e.g., by the "ring around the rosy" method. The new tableau is given in Table 8–6.

In the new tableau only $x_{B1} < 0$. Therefore $\mathbf{a}_3$ is removed at the next step. The vector to go in is determined from

$$\max \left\{ \frac{1/3}{-1/3}, \frac{7/3}{-1/3} \right\} = -1.$$

Thus $\mathbf{a}_4$ goes in. The new tableau is given in Table 8–7.

All x_{Bi} are now ≥ 0, and the optimality criterion is satisfied. Hence an optimal solution has been found. The graphic solution of the problem is a

TABLE 8–7 — TABLEAU 3

c_B	Vectors in Basis	c_j b	-3 a_1	-1 a_2	0 a_3	0 a_4
0	a_4	1	1	0	-3	1
-1	a_2	1	1	1	-1	0
	$z_j - c_j$	-1	2	0	1	0

simple matter and we can easily see that this answer is correct. Although we were using criteria which applied to the dual problem, the actual computations were carried out completely in terms of the primal. Note that the value of the function to be maximized did not increase at each iteration. Instead, z decreased at each step. There is no reason why it should have increased since the basic solutions were not feasible until an optimal solution was reached. In fact, z should decrease or remain unchanged at each iteration since when using the dual simplex method, we always have $z = Z$, and Z is being minimized in the dual problem.

8–11 A geometric interpretation. An interesting geometric interpretation can be given to the dual linear programming problem and the dual simplex algorithm. If we write the primal as

$$\sum_{j=1}^{n} x_j a_j = b,$$
$$x \geq 0, \tag{8–89}$$
$$\max z = cx,$$

then the dual problem is

$$w'a_j \geq c_j, \quad j = 1, \ldots, n, \tag{8–90}$$
$$\min Z = b'w.$$

The activity vectors a_j in the primal become normals to half-spaces representing the constraints in the dual. The requirements vector b of the primal becomes a normal to the hyperplane $Z = b'w$ in the dual. The actual geometry is best illustrated by means of an example.

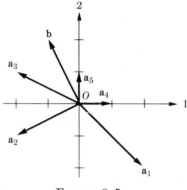

FIGURE 8–5

EXAMPLE: Given the linear programming problem

$$x_1\mathbf{a}_1 + \cdots + x_5\mathbf{a}_5 = \mathbf{b}, \qquad x_j \geq 0, \qquad j = 1, \ldots, 5,$$
$$\max z = -3x_1 - 4x_2 - 2x_3,$$

where

$$\mathbf{b} = [-1, 2], \qquad \mathbf{a}_1 = [2, -2], \qquad \mathbf{a}_2 = [-2, -1], \qquad \mathbf{a}_3 = [-2, 1],$$
$$\mathbf{a}_4 = [1, 0], \qquad \mathbf{a}_5 = [0, 1].$$

The dual problem is:

$$2w_1 - 2w_2 \geq -3,$$
$$-2w_1 - w_2 \geq -4,$$
$$-2w_1 + w_2 \geq -2,$$
$$w_1 \qquad\quad \geq \quad 0,$$
$$w_2 \geq \quad 0,$$
$$\min Z = -w_1 + 2w_2.$$

Because of the appearance of slack variables in the primal, the dual variables are non-negative.

The requirements-space configuration for the primal is shown in Fig. 8–5. For the dual problem, the convex set of feasible solutions in w_1w_2-space is represented by the shaded convex polyhedron shown in Fig. 8–6.* Whenever two of the dual constraints hold as strict equalities, the vectors normal to the constraints can be imagined to form a basis for the primal if the normals are linearly independent. In w_1w_2-space, the point $\mathbf{w}$ where two

---

* When illustrating graphically a vector normal to a line, we shall find it sometimes convenient to have the vector originate on the line rather than at the origin. This is done in Fig. 8–6 for greater clarity.

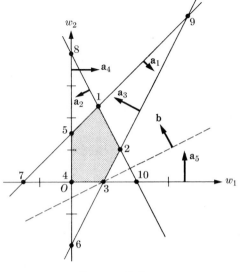

FIGURE 8–6

dual constraints hold as strict equalities is the intersection of the two lines representing these two constraints. A basic solution to the primal problem can then be associated with the intersection of each pair of bounding lines for the half-spaces representing the dual constraints.

There can be $5!/3!2! = 10$ basic solutions to the primal. All these exist and are represented by the numbered points in Fig. 8–6. For example, point 1 corresponds to having a_1, a_2 in the primal basis. The only feasible basic solutions to the primal are those corresponding to points 3, 6, 10. The points corresponding to feasible solutions to the dual and to basic solutions to the primal are the extreme points 1, 2, 3, 4, 5 of the convex polyhedron. Only one of these points, 3, also corresponds to a feasible solution to the primal. This then should be an optimal extreme point for the dual. On considering the dual objective function $Z = b'w$, we see that this is indeed the case. Using the dual simplex method, we move from one extreme point of the convex polyhedron to an adjacent one until an optimal extreme point is reached. At this point, the corresponding solution to the primal becomes feasible and, hence, optimal.

8–12 A primal-dual algorithm. When it is necessary to add artificial variables to a linear programming problem, both the two-phase method and Charnes' $-M$-method first drive the artificial variables to zero and thus obtain a feasible solution to the problem before working towards optimality. Unfortunately, in the process of driving the artificial variables to zero, they are not necessarily working towards optimality because the criterion used to select the vectors to enter the basis is only concerned with driving the artificial variables to zero. Hence at the end of Phase I (and, similarly, when the artificial variables are zero in Charnes' $-M$-method), the resulting feasible solution may not be anywhere near optimal. Consequently, a large number of iterations may be required in Phase II to achieve optimality.

It would be very desirable if both objectives could be attained in Phase I, so that it might become possible to reduce considerably the total number of iterations. A great deal of work has been expended in trying to develop such an algorithm. The primal-dual algorithm to be discussed in this section is a result of such efforts.

We have seen that the dual simplex algorithm can be used in certain circumstances to eliminate the necessity of introducing artificial variables. This algorithm does not have general applicability because it is often not easy to find a basic solution with all $z_j - c_j \geq 0$. The primal-dual algorithm developed by Dantzig, Ford, and Fulkerson [3] does introduce artificial variables into the primal and hence does require a Phase I. The vectors to enter the basis in Phase I are chosen in a way quite different from that employed previously. The dual problem is used to determine which vectors can enter the primal basis. The computational procedure is such that when Phase I terminates we have found an optimal as well as a feasible solution to the given problem.

The procedure is rather interesting. We begin with a solution to the dual. This solution releases certain legitimate vectors of the primal for insertion into the primal basis. Then we work on the primal until the optimality criterion is satisfied for the vectors released to enter the primal basis. A new solution to the dual can be found which releases one or more additional primal vectors for entry into the basis. Each time a new solution to the dual is found there is a strict decrease in the dual objective function. Complementary slackness is maintained at each step so that when a feasible solution to the primal is found it is also optimal. Hence, in the primal, we are working on feasibility and optimality at the same time.

We shall assume that the primal problem is

$$\mathbf{Ax} = \mathbf{b}, \qquad \mathbf{x} \geq \mathbf{0}, \qquad \max z = \mathbf{cx}. \qquad (8\text{–}91)$$

It has been seen in the discussion of the dual simplex algorithm that it may not be easy to find an immediate solution to the dual of (8–91). Beale [1], however, has suggested a very simple modification of (8–91) which leads to an immediate solution for the dual. Suppose that we replace (8–91) by a modified primal problem,

$$\begin{bmatrix} 1 & 1 \\ 0 & \mathbf{A} \end{bmatrix} \begin{bmatrix} x_0 \\ \mathbf{x} \end{bmatrix} = \begin{bmatrix} b_0 \\ \mathbf{b} \end{bmatrix}, \qquad [x_0, \mathbf{x}] \geq \mathbf{0}, \qquad \max z = \mathbf{cx}. \qquad (8\text{–}92)$$

We have introduced an additional constraint $x_0 + \sum_{j=1}^n x_j = b_0$ and an additional variable $x_0 \geq 0$ which appears only in the new constraint. The price of x_0 is zero. It is assumed that b_0 can be made arbitrarily large so that the new constraint places no additional restrictions on the x_j, $j = 1, \ldots, n$. For hand computations it is unnecessary to give a numerical value to b_0.

The dual of (8–92), called the modified dual, is

$$\begin{bmatrix} 1 & \mathbf{0} \\ \mathbf{1}' & \mathbf{A}' \end{bmatrix} \begin{bmatrix} w_0 \\ \mathbf{w} \end{bmatrix} \geq \begin{bmatrix} 0 \\ \mathbf{c}' \end{bmatrix},$$

$$\min Z = b_0 w_0 + \mathbf{b}'\mathbf{w}; \tag{8–93}$$

the components of $\mathbf{w}$ are unrestricted in sign, but the first constraint of (8–93) requires $w_0 \geq 0$. However, we can immediately obtain a solution to this dual problem. One such solution is

$$\mathbf{w} = \mathbf{0}; \qquad w_0 = \max c_j, \qquad j = 0, 1, \ldots, n;$$

where

$$c_0 = 0. \tag{8–94}$$

After adding surplus variables to the modified dual [Eq. (8–93)], we can write

$$\begin{bmatrix} 1 & \mathbf{0} \\ \mathbf{1}' & \mathbf{A}' \end{bmatrix} \begin{bmatrix} w_0 \\ \mathbf{w} \end{bmatrix} - \begin{bmatrix} 1 & \mathbf{0} \\ \mathbf{0} & \mathbf{I}_n \end{bmatrix} \begin{bmatrix} w_{s0} \\ \mathbf{w}_s \end{bmatrix} = \begin{bmatrix} 0 \\ \mathbf{c}' \end{bmatrix}, \tag{8–95}$$

and $[w_{s0}, \mathbf{w}_s] \geq \mathbf{0}$. If $w_0 = 0$, any solution to the modified dual problem (8–93) will also be a solution to the dual of (8–91).

In Section 8–8, we noted that if $\mathbf{x}'\mathbf{w}_s = 0$, or equivalently for dual problems [Eqs. (8–92), (8–95)], if

$$x_0 w_{s0} + \mathbf{x}'\mathbf{w}_s = 0, \tag{8–96}$$

then $Z = z$, assuming that $[w_{s0}, \mathbf{w}_s] \geq \mathbf{0}$ and $\mathbf{x}$ is any solution (not necessarily feasible) to the primal. If $[x_0, \mathbf{x}]$ is a feasible solution to the modified primal and (8–96) holds, then $[x_0, \mathbf{x}]$ is an optimal solution to the modified primal, and $[w_0, \mathbf{w}]$ is an optimal solution to the modified dual. If, in addition, $w_0 = 0$, then $z = \mathbf{cx} = Z = \mathbf{b}'\mathbf{w}$, and from (8–96), $\mathbf{x}'\mathbf{w}_s = 0$. Consequently, $\mathbf{x}$ is an optimal solution to the given primal problem, and $\mathbf{w}$ is an optimal solution to its dual. If we have a solution to the modified dual with $w_0 \neq 0$ and a feasible solution to the modified primal such that (8–96) is satisfied (this implies $x_0 = 0$), then

$$z = Z = b_0 w_0 + \mathbf{b}'\mathbf{w}. \tag{8–97}$$

We have seen that b_0 can be made arbitrarily large without affecting the solution to (8–91), and since z for (8–91) is the same as for (8–92), we see from (8–97) that z can be made arbitrarily large, and (8–91) has an unbounded solution.† This result will be of use to us later.

Let us now add artificial variables to (8–92) as if we were to make the usual Phase I calculation. We also assign prices of -1 to the artificial variables and zero prices to the legitimate variables. This gives us the problem (called the extended primal)

$$\begin{bmatrix} 1 & 1 \\ 0 & A \end{bmatrix} \begin{bmatrix} x_0 \\ x \end{bmatrix} + \begin{bmatrix} 1 & 0 \\ 0 & I_m \end{bmatrix} \begin{bmatrix} x_{a0} \\ x_a \end{bmatrix} = \begin{bmatrix} b_0 \\ b \end{bmatrix},$$

$$[x_0, x] \geq 0, \qquad [x_{a0}, x_a] \geq 0, \tag{8–98}$$

$$\max z^* = -1 x_{a0} - 1 x_a.$$

We shall denote the $(m+1)$-component legitimate activity vectors by $a_j^{(1)} (j = 0, 1, \ldots, n)$ and a basis matrix for the constraints by B_1. The vector containing the prices c_j^* of the variables in the basis will be denoted by $c_{B_1}^*$ (these prices are 0 or -1), and $z_j^* - c_j^* = c_{B_1}^* B_1^{-1} a_j^{(1)} - c_j^*$.

When we begin the primal-dual algorithm, only artificial variables are in the primal basis. To determine the first vector to enter the basis, we do not use immediately the $z_j^* - c_j^*$. Instead we turn to the dual problem (8–95). An initial solution to this problem is given by (8–94), and for this solution,

$$w_s = w_0 1' - c'.$$

It follows from the manner of selecting w_0 that at least one component of $[w_{s0}, w_s]$ will vanish.

Now we shall proceed in such a way that (8–96) is always satisfied. Then, when $z^* = 0$ and we have found a feasible solution to the primal, it will be optimal, and the maximum value of z is the Z for the corresponding solution to the dual. Thus we completely eliminate the need for a Phase II. When Phase I is ended, we have an optimal solution to the primal.

Next we denote by S the set of w_{sj} which vanish for the solution (8–94) to the modified dual. All other w_{sj} are strictly positive. We then allow the set P of vectors $a_j^{(1)}$ for which the corresponding w_{sj} are in S to enter the extended primal basis. In this way, all x_j for which $w_{sj} > 0$ remain at a zero level. Since S is nonempty, there will be at least one $a_j^{(1)}$ which can enter the extended primal basis. Now the simplex method is applied to the

---

† Note that for a fixed b_0, (8–92) can never have an unbounded solution because the variables must sum to b_0. Thus the modified dual always has a solution even if there exists no solution to the dual of (8–91).

extended primal, and only the vectors in P are considered for entry into the basis. This problem will be referred to as a restricted primal. We continue to apply the simplex method to the restricted primal, inserting vectors from P until $z_j^* - c_j^* \geq 0$ for each $\mathbf{a}_j^{(1)}$ in P, that is, the optimality criterion is satisfied for these vectors which can enter the basis. Let $\mathbf{B}_1$ be the extended primal basis matrix when the optimality criterion is satisfied for the vectors in P, and let $\mathbf{c}_{B_1}^*$ be the vector containing the prices in the basis. If we write

$$\boldsymbol{\sigma} = (\sigma_0, \sigma_1, \ldots, \sigma_m) = \mathbf{c}_{B_1}^* \mathbf{B}_1^{-1}, \qquad (8\text{-}99)$$

we shall prove that there exists a $\theta > 0$ for which

$$(\hat{w}_0, \hat{\mathbf{w}}') = (w_0, \mathbf{w}') + \theta\boldsymbol{\sigma} \qquad (8\text{-}100)$$

is a new solution to the dual with $\hat{Z} < Z$.

For all $\mathbf{a}_j^{(1)}$ in P,

$$z_j^* - c_j^* = \mathbf{c}_{B_1}^* \mathbf{B}_1^{-1} \mathbf{a}_j^{(1)} = \boldsymbol{\sigma}\mathbf{a}_j^{(1)} \geq 0, \qquad (8\text{-}101)$$

since in the restricted primal the optimality criterion is satisfied; furthermore, if $\mathbf{a}_j^{(1)}$ is in the basis, $\boldsymbol{\sigma}\mathbf{a}_j^{(1)} = 0$. Then

$$(\hat{w}_0, \hat{\mathbf{w}}')\mathbf{a}_j^{(1)} = (w_0, \mathbf{w}')\mathbf{a}_j^{(1)} + \theta\boldsymbol{\sigma}\mathbf{a}_j^{(1)} \geq c_j,$$
$$\text{all } \mathbf{a}_j^{(1)} \text{ in } P, \quad \text{any } \theta \geq 0, \qquad (8\text{-}102)$$

since for all $\mathbf{a}_j^{(1)}$ in P, $(w_0, \mathbf{w}')\mathbf{a}_j^{(1)} = c_j$, that is, $w_{sj} = 0$; this result, together with (8–101), yields (8–102).

Next consider the $\mathbf{a}_j^{(1)}$ not in P (these were not considered for entry into the basis). For these $\mathbf{a}_j^{(1)}$, $(w_0, \mathbf{w}')\mathbf{a}_j^{(1)} > c_j$. It will also be true that

$$(\hat{w}_0, \hat{\mathbf{w}}')\mathbf{a}_j^{(1)} = (w_0, \mathbf{w}')\mathbf{a}_j^{(1)} + \theta\boldsymbol{\sigma}\mathbf{a}_j^{(1)} \geq c_j$$

for any

$$\theta, \quad 0 \leq \theta \leq \theta_0 = \min_j - \frac{[(w_0, \mathbf{w}')\mathbf{a}_j^{(1)} - c_j]}{\boldsymbol{\sigma}\mathbf{a}_j^{(1)}}, \quad \boldsymbol{\sigma}\mathbf{a}_j^{(1)} < 0.$$

When all $\boldsymbol{\sigma}\mathbf{a}_j^{(1)} \geq 0$, θ can be made arbitrarily large, and $(\hat{w}_0, \hat{\mathbf{w}}')$ will be a solution to the dual. Note, however, that for all j, $\boldsymbol{\sigma}\mathbf{a}_j^{(1)} = z_j^* - c_j^*$, and $w_{sj} = (w_0, \mathbf{w}')\mathbf{a}_j^{(1)} - c_j$ so that the largest θ for which $(\hat{w}_0, \hat{\mathbf{w}}')$ is a solution is

$$\theta_0 = \min_j \frac{w_{sj}}{c_j^* - z_j^*}, \quad z_j^* - c_j^* < 0,$$

or

$$\theta_0 = \infty, \qquad (8\text{-}103)$$

and in every case, $\theta_0 > 0$. Now

$$
\begin{aligned}
\hat{Z} &= (\hat{w}_0, \hat{\mathbf{w}}')[b_0, \mathbf{b}] \\
&= (w_0, \mathbf{w}')[b_0, \mathbf{b}] + \theta\boldsymbol{\sigma}[b_0, \mathbf{b}] \qquad\qquad (8\text{--}104) \\
&= Z + \theta z^*,
\end{aligned}
$$

and since $z^* < 0$, $\hat{Z} < Z$. To obtain the greatest possible decrease in Z we wish to use the largest possible value of θ, that is θ_0, if the maximum value of θ is finite. Observe that if θ can be made arbitrarily large, Z can be made arbitrarily small so that the dual has an unbounded solution and the primal has no solution. This can also be seen directly from the primal: If all $z_j^* - c_j^* \geq 0$ and $z^* < 0$, we know that there is no feasible solution to the primal.

Assuming that $\theta_0 \neq \infty$, we obtain a new solution to the dual; this can be characterized by the new surplus variables $\hat{w}_{sj} = w_{sj} + \theta_0(z_j^* - c_j^*)$. There will be at least one $\hat{w}_{sj} = 0$ for which w_{sj} was not in S because of the manner in which θ_0 was chosen. Hence, at least one new vector $\mathbf{a}_j^{(1)}$ which was not in the previous set P will be released to enter the primal basis. Consider the new set $\hat{P}$ of vectors $\mathbf{a}_j^{(1)}$ for which $\hat{w}_{sj} = 0$. This new set will include at least one $\mathbf{a}_j^{(1)}$ not in P and also those vectors in P for which $z_j^* - c_j^* = 0$ (in particular, this means that $\hat{P}$ includes the vectors from P in $\mathbf{B}_1$).

At this point, we return to the primal, take up where we left off, and iterate until $z_j^* - c_j^* \geq 0$ for all vectors in $\hat{P}$, that is, we solve the new restricted primal. This yields a new basis $\hat{\mathbf{B}}_1$ which gives a $\hat{\boldsymbol{\sigma}}$ that can be used to obtain another solution to the dual with a still smaller value of Z. The new solution to the dual releases one or more vectors to be inserted into the primal basis, etc. It is important to note that after a new solution to the dual is obtained, the initial tableau for the new restricted primal is the optimal tableau for the previous restricted primal.

We have noted previously that when $z^* = 0$, we have an optimal solution to the primal, and max $z = Z$ for the dual, provided $w_{s0} = w_0 = 0$. If $w_{s0} \neq 0$, the primal has an unbounded solution. If at any stage $z^* < 0$, $z_j^* - c_j^* \geq 0$ for all j, the primal has no feasible solution. This covers all possibilities. If one of the methods already discussed is used to avoid degeneracy in the primal, then since Z decreases at each dual iteration, the algorithm will terminate in a finite number of steps. Interestingly enough, the whole primal-dual algorithm can be performed by means of the simplex tableau. One only has to add an extra row which has $Z = z$ in the column headed $\mathbf{b}^{(1)}$ and w_{sj} in the $\mathbf{a}_j^{(1)}$-columns. The pertinent new equations are (8–103) and $\hat{w}_{sj} = w_{sj} + \theta_0(z_j^* - c_j^*)$.

At the present time, not enough work has actually been carried out to show definitively that the primal-dual algorithm is really superior to the two-phase method, although it would seem so theoretically.*

8–13 The primal-dual algorithm; an example. Let us illustrate the use of the primal-dual algorithm by solving the problem

$$x_1 + x_2 \geq 2,$$
$$x_1 + 3x_2 \leq 3,$$
$$x_1, x_2 \geq 0,$$
$$\max z = x_1 + 6x_2.$$

After adding slack and surplus variables and annexing the additional constraint needed to find an initial solution to the dual, we obtain the modified primal

$$x_0 + x_1 + x_2 + x_3 + x_4 = b_0,$$
$$x_1 + x_2 - x_3 \qquad\quad = 2,$$
$$x_1 + 3x_2 \qquad\quad + x_4 = 3,$$
$$x_j \geq 0, \qquad j = 0, \ldots, 4,$$
$$\max z = x_1 + 6x_2.$$

For the initial solution to the dual, $w_0 = \max c_j$, $c_j > 0$; hence, $w_0 = \max (1, 6) = 6$. Thus $w_{s0} = 6$ and $\mathbf{w}_s = w_0 \mathbf{1}' - \mathbf{c}'$ or $w_{s1} = 6 - 1 = 5$, $w_{s2} = 6 - 6 = 0$, $w_{s3} = 6 - 0 = 6$, $w_{s4} = 6 - 0 = 6$. Also, $Z = w_0 b_0 + \mathbf{w}'\mathbf{b} = w_0 b_0 = 6b_0$. The initial tableau is shown in Table 8–8. The last row gives the surplus variables for the dual problem and, in the first position, the value of Z. We begin with all artificial variables in the primal basis. Only $w_{s2} = 0$; hence, in the first restricted primal problem, only $\mathbf{a}_2^{(1)}$ can enter the basis. In this first tableau, it is convenient to list the actual prices of the variables in the first row as an aid in obtaining the initial w_{sj}-values. The prices actually used are, of course, $c_j^* = 0$ for any legitimate vector and $c_j^* = -1$ for any artificial vector.

The vector to be removed from the basis is determined in the usual way. It is assumed that b_0 is so large that $\mathbf{q}_0^{(1)}$ will never be removed if it is possible to remove any other vector. From Table 8–8 it is clear that $\mathbf{q}_2^{(1)}$ should be

---

* A recent master's thesis by Richard Mills (June 1960) at the School of Industrial Management, MIT, was devoted to a study of the efficiency of the primal-dual algorithm. A code to solve linear programming problems on the IBM 704 by the primal-dual algorithm was developed. Several problems were solved by using this code and the RAND code for the revised simplex method. The results, however, were inconclusive. In one or two cases, the primal-dual algorithm required a little less time than the revised simplex method, while in other cases it was somewhat more time-consuming.

TABLE 8–8 — TABLEAU 1

	c_j		0	1	6	0	0
$c_{B_1}^*$	Vectors in Basis	$b^{(1)}$	$a_0^{(1)}$	$a_1^{(1)}$	$a_2^{(1)}$	$a_3^{(1)}$	$a_4^{(1)}$
-1	$q_0^{(1)}$	b_0	1	1	1	1	1
-1	$q_1^{(1)}$	2	0	1	1	-1	0
-1	$q_2^{(1)}$	3	0	1	3	0	1
	$z_j^* - c_j^*$	$-5 - b_0$	-1	-3	-5	0	-2
	w_{sj}	$6b_0$	6	5	0	6	6

TABLE 8–9 — TABLEAU 2

$c_{B_1}^*$	Vectors in Basis	$b^{(1)}$	$a_0^{(1)}$	$a_1^{(1)}$	$a_2^{(1)}$	$a_3^{(1)}$	$a_4^{(1)}$
-1	$q_0^{(1)}$	$b_0 - 1$	1	$\frac{2}{3}$	0	1	$\frac{2}{3}$
-1	$q_1^{(1)}$	1	0	$\frac{2}{3}$	0	-1	$-\frac{1}{3}$
0	$a_2^{(1)}$	1	0	$\frac{1}{3}$	1	0	$\frac{1}{3}$
	$z_j^* - c_j^*$	$-b_0$	-1	$-\frac{4}{3}$	0	0	$-\frac{1}{3}$
	w_{sj}	$6b_0$	6	5	0	6	6
	$\hat{w}_{sj}$	$2\frac{1}{4}b_0$	$2\frac{1}{4}$	0	0	6	$4\frac{3}{4}$

removed. After inserting $a_2^{(1)}$ into the basis, we obtain Table 8–9. Now the $z_j^* - c_j^* \geq 0$ for the vectors allowed to enter the primal basis, i.e., for $a_2^{(1)}$. Hence, we must find new values for the w_{sj}. For those $z_j^* - c_j^* < 0$, we compute $w_{sj}/(c_j^* - z_j^*)$, and pick the smallest ratio. Call this ratio θ. Only $z_0^* - c_0^*$, $z_1^* - c_1^*$, $z_4^* - c_4^*$ are <0, and

$$\frac{w_{s0}}{c_0^* - z_0^*} = 6; \qquad \frac{w_{s1}}{c_1^* - z_1^*} = \frac{15}{4}; \qquad \frac{w_{s4}}{c_4^* - z_4^*} = 18;$$

TABLE 8-10 — TABLEAU 3

$c_{B_1}^*$	Vectors in Basis	$\mathbf{b}^{(1)}$	$\mathbf{a}_0^{(1)}$	$\mathbf{a}_1^{(1)}$	$\mathbf{a}_2^{(1)}$	$\mathbf{a}_3^{(1)}$	$\mathbf{a}_4^{(1)}$
-1	$\mathbf{q}_0^{(1)}$	$b_0 - 2$	1	0	0	2	1
0	$\mathbf{a}_1^{(1)}$	$\frac{3}{2}$	0	1	0	$-\frac{3}{2}$	$-\frac{1}{2}$
0	$\mathbf{a}_2^{(1)}$	$\frac{1}{2}$	0	0	1	$\frac{1}{2}$	$\frac{1}{2}$
	$z_j^* - c_j^*$	$-b_0 + 2$	-1	0	0	-2	-1
	w_{sj}	$2\frac{1}{4}b_0$	$2\frac{1}{4}$	0	0	6	$4\frac{3}{4}$
	$\hat{w}_{sj}$	$4\frac{1}{2}$	0	0	0	$1\frac{1}{2}$	$2\frac{1}{2}$

TABLE 8-11 — TABLEAU 4

$c_{B_1}^*$	Vectors in Basis	$\mathbf{b}^{(1)}$	$\mathbf{a}_0^{(1)}$	$\mathbf{a}_1^{(1)}$	$\mathbf{a}_2^{(1)}$	$\mathbf{a}_3^{(1)}$	$\mathbf{a}_4^{(1)}$
0	$\mathbf{a}_0^{(1)}$	$b_0 - 2$	1	0	0	2	1
0	$\mathbf{a}_1^{(1)}$	$\frac{3}{2}$	0	1	0	$-\frac{3}{2}$	$-\frac{1}{2}$
0	$\mathbf{a}_2^{(1)}$	$\frac{1}{2}$	0	0	1	$\frac{1}{2}$	$\frac{1}{2}$
	$z_j^* - c_j^*$	0	0	0	0	0	0
	w_{sj}	$4\frac{1}{2}$	0	0	0	$1\frac{1}{2}$	$2\frac{1}{2}$

hence $\theta = \frac{15}{4}$. Then $\hat{w}_{sj} = w_{sj} + \theta(z_j^* - c_j^*)$; $\hat{Z} = Z + \theta z^*$. For example, $Z = 6b_0 + \frac{15}{4}(-b_0) = 2\frac{1}{4}b_0$; $\hat{w}_{s4} = 6 + \frac{15}{4}(-\frac{1}{3}) = 4\frac{3}{4}$. The $\hat{w}_{sj}$ are also given in Table 8-9. Only $\hat{w}_{s1}$, $\hat{w}_{s2} = 0$. Consequently, at the next step, only $\mathbf{a}_1^{(1)}$ can enter the basis. The remaining tableaux are shown in Tables 8-10 and 8-11. At the last step, $\mathbf{a}_0^{(1)}$ enters the basis, and we obtain a feasible and optimal solution to the modified primal. Since $w_0 = w_{s0} = 0$, we also have an optimal solution to the given primal problem. It is $x_1 = \frac{3}{2}$, $x_2 = \frac{1}{2}$, $z = Z = 4\frac{1}{2}$. The correctness of the result can easily be checked by solving the given problem graphically.

For this particular example, the primal-dual algorithm certainly did not reduce the amount of work required to solve the problem. However, one should not judge the merits of the method on such a small problem, which was introduced only for the purpose of illustrating the way in which the primal-dual algorithm can be used.

REFERENCES

1. E. M. L. BEALE, "An Alternative Method for Linear Programming," *Proceedings of the Cambridge Philosophical Society,* **50,** 4, 1954, pp. 513–523.

2. G. B. DANTZIG, "The Dual Simplex Algorithm," *RM*-**1270,** The RAND Corp., July, 1954.

3. G. B. DANTZIG, L. R. FORD, and D. R. FULKERSON, "A Primal-Dual Algorithm for Linear Programming," *Linear Inequalities and Related Systems.* Kuhn and Tucker, eds. Princeton: Princeton University Press, 1956; also *RM*-**1709,** The RAND Corp., May, 1956.

4. G. B. DANTZIG, "Composite Simplex-Dual Simplex Algorithm—I," *RM*-**1274,** The RAND Corp., April, 1954.

This article and the report of Orchard-Hays listed below present other primal-dual type algorithms.

5. G. B. DANTZIG and A. ORDEN, "Duality Theorems," *RM*-**1265,** The RAND Corp., Oct., 1953.

6. A. J. GOLDMAN, and A. W. TUCKER, "Theory of Linear Programming," *Linear Inequalities and Related Systems.* Kuhn and Tucker, eds. Princeton: Princeton University Press, 1956.

7. E. A. GUILLEMIN, *Introductory Circuit Theory.* New York: Wiley, 1953.

8. C. E. LEMKE, "The Dual Method of Solving The Linear Programming Problem," *Naval Research Logistics Quarterly,* **1,** 1954, pp. 48–54.

9. W. ORCHARD-HAYS, "A Composite Simplex Algorithm—II," *RM*-**1275,** The RAND Corp., May, 1954.

PROBLEMS

8–1. Give the dual of the following problem in a form such that the dual variables are non-negative.

$$2x_1 + 3x_2 + 5x_3 \geq 2,$$
$$3x_1 + x_2 + 7x_3 \leq 3,$$
$$x_1 + 4x_2 + 6x_3 \leq 5,$$
$$x_1, x_2, x_3 \geq 0,$$
$$\min z = 2x_1 + 2x_2 + 4x_3.$$

8–2. Give the dual of the following problem in a form such that the dual variables are non-negative.

$$3x_1 + 7x_2 + 8x_3 + 5x_4 + x_5 = 2,$$
$$2x_1 + x_2 + 3x_3 + 2x_4 + 9x_5 = 6,$$
$$x_1, x_2, x_3, x_4 \geq 0, \quad x_5 \text{ unrestricted,}$$
$$\max z = 6x_1 + 4x_2 + x_3 + 7x_4 + 5x_5.$$

8–3. Give the dual of the following problem in a form such that the dual variables are non-negative, and no strict equalities appear in the dual constraints.

$$2.4x_1 + 3.2x_2 + 4x_3 + 7.2x_4 = 21,$$
$$3x_1 + 17x_2 + 80x_3 + 2x_4 \leq 48,$$
$$x_1, x_2 \geq 0, \quad x_3, x_4 \text{ unrestricted,}$$
$$\max z = 1.8x_1 + 2.4x_2 + 6x_3 + x_4.$$

8–4. Using the duality theory, solve the following linear programming problem, and verify the result by solving the problem graphically.

$$18x_1 + 16x_2 \geq 0.5,$$
$$0.1x_1 + 0.2x_2 \leq 4,$$
$$x_1 + 30x_2 \leq 50,$$
$$14x_1 + x_2 \geq 0.1,$$
$$x_1 + 0.05x_2 \leq 6,$$
$$x_1, x_2 \geq 0,$$
$$\max z = 3x_1 + 2x_2.$$

8–5. Using the duality theory, solve the following linear programming problem:

$$3x_1 + 5x_2 + 4x_3 \geq 7,$$
$$6x_1 + x_2 + 3x_3 \geq 4,$$
$$7x_1 - 2x_2 - x_3 \leq 10,$$
$$x_1 - 2x_2 + 5x_3 \geq 3,$$
$$4x_1 + 7x_2 - 2x_3 \geq 2,$$
$$x_1, x_2, x_3 \geq 0,$$
$$\min z = 3x_1 - 2x_2 + 4x_3.$$

8–6. By means of the duality theory, solve and illustrate geometrically the following linear programming problem:

$$x_1 + x_2 \geq 1,$$
$$x_1 + x_2 \leq 7,$$
$$x_1 + 2x_2 \geq 10,$$
$$x_2 \leq 3,$$
$$x_1, x_2 \geq 0,$$
$$\max z = 3x_1 + 2x_2.$$

8–7. Starting with the primal problem in the form of (8–13), and using arguments of the type developed in Section 8–3, show that if the primal problem has an optimal solution, so does the dual. Construct the solution to the dual. Work with (8–13) directly, i.e., do not convert it to the form of (8–7).

8–8. Prove that a necessary and sufficient condition for the primal and dual to have optimal solutions is that both have feasible solutions.

8–9. For the dual problems (8–33), (8–34); (8–35), (8–36); (8–37), (8–38); (8–39), (8–40), show that if $\mathbf{B}$ is an optimal basis matrix for the primal and $\mathbf{c}_B$ contains the prices in the basis, then $\mathbf{c}_B \mathbf{B}^{-1}$ is an optimal solution to the dual. Note that, in general, the dual variables will not be non-negative here.

8–10. It was shown in the text that the dual of $\mathbf{A}\mathbf{x} = \mathbf{b}$, $\mathbf{x} \geq 0$, max $z = \mathbf{c}\mathbf{x}$, has unrestricted variables. However, if some slack and/or surplus vectors appear in $\mathbf{A}$, show that the dual variable for a constraint having a slack variable is non-negative, and that the dual variable for a constraint having a surplus variable is nonpositive. Hence, demonstrate that the only dual variables which are really unrestricted are those corresponding to constraints which were originally equations. In this way, show that the dual of any linear programming problem is unique (except for trivial changes in form), and is independent of the particular manner in which we write the primal.

8–11. If in an optimal solution to the primal the kth constraint is an equality, under what conditions is it true that the kth constraint of the dual is a strict inequality? Assume the constraints are numbered as in (8–46). When does the above not hold? How are these results related to alternative optima in the primal and to degeneracy?

8–12. Consider an optimal basic solution to the primal and to the dual of the type constructed in Section 8–8. Show that if an optimal basic solution to the primal is degenerate, then there are alternative optima in the dual. Furthermore, if there are alternative optima in the primal due to some $z_j - c_j = 0$ for $\mathbf{a}_j$ not in the basis, then the corresponding optimal solution to the dual will be degenerate.

8–13. Prove that if the primal has an optimal solution, then there is an optimal solution $\mathbf{x}$ to the primal (not necessarily basic) and an optimal solution $\mathbf{w}$ to the dual such that if $x_j = 0$, then $w_{sj} > 0$, and if $x_{si} = 0$, then $w_i > 0$. Hint: After a review of Section 8–5, use the results of Problem 8–12 to prove this. Consider first the case where the primal has a unique optimal solution which is not degenerate. Then consider the case where the primal has alternative optima, but none is degenerate. Finally, consider the case where degeneracy appears in an optimal solution to the primal and where, in addition, there are alternative optima.

8–14. Construct an example different from that given in Section 8–6 to show that both the primal and dual problems may have no solution.

8–15. Consider the primal problem $\mathbf{A}\mathbf{x} = \mathbf{b}$, $\mathbf{x} \geq 0$, max $z = \mathbf{c}\mathbf{x}$. Suppose that we multiply the kth constraint by the scalar $\lambda \neq 0$. If $\mathbf{w}$ is an optimal solution to the dual of the above primal problem, what is an optimal solution to the dual of the primal problem whose kth constraint is multiplied by λ? Hint: Note that the optimal solution to the new primal is unchanged.

8-16. Assume that we are given the primal problem $\mathbf{Ax} = \mathbf{b}$, $\mathbf{x} \geq \mathbf{0}$, max $z = \mathbf{cx}$, and an optimal solution, $\mathbf{w}$, to the dual of the problem. Suppose that we form a new primal problem by adding ($\lambda \neq 0$) times constraint k to constraint r. What is an optimal solution to the dual of this new problem?

8-17. Consider the primal of Problem 8-16. Suppose that we add a multiple $\lambda \neq 0$ of row k of $\mathbf{A}$ to $\mathbf{c}$. How does an optimal solution to the resulting primal compare with an optimal solution to the original problem? Given an optimal solution, $\mathbf{w}$, to the dual of the original problem, what is an optimal solution to the dual of the new problem?

8-18. Solve the following linear programming problem by the dual simplex algorithm:

$$2x_1 + x_2 \geq 4,$$
$$x_1 + 7x_2 \geq 7,$$
$$x_1, x_2 \geq 0,$$
$$\min z = x_1 + x_2.$$

8-19. Solve the following linear programming problem by the dual simplex algorithm:

$$2x_1 + 4x_2 + 5x_3 + x_4 \geq 10,$$
$$3x_1 - x_2 + 7x_3 - 2x_4 \geq 2,$$
$$5x_1 + 2x_2 + x_3 + 6x_4 \geq 15,$$
$$x_1, x_2, x_3, x_4 \geq 0,$$
$$\min z = 3x_1 + 2x_2 + x_3 + 4x_4.$$

8-20. Solve Problem 8-19 by the simplex method, using the two-phase technique, and compare the number of iterations required in both methods.

8-21. Solve the following linear programming problem by the dual simplex algorithm:

$$4x_1 - x_2 + 2x_3 + 3x_4 - 5x_5 + 6x_6 \geq 2,$$
$$x_1 + 3x_2 - 4x_3 + 5x_4 - x_5 + 2x_6 \geq 13,$$
$$3x_1 + 7x_2 + x_3 - 2x_4 + x_5 - 9x_6 \geq 7,$$
$$5x_1 - 3x_2 + 8x_3 - 4x_4 + 6x_5 + x_6 \geq 6,$$
$$x_1, x_2, x_3, x_4 \geq 0,$$
$$\min z = x_1 + 3x_2 + 7x_3 + 5x_4 + 2x_5 + 8x_6.$$

8-22. Solve Problem 8-21 by the simplex method, using the two-phase technique. Compare the number of iterations required in each case.

8-23. Lemke has suggested the following procedure as a possible technique for getting started on the dual simplex algorithm: We are given the problem $\mathbf{Ax} = \mathbf{b}$, $\mathbf{x} \geq \mathbf{0}$, max $z = \mathbf{cx}$. Find m linearly independent activity vectors from $\mathbf{A}$. Let the vector $\mathbf{b}^*$ be a linear combination of these vectors, with each scalar coefficient positive. Then solve the problem $\mathbf{Ax} = \mathbf{b}^*$, $\mathbf{x} \geq \mathbf{0}$, max $z = \mathbf{cx}$ by the simplex method. In the optimal solution replace $\mathbf{b}^*$ by $\mathbf{b}$. This gives a basic (although not necessarily feasible) solution to the original problem, with all $z_j - c_j \geq 0$. The dual simplex algorithm can now be applied. Discuss why this procedure works. Are there any cases where difficulties may arise? Can this be considered a practical procedure for getting started on the dual simplex algorithm?

8–24. In the special case when all $c_j \leq 0$, Dantzig has suggested a more straightforward way of getting started on the dual simplex algorithm. His method involves the direct use of the dual. Begin with the dual basis $\overline{\mathbf{B}} = -\mathbf{I}_n$ so that $w_{sj} = -c_j \geq 0$. Since $\mathbf{a}^1, \ldots, \mathbf{a}^m$ should be in the dual basis, use an arbitrary rule to insert these vectors. Discuss in detail how this method yields an initial solution for the application of the dual simplex method to the primal. Also, suggest a rule for inserting the $\mathbf{a}^i$. Does this method appear practical?

8–25. Using Charnes' perturbation method, resolve the degeneracy problem in the dual simplex algorithm. Hint: Applying Charnes' method directly to the dual problem and using only a set of linearly independent vectors, we should replace $\mathbf{c}'$ by $\mathbf{c}' - \sum_{j=1}^{n} \epsilon^j \mathbf{e}_j$ or $c_j(\epsilon) = c_j - \epsilon^j$. Then $z_j(\epsilon) - c_j(\epsilon) = \mathbf{c}_B(\epsilon)\mathbf{y}_j - c_j + \epsilon^j$. What is the rule for choosing the vector to enter? Note that, in this case, one must be concerned about the question whether the lowest powers of ϵ are in the basis. If, for example, c_1 is not in the basis, ϵ^1 appears only in $z_1(\epsilon) - c_1(\epsilon)$. Show that a tie will never be resolved on the power of ϵ corresponding to the vector $-\mathbf{e}_j$ which is to leave the basis, and consequently, we need not be concerned about losing from the basis the power of ϵ for which the tie was resolved.

8–26. For each of the pairs of dual problems in Section 8–4, show that the dual of the dual is the primal.

8–27. If the addition of only a relatively small number of artificial variables to a given problem permits us to use the two-phase method, would this method or the primal-dual algorithm seem to be more efficient? Why? Under what circumstances can one expect the primal-dual algorithm to be better than the two-phase method, and conversely? Note that all these alternatives are essentially conjectures, and that no real evidence has been accumulated which allows any definite conclusions.

8–28. Using the primal-dual algorithm of Section 8–12, solve and illustrate graphically the following problem:

$$3x_1 + 2x_2 \geq 6,$$
$$x_1 + 6x_2 \geq 3,$$
$$x_1, x_2 \geq 0,$$
$$\max z = x_1 + 2x_2.$$

8–29. Using the primal-dual algorithm, solve the following problem:

$$3x_1 + 5x_2 - 6x_3 + 2x_4 + 4x_5 = 27,$$
$$x_1 + 2x_2 + 3x_3 - 7x_4 + 6x_5 \geq 2,$$
$$9x_1 - 4x_2 + 2x_3 + 5x_4 - 2x_5 = 16,$$
$$x_j \geq 0, \qquad j = 1, \ldots, 5,$$
$$\max z = 7x_1 + 2x_2 + x_3 + 4x_4 + 6x_5.$$

8–30. Solve the following problem by means of the primal-dual algorithm:

$$x_1 + 5x_2 + 2x_3 + 7x_4 + 4x_5 + 6x_6 = 25,$$
$$3x_1 - 2x_2 - x_3 + 8x_5 + x_6 = 9,$$
$$4x_1 + x_2 + 7x_3 - 3x_4 - 2x_5 \geq 3,$$
$$2x_1 + 6x_2 - 3x_3 + 4x_5 + x_6 \geq 5,$$
$$x_j \geq 0, \qquad j = 1, \ldots, 6,$$
$$\max z = 3x_1 - 2x_2 + 4x_3 + x_4 + 6x_5 + 9x_6.$$

8–31. Given an optimal tableau for the linear programming problem $\mathbf{Ax} = \mathbf{b}$, $\mathbf{x} \geq \mathbf{0}$, $\max z = \mathbf{cx}$, solved by the simplex method, show how to find an optimal solution to the dual from this tableau.

Consider both cases: (a) where it is necessary to add artificial variables, and (b) where artificial variables are not needed.

8–32. Consider the primal-dual algorithm discussed in Section 8–12. How do we know that on adding the constraint $x_0 + \sum_{j=1}^{n} x_j = b_0$, we cannot have $m + 1$ vectors from $\mathbf{A}$ in an optimal solution? Hint: Recall that b_0 can be arbitrarily large. If x_0 is not in basis, the other x_{Bi} must depend on b_0. As b_0 is increased, z will either increase or decrease.

8–32. Why must we be concerned about degeneracy in the primal-dual algorithm, when it was shown that, for the dual, Z strictly decreases at each dual iteration? Hint: Is the value of Z changed for each primal iteration?

8–33. Given an optimal basic solution to a linear programming problem. Can one obtain an unbounded solution by changing the requirements vector? What is the geometrical interpretation of this result? Hint: Is there a solution to the dual?

8–34. Prove that if a given basic feasible solution to some linear programming problem is optimal, the same basis vectors will yield an optimal solution for any requirements vector which lies in the cone spanned by these basis vectors.

8–35. Show that an optimal basic solution to $\mathbf{Ax} = \mathbf{b}$, $\mathbf{x} \geq \mathbf{0}$, $\max z = \mathbf{cx}$ is also an optimal solution to the same problem if it is converted to the form $\mathbf{Dx}_r \leq \mathbf{d}$, $\mathbf{x}_r \geq \mathbf{0}$, $\max z = \mathbf{c}_r\mathbf{x}_r$ before application of the simplex method. Note that if there are any equations in the original formulation of the problem. $\mathbf{D}$ will have more rows than $\mathbf{A}$; this implies that there will be more basic variables when the second formulation is used. What will these additional basic variables be? Hint: What is the rank of $\mathbf{D}$?

8–36. After a new solution to the dual has been obtained, under what circumstances will more than a single additional vector be released to enter the restricted primal basis in the primal-dual algorithm? If more than a single vector is released to enter the restricted primal basis, is it expected that this will increase or reduce the total amount of time required to solve the problem?

8–37. Solve the example of Section 8–13 by the primal-dual algorithm without annexing the constraint $x_0 + \sum x_j = b_0$, that is, find a solution to the dual of the given problem without using w_0.

8–38. Why did we include the artificial vector $\mathbf{q}_0^{(1)}$ in the example of Section 8–13 when $\mathbf{a}_0^{(1)}$ is a unit vector?

8–39. Discuss the simplifications introduced into the primal-dual algorithm when one can find an initial solution to the dual without annexing the additional constraint to the primal.

8–40. It has been shown that if $\mathbf{x}_B = \mathbf{B}^{-1}\mathbf{b}$, $z = \mathbf{c}_B\mathbf{x}_B$ is an optimal basic solution to some linear programming problem, then $\mathbf{w}' = \mathbf{c}_B\mathbf{B}^{-1}$ is an optimal solution to the dual. Will this optimal solution to the dual always be a basic solution?

8–41. We have shown above that a given optimal basic feasible solution to the linear programming problem $\mathbf{Ax} = \mathbf{b}$, $\mathbf{x} \geq \mathbf{0}$, max $z = \mathbf{cx}$ uniquely determines an optimal solution to the dual if $r(\mathbf{A}) = m$. Show that if there is redundancy in the constraints, then an optimal basic solution to the primal with one or more artificial variables in the basis does not really uniquely determine the dual variables in the corresponding optimal solution to the dual $\mathbf{c}_B\mathbf{B}^{-1}$, that is, there is an infinite number of solutions to the dual, which yield the proper $(z_j - c_j)$-values for the legitimate primal vectors.

CHAPTER 9

TRANSPORTATION PROBLEMS

"Under a world of whistles, wires and steam
Caboose—like they go ruminating through
Ohio, Indiana—blind baggage—
To Cheyenne tagging . . . maybe "Kalamazoo."

Hart Crane.

9–1 Introduction. A certain class of linear programming problems, known as transportation type problems, arises very frequently in practical applications. In Chapter 1, the general transportation problem was formulated as follows: A product is available in known quantities at each of m origins. It is required that given quantities of the product be shipped to each of n destinations. The minimum cost of shipping a unit of the product from any origin to any destination is known. We wish to determine the shipping schedule which minimizes the total cost of shipment.

Let a_i be the quantity of the product available at origin i, and b_j the quantity of the product required at destination j. The cost of shipping one unit from origin i to destination j will be written c_{ij}. We shall assume that

$$\sum_{i=1}^{m} a_i = \sum_{j=1}^{n} b_j, \qquad (9\text{–}1)$$

so that the total quantity required at the destinations is precisely the same as the amount available at the origins. Then if x_{ij} is the quantity shipped from origin i to destination j, we wish to find $x_{ij} \geq 0$ which satisfy the $m + n$ constraints

$$\sum_{j=1}^{n} x_{ij} = a_i, \qquad a_i > 0, \qquad i = 1, \ldots, m, \qquad (9\text{–}2)$$

$$\sum_{i=1}^{m} x_{ij} = b_j, \qquad b_j > 0, \qquad j = 1, \ldots, n, \qquad (9\text{–}3)$$

and which minimize

$$z = \sum_{i,j} c_{ij} x_{ij}. \qquad (9\text{–}4)$$

From Eq. (9–1) it follows that, in our present formulation of the problem, the strict equality sign holds in every constraint. The formulation in

Chapter 1 allowed the constraints (9–2) to have a $\leq$ sign since the total amount available at the origins was permitted to be greater than the total amount required at the destinations. In reality, however, the formulation in Chapter 1 was no more general than our present one. Since any transportation problem can be converted to the form of Eqs. (9–2) through (9–4) (see Section 9–12), there is no loss in generality if we concentrate our attention on problems which can be cast into this form.

First, let us convert the constraints of the transportation problem into our standard matrix form for a linear programming problem, $\mathbf{Ax} = \mathbf{b}$. Write

$$\mathbf{x} = [x_{11}, \ldots, x_{1n}, x_{21}, \ldots, x_{2n}, \ldots, x_{mn}],$$
$$\mathbf{b} = [a_1, \ldots, a_m, b_1, \ldots, b_n].$$

$$(9–5)$$

If the constraints are written as

$$
\begin{aligned}
x_{11} + x_{12} + \cdots + x_{1n} && && && &= a_1, \\
&& x_{21} + \cdots + x_{2n} && && &= a_2, \\
&&&& \ddots && &\ \ \vdots \\
&&&& x_{m1} + \cdots + x_{mn} &= a_m, \\
x_{11} && + x_{21} + \cdots + && x_{m1} && &= b_1, \\
&& \ddots && && &\ \ \vdots \\
x_{1n} && + && x_{2n} + && \cdots + x_{mn} &= b_n,
\end{aligned}
$$

$$(9–6)$$

they take the form $\mathbf{Ax} = \mathbf{b}$ provided

$$
\mathbf{A} = \left.\begin{bmatrix}
\mathbf{1}_n & \mathbf{0} & \mathbf{0} & \cdots & \mathbf{0} \\
\mathbf{0} & \mathbf{1}_n & \mathbf{0} & \cdots & \mathbf{0} \\
\mathbf{0} & \mathbf{0} & \mathbf{1}_n & \cdots & \mathbf{0} \\
\vdots & & & & \vdots \\
\mathbf{0} & \mathbf{0} & \mathbf{0} & \cdots & \mathbf{1}_n \\
\mathbf{I}_n & \mathbf{I}_n & \mathbf{I}_n & \cdots & \mathbf{I}_n
\end{bmatrix}\right\}
\begin{array}{l} m \text{ rows}, \\[3em] \} \ n \text{ rows} \end{array}
$$

$$(9–7)$$

$$\underbrace{\phantom{mn \text{ columns}}}_{mn \text{ columns}}$$

where $\mathbf{A}$ is an $(m + n) \times (mn)$ matrix. Of course, $\mathbf{1}$ is the sum vector and the subscript n implies that it has n components. Note that a given variable appears in two and only two of the constraints.

Equation (9–7) can be used to provide a rigorous definition of what we mean by a transportation problem. Any linear programming problem $\mathbf{Ax} = \mathbf{b}$, $\mathbf{x} \geq \mathbf{0}$, max or min $z = \mathbf{cx}$ will be called a transportation problem if it can be cast into such a form that the matrix of the coefficients $\mathbf{A}$ has the structure (9–7).

EXAMPLE: For the specific case of two origins and four destinations, $\mathbf{Ax} = \mathbf{b}$ becomes

$$
\begin{bmatrix}
1 & 1 & 1 & 1 & 0 & 0 & 0 & 0 \\
0 & 0 & 0 & 0 & 1 & 1 & 1 & 1 \\
1 & 0 & 0 & 0 & 1 & 0 & 0 & 0 \\
0 & 1 & 0 & 0 & 0 & 1 & 0 & 0 \\
0 & 0 & 1 & 0 & 0 & 0 & 1 & 0 \\
0 & 0 & 0 & 1 & 0 & 0 & 0 & 1
\end{bmatrix}
\begin{bmatrix}
x_{11} \\ x_{12} \\ x_{13} \\ x_{14} \\ x_{21} \\ x_{22} \\ x_{23} \\ x_{24}
\end{bmatrix}
=
\begin{bmatrix}
a_1 \\ a_2 \\ b_1 \\ b_2 \\ b_3 \\ b_4
\end{bmatrix}.
$$

We have cast the transportation problem into the form of the standard linear programming problem, and hence the simplex method could be applied directly to any transportation problem. However, because $\mathbf{A}$ has a very simple and special structure, it is possible to develop algorithms for solving transportation problems which are much more efficient computational procedures than the simplex method. This chapter will be devoted to a study of some of these special algorithms.

9–2 Properties of the matrix A. The matrix $\mathbf{A}$ of (9–7) has $m + n$ rows and mn columns. Column $(i - 1)n + j$ of $\mathbf{A}$ will be denoted by $\mathbf{p}_{ij}$. We shall find it convenient to use a double-subscript notation for the activity vectors just as we are using a double subscript on the variables. Each $\mathbf{p}_{ij}$ is an $(m + n)$-component vector, and only two components of $\mathbf{p}_{ij}$ differ from zero. In fact, we can write

$$
\mathbf{p}_{ij} = \mathbf{e}_i + \mathbf{e}_{m+j}, \tag{9–8}
$$

where the $\mathbf{e}_k$ are the unit vectors for E^{m+n}.

The rows of $\mathbf{A}$ fall naturally into two sets: the first m rows which come from the origin (or source) constraints and the last n rows which come from the destination constraints. We shall call these two sets the origin (or source) rows and destination rows of $\mathbf{A}$, respectively. From (9–7) note that adding the first m rows of $\mathbf{A}$ (the origin rows) yields $\mathbf{1}_{(mn)}$, and adding the last n rows of $\mathbf{A}$ (the destination rows) also yields $\mathbf{1}_{(mn)}$. Thus the sum of the first m rows of $\mathbf{A}$ minus the sum of the last n rows of $\mathbf{A}$ gives a null vector. Consequently, the rank of $\mathbf{A}$ is less than $m + n$. In fact, the rank of $\mathbf{A}$ is $m + n - 1$, as we can easily show by finding a determinant of order $m + n - 1$ in $\mathbf{A}$ which does not vanish. Consider the matrix $\mathbf{D}$ formed from $\mathbf{A}$ by taking columns $n, 2n, \ldots, mn, 1, \ldots, n - 1$ and rows $1, \ldots, m + n - 1$ (the last row of $\mathbf{A}$ being omitted). Then

$$|\mathbf{D}| = \begin{vmatrix} \mathbf{I}_m & \mathbf{F} \\ \mathbf{0} & \mathbf{I}_{n-1} \end{vmatrix} = 1, \quad \text{where} \quad \mathbf{F} = \begin{bmatrix} \mathbf{1}_{n-1} \\ \mathbf{0} \end{bmatrix}. \quad (9\text{--}9)$$

Since $\mathbf{D}$ is a square matrix of order $m + n - 1$, $r(\mathbf{A}) = m + n - 1$.

Let us denote the origin rows of $\mathbf{A}$ by $\mathbf{s}^i$, $i = 1, \ldots, m$, and the destination rows by $\mathbf{d}^j$, $j = 1, \ldots, n$. Then the relation expressing the linear dependence between the rows of $\mathbf{A}$ can be written

$$\sum_{i=1}^{m} \mathbf{s}^i - \sum_{j=1}^{n} \mathbf{d}^j = \mathbf{0}. \quad (9\text{--}10)$$

It is important to note that the coefficient of every row vector is either $+1$ or -1. This means that any row of $\mathbf{A}$ can be expressed as a linear combination of the remaining $m + n - 1$ rows. In other words, we can cross out any one row of $\mathbf{A}$, and the resulting $(m + n - 1) \times (mn)$ matrix will have rank $m + n - 1$. This follows because we know that at least one set of $m + n - 1$ rows is linearly independent, and by $(9\text{--}10)$, the remaining row can replace any row of the linearly independent set, and the new set will also be linearly independent.

What we have just proved is equivalent to saying that only $m + n - 1$ of the constraints $(9\text{--}2)$, $(9\text{--}3)$ are independent. Furthermore, we can remove any one constraint, and the remaining $m + n - 1$ constraints will be independent. Intuitively, all this is obvious. Since we are assuming that $(9\text{--}1)$ holds, any set of x_{ij} which satisfies all but one of the constraints must automatically satisfy this remaining constraint.

It is also interesting to note that the same sort of linear dependence holds for the rows of any $(m + n) \times k$ matrix $\mathbf{R}$ formed by choosing any $k \leq mn$ columns of $\mathbf{A}$. If we denote the source rows of $\mathbf{R}$ by $\mathbf{s}^i$ and the destination rows by $\mathbf{d}^j$, then $(9\text{--}10)$ holds. In fact, $(9\text{--}10)$ also holds for a single vector $\mathbf{p}_{ij}$. *As a particular case, assume that $\mathbf{R}$ is formed from any $m + n - 1$ linearly independent columns of $\mathbf{A}$. Then we know that $r(\mathbf{R}) = m + n - 1$. Furthermore, we know from $(9\text{--}10)$ that since any row of $\mathbf{R}$ is a linear combination of the remaining $m + n - 1$ rows, every set of $m + n - 1$ rows of $\mathbf{R}$ is linearly independent. This means that if any single row of $\mathbf{R}$ is crossed out, the remaining matrix of order $m + n - 1$ will be nonsingular. Similarly, if we have an $(m + n) \times (m + n - 1)$ matrix $\mathbf{R}$ formed from $m + n - 1$ columns of $\mathbf{A}$, and if there is one minor of order $m + n - 1$ in $\mathbf{R}$ which does not vanish (implying that $r(\mathbf{R}) = m + n - 1$), then all $m + n$ minors of order $m + n - 1$ in $\mathbf{R}$ are different from zero.*

An interesting and important property of the matrix $\mathbf{A}$ is that every minor of $\mathbf{A}$ can only have the value ± 1 or 0. (This is sometimes referred to as the unimodular property of the matrix $\mathbf{A}$.) Let $\mathbf{A}_k$ be a kth-order submatrix formed from any k different columns and k different rows of $\mathbf{A}$. We wish to prove that

$$|\mathbf{A}_k| = \pm 1 \quad \text{or} \quad 0. \tag{9–11}$$

First note that each column of $\mathbf{A}_k$ contains either two 1's, a single 1, or no 1. If $\mathbf{A}_k$ contains one or more columns of zeros, then clearly $|\mathbf{A}_k| = 0$. If, on the other hand, each column of $\mathbf{A}_k$ contains two 1's, then for every column in $\mathbf{A}_k$, one of the 1's must occur in an origin row, and the other in a destination row. Taking the sum of the origin rows minus the sum of the destination rows, we obtain a null vector; hence, the rows of $\mathbf{A}_k$ are not linearly independent, and again $|\mathbf{A}_k| = 0$. Finally, if every column of $\mathbf{A}_k$ contains one or two 1's, and at least one column contains only a single 1, then we expand $|\mathbf{A}_k|$ by any one of the columns which contain a single 1. This gives

$$|\mathbf{A}_k| = \pm |\mathbf{A}_{k-1}|,$$

where $|\mathbf{A}_{k-1}|$ is a minor of $\mathbf{A}$ of order $k - 1$. Now the same arguments can be applied to $\mathbf{A}_{k-1}$. Either $|\mathbf{A}_{k-1}| = 0$ or $|\mathbf{A}_{k-1}| = \pm |\mathbf{A}_{k-2}|$, etc. However, we observe that every $|\mathbf{A}_1| = 0, 1$ since each matrix element of $\mathbf{A}$ has the value 0 or 1. Thus we have proved that every minor of $\mathbf{A}$ has the value ± 1 or 0. This very important property of the $\mathbf{A}$ matrix allows us to develop algorithms for solving the transportation problem which are much more efficient than the direct application of the simplex method.

EXAMPLE: It is easily checked that the minors of the matrix $\mathbf{A}$ in the example on page 275 have only the values $\pm 1, 0$. Consider the minor formed from columns 1, 2, 3 and rows 1, 3, 5. It is

$$\begin{vmatrix} 1 & 1 & 1 \\ 1 & 0 & 0 \\ 0 & 0 & 1 \end{vmatrix} = - \begin{vmatrix} 1 & 0 \\ 0 & 1 \end{vmatrix} = -1.$$

The minor formed from columns 2, 4, 6 and rows 3, 4, 5 is

$$\begin{vmatrix} 0 & 0 & 0 \\ 1 & 0 & 1 \\ 0 & 0 & 0 \end{vmatrix} = 0.$$

The minor formed from columns 1, 7 and rows 3, 5 is

$$\begin{vmatrix} 1 & 0 \\ 0 & 1 \end{vmatrix} = 1.$$

9–3 The simplex method and transportation problems. Let us examine the problems involved in applying the simplex method directly to a transportation problem. When the constraints are written in the form $\mathbf{Ax = b}$, $\mathbf{A}$ does not contain an identity matrix. In fact, there are no unit vectors at all in $\mathbf{A}$. Thus, to begin with a basis matrix which is an identity matrix, it is necessary to annex artificial vectors. The initial basis matrix will contain only artificial vectors. We noted above that there is redundancy in the constraints (9–2), (9–3); in addition, we saw that any one constraint can be dropped, and the remaining constraints will be independent. Although we could eliminate a constraint before applying the simplex method, we shall find it convenient to retain all $m + n$ constraints. Then we add $m + n$ artificial vectors. We know that an optimal solution to the problem must have one artificial vector in the basis at a zero level, i.e., every basic feasible solution to the set of constraints

$$(\mathbf{A, I}) \begin{bmatrix} \mathbf{x} \\ \mathbf{x}_a \end{bmatrix} = \mathbf{b} \tag{9–12}$$

will contain at least one artificial vector. The following important result immediately follows from the fact that $r(\mathbf{A}) = m + n - 1$: *An optimal solution to a transportation problem with m origins and n destinations never need have more than $m + n - 1$ of the x_{ij} different from zero.*

It is not uncommon in practice to find transportation problems which have, for example, 25 origins and 1,000 destinations. For this problem, there are 1,025 constraints and about 25,000 variables. None of the presently available computer codes for the simplex method will handle a problem of this magnitude. Even if they did, the solutions would require a great deal of time. It is quite clear that to solve practical problems of this sort, a much more efficient algorithm than the direct application of the simplex method must be found. Interestingly enough, if we study theoretically the application of the simplex method to the transportation problem, a number of simplifications become apparent, permitting the development of an algorithm which, with the aid of a large scale computer, can easily solve a problem involving 25 origins and 1,000 destinations.

Before going on, let us note that if (9–1) holds, the transportation problem always has a feasible solution and hence an optimal feasible solution. Intuitively, this is obvious. There are many ways of obtaining a feasible solution. Clearly,

$$x_{ij} = \frac{a_i b_j}{\alpha}, \qquad \alpha = \sum_{i=1}^{m} a_i = \sum_{j=1}^{n} b_j \tag{9–13}$$

is a feasible solution. Another way is to begin with origin 1: We ship $\min (b_1, a_1)$ to destination 1. If $b_1 < a_1$, we ship $\min (b_2, a_1 - b_1)$ to destination 2. If $b_1 > a_1$, we move to origin 2 and ship $\min (b_1 - a_1, a_2)$

to destination 1, etc. Continuing in this manner, we finally satisfy all origin and destination requirements. A particularly interesting feature of this method is that, at each step, we satisfy either one of the origin requirements or one of the destination requirements. Thus we obtain a feasible solution in which no more than $m + n - 1$ of the x_{ij} are different from zero.

We might also note that there is no feasible solution to (9–2) and (9–3) unless (9–1) holds. To see this we only need to sum (9–2) over i and (9–3) over j. This requires that any solution to (9–2), (9–3) must satisfy

$$\sum_{i=1}^{m} \sum_{j=1}^{n} x_{ij} = \sum_{i=1}^{m} a_i, \tag{9–14}$$

$$\sum_{j=1}^{n} \sum_{i=1}^{m} x_{ij} = \sum_{j=1}^{n} b_j. \tag{9–15}$$

The same quantity appears on the left-hand side of (9–14), (9–15). Thus if there is a solution, (9–1) must hold. We have shown that a necessary and sufficient condition for a feasible solution to (9–2), (9–3) to exist is that (9–1) holds.

Since a transportation problem has a feasible solution if (9–1) holds, it follows that the artificial variables can always be driven to zero in Phase I. Consider a basic feasible solution to (9–12) which is also a feasible solution to $\mathbf{Ax} = \mathbf{b}$. Let $\mathbf{B}$ be the basis matrix (of order $m + n$). In general, $\mathbf{B}$ will contain $m + n - 1$ of the $\mathbf{p}_{ij}$ and one artificial vector $\mathbf{q}$ which will be at a zero level in the basic feasible solution. Furthermore, any $\mathbf{p}_{ij}$ in $\mathbf{A}$ can be expressed as a linear combination of the $m + n - 1$ vectors from $\mathbf{A}$ in $\mathbf{B}$. Thus, in reality, we never have to make explicit use of the artificial vector. For this reason, we shall refer to any set of $m + n - 1$ linearly independent vectors from $\mathbf{A}$ as a set of basis vectors for the transportation problem. A particular vector from such a set of basis vectors will be denoted by $\mathbf{p}_{\alpha\beta}^B$, and the corresponding basic variables will be denoted by $x_{\alpha\beta}^B$.

Any vector $\mathbf{p}_{ij}$ from $\mathbf{A}$ can be written as a linear combination of the basis vectors in the following way:

$$\mathbf{p}_{ij} = \sum_{\alpha\beta} y_{ij}^{\alpha\beta} \mathbf{p}_{\alpha\beta}^B, \tag{9–16}$$

where $\sum_{\alpha\beta}$ means a summation over the basis vectors. The two subscripts and superscripts on the $y_{ij}^{\alpha\beta}$ are rather clumsy, but we use them for clarity. Fortunately, we do not need to write these $y_{ij}^{\alpha\beta}$ very often; they are, of course, the numbers that would appear in the usual simplex tableau. We know that the artificial vector $\mathbf{q}$ is not needed in (9–16) so that $y_{ij}^q = 0$

for all i, j, that is, a row of zeros in the simplex tableau corresponds to the artificial vector.

We shall next prove the interesting result that every $y_{ij}^{\alpha\beta}$ is 0 or ± 1. Observe that (9–16) is a set of $m + n$ linear equations in $m + n - 1$ unknowns, the $y_{ij}^{\alpha\beta}$. In matrix form, it can be written $\mathbf{R}y_{ij} = \mathbf{p}_{ij}$, and $\mathbf{R}$ is a matrix formed from $m + n - 1$ linearly independent columns of $\mathbf{A}$. Recall from Section 9–2 that any one row of $\mathbf{R}$ can be crossed out, and the resulting matrix will be nonsingular. Let us then drop equation i from (9–16). Note that the ith component of $\mathbf{p}_{ij}$ contains a 1. The new set of equations obtained after eliminating the ith equation can be written $\mathbf{T}y_{ij} = \mathbf{e}_{j+m-1}$, where $\mathbf{e}_{j+m-1}$ is a unit vector containing $m + n - 1$ components and $\mathbf{T}$ is obtained from $\mathbf{R}$ by deleting row i. When a row of $\mathbf{p}_{ij}$ containing a 1 is crossed off, we are left with a unit vector. But $\mathbf{T}$ is nonsingular, so we can write

$$\mathbf{y}_{ij} = \mathbf{T}^{-1}\mathbf{e}_{j+m-1} = \boldsymbol{\tau}_{j+m-1}, \qquad (9\text{–}17)$$

where $\boldsymbol{\tau}_{j+m-1}$ is the $(j + m - 1)$-column of $\mathbf{T}^{-1}$. However, each component of $\boldsymbol{\tau}_{j+m-1}$ is some minor of order $m + n - 2$ from $\mathbf{T}$ divided by $|\mathbf{T}|$. Furthermore, $|\mathbf{T}|$ and the minors of $\mathbf{T}$ are minors of $\mathbf{A}$. Consequently, each element of $\boldsymbol{\tau}_{j+m-1}$ is ± 1, 0, and hence each $y_{ij}^{\alpha\beta}$ is ± 1, 0.

9–4 Simplifications resulting from all $y_{ij}^{\alpha\beta} = \pm 1$ or 0. We are now in a position to obtain some important results. In going from one simplex tableau to the next, let us first consider the transformation formula for the basic variables. When the double subscript notation is used, it is

$$\hat{x}_{\alpha\beta}^{B} = x_{\alpha\beta}^{B} - \frac{y_{st}^{\alpha\beta}}{y_{st}^{uv}} x_{uv}^{B}, \qquad \alpha\beta \neq uv; \qquad \hat{x}_{st} = \frac{x_{uv}^{B}}{y_{st}^{uv}},$$

where $\mathbf{p}_{st}$ is the vector entering the basis, and $\mathbf{p}_{uv}^{B}$ the vector to be removed. But by our above discussion, it must be true that $y_{st}^{uv} = 1$, $y_{st}^{\alpha\beta} = \pm 1$, 0 so that $\hat{x}_{\alpha\beta}^{B} = x_{\alpha\beta}^{B}$ or $x_{\alpha\beta}^{B} \pm x_{uv}^{B}$. Note that division is no longer needed. The new value of the variable is found from the original one by means of simple addition or subtraction. Suppose that the a_i, b_j in the requirements vector are integers. Then the basic variables in the initial basic feasible solution to (9–12), $\mathbf{x}_a = \mathbf{b}$, will be integers. Since the transformation formula for the basic variables requires only addition or subtraction, the basic variables in every basic feasible solution will have integral values. This means that the basic variables in any optimal basic solution will be integers, i.e., we arrive at the following theorem.

INTEGRALITY PROPERTY: *If the a_i, b_j of (9–2), (9–3) are integers, then any optimal basic solution to the transportation problem will have the property that all positive x_{ij} will be integers.*

This integrality property is peculiar to the transportation problem. The reader will recall that we cannot, in general, expect that an optimal solution to an arbitrary linear programming problem will have integral values for the variables. In fact, if we require that the variables be integers, a linear programming problem usually becomes a nonlinear programming problem. Intuitively, this integrality property is expected to follow from the physical nature of the problem: If it is profitable to ship a fraction of a unit to any destination, it is profitable to ship as large a quantity as possible. Since an integral number of units is required at each destination, an integral number of units will be shipped.

When numerical computations are performed by the simplex method, the bulk of the work consists of determining the $\hat{y}_{ij}$ from the y_{ij} at each iteration. For the transportation problem, the $y_{ij}^{\alpha\beta}$ are always 0, ± 1. This suggests that by not transforming the $y_{ij}^{\alpha\beta}$ at each iteration, we might be able to avoid a large part of the work required in the simplex method. Fortunately, this is correct. It is instructive to examine more closely the problem of expressing any $\mathbf{p}_{ij}$ in terms of the basis vectors $\mathbf{p}_{\alpha\beta}^{B}$. If the $\mathbf{p}_{\alpha\beta}^{B}$ for which $y_{ij}^{\alpha\beta} = 0$ are omitted, our above discussion shows that the relation expressing the linear dependence between $\mathbf{p}_{ij}$ and the $\mathbf{p}_{\alpha\beta}^{B}$ can be written

$$\mathbf{p}_{ij} = \sum (\pm)\mathbf{p}_{\alpha\beta}^{B}. \tag{9–18}$$

Each of the vectors $\mathbf{p}_{ij}$, $\mathbf{p}_{\alpha\beta}^{B}$ has the form (9–8). Consequently, since the coefficient of each $\mathbf{p}_{\alpha\beta}^{B}$ is ± 1, there must be one $\mathbf{p}_{\alpha\beta}^{B}$, of the form $\mathbf{p}_{iu}^{B} = \mathbf{e}_i + \mathbf{e}_{m+u}$, whose coefficient is $+1$ in (9–18), so that there will be a 1 in the ith component of $\mathbf{p}_{ij}$. Then if $u \neq j$, there must be a $\mathbf{p}_{\alpha\beta}^{B}$, of the form $\mathbf{p}_{vu}^{B} = \mathbf{e}_v + \mathbf{e}_{m+u}$, $v \leq m$, whose coefficient is -1 in (9–18), so that the 1 in the $(m + u)$th component of $\mathbf{p}_{iu}^{B}$ will be cancelled out. Continuing in this way, we must reach, in a finite number of steps ($\leq m + n - 1$), a vector $\mathbf{p}_{\alpha\beta}^{B}$, of the form $\mathbf{p}_{wj}^{B} = \mathbf{e}_w + \mathbf{e}_{m+j}$, whose coefficient is positive in (9–18). The 1 in the wth component will cancel the wth component of the immediately preceding vector (whose coefficient is -1), and the $(m + j)$th component of $\mathbf{p}_{wj}^{B}$ will give the $(m + j)$th component of $\mathbf{p}_{ij}$. Thus we see that the expression of any $\mathbf{p}_{ij}$ in terms of a set of basis vectors will have a remarkably simple form. Furthermore, since the representation of any vector in terms of a set of basis vectors is unique, the above representation is unique.

The preceding discussion has shown that the representation of $\mathbf{p}_{ij}$ in terms of the $\mathbf{p}_{\alpha\beta}^{B}$ can be written

$$\mathbf{p}_{ij} = \mathbf{p}_{iu}^{B} - \mathbf{p}_{vu}^{B} + \mathbf{p}_{vt}^{B} - \cdots - \mathbf{p}_{ws}^{B} + \mathbf{p}_{wj}^{B}. \tag{9–19}$$

Since in (9–19) we begin and end with a plus sign, and since the signs are alternately plus and minus, it follows that an odd number of basis vectors at a nonzero level is always used to express any vector from $\mathbf{A}$ in terms of the basis vectors.

EXAMPLE: For the matrix $\mathbf{A}$ given in the example on page 275, the reader can quickly verify that the vectors $\mathbf{p}_{11}$, $\mathbf{p}_{12}$, $\mathbf{p}_{22}$, $\mathbf{p}_{23}$, $\mathbf{p}_{24}$ are linearly independent, and hence any vector in $\mathbf{A}$ can be represented as a linear combination of these five vectors. Three vectors, $\mathbf{p}_{21}$, $\mathbf{p}_{13}$, $\mathbf{p}_{14}$, are not in the above set. We see that

$$\mathbf{p}_{21} = \mathbf{p}_{22} - \mathbf{p}_{12} + \mathbf{p}_{11}, \qquad \mathbf{p}_{13} = \mathbf{p}_{12} - \mathbf{p}_{22} + \mathbf{p}_{23},$$

$$\mathbf{p}_{14} = \mathbf{p}_{12} - \mathbf{p}_{22} + \mathbf{p}_{24}.$$

It is suggested that the reader write out the vectors explicitly to verify that all the intermediate 1's do cancel. In each case, the expression of a vector in terms of the basis vectors has the form (9–19). Furthermore, an odd number of basis vectors appears at a nonzero level in every instance, but not every basis vector appears at a nonzero level in any one expression. However, each basis vector does appear in at least one of the three expressions.

Consider the following symbolic matrix of the $\mathbf{p}_{ij}$ (the basis vectors are circled). Note the interesting fact that each $\mathbf{p}_{ij}$ not in the basis and the basis vectors which appear at a nonzero level in (9–19) form what we might call a loop in this matrix.

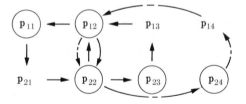

The idea introduced in the above example of representing the $\mathbf{p}_{ij}$ as a symbolic matrix is very important. If we circle a set of $m + n - 1$ linearly independent vectors in the matrix $\|\mathbf{p}_{ij}\|$, we can see immediately how to express any other vector $\mathbf{p}_{ij}$ in this matrix in terms of the basis vectors. Beginning with $\mathbf{p}_{ij}$, we move in row i until we encounter a basis vector $\mathbf{p}_{iu}^{B}$ such that there is another basis vector in column u of the matrix. A coefficient of $+1$ is assigned to $\mathbf{p}_{iu}^{B}$. Next, we move in column u from $\mathbf{p}_{iu}^{B}$ to a basis vector $\mathbf{p}_{vu}^{B}$ which has another basis vector in row v. A coefficient of -1 is assigned to $\mathbf{p}_{vu}^{B}$. Then, we find a basis vector $\mathbf{p}_{vt}^{B}$ which has another basis vector in column t, etc. Ultimately, we must close the loop with some basis vector $\mathbf{p}_{wj}^{B}$. In this way, we obtain (9–19) without having to compute explicitly the $y_{ij}^{\alpha\beta}$.

It is important to note that we did not imply in the above paragraph that any "path" formed in this way will ultimately close the loop. There may be some "blind alleys." However, we are sure that there will be *one* path that will close the loop. Furthermore, there will be only one such path, i.e., the loop is unique. Observe that instead of finding at the first step a basis vector $\mathbf{p}_{iu}^{B}$ in the same row as $\mathbf{p}_{ij}$ such that there is another basis vector in column u, we can equally well find a basis vector $\mathbf{p}_{sj}^{B}$ in the same column as $\mathbf{p}_{ij}$ such that there is another basis vector in row s, and obtain precisely the same loop; however, we traverse it in the opposite direction.

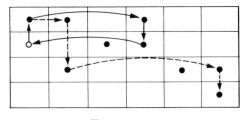

FIGURE 9–1

EXAMPLE: Consider a transportation problem having four origins and six destinations. It is easily shown that the nine vectors $\mathbf{p}_{11}$, $\mathbf{p}_{12}$, $\mathbf{p}_{32}$, $\mathbf{p}_{23}$, $\mathbf{p}_{14}$, $\mathbf{p}_{24}$, $\mathbf{p}_{35}$, $\mathbf{p}_{36}$, $\mathbf{p}_{46}$ are linearly independent. One only needs to evaluate any 9th-order minor in the matrix formed from these vectors (this is really quite easy to do—try it). Thus, for this problem, any vector in the $\mathbf{A}$ matrix can be expressed as a linear combination of these basis vectors which are represented by dots in Fig. 9–1. Suppose that we wish to express $\mathbf{p}_{21}$ in terms of the basis vectors. Consider Fig. 9–1, where the cell representing $\mathbf{p}_{21}$ is indicated by a circle. Beginning with $\mathbf{p}_{21}$, let us find a basis vector in column 1, $\mathbf{p}_{i1}^{B}$, which has another basis vector in row i. There is only one basis vector, $\mathbf{p}_{11}$, in column 1. In addition to $\mathbf{p}_{11}$, row 1 contains two other basis vectors, $\mathbf{p}_{12}$, $\mathbf{p}_{14}$. Note that there is a basis vector $\mathbf{p}_{32}$ in column 2 and a basis vector $\mathbf{p}_{24}$ in column 4. If we choose $\mathbf{p}_{12}$ as the next basis vector, we must follow the dotted path in Fig. 9–1. It is a blind alley and does not lead to a loop. On the other hand, if we choose $\mathbf{p}_{14}$ as the second basis vector, we are led to the loop shown in solid lines. From this loop, we see that $\mathbf{p}_{21}$ can be written as a linear combination of the basis vectors in the following way:

$$\mathbf{p}_{21} = \mathbf{p}_{11} - \mathbf{p}_{14} + \mathbf{p}_{24}.$$

All other basis vectors have zero coefficients.

Let us now turn our attention to the computation of the $z_j - c_j$. For the transportation problem, it is convenient to use two subscripts here also, so that we shall write $z_{ij} - c_{ij}$. If $c^B_{\alpha\beta}$ is the price corresponding to the basis vector $\mathbf{p}^B_{\alpha\beta}$, then

$$z_{ij} - c_{ij} = \sum_{\alpha\beta} y^{\alpha\beta}_{ij} c^B_{\alpha\beta} - c_{ij} \qquad (9\text{--}20)$$

or

$$z_{ij} - c_{ij} = \sum(\pm) c^B_{\alpha\beta} - c_{ij}. \qquad (9\text{--}21)$$

For the vector $\mathbf{p}_{ij}$ of (9–19), we can write

$$z_{ij} - c_{ij} = c^B_{iu} - c^B_{vu} + c^B_{vt} - \cdots - c^B_{ws} + c^B_{wj} - c_{ij}. \qquad (9\text{--}22)$$

If we arrange the c_{ij} into a matrix $||c_{ij}||$, then we can compute all the $z_{ij} - c_{ij}$, using the same technique of finding a loop involving c_{ij} and the $c^B_{\alpha\beta}$ that was used to express $\mathbf{p}_{ij}$ in terms of the $\mathbf{p}^B_{\alpha\beta}$. For the above example, we see that

$$z_{21} - c_{21} = c_{11} - c_{14} + c_{24} - c_{21}.$$

In this section, we have examined the theory underlying the application of the simplex method to any transportation problem with the following results. Some remarkable simplifications are introduced into the transformation formulas by the fact that the $y^{\alpha\beta}_{ij}$ are always either 0 or ± 1. If we arrange the $\mathbf{p}_{ij}$ into a symbolic matrix $||\mathbf{p}_{ij}||$, it is very easy to determine the $y^{\alpha\beta}_{ij}$ for a given basis without any computation whatever. Furthermore, if the c_{ij} are arranged into the same type of matrix, we can compute the $z_{ij} - c_{ij}$ directly, using only the operations of addition and subtraction. Here we have the key to the development of an efficient algorithm for solving transportation problems.

9–5 The transportation-problem tableau. The results of the preceding section suggest that we should focus our attention on a matrix tableau involving m rows and n columns rather than on a simplex tableau with $m + n + 1$ rows and $mn + m + n + 1$ columns. Let us consider the tableau shown in Table 9–1. In cell (i, j) enter c_{ij} and x_{ij}. Note that if the x_{ij} entered in the tableau represent a feasible solution, it must be true that addition of the x_{ij} in row i yields a_i, $i = 1, \ldots, m$. Similarly, if we sum the x_{ij} in column j, we must obtain b_j, $j = 1, \ldots, n$. Hence, all the constraints are conveniently represented, and it is easy to check whether any set of x_{ij} is a feasible solution by simply summing the rows and columns.

In the last column we enter the origin availabilities and in the last row the destination requirements. It is also convenient to use D_j as a heading for column j to indicate that this column pertains to destination j. Similarly O_i is placed at the beginning of row i to indicate that this row pertains to origin i. We can, of course, also associate the vector $\mathbf{p}_{ij}$ with the cell

TABLE 9–1 — TABLEAU FOR TRANSPORTATION PROBLEM

	D_1	D_2		D_j		D_n	a_i
O_1	c_{11} x_{11}	c_{12} x_{12}	$\cdots$	c_{1j} x_{1j}	$\cdots$	c_{1n} x_{1n}	a_1
O_2	c_{21} x_{21}	c_{22} x_{22}	$\cdots$	c_{2j} x_{2j}	$\cdots$	c_{2n} x_{2n}	a_2
	$\vdots$	$\vdots$	$\cdots$	$\vdots$	$\cdots$	$\vdots$	$\vdots$
O_i	c_{i1} x_{i1}	c_{i2} x_{i2}	$\cdots$	c_{ij} x_{ij}	$\cdots$	c_{in} x_{in}	a_i
	$\vdots$	$\vdots$	$\cdots$	$\vdots$	$\cdots$	$\vdots$	$\vdots$
O_m	c_{m1} x_{m1}	c_{m2} x_{m2}	$\cdots$	c_{mj} x_{mj}	$\cdots$	c_{mn} x_{mn}	a_m
b_j	b_1	b_2	$\cdots$	b_j	$\cdots$	b_n	$\sum a_i = \sum b_j$

(i, j). However, we shall never make explicit use of these vectors. In the lower right-hand cell of Table 9–1, it is often desirable to enter the total amount to be shipped, i.e., $\sum a_i = \sum b_j$.

When dealing with basic solutions, we know that no more than $m + n - 1$ of the x_{ij} in Table 9–1 will be positive. If more than $m + n - 1$ of the x_{ij} are positive, the vectors $\mathbf{p}_{ij}$ corresponding to these variables will be linearly dependent. Since we shall be concerned only with basic feasible solutions, no more than $m + m - 1$ of the x_{ij} will ever be > 0. Only the values of the basic variables will be entered in the tableau; i.e., we shall not fill in the zeros for the nonbasic variables. However, zero values of the basic variables will be written in.

In the previous section, the notions of a path and a loop were introduced in an intuitive fashion. Now we shall find it desirable to make these concepts more precise.

DIRECTED PATH JOINING TWO CELLS: *A directed path from the cell (i, j) to the cell (v, w) in Table 9–1 is defined to be an ordered set of cells $\{(i, j), (i, k), (q, k), (q, r), \ldots, (v, w)\}$ or $\{(i, j), (s, j), (s, t), \ldots, (v, w)\}$ such that any two adjacent cells in the ordered sets lie in the same row or same column, while any three adjacent cells do not lie in the same row or same*

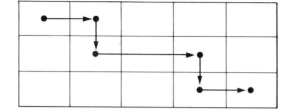

FIGURE 9–2

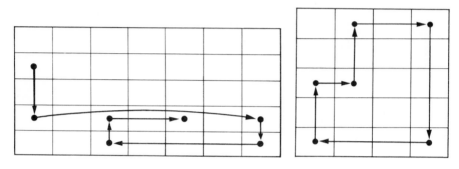

FIGURE 9–3   FIGURE 9–4

column. Furthermore, each cell (except the last) must appear only once in the ordered sets. The cell (i, j) is called the initial cell of the path, and (v, w) is called the terminal cell.

It is convenient to be able to illustrate graphically a path connecting two cells in Table 9–1. To do this we simply join by line segments the ordered set of cells which form the path. The direction is indicated by an arrowhead on the line. These line segments will be called branches.

DIRECTED BRANCH: *A directed branch is a line segment joining an ordered pair of cells which lie either in the same row or the same column of Table 9–1. The first cell of the ordered pair is called the initial point of the branch, and the second cell is called the end point of the branch.*

A path, as we have defined it, may contain only a single element. If it contains more than a single element, it can be represented by a sequence of one or more branches. The end point of one branch is the initial point for the immediately succeeding branch. In addition, each branch is orthogonal to the branch immediately preceding it. A typical directed path from cell $(1, 1)$ to cell $(3, 5)$ is shown in Fig. 9–2. The ordered set of elements which describe the path is $\{(1, 1), (1, 2), (2, 2), (2, 4), (3, 4), (3, 5)\}$. Of course, there are many other directed paths from $(1, 1)$ to $(3, 5)$. Note that our definition permits a directed path such as that connecting $(2, 1)$ with $(4, 5)$ in Fig. 9–3.

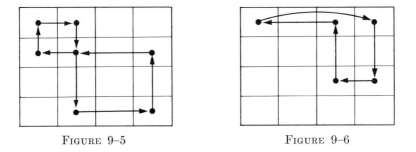

FIGURE 9–5   FIGURE 9–6

DIRECTED LOOP: *A directed loop in Table 9–1 is a directed path such that the first cell in the ordered set is the same as the last cell, and the first branch is orthogonal to the last branch.*

A typical directed loop is shown in Fig. 9–4. Two types of loops not allowed by our definition are shown in Figs. 9–5, 9–6. The loop in Fig. 9–5 is not permitted because, according to our definition of a directed path, each cell (except the last) must appear only once in the ordered set. In Fig. 9–5, $(2, 2)$ appears twice. The loop in Fig. 9–6 is not allowed because, if $(1, 1)$ is chosen as the initial cell, the first and last branches are not orthogonal. It is still not allowed if any other cell is chosen for the initial cell because then it is not true that each pair of adjacent branches is orthogonal. Note that we cannot know by looking at a loop such as that shown in Fig. 9–4 which element is to be considered the first one.

From the above definition of a directed loop it is clear that there is always an even number of distinct cells in the set which defines the loop. Furthermore, the vectors $\mathbf{p}_{ij}$ from $\mathbf{A}$ associated with the cells in a loop are linearly dependent. To see this it is only necessary to start with any cell in the loop, and assign a coefficient of $+1$ to the selected vector. We move on to the next cell (which is in either the same row or column as the first one) and assign a coefficient of -1 to that vector. Proceeding in this way, alternately assigning coefficients of $+1$, -1 to the vectors, we obtain something like

$$\mathbf{p}_{ij} - \mathbf{p}_{rj} + \mathbf{p}_{rs} - \cdots + \mathbf{p}_{vw} - \mathbf{p}_{iw} = \mathbf{0},$$

which expresses the linear dependence of the vectors associated with the cells in the loop.

In Section 9–3 we discussed the representation of any vector in terms of a set of basis vectors (or equivalently, any vector in a set of linearly dependent vectors in terms of a subset of linearly independent vectors from the given set). We showed that the relation of linear dependence must have the form (9–19). But from our definition of a directed loop, we see that the cells corresponding to the ordered set of vectors $\{\mathbf{p}_{ij}, \mathbf{p}_{iu}^{B}, \mathbf{p}_{vu}^{B}, \ldots, \mathbf{p}_{wj}^{B}, \mathbf{p}_{ij}\}$ form a loop in Table 9–1.

9–6 Bases in the transportation tableau. We can now make an interesting and useful observation. We have demonstrated that the vectors from **A** associated with the cells which form a loop in Table 9–1 are linearly dependent. Furthermore, it has been shown that if a given set of vectors from **A** is linearly dependent, then the cells associated with some subset of these vectors form a loop in Table 9–1. Hence we conclude that any set of vectors for which no loop exists in the corresponding cells of Table 9–1 is linearly independent. *Thus a set of basis vectors from* **A** *is a set of $m + n - 1$ vectors such that no loop exists in the set of cells (Table 9–1) corresponding to these vectors.* Here we have a simple criterion for deciding whether any feasible solution given in Table 9–1 is a basic feasible solution.

We shall introduce a few additional concepts in order to obtain an even more vivid geometrical interpretation of the bases and linear dependence in Table 9–1.

SIMPLE DIRECTED PATH: *A simple directed path from cell (i, j) to cell (u, v) (Table 9–1) is a directed path such that in any row or column of Table 9–1 there are no more than two cells in the set of cells which defines the path.*

Figure 9–2 shows a simple directed path. If any given directed path connecting two elements in Table 9–1 is not simple, it can be reduced to a simple path by eliminating some of the cells in the path. To prove this, suppose that in row k of Table 9–1 there appear more than two cells of the path. Let (k, p), (k, q), $\ldots$, (k, w) be the cells of the path in row k. Furthermore, assume that they are written in the order in which they appear in the ordered set describing the path. Now we drop *all* elements in the ordered set which lie between (k, p) and (k, w), so that, in the new ordered set, (k, p), (k, w) are adjacent cells. We do this for every row and column where more than two cells of the path appear. The resulting path is a simple path.

An example will illustrate this procedure: The path shown in Fig. 9–3 is represented by the ordered set

$$\{(2, 1), (4, 1), (4, 7), (5, 7), (5, 3), (4, 3), (4, 5)\}.$$

In row 4, there are 4 elements of the path, and their order in the set is $(4, 1)$, $(4, 7)$, $(4, 3)$, $(4, 5)$. According to the above discussion, we drop all elements of the path between $(4, 1)$ and $(4, 5)$. This gives the new path $\{(2, 1), (4, 1), (4, 5)\}$, which should be a simple path since row 4 was the only row or column which contained more than two cells of the original path. We see that it is indeed a simple path.

SIMPLE DIRECTED LOOP: *A simple directed loop is a directed loop which has no more than two cells in any row or column of Table 9–1.*

We have shown that any directed path can be reduced to a simple directed path. It follows that any directed loop can be reduced to a simple directed loop in the same fashion. Clearly, if a loop has one element in a given row or column, it must have at least two elements. A simple loop has precisely two elements in every row and column where one element of the loop appears.

Now consider the set consisting of $m + n - 1$ linearly independent basis vectors and one other vector $\mathbf{p}_{ij}$. The set of $m + n$ vectors is linearly dependent since $\mathbf{p}_{ij}$ can be written as a linear combination of the basis vectors. Hence a loop exists in some subset of the $m + n$ cells (Table 9–1) corresponding to these vectors. Furthermore, the loop is unique (except for the direction of traversing the loop) since a vector can be expressed in terms of a set of basis vectors in only one way. We conclude, therefore, that *this unique loop must be simple.* This follows because we know that if there is a directed loop, then there is a simple directed loop. If there were a directed loop other than a simple one, the representation of $\mathbf{p}_{ij}$ in terms of the basis vectors would not be unique. Hence, given any $\mathbf{p}_{ij}$ and a set of $m + n - 1$ basis vectors, there always exists a simple directed loop in Table 9–1 involving only the cells corresponding to $\mathbf{p}_{ij}$ and the basis vectors.

CONNECTED SET OF CELLS: *A set of cells in Table 9–1 is said to be connected if there exists a directed path (and hence a simple directed path) involving only cells in the set, that joins any cell in the set to any other cell in the set.*

It is very easy to prove that the cells in Table 9–1 corresponding to $m + n - 1$ basis vectors are connected. Assume that there is no path joining the cells (s, t), (u, v) corresponding to the basis vectors $\mathbf{p}_{st}^{B}$, $\mathbf{p}_{uv}^{B}$, which involves only cells that correspond to the remaining basis vectors. Then consider the cell (s, v) corresponding to the vector $\mathbf{p}_{sv}$. But $\mathbf{p}_{sv}$ is linearly dependent on the basis vectors, and hence there is a simple loop which involves only (s, v) and the cells corresponding to the basis vectors. This leads to a contradiction, because the loop implies that a directed path exists which involves only cells corresponding to the basis vectors and which joins two cells corresponding to the basis vectors $\mathbf{p}_{sw}^{B}$ and $\mathbf{p}_{qv}^{B}$; these cells are in the same row and column, respectively, as (s, v). If $\mathbf{p}_{sw}^{B} \neq \mathbf{p}_{st}^{B}$, they can be connected by a directed branch. The same is true if $\mathbf{p}_{qv}^{B} \neq \mathbf{p}_{uv}^{B}$. Thus the cells corresponding to a set of basis vectors are connected.

BASIS CELLS: *The cells of Table 9–1 corresponding to a given set of $m + n - 1$ basis vectors will be referred to as basis cells of the tableau for the given basis.*

TREE: *A tree in Table 9–1 is a connected set of cells without loops.*

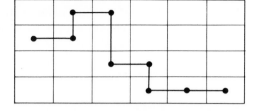

FIGURE 9-7

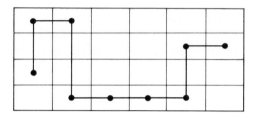

FIGURE 9-8

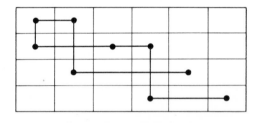

FIGURE 9-9

As a result of the above discussion we conclude that a set of basis cells in Table 9–1 forms a tree with $m + n - 1$ cells. Conversely, the vectors corresponding to the cells in any tree containing $m + n - 1$ elements form a basis. A tree containing $m + n - 1$ cells will be called a basic tree. Observe that *a basic tree has at least one cell in every row and column of Table 9–1.* This follows because the vectors corresponding to the basic cells form a basis. If there is no cell in row i, then it is not possible to form a loop consisting of one cell in row i and the basic cells. This contradicts the fact that we actually have a basis.

EXAMPLE: Two basic trees for a transportation problem involving four origins and six destinations are shown in Figs. 9–7 and 9–8. It is important to note that the branches of a tree may cross each other orthogonally provided that there is no cell of the tree at the point of intersection. For example, in Fig. 9–9, the branches of a tree cross, but no loop is formed since there are no cells of the set at the points of intersection of the branches.

The reader should now be able to see how the tableau form of Table 9–1 can be used to solve transportation problems in a way that requires considerably fewer computations than the direct application of the simplex method. We shall next present the details of this computational algorithm.

9–7 The stepping-stone algorithm. Let us suppose that we have a basic feasible solution to a given transportation problem such that the $m + n - 1$ basic variables x_{ij} are positive. Then we construct a tableau of the form of Table 9–1. We enter the values of the nonzero x_{ij} in the appropriate cells and circle these values so that we know which are the basic cells. All the costs are also entered into the tableau. To determine whether the given basic feasible solution is optimal, we must determine the $z_{ij} - c_{ij}$ for the $\mathbf{p}_{ij}$ not in the basis.

It is easy to compute $z_{ij} - c_{ij}$ for the vector $\mathbf{p}_{ij}$, i.e., for cell (i, j). We find the unique loop involving (i, j) and the basic cells. Suppose that the ordered set of cells is

$$\{(i, j), (i, r), (u, r), \ldots, (s, w), (s, j), (i, j)\}.$$

Then from (9–22),

$$z_{ij} - c_{ij} = c_{ir}^B - c_{ur}^B + \cdots - c_{sw}^B + c_{sj}^B - c_{ij}. \qquad (9\text{–}23)$$

Starting from cell (i, j), we move around the loop, alternately assigning plus and minus signs to the costs. Note that $z_{ij} - c_{ij}$ is the same, no matter in which direction we traverse the loop. Enter the value of $z_{ij} - c_{ij}$ in the space reserved for x_{ij} (this space is not used since $x_{ij} = 0$ for this cell). In this way, we can evaluate all $z_{ij} - c_{ij}$ for vectors $\mathbf{p}_{ij}$ not in the basic solution, and enter them in the tableau. Recall that we are solving a minimization problem. Thus, if all $z_{ij} - c_{ij} \leq 0$, the basic feasible solution is optimal.

If one or more of the $z_{ij} - c_{ij} > 0$, we know that the value of z can be reduced. This follows since we have assumed that the solution has $m + n - 1$ positive x_{ij}, i.e., the basic solution is not degenerate. For the moment, we shall assume that degeneracy does not occur. Later we shall see that it is very easy to handle degeneracy in the transportation tableau. The reader might note that we never need worry about an unbounded solution in a transportation problem. The absolute minimum cost is zero.

We are now ready to determine a new basic solution. As in the simplex method, we compute

$$z_{st} - c_{st} = \max (z_{ij} - c_{ij}) \qquad \text{for} \qquad z_{ij} - c_{ij} > 0. \qquad (9\text{–}24)$$

This means that, in the simplex method, $\mathbf{p}_{st}$ enters the basis, that is, x_{st}

becomes positive in the next tableau, and the vector to leave would be
determined from

$$\min \frac{x_{\alpha\beta}^{B}}{y_{st}^{\alpha\beta}}, \qquad y_{st}^{\alpha\beta} > 0.$$

However, the $y_{st}^{\alpha\beta} > 0$ have the value unity. Hence the variable that is
driven to zero in the current basic solution is the smallest $x_{\alpha\beta}^{B}$ of those $x_{\alpha\beta}^{B}$ for
which the coefficient of $c_{\alpha\beta}^{B}$ in (9–23) is $+1$ when $z_{st} - c_{st}$ appears on the
left-hand side of the expression. In other words, to find the variable to
be removed from the current basis, we determine the loop involving (s, t)
and the basis cells. From the cells for which the coefficient of $c_{\alpha\beta}^{B}$ is $+1$
when z_{st} is written in terms of prices in the basis, we choose the smallest
$x_{\alpha\beta}^{B}$, say x_{qr}^{B}.

Then the values of the basic variables for the new basic solution are
easily computed. These new values will be denoted by a caret. We have

$$\hat{x}_{st} = x_{qr}^{B} \tag{9–25a}$$

and

$$\hat{x}_{\alpha\beta}^{B} = x_{\alpha\beta}^{B} - x_{qr}^{B} \tag{9–25b}$$

for those $x_{\alpha\beta}^{B}$ in the loop involving (s, t) for which $c_{\alpha\beta}^{B}$ had a coefficient of $+1$.
Also,

$$\hat{x}_{\alpha\beta}^{B} = x_{\alpha\beta}^{B} + x_{qr}^{B} \tag{9–25c}$$

for those $x_{\alpha\beta}^{B}$ in the loop involving (s, t) for which $c_{\alpha\beta}^{B}$ had a coefficient of -1.
Finally,

$$\hat{x}_{\alpha\beta}^{B} = x_{\alpha\beta}^{B} \tag{9–25d}$$

for those $x_{\alpha\beta}^{B}$ that were not in the loop involving (s, t). Although this
explanation may seem a little complicated, an example will illustrate that
the procedure is really quite simple. Noting that the $y_{st}^{\alpha\beta}$ can only take on
the values $\pm 1, 0$, we see that the above formulas follow directly from the
transformation formulas of the simplex method.

A new tableau is constructed for this new basic solution. The new
values of the basic variables are entered in this tableau and are circled.
Again, all the $z_{ij} - c_{ij}$ are computed as described above, and the whole
procedure is repeated. When all $z_{ij} - c_{ij} \leq 0$, we have found an optimal
solution to the transportation problem.

Here we have developed a very simple algorithm for solving any transportation problem, given an initial basic feasible solution. This algorithm
is, in fact, the simplex method. However, because all $y_{ij}^{\alpha\beta}$ are $\pm 1, 0$, most
of the work involved in the simplex method can be eliminated since we
never need to compute the $y_{ij}^{\alpha\beta}$. This allows us to solve the problem simply
by means of addition and subtraction, and furthermore, it enables us to

use a tableau involving only m rows and n columns rather than the much larger simplex tableau. The above algorithm is sometimes referred to as the stepping-stone method; it was introduced by Charnes and Cooper [1]. However, Dantzig [8] was the first to find a short-cut method of solving the transportation problem and to develop the tableau form of Table 9–1; he uses duality to compute the $z_{ij} - c_{ij}$ in a different and more efficient way. We shall introduce this additional computational short cut later.

If the simplex method is directly applied to the transportation problem, it is necessary to begin with a basis containing only artificial vectors. Fortunately, an initial basic feasible solution can be obtained directly from the tableau form of Table 9–1. Artificial vectors are never needed. A particularly simple method of determining an initial basic feasible solution is the so-called northwest-corner rule, introduced by Charnes and Cooper. We begin with cell $(1, 1)$. Set $x_{11} = \min (a_1, b_1)$. At this first step, we satisfy either an origin or a destination requirement. If $a_1 > b_1$, we move to cell $(1, 2)$ and set $x_{12} = \min (a_1 - b_1, b_2)$. On the other hand, if $b_1 > a_1$, we move to cell $(2, 1)$ and set $x_{21} = \min (b_1 - a_1, a_2)$. (When $a_1 = b_1$, degeneracy occurs; this will be treated later.) At the second step, we satisfy either the second origin or the second destination requirement. We continue in this way, satisfying at the kth step either an origin or a destination requirement. Ultimately, we obtain a feasible solution. Now we note that this method cannot yield more than $m + n - 1$ positive x_{ij} because, at each step, we satisfy an origin or a destination requirement. After $m + n - 1$ steps, $m + n - 1$ of the constraints will be satisfied. Since $r(\mathbf{A}) = m + n - 1$, the remaining constraint will be automatically satisfied at this point. In the absence of degeneracy, we do not obtain less than $m + n - 1$ positive x_{ij}. In this case, it is clear that the resulting solution is basic because the method of constructing the solution rules out any possibility of loops, that is, at each step, we satisfy a row or column constraint and, in constructing the solution, we move down and to the right. We never double back, and hence a loop cannot be formed. By moving down and to the right we mean that if at step $k - 1$, we assign a positive value to x_{ij}, then at step k, we assign a positive value to $x_{i,j+1}$ or $x_{i+1,j}$. At each step, one subscript increases, and the other remains unchanged. The following example (Section 9–8) will clarify the above exposition.

The basic feasible solution obtained by means of the northwest-corner rule may be far from optimal since the costs were completely ignored. Later we shall discuss methods of determining an initial basic feasible solution which do take account of the costs. The additional effort spent in obtaining a good initial basic solution is worth while because it can considerably reduce the number of iterations which will be required to find an optimal solution.

We wish to note that a standard simplex tableau can be constructed quite easily from the information contained in a transportation tableau. From our knowledge of the basic variables we know which vectors are in the basic solution. These $m + n - 1$ vectors, along with any artificial vector, will yield an $(m + n)$th-order basis matrix. The $z_{ij} - c_{ij}$ are given in the transportation tableau. The $y_{ij}^{\alpha\beta}$ can be determined very quickly by finding the loop which connects cell (i, j) and the basis cells.

The stepping-stone algorithm permits us to solve transportation problems that are too large to lend themselves to direct application of the simplex method. For example, on a computer, it is not difficult to solve a transportation problem involving 1,000 destinations and 25 origins by means of the stepping-stone algorithm or some of its variants. As previously noted, no computer is large enough to solve the same problem by direct application of the simplex method. The stepping-stone algorithm has another property which is very important when a digital computer is to be used: It requires only the arithmetic operations of addition and subtraction. A digital computer can be made to operate (in so-called fixed-point arithmetic) so that no rounding-off errors occur in addition or subtraction. Thus, the stepping-stone algorithm makes it possible to avoid the problem of rounding-off errors which limit the size of the problems that can be solved by the simplex method. A transportation problem may require an arbitrarily large number of iterations, and no loss of accuracy due to rounding-off will occur if fixed-point arithmetic is used.*

9–8 An example. The general discussion presented above will now be applied to a very simple example. Consider a transportation problem involving 4 origins and 6 destinations. The origin availabilities, the destination requirements, and the costs are given in Tableau 1, Table 9–2.

An initial basic feasible solution can be obtained by means of the northwest-corner rule. We set $x_{11} = \min (a_1, b_1) = \min (50, 30) = 30$. Thus we have satisfied the requirements of destination 1. We have not used all units available at origin 1; hence we set $x_{12} = \min (a_1 - b_1, b_2) = \min (20, 50) = 20$. Now the first origin constraint is satisfied. Since an additional 30 units must be shipped to destination 2, we move to cell $(2, 2)$ and set $x_{22} = \min (b_2 - 20, a_2) = \min (30, 40) = 30$. Thus the requirements of destination 2 are satisfied. Ten units are still available at origin 2; thus $x_{23} = \min (10, b_3) = 10$. An additional 10 units must be shipped to destination 3; set $x_{33} = 10$. This leaves 50 units still to be shipped from origin 3. We set $x_{34} = 40 = b_4$ and satisfy the requirement of destination 4. Since 10 units remain to be shipped from origin 3, we set

---

* This is not true, however, if floating-point arithmetic is used. In this case, rounding-off errors can occur.

$x_{35} = 10$. The requirement at destination 5 is 30; set $x_{45} = 20$. This leaves 11 units to be shipped from origin 5, which is precisely the number of units required at destination 6. We circle the x_{ij}-values just obtained and note that they are $9 = m + n - 1$ in number. Furthermore, these cells do not form a loop. Thus we have a basic feasible solution. All other x_{ij} are zero. We do not fill in these zeros. This initial basic feasible solution is given in Table 9–2.

The next task is to compute the $z_{ij} - c_{ij}$. Let us illustrate the procedure by calculating $z_{41} - c_{41}$. First, we find the unique loop involving (4, 1) and the basis cells. This loop, shown in Table 9–2, is indeed unique and simple. For this special case, (9–23) becomes

$$z_{41} - c_{41} = c_{45} - c_{35} + c_{33} - c_{23} + c_{22} - c_{12} + c_{11} - c_{41},$$

or

$$z_{41} - c_{41} = 2 - 4 + 4 - 2 + 2 - 1 + 2 - 4 = -1.$$

The value -1 is now entered in cell (4, 1). We use boldface type for the $z_{ij} - c_{ij}$ to avoid confusion with the costs. In the actual working of problems by hand, it is often helpful to use different colors for the c_{ij}, $z_{ij} - c_{ij}$, and the basic variables. Note that we obtain the same value of $z_{41} - c_{41}$, regardless of the direction in which we traverse the loop, i.e.,

$$z_{41} - c_{41} = c_{11} - c_{12} + c_{22} - c_{23} + c_{33} - c_{35} + c_{45} - c_{41}.$$

All the other $z_{ij} - c_{ij}$ are computed in the same way. We do not compute the $z_{ij} - c_{ij}$ for the basic cells because we know that $z_{ij} - c_{ij} = 0$ for these cells. However, zero values of the $z_{ij} - c_{ij}$ for nonbasic cells are written in.

Not all $z_{ij} - c_{ij} \leq 0$, so the initial basic feasible solution is not optimal. The largest $z_{ij} - c_{ij}$ is $z_{36} - c_{36} = 3$. At the next stage, x_{36} becomes positive ($\mathbf{p}_{36}$ enters the basis in the simplex method). To determine the variable to leave the basis we find the loop involving (3, 6) and the basis cells. This loop is the dashed line shown in Table 9–2. We note that

$$z_{36} - c_{36} = c_{35} - c_{45} + c_{46} - c_{36}.$$

Only c_{35} and c_{46} have plus signs; hence only these basic cells give $y_{ij}^{\alpha\beta} = +1$. Now $x_{35} = 10$, $x_{46} = 11$. The smallest of these is $x_{35} = 10$. For the new basic solution,

$$\hat{x}_{36} = x_{35} = 10, \qquad \hat{x}_{45} = 20 + x_{35} = 30, \qquad \hat{x}_{46} = 11 - x_{35} = 1.$$

All basic variables not in the loop are unchanged in value. These results follow from (9–25).

Without worrying about the $y_{ij}^{\alpha\beta}$, we can easily see how the x_{ij} should change when a given variable is to be brought into the solution. Examination of the loop involving cell $(3, 6)$ and the basis cells shows that to satisfy origin constraint 3, x_{35} must be decreased by θ if x_{36} is increased by θ. In order to satisfy destination constraint 5, x_{45} must be increased by θ, and to satisfy origin constraint 4, x_{46} must be decreased by θ. The largest permissible value of θ is that which first drives one of the basic variables to zero. As soon as one knows the cells which are in the basic solution, the values of the basic variables can be easily determined by satisfying the constraints. No transformation formula is needed.

The new basic feasible solution is given in Table 9–3. It should be observed that it is very easy to obtain the new basic feasible solution. The bulk of the work in the stepping-stone algorithm comes in evaluating the $z_{ij} - c_{ij}$. Having found a new basic feasible solution, we must determine the new $z_{ij} - c_{ij}$. We can evaluate these by the loop method just as we did for the first tableau. These new $z_{ij} - c_{ij}$ are given in Table 9–3. On occasions, it can be a little tricky to find the required loop, especially, if a fairly large problem is being solved. (In Table 9–3, we have drawn the loop needed to evaluate $z_{25} - c_{25}$, for example.)

The remaining tableaux are presented in Tables 9–4 through 9–6. In Table 9–3, the choice of the vector to enter the basis is not uniquely determined by (9–24). Cell $(4, 3)$ was chosen arbitrarily to enter the basis. The tableaux do not contain the value of the objective function. Therefore, we must compute the minimum value of z from the last tableau. We see that

$$\min z = 2(20) + 3(10) + 1(30) + 2(20) + 2(20) + 2(39) + 1(1)$$
$$+ 2(30) + 1(11) = 330.$$

This can be compared with the cost for the initial basic feasible solution, which is

$$z = 2(30) + 1(20) + 2(30) + 2(10) + 4(10) + 2(40) + 4(10)$$
$$+ 2(20) + 2(11) = 382.$$

The reader may find it instructive to draw in the branches of the basic trees in Tables 9–2 through 9–6. Some of these have an interesting structure.

Note: To compute the $z_{ij} - c_{ij}$, for all tableaux after the first, one could use the standard transformation formula of the simplex method. For the transportation problem, this transformation formula is

$$\hat{z}_{ij} - c_{ij} = z_{ij} - c_{ij} - \frac{y_{ij}^{qr}}{y_{st}^{qr}}(z_{st} - c_{st}), \qquad (9\text{–}26)$$

TABLE 9–2 — TABLEAU 1

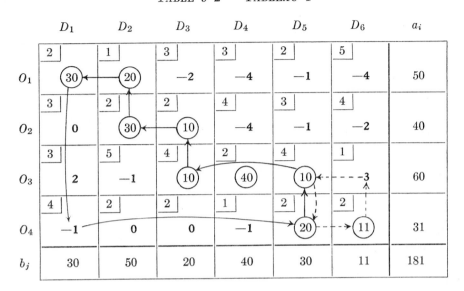

	D_1	D_2	D_3	D_4	D_5	D_6	a_i
O_1	2 | (30)	1 | (20)	3 | −2	3 | −4	2 | −1	5 | −4	50
O_2	3 | 0	2 | (30)	2 | (10)	4 | −4	3 | −1	4 | −2	40
O_3	3 | 2	5 | −1	4 | (10)	2 | (40)	4 | (10)	1 | −3	60
O_4	4 | −1	2 | 0	2 | 0	1 | −1	2 | (20)	2 | (11)	31
b_j	30	50	20	40	30	11	181

TABLE 9–3 — TABLEAU 2

	D_1	D_2	D_3	D_4	D_5	D_6	a_i
O_1	2 | (30)	1 | (20)	3 | −2	3 | −4	2 | −4	5 | −7	50
O_2	3 | 0	2 | (30)	2 | (10)	4 | −4	3 | −4	4 | −5	40
O_3	3 | 2	5 | −1	4 | (10)	2 | (40)	4 | −3	1 | (10)	60
O_4	4 | 2	2 | 3	2 | 3	1 | 2	2 | (30)	2 | (1)	31
b_j	30	50	20	40	30	11	181

TABLE 9–4 — TABLEAU 3

	D_1	D_2	D_3	D_4	D_5	D_6	a_i
O_1	2 (30)	1 (20)	3 −2	3 −4	2 −1	5 −7	50
O_2	3 0	2 (30)	2 (10)	4 −4	3 −1	4 −5	40
O_3	3 2	5 −1	4 (9)	2 (40)	4 0	1 (11)	60
O_4	4 −1	2 0	2 (1)	1 −1	2 (30)	2 −3	31
b_j	30	50	20	40	30	11	181

TABLE 9–5 — TABLEAU 4

	D_1	D_2	D_3	D_4	D_5	D_6	a_i
O_1	2 (21)	1 (29)	3 −2	3 −2	2 −1	5 −5	50
O_2	3 0	2 (21)	2 (19)	4 −2	3 −1	4 −3	40
O_3	3 (9)	5 −3	4 −2	2 (40)	4 −2	1 (11)	60
O_4	4 −1	2 0	2 (1)	1 1	2 (30)	2 −1	31
b_j	30	50	20	40	30	11	181

TABLE 9–6 — TABLEAU 5

	D_1	D_2	D_3	D_4	D_5	D_6	a_i
O_1	2 (20)	1 (30)	3 −2	3 −2	2 0	5 −5	50
O_2	3 0	2 (20)	2 (20)	4 −2	3 0	4 −3	40
O_3	3 (10)	5 −3	4 −2	2 (39)	4 −1	1 (11)	60
O_4	4 −2	2 −1	2 −1	1 (1)	2 (30)	2 −2	31
b_j	30	50	20	40	30	11	181

where $y_{st}^{qr} = +1$. The value of y_{ij}^{qr} can be 0, ± 1. This method is easier than the loop method since, at worst, we only need to add or subtract two numbers. We must, however, determine y_{ij}^{qr}. This requires that we find the loop involving (i, j) and the basis cells in the previous tableau (not in the new tableau where we enter the values of the $z_{ij} - c_{ij}$).

Let us illustrate the computation of $z_{41} - c_{41}$ for tableau 2 from the information in tableau 1. From (9–26) we see that

$$\hat{z}_{41} - c_{41} = z_{41} - c_{41} - 3y_{41}^{35} = -1 - 3y_{41}^{35},$$

since $z_{st} - c_{st} = z_{36} - c_{36} = 3$. To determine y_{41}^{35}, we go back to Table 9–2 and find the loop (plotted) connecting $(4, 1)$ and the basis elements. We see that $y_{41}^{35} = -1$, so that $\hat{z}_{41} - c_{41} = -1 + 3 = 2$; this is the value shown in Table 9–3. The transformation formula (9–26) is seldom used to find the $z_{ij} - c_{ij}$, because it is simpler to work with a single tableau than with two tableaux.

9–9 Degeneracy and the transportation tableau. A feasible solution to a transportation problem is degenerate if less than $m + n - 1$ of the x_{ij} are positive. Degeneracy may be encountered in the process of determining the initial basic feasible solution or at some subsequent iteration. From the practical point of view, degeneracy does not cause any difficulties, just as it did not cause any real difficulties in the simplex method. No transportation problem has ever been known to cycle. In the simplex method, the degeneracy problem can be eliminated by the use of a perturbation method. The same is true for the transportation problem; however, a much simpler perturbation method can be used.

Let us begin our discussion by showing how degeneracy can be handled in practice, without introducing some technique which ensures that cycling will not occur. If the method used to provide an initial solution yields a feasible solution with $h < m + n - 1$ of the $x_{ij} > 0$, we encounter degeneracy at the outset. The cells associated with the positive x_{ij} do not form a basic tree. To obtain an initial basic solution and a basic tree in the tableau, we must add $m + n - 1 - h$ additional cells at a zero level. We choose the cells to be added such that the resulting $m + n - 1$ cells form a basic tree. We enter a zero into the cells added and circle these zeros to indicate that they are part of the initial basic solution. In manual computations, it is very easy to choose cells which will yield a basic tree (there may be, of course, many different combinations). In the next section, we shall present a simple method of automatically determining the cells to be added at a zero level, which is useful when the problem is to be solved on a digital computer. Having determined a basic solution, we proceed in the usual way. In this case a variable can enter and leave the solution at a zero level.

EXAMPLE: Consider the tableau in Table 9–7. Costs are omitted since they are not relevant to the discussion. Using the northwest-corner rule to find an initial feasible solution, we obtain the results shown in Table 9–7. Here we have only 8 positive x_{ij}, although $m + n - 1 = 10$. It will be noted that the set of cells corresponding to the positive x_{ij} is not connected.

TABLE 9–7

	D_1	D_2	D_3	D_4	D_5	D_6	a_i
O_1	(20)	(5)					25
O_2		(25)	+ (0) ← x				25
O_3			−(40) → (10) +				50
O_4				(40)	(0)		40
O_5					(10)	(20)	30
b_j	20	30	40	50	10	20	170

Two more cells are needed to obtain a basic tree. Clearly, if we add cells (2, 3), (4, 5) (dashed circles), a basic tree results. The value zero is entered into these cells, and we have a basic (degenerate) feasible solution. The annexed cells were by no means the only two cells which could have been added to yield a basic tree.

If the $z_{ij} - c_{ij}$ are such that cell (2, 4) should appear in the basic tree at the next iteration, it will be observed that x_{24} will enter the basic solution at a zero level. The values of the variables in the basic solution remain unchanged. We only have to replace cell (2, 3) by cell (2, 4) to obtain a new basic tree.

Degeneracy can also appear at some later iteration if there is a tie for the variable to leave the basic solution. As in the simplex method, we can choose arbitrarily any one of the tied variables as the variable to leave the basis. At the next stage, the variables that were tied with the removed variable will be at a zero level. However, we keep these variables in the basic solution (i.e., they remain circled) and proceed as usual.

EXAMPLE: Suppose that in the problem set forth in Table 9–2, we change the availability at origin 4 to 30 and the requirement at destination 6 to 10. For this new problem, the northwest-corner rule yields the initial basic feasible solution shown in Table 9–8.

The $z_{ij} - c_{ij}$ are the same as in Table 9–2, so x_{36} enters the basic solution at the next stage. Now, however, there is a tie for the variable to be removed. Either x_{35} or x_{46} can be replaced by x_{36}. If we arbitrarily decide to replace x_{35}, the new basic solution is that shown in Table 9–9. One of the basic variables is now zero, and degeneracy has appeared. Again, the

TABLE 9–8

	D_1	D_2	D_3	D_4	D_5	D_6	a_i
O_1	(30)	(20)					50
O_2		(30)	(10)				40
O_3			(10)	(40)	(10)		60
O_4					(20)	(10)	30
b_j	30	50	20	40	30	10	180

TABLE 9–9

	D_1	D_2	D_3	D_4	D_5	D_6	a_i
O_1	(30)	(20)					50
O_2		(30)	(10)				40
O_3			(10)	(40)		(10)	60
O_4					(30)	(0)	30
b_j	30	50	20	40	30	10	180

$z_{ij} - c_{ij}$ are the same as in Table 9–3. If x_{43} is chosen to enter the basis, it enters at a zero level.

Let us now turn our attention to the study of a method which completely eliminates the possibility of degeneracy. We begin our discussion by showing that if degeneracy occurs at any stage, then at least one proper subset I of the a_i and at least one proper subset J of the b_j exist such that $\sum_{i \in I} a_i = \sum_{j \in J} b_j$, the summations being taken over the a_i, b_j in the appropriate subsets. Before presenting the proof, we wish to note that this was indeed the case in the preceding examples where degeneracy occurred. In Table 9–7, $a_1 + a_2 = b_1 + b_2 = 50$, and $a_5 = b_5 + b_6$. In addition to these subsets, there is a number of other proper subsets in Table 9–7 such that $\sum a_i = \sum b_j$. In Table 9–8, $a_1 + a_4 = b_1 + b_2 = 80$, $a_2 + a_3 = b_2 + b_4 + b_6$, etc.

Suppose then, that we have a degenerate basic feasible solution. Without loss in generality, we can assume $n \geq m$. Thus for the basic feasible solution, there will be at least one column of Table 9–1 which contains only one positive x_{ij}. Otherwise there would have to be at least $2n$ positive values of x_{ij} in the basic solution, with the result that $2n \leq m + n - 1$ or $n \leq m - 1$, which contradicts our assumption. For any such x_{ij}, we must have $x_{ij} = b_j$. Now we cross off column j, replace a_i by $a_i^{(1)} = a_i - b_j$, and consider the new tableau containing m rows and $n^{(1)} = n - 1$ columns. For this new tableau, $n^{(1)} \geq m$ or $m \geq n^{(1)}$ so that there will be at least one row or column which contains only one positive x_{ij}. Suppose x_{uv} is the only positive x_{uj} in row u. We cross off row u and replace b_v by $b_v^{(2)} = b_v - a_u$.

After k steps we are left with a tableau containing a total of $m + n - k$ rows and columns. Furthermore, the $a_i^{(k)}$, $b_j^{(k)}$, which are the origin availabilities and destination requirements for this tableau, will have the form

$$a_i^{(k)} = a_i - \Sigma b_j + \Sigma a_i, \qquad b_j^{(k)} = b_j - \Sigma a_i + \Sigma b_j, \qquad (9\text{--}27)$$

the summations being taken over some subsets of the crossed-off rows and columns. When we reach one of the basic variables for which $x_{st} = 0$, either the $a_s^{(k)}$ or $b_t^{(k)}$ will be zero (since x_{st} is the only basic variable in row s or column t). In both cases, Eq. (9–27) leads to the conclusion that $\Sigma a_i = \Sigma b_j$ for some proper subsets of a_i, b_j in the original tableau.

EXAMPLE: For the degenerate basic solution given in Table 9–7, x_{11} is the only basic variable in column 1. We cross off column 1 and replace a_1 by $a_1^{(1)} = a_1 - b_1$ in the new tableau. Now x_{12} is the only basic element in row 1. We cross off row 1 and replace b_2 by $b_2^{(2)} = b_2 - a_1^{(1)} = b_2 - a_1 + b_1$. Then x_{22} is the only basic element in column 1 of the new tableau (column 2 of Table 9–7). We cross off this column and replace a_2 by $a_2^{(3)} = a_2 - b_2^{(2)} = a_2 - b_2 + a_1 - b_1 = 0$. But $x_{23} = 0$ is the only element in this row. Since $a_2^{(3)} = 0$, everything works out properly. However, $a_2^{(3)} = 0$ implies that $a_1 + a_2 = b_1 + b_2$, as mentioned above.

This result proves that degeneracy can never appear in a transportation problem unless the sum of some proper subset of the a_i is equal to the sum of some proper subset of the b_j. Imagine now that we perturb the problem slightly, that is, the origin availabilities are $a_i' = a_i + \epsilon, i = 1, \ldots, m$, and the destination requirements are $b_j' = b_j, j = 1, \ldots, n - 1, b_n' = b_n + m\epsilon$. We note that

$$\sum_{i=1}^{m} (a_i + \epsilon) = \sum_{j=1}^{n-1} b_j + b_n + m\epsilon,$$

so that the problem still has a solution. We shall demonstrate that there exists an $\epsilon_0 > 0$ such that for all $\epsilon, 0 < \epsilon < \epsilon_0$, degeneracy will never occur.

In the original problem, there is only a finite number of partial sums of the a_i, b_j. Consider all sets of partial sums containing the a_i', b_j'. These partial sums will not satisfy $\Sigma a_i' = \Sigma b_j'$ for all ϵ since ϵ will never cancel out in such an expression. They are linear in ϵ, and in each case we can solve for the ϵ such that $\Sigma a_i' = \Sigma b_j'$. If we choose ϵ_0 to be the smallest of the resulting positive ϵ's*, then for any $\epsilon, 0 < \epsilon < \epsilon_0$, it can never be true that any partial sums satisfy $\Sigma a_i' = \Sigma b_j'$. Hence degeneracy can never appear in the perturbed problem.

When solving a transportation problem by hand, we can easily carry along the ϵ's. It is never necessary to determine ϵ_0 explicitly. There is no need to introduce the ϵ's until a tie occurs; then they can be introduced to break the tie. Naturally, when an optimal solution is found, we drop the ϵ's to obtain the solution to the original problem.

---

* Note that if no $\epsilon > 0$, ϵ_0 can be arbitrarily large.

TABLE 9–10

	D_1	D_2	D_3	D_4	D_5	D_6	a_i
O_1	(20)	($5+\epsilon$)					$25+\epsilon$
O_2		($25-\epsilon$)	(2ϵ)				$25+\epsilon$
O_3			($40-2\epsilon$)	($10+3\epsilon$)			$50+\epsilon$
O_4				($40-3\epsilon$)	(4ϵ)		$40+\epsilon$
O_5					($10-4\epsilon$)	($20+5\epsilon$)	$30+\epsilon$
b_j	20	30	40	50	10	$20+5\epsilon$	$170+5\epsilon$

EXAMPLE: If the ϵ's are introduced into Table 9–7, we obtain Table 9–10.

If $\sum a_i = \sum b_j$ for one or more partial sums, one should be careful not to infer that degeneracy will occur. In the example worked out in Tables 9–2 through 9–6, it will be noted that $a_2 + a_3 = b_2 + b_3 + b_5$, $a_2 = b_4$, etc. However, degeneracy did not appear in the solution of this example.

9–10 Determination of an initial basic feasible solution. The northwest-corner rule for determining an initial basic feasible solution to a transportation problem has already been discussed. Now we shall present some other methods which often yield a result which is much closer to an optimal solution than that obtained by the northwest-corner rule. As suggested before, it is worth while to spend some time finding a "good" initial solution because it can considerably reduce the total number of iterations required to reach an optimal solution.

Most of the methods for determining an initial basic feasible solution assign a positive value to one variable and, at the same time, satisfy either a row or column constraint at each step. We shall now prove that any procedure for determining a feasible solution which assigns a positive value to one variable and satisfies either a row or column constraint at each step will automatically yield a basic feasible solution, and in the absence of degeneracy, the resulting cells will form a basic tree. Note first of all that such a technique cannot give more than $m + n - 1$ positive variables since, after $m + n - 1$ steps, $m + n - 1$ of the constraints will be satisfied, and the remaining constraint is automatically satisfied.

All that remains is to demonstrate that a loop cannot be formed. Suppose that at step k a positive value is assigned to x_{ij}, and cell (i, j), together with some or all of the $k - 1$ cells corresponding to previously determined positive values of the variables, forms a loop. Let the loop be described by the ordered set

$$(i, j), \ (i, r), \ (s, r), \ \ldots, \ (v, u), \ (v, j), \ (i, j).$$

Since we are allowed to assign a positive value to x_{ij}, it must be true that by assigning a positive value to x_{ir} we have satisfied the column constraint r rather than the row constraint i. This means that a positive value must have been assigned to x_{sr} before it was assigned to x_{ir}, and at that step, the row constraint s had been satisfied. Proceeding in this way, we conclude that the column constraint j was satisfied by assigning a positive value to x_{vj}. However, we are now assigning a positive value to x_{ij}, which contradicts the fact that the constraint j has been satisfied. Thus no loop can be formed, and a basic solution is obtained. In the absence of degeneracy, the basic cells will be $m + n - 1$ in number and will form a basic tree. When degeneracy occurs, one or more additional cells must be included at a zero level to yield a basic tree.

When degeneracy occurs, an automatic procedure for adding cells at a zero level in order to obtain a basic tree follows immediately if the initial solution is found by assigning at each step a value to one variable such that either a row or column constraint is satisfied. For example, suppose that at step k, a row and a column constraint are satisfied simultaneously. This means that degeneracy has appeared. At this point, imagine that either the row or the column constraint satisfied at step k is perturbed by increasing its requirement by ϵ. Then continue the process of finding the initial solution. The above proof shows that the resulting solution will be basic, and when the ϵ's are set to zero, a degenerate basic solution is found. It is really unnecessary to introduce the ϵ's explicitly. The important thing is that both a row and a column are never dropped simultaneously.* This observation is valuable when the technique is to be used with digital computers, since it eliminates the necessity of introducing numerical values for the ϵ's.

We shall now present four methods for obtaining an initial basic feasible solution. All make some use of the costs. In the following, whenever we say, at any one step, "cross off" a row or column, we mean that no cells from that row or column can be chosen for basis cells at a later step in the determination of an initial basic feasible solution.

---

* Interestingly enough, an entire paper [4] has been devoted to explaining this simple procedure for adding cells at a zero level in order to obtain an initial degenerate basic feasible solution.

TABLE 9–11

	D_1	D_2	D_3	D_4	D_5	D_6	a_i
O_1	2 ⟨30⟩	1 ⟨20⟩	3	3	2	5	50
O_2	3	2 ⟨30⟩	2 ⟨10⟩	4	3	4	40
O_3	3	5	4	2 ⟨19⟩	4 ⟨30⟩	1 ⟨11⟩	60
O_4	4	2	2 ⟨10⟩	1 ⟨21⟩	2	2	31
b_j	30	50	20	40	30	11	181

(1) *Column minima:* Beginning with column 1 of the tableau, choose the minimum cost in this column. Suppose that it occurs in row r. Then set $x_{r1} = \min (a_r, b_1)$. If $x_{r1} = b_1$, cross off column 1 and move to column 2. If $x_{r1} = a_r$, cross off row r from the tableau, and choose the next lowest cost in column 1. Assume that it occurs in row s. Set $x_{s1} = \min (a_s, b_1 - a_r)$. Continue in this way until the requirement at the first destination is satisfied. If the minimum cost is not unique, select any one of the minima. When the requirement of column 1 is satisfied, cross off column 1 and repeat the above procedure for column 2. Continue until the requirement of column n is satisfied.

In the event that a row constraint and a column constraint, say column k, are satisfied simultaneously, cross off only the row. Then move to the cell in column k having the next lowest cost. Assign a value of zero to this cell and assume it to be in the basic solution. Now cross off column k and move to column $k + 1$. This will yield a degenerate basic feasible solution.

If this procedure is used to obtain an initial basic solution for the example solved in Tables 9–2 through 9–6, we obtain Table 9–11 for the first tableau provided that in columns 2, 3 the row with the lowest index is chosen when the minimum cost is not unique.

(2) *Row minima:* Beginning with row 1, we choose the minimum cost in this row. Suppose that it occurs in column r. Set $x_{1r} = \min (a_1, b_r)$. If $x_{1r} = a_1$, cross off row 1 and move to row 2. If $x_{1r} = b_r$, cross off column r and determine the next lowest cost in row 1. Assume it occurs in column s.

TABLE 9–12

	D_1	D_2	D_3	D_4	D_5	D_6	a_i
O_1	2 (0)	1 (50)	3	3	2	5	50
O_2	3 (20)	2	2 (20)	4	3	4	40
O_3	3 (9)	5	4	2 (40)	4	1 (11)	60
O_4	4 (1)	2	2	1	2 (30)	2	31
b_j	30	50	20	40	30	11	181

Set $x_{1s} = \min\,(a_1 - b_r, b_s)$. Continue in this way until the first row constraint is satisfied. When the requirement of the first row is satisfied, cross off row 1 and repeat the above procedure for row 2. Continue until the row constraint m is satisfied. Whenever a minimum cost is not unique, make an arbitrary choice among the minima.

In the event that a row constraint, say row k, and a column constraint are satisfied simultaneously, cross off only the column. Then find the next lowest cost in row k, and insert this cell into the solution at a zero level. Then cross off row k, and move on to row $k + 1$.

If this technique is used to obtain a first solution for the problem of Table 9–11, Table 9–12 results. Note that degeneracy appears. According to our rule, either cell $(1, 1)$ or $(1, 5)$ could have been added at a zero level. We chose $(1, 1)$.

(3) *Matrix minima:* Determine the smallest cost in the entire tableau. Suppose this occurs for cell (i, j). Set $x_{ij} = \min\,(a_i, b_j)$. Then cross off either row i or column j, depending on which requirement is satisfied. If $x_{ij} = a_i$, decrease b_j by a_i, and if $x_{ij} = b_j$, decrease a_i by b_j. Repeat the process for the resulting tableau. Whenever the minimum cost is not unique, make an arbitrary choice among the minima. As usual, if a row and a column constraint are satisfied simultaneously, cross off only the row or the column, not both.

This method yields the initial solution (shown in Table 9–13) for the example under consideration if, in the absence of a unique minimum, we choose the cell for which $i + j$ is smallest. Here again degeneracy appears.

TABLE 9–13

	D_1	D_2	D_3	D_4	D_5	D_6	a_i
O_1	2 (0)	1 (50)	3	3	2	5	50
O_2	3 (20)	2	2 (20)	4	3	4	40
O_3	3 (10)	5	4	2 (9)	4 (30)	1 (11)	60
O_4	4	2	2	1 (31)	2	2	31
b_j	30	50	20	40	30	11	181

(4) *Vogel's method:* This technique has been suggested by Vogel [9]. For each row, find the lowest cost c_{ij} and the next lowest cost c_{it} in that row. Compute $c_{it} - c_{ij}$. In this way, m numbers are obtained. Proceed in precisely the same way for each of the columns and obtain n more numbers. Choose the largest of these $m + n$ differences. Suppose that the largest of these numbers was associated with the difference in column j. Furthermore, let cell (i, j) contain the lowest cost in column j. Then set $x_{ij} = \min(a_i, b_j)$. Cross off either row i or column j, depending on which requirement is satisfied, and repeat the whole process for the resulting tableau. As usual, when the maximum difference is not unique, an arbitrary choice can be made, and if a row and a column constraint are satisfied simultaneously, cross off only the row or the column, not both.

For our example, this method yields the solution shown in Table 9–14. It is convenient to list the row differences in a column to the right of the tableau and the column differences in a row at the bottom of the tableau. The differences shown in the difference row and column are those for the first step, i.e., those which are to be used in selecting the first basis cell. Here we have the worst possible case; every difference has the same value. The tie is resolved by choosing the cell with the smallest value of $i + j$. At each step, a new set of differences must be computed.

Many other techniques for determining an initial solution might have been discussed. However, those presented above are most commonly used for hand computations and for digital computers. It is by no means established that any one of the methods is better than the others. In fact,

TABLE 9–14

	D_1	D_2	D_3	D_4	D_5	D_6	a_i	
O_1	2 ⟨30⟩	1 ⟨20⟩	3	3	2	5	50	1
O_2	3	2 ⟨30⟩	2 ⟨10⟩	4	3	4	40	1
O_3	3	5	4	2 ⟨40⟩	4 ⟨9⟩	1 ⟨11⟩	60	1
O_4	4	2	2 ⟨10⟩	1	2 ⟨21⟩	2	31	1
b_j	30	50	20	40	30	11	181	
	1	1	1	1	1	1		

for our particular example, it is not even certain that these methods are more efficient than the northwest-corner rule. However, the northwest-corner rule looked as good as it did only because we arranged the data so that the lowest prices were near the main diagonal. To decide which method for determining on initial basic feasible solution leads to the smallest number of iterations for our example, it would be necessary to solve the problem in each case. This task is left to the problems.

9–11 Alternative procedure for computing $z_{ij} - c_{ij}$; duality. In his original work on the transportation problem, Dantzig [8] presented a method for evaluating the $z_{ij} - c_{ij}$ which is simpler than the stepping-stone technique. Let $c_{ir}^B, c_{qr}^B, c_{qt}^B, \ldots, c_{ws}^B, c_{wj}^B$ be the $m + n - 1$ prices corresponding to the variables in any basic feasible solution to a transportation problem with m origins and n destinations. Now suppose that we write

$$
\begin{aligned}
u_i + v_r &= c_{ir}^B, \\
u_q + v_r &= c_{qr}^B, \\
u_q + v_t &= c_{qt}^B, \\
&\;\vdots \\
u_w + v_s &= c_{ws}^B, \\
u_w + v_j &= c_{wj}^B.
\end{aligned}
\tag{9–28}
$$

Consider (9–28) to be a set of $m + n - 1$ simultaneous linear equations in the $m + n$ variables u_α, v_β. If we write (9–28) in matrix form, numbering the variables so that the u_α starting with the lowest subscript come first and are followed by the v_β arranged in the same order, it will be observed that the rows of the matrix of the coefficients are simply the vectors $\mathbf{p}_{\alpha\beta}^B$ in the basic solution. Thus the rank of the matrix of the coefficients is $m + n - 1$. We can assign an arbitrary value to one of the u_α, v_β and solve uniquely for the remaining $m + n - 1$ variables. These equations are extremely easy to solve since they can be solved sequentially. If, for example, we set $u_i = 0$, then $v_r = c_{ir}^B$, $u_q = c_{qr}^B - c_{ir}^B$, etc. Note that, in solving the above set of equations, we obtain m, u_α and n, v_β so that there is a u_α corresponding to each row and a v_β corresponding to each column of the tableau.

The introduction of the u_α, v_β has an interesting result: For any cell (i, j),

$$z_{ij} - c_{ij} = u_i + v_j - c_{ij}, \qquad (9\text{–}29)$$

and the savings in computational effort become apparent. As soon as the u_α, v_β are determined, all the $z_{ij} - c_{ij}$ can be found by adding two numbers and subtracting a third. The proof is trivial. We can write

$$z_{ij} - c_{ij} = c_{ir}^B - c_{qr}^B + \cdots - c_{ws}^B + c_{wj}^B - c_{ij};$$

but by (9–28),

$$z_{ij} - c_{ij} = u_i + v_r - u_q - v_r + \cdots - u_w - v_s + u_w + v_j - c_{ij}$$
$$= u_i + v_j - c_{ij}. \qquad (9\text{–}30)$$

For hand computations, it is convenient to augment the tableau by an additional column which gives the u_α and an additional row which gives the v_β. Then the $z_{ij} - c_{ij}$ are determined as follows: We move in row i to the u-column to find u_i, and in column j to the v-row to find v_j; the value of $z_{ij} - c_{ij}$ is given by (9–29).

EXAMPLE: Let us use the u_i, v_j to compute the $z_{ij} - c_{ij}$ in Table 9–6. The prices in the basis are c_{11}, c_{31}, c_{12}, c_{22}, c_{23}, c_{34}, c_{44}, c_{45}, c_{36}. The set of simultaneous equations to be solved is

$$u_1 + v_1 = c_{11} = 2, \qquad u_1 + v_2 = c_{12} = 1, \qquad u_2 + v_2 = c_{22} = 2,$$

$$u_2 + v_3 = c_{23} = 2, \qquad u_3 + v_1 = c_{31} = 3, \qquad u_3 + v_4 = c_{34} = 2,$$

$$u_3 + v_6 = c_{36} = 1, \qquad u_4 + v_4 = c_{44} = 1, \qquad u_4 + v_5 = c_{45} = 2.$$

Setting $u_1 = 0$, we find $v_1 = 2, v_2 = 1, u_2 = 1, v_3 = 1, u_3 = 1, v_4 = 1$

TABLE 9–15

	D_1	D_2	D_3	D_4	D_5	D_6	a_i	u_i
O_1	2 (20)	1 (30)	3 −2	3 −2	2 0	5 −5	50	0
O_2	3 0	2 (20)	2 (20)	4 −2	3 0	4 −3	40	1
O_3	3 (10)	5 −3	4 −2	2 (39)	4 −1	1 (11)	60	1
O_4	4 −2	2 −1	2 −1	1 (1)	2 (30)	2 −2	31	0
b_j	30	50	20	40	30	11	181	
v_j	2	1	1	1	2	0		

$u_4 = 0$, $v_5 = 2$, $v_6 = 0$. We can then construct the tableau given in Table 9–15. For example: To compute $z_{41} - c_{41}$, we note that $u_4 = 0$, $v_1 = 2$, $c_{41} = 4$, and hence $z_{41} - c_{41} = 0 + 2 - 4 = -2$. The $(z_{ij} - c_{ij})$-values in Table 9–15 check with those obtained in Table 9–6.

After using the uv-method (as we shall call the present technique*) on several tableaux, the reader will be convinced that it involves much less work than the stepping-stone technique, especially for large tableaux. Furthermore, the chances of making a numerical mistake are considerably reduced. Almost all digital computer codes for solving transportation problems use the uv-method to evaluate the $z_{ij} - c_{ij}$ rather than the stepping-stone technique.

The u_i, v_j introduced above are, of course, nothing but the variables for the dual of the transportation problem. Taking the dual of (9–2), (9–3), and (9–4), we can write

$$u_i + v_j \leq c_{ij}, \qquad i = 1, \ldots, m, \qquad j = 1, \ldots, n,$$

$$\max Z = \sum_{i=1}^{m} a_i u_i + \sum_{j=1}^{n} b_j v_j,$$

---

* This method is sometimes also referred to as the MODI method.

where the u_i, v_j are unrestricted in sign. The dual problem has mn constraints and $m + n$ variables.

The values of the dual variables obtained from (9–28) do not satisfy the dual constraints unless the solution to the primal is optimal. Note that if $x_{ij} > 0$, then $u_i + v_j = c_{ij}$, so that the complementary slackness condition is always satisfied. The dual variables are not uniquely determined from these $m + n - 1$ equations (9–28) because one of the $m + n$ constraints of the primal is redundant, and we have a dual variable which corresponds to this redundant constraint.

9–12 Inequalities in the constraints of a transportation problem. Let us return to the formulation of the transportation problem given in Chapter 1. It had the form

$$\sum_{j=1}^{n-1} x_{ij} \leq a_i, \qquad i = 1, \ldots, m,$$

$$\sum_{i=1}^{m} x_{ij} = b_j, \qquad j = 1, \ldots, n - 1, \qquad (9\text{–}31)$$

$$x_{ij} \geq 0, \qquad \text{all } i, j,$$

$$\min z = \sum_{i,j} c_{ij} x_{ij}.$$

For a reason that will soon become clear, we here use $n - 1$ rather than n. The first m constraints now contain a $\leq$ sign rather than an equality sign. Physically, this simply means that more units may be available at the origins than are required at the destinations.

The inequalities can be converted to equalities by the addition of m slack variables. These slack variables will be written x_{in}, $i = 1, \ldots, m$. Then the constraints become

$$\sum_{j=1}^{n-1} x_{ij} + x_{in} = a_i, \qquad i = 1, \ldots, m, \qquad (9\text{–}32)$$

$$\sum_{i=1}^{m} x_{ij} = b_j, \qquad j = 1, \ldots, n - 1. \qquad (9\text{–}33)$$

Sum (9–32) over i and subtract from the result the sum of (9–33) over j. This gives

$$\sum_{i=1}^{m} x_{in} = \sum_{i=1}^{m} a_i - \sum_{j=1}^{n-1} b_j = b_n. \qquad (9\text{–}34)$$

Here we have the interesting and intuitively obvious result that the total slack, i.e. the sum of the slack variables, remains constant and is the difference, denoted by b_n, between the origin availabilities and the destination requirements. Note that if we annex (9–34) to (9–33), we have reduced the problem expressed by (9–31) to the problem formulated in Eqs. (9–2) through (9–4); i.e., to the problem considered above. To construct the tableau, we simply add one more column, i.e., an additional destination for the slack. Intuitively, this approach is to be expected since the units not shipped can be considered to be shipped to ourselves at no cost. As usual, the cost c_{in} associated with the slack variable x_{in} is zero.

Instead of Eq. (9–31) we shall now consider the following meaningful problem:

$$\sum_{j=1}^{n} x_{ij} = a_i, \qquad i = 1, \ldots, m-1,$$

$$\sum_{i=1}^{m-1} x_{ij} \geq b_j, \qquad j = 1, \ldots, n,$$

$$x_{ij} \geq 0, \qquad \text{all } i, j,$$

$$\max z = \sum_{i,j} c_{ij} x_{ij}.$$

(9–35)

Introduce the surplus variables $x_{mj}, j = 1, \ldots, n$ and note that

$$-\sum_{j=1}^{n} x_{mj} = \sum_{j=1}^{n} b_j - \sum_{i=1}^{m-1} a_i = a_m \leq 0. \qquad (9\text{–}36)$$

The constraints of (9–35) can therefore be converted into the set of equations

$$\sum_{j=1}^{n} x_{ij} = a_i, \qquad i = 1, \ldots, m-1,$$

$$-\sum_{j=1}^{n} x_{mj} = a_m,$$

$$\sum_{i=1}^{m-1} x_{ij} - x_{mj} = b_j, \qquad j = 1, \ldots, n.$$

(9–37)

Here, a new difficulty arises because the coefficients of the surplus variables are -1 instead of 1. Again, it is easy to show that all minors of the matrix of the coefficients have the value ± 1, 0. The computational method is precisely the same as before except that we use $z_{mj} = -u_m - v_j$ for computing $z_{mj} - c_{mj}$. This follows immediately from the dual. To solve this problem, we add one more row to the tableau, i.e., an additional origin containing the negative of the total surplus. A detailed discussion of the above example is left for Problem 9–27.

We wish to note that, provided all costs are positive, then in the optimal solution to a problem of the form

$$\sum_{j=1}^{n} x_{ij} \leq a_i, \qquad i = 1, \ldots, m,$$

$$\sum_{i=1}^{m} x_{ij} \geq b_j, \qquad j = 1, \ldots, n,$$

$$x_{ij} \geq 0, \qquad \text{all } i, j,$$

$$\text{max or min } z = \sum_{i,j} c_{ij} x_{ij},$$

$$(9\text{--}38)$$

strict equalities will hold (a) in the destination constraints if z is to be minimized and (b) in the origin constraints if z is to be maximized. Physically, this means that if we are minimizing the cost, no more will be shipped than necessary, and if we are maximizing z, as much will be shipped as possible. It is easy to prove these facts rigorously; the details are left for Problems 9–24 and 9–25.

Finally, we might note that once a transportation problem has been cast into the form (9–2) through (9–4), we can replace each c_{ij} by $c_{ij} + \lambda$ for any constant λ without changing the x_{ij} which yield an optimal solution. This can be done because the substitution of $c_{ij} + \lambda$ for each c_{ij} changes the value of the objective function merely by the constant $\lambda \sum_{i=1}^{m} a_i$.

9–13 Generalized transportation problems. Consider a linear programming problem of the following form: We wish to find $x_{ij} \geq 0$, $x_{si} \geq 0$, which satisfy the constraints

$$\sum_{j=1}^{n} d_{ij} x_{ij} \pm x_{si} = a_i, \qquad a_i > 0, \qquad i = 1, \ldots, m, \qquad (9\text{--}39)$$

$$\sum_{i=1}^{m} x_{ij} = b_j, \qquad b_j > 0, \qquad j = 1, \ldots, n, \qquad (9\text{--}40)$$

and which maximize or minimize the linear form

$$z = \sum_{i,j} c_{ij} x_{ij}. \qquad (9\text{--}41)$$

The x_{si} can be considered to be slack or surplus variables. This linear programming problem differs from the transportation problem in that the coefficients of the x_{ij} in (9–39) are the arbitrary numbers d_{ij} rather than unity. Problems of this type arise in practice in a variety of applications. One particular example (to be considered in Chapter 12) is that of machine assignments.

Clearly, the simplex method can be used to solve linear programming problems of the form (9–39) through (9–41). However, the structure of these problems is so similar to that of the transportation problem that we should be able to devise an algorithm for their solution which requires less work than the simplex method. This can be done, and it will be shown how the uv-algorithm for the transportation problem can be modified to solve such problems. We shall call (9–39) through (9–41) a generalized transportation problem. The constraints (9–39) arise frequently because of limitations of the various available resources. Hence we shall call them resource constraints. The constraints (9–40) often specify the requirements, and therefore we shall refer to them as requirement constraints.

There are several important differences between transportation problems and generalized transportation problems. First of all, the rank of the matrix of the coefficients of the x_{ij} in (9–39) and (9–40) is, in general, $m + n$ rather than $m + n - 1$, i.e., all constraints are independent. In the discussions which follow, we shall assume that the coefficient matrix has rank $m + n$. Furthermore, the $y_{ij}^{\alpha\beta}$ for the generalized transportation problem can take on values different from $\pm 1, 0$. This in turn means that division cannot be eliminated in the generalized transportation problem. Consequently, the integrability property of optimal basic solutions which held for transportation problems does not hold for generalized transportation problems. An optimal basic solution may involve nonintegral values of the x_{ij}, even though the a_i, b_j are integers.

If we arrange the variables and constraints for the generalized transportation problem as in (9–5) and (9–6), the activity vector $\mathbf{p}_{ij}$ corresponding to x_{ij} is

$$\mathbf{p}_{ij} = d_{ij}\mathbf{e}_i + \mathbf{e}_{m+j}, \qquad (9\text{–}42)$$

and the activity vector corresponding to x_{si} is $\pm\mathbf{e}_i$.

Denoting by $\mathbf{p}_{\alpha\beta}^B$ the $m + n$ activity vectors in any given basic solution, we can write any $\mathbf{p}_{ij}$ as

$$\mathbf{p}_{ij} = \sum_{\alpha\beta} y_{ij}^{\alpha\beta}\mathbf{p}_{\alpha\beta}^B, \qquad (9\text{–}43)$$

and if $\mathbf{B}$ is the basis matrix containing the $\mathbf{p}_{\alpha\beta}^B$, then $\mathbf{p}_{ij} = \mathbf{B}\mathbf{y}_{ij}$. When

z in (9–41) is to be minimized, the dual of (9–39) through (9–41) is

$$d_{ij}u_i + v_j \leq c_{ij}, \quad i = 1, \ldots, m, \quad j = 1, \ldots, n, \quad (9\text{–}44)$$

$$\pm u_i \leq 0, \quad i = 1, \ldots, m, \quad (9\text{–}45)$$

$$\max Z = \sum_{i=1}^{m} a_i u_i + \sum_{j=1}^{n} b_j v_j. \quad (9\text{–}46)$$

The constraints (9–45) come from the slack or surplus variables; a plus sign holds for slack variables and a minus sign for surplus variables.

For any basic feasible solution to the primal, denote by $c_{\alpha\beta}^B$ the prices in the primal basis. Then consider the m, u_α and n, v_β which are the solutions to the set of $m + n$ equations

$$\left. \begin{array}{c} d_{\alpha\beta}u_\alpha + v_\beta = c_{\alpha\beta}^B, \\ u_\alpha = 0 \end{array} \right\} \ m + n \text{ equations.} \quad (9\text{–}47)$$

An equation of the form $u_\alpha = 0$ appears if the slack or surplus variable $x_{s\alpha}$ is in the primal basis. When the u_α, v_β are arranged in the proper order into a row vector $(\mathbf{u}, \mathbf{v}) = (u_1, \ldots, u_m, v_1, \ldots, v_n)$, then $(\mathbf{u}, \mathbf{v}) = \mathbf{c}_B \mathbf{B}^{-1}$. Hence, once the u_α, v_β are known, we can immediately compute the $z_{ij} - c_{ij}$ for the corresponding basic solution to the primal from

$$z_{ij} - c_{ij} = \mathbf{c}_B \mathbf{B}^{-1} \mathbf{p}_{ij} - c_{ij} = (\mathbf{u}, \mathbf{v})\mathbf{p}_{ij} - c_{ij} = d_{ij}u_i + v_j - c_{ij}, \quad \text{all } i, j,$$

and $\hspace{9cm} (9\text{–}48)$

$$z_{si} - c_{si} = (\mathbf{u}, \mathbf{v})(\pm \mathbf{e}_i) = u_i \text{ (slack variable)}, \quad -u_i \text{ (surplus variable)}.$$

9–14 Solving the generalized transportation problem. We are now in a position to solve the generalized transportation problem. The tableau is the same as that used in solving the transportation problem (see Table 9–16). Now, however, we must include d_{ij} as well as c_{ij} in each cell (i, j). We denote row i by R_i and column j by P_j. It will be noted that a_i is obtained for R_i if we multiply x_{ij} by d_{ij} and sum across the row. When we sum the x_{ij} in P_j, then b_j is obtained. In this tableau, however, the sum of the variables in the slack or surplus column has no meaning. For a generalized transportation problem, the total slack or surplus does not need to remain constant. Furthermore, it need not be true that $\sum a_i = \sum b_j$. The slack or surplus variables enter only when we sum across rows in the way indicated above.

An initial basic feasible solution for the above problem can be obtained in almost the same way as for transportation problems. Any unique feasible solution involving exactly $m + n$ positive x_{ij} will be a basic feasible solution (see Chapter 2). All the methods suggested in Section

TABLE 9–16

	P_1		P_2			P_m		Slack or Surplus a_i		u_i
R_1	c_{11} d_{11}	x_{11}	c_{12} d_{12}	x_{12}	$\ldots$	c_{1n} d_{1n}	x_{1n}	0 1	x_{s1}	a_1	u_1
R_2	c_{21} d_{21}	x_{21}	c_{22} d_{22}	x_{22}	$\ldots$	c_{2n} d_{2n}	x_{2n}	0 1	x_{s2}	a_2	u_2
$\vdots$					$\ldots$					$\vdots$
R_m	c_{m1} d_{m1}	x_{m1}	c_{m2} d_{m2}	x_{m2}	$\ldots$	c_{mn} d_{mn}	x_{mn}	0 1	x_{sm}	a_m	u_m
b_j	b_1		b_2		$\ldots$	b_n				
v_j	v_1		v_2		$\ldots$	v_n				

9–10 can be used to obtain a basic feasible solution. There is only one difference: When considering the resource constraints, we must remember that $d_{ij}x_{ij}$ rather than x_{ij} is the amount used of resource i. Of course, we can always obtain a basic feasible solution (if there is one) by adding artificial variables. Problem 9–35 asks the reader to show how this can be done within the framework of the tableau format of Table 9–16. For the generalized transportation problem, it need not be true that the cells (in Table 9–16) corresponding to a basic solution form a tree. It is quite possible that a loop exists in the set of basic cells. Loops no longer imply that the vectors in the loop are linearly dependent (why?). Furthermore, it is not necessarily true that the cells for a basic solution yield a connected graph.

After a basic feasible solution is obtained, the $z_{ij} - c_{ij}$ must be computed to determine whether this solution is optimal. First we compute the u_α, v_β by solving the set of equations (9–47); then we use (9–48) to find the $z_{ij} - c_{ij}$. The equations (9–47) are fairly easy to solve, and they can often be solved sequentially just as they can for transportation problems. For generalized transportation problems, the u_α, v_β are uniquely determined by (9–47). It is not possible to assign an arbitrary value to one or more of these variables.

When z is to be minimized and the basic solution is not optimal, the vector $\mathbf{p}_{st}$ to enter the basis is computed, as usual, from $z_{st} - c_{st} = \max\,(z_{ij} - c_{ij})$, $z_{ij} - c_{ij} > 0$. To determine the vector to leave the basis, the $y_{st}^{\alpha\beta}$ must be found. Frequently, this can be done very easily by solving directly the set of equations (9–43) which, just as the set of equations for the u_α, v_β, can often be solved sequentially. It is also possible to compute the y_{st}^α by finding a loop in the tableau connecting cell (s, t) and the basic cells. However, the technique here is not so simple as in the case of transportation problems because vectors outside the loop may be needed, and because one can get off to wrong starts in going around the loop. These difficulties will be illustrated in the example of the next section.

The criterion used in the simplex method determines the vector $\mathbf{p}_{qr}$ to leave the basis, i.e.,

$$\frac{x_{qr}^B}{y_{st}^{qr}} = \theta = \min\left\{\frac{x_{\alpha\beta}^B}{y_{st}^{\alpha\beta}}\right\}, \qquad y_{st}^{\alpha\beta} > 0. \tag{9–49}$$

The new basic feasible solution is most easily found by setting $x_{st} = \theta$, $x_{qr} = 0$ and making the appropriate adjustments in the tableau to obtain a new solution. This is also illustrated in the example. Of course, the new basic variables can be computed from the standard transformation formulas

$$\hat{x}_{\alpha\beta}^B = x_{\alpha\beta}^B - \theta y_{st}^{\alpha\beta},$$
$$\hat{x}_{st} = \theta. \tag{9–50}$$

The technique discussed in this section can also be used to solve somewhat more general problems in which (9–40) is replaced by

$$\sum_{i=1}^m f_{ij}x_{ij} \pm x_{sj} = b_j, \qquad j = 1, \ldots, n. \tag{9–51}$$

A variety of the algorithm described here has been programmed for the IBM 709 digital computer by K. Eisemann. Hence, generalized transportation problems can be solved efficiently on this computer, and it is not necessary to use the relatively inefficient simplex method for problems which are too large to be worked out by hand. The generalized transportation problem has been discussed by Charnes and Cooper [2], and Ferguson and Dantzig [5].

9–15 Generalized transportation problem; an example. An example should help a great deal to clarify the method (discussed in Section 9–4) for solving generalized transportation problems. Consider the problem given in Table 9–17; assume that we wish to minimize the cost $z = \sum c_{ij} x_{ij}$.

There are three resources and four requirements (products), and therefore a nondegenerate basic feasible solution should have exactly seven positive x_{ij}. To determine the initial basic feasible solution, we shall use the column-minima method. The lowest cost in column 1 is $c_{11} = 0.25$, and hence we set

$$x_{11} = \min \left(b_1, \frac{a_1}{d_{11}} \right) = \min \left(200, \frac{200}{0.35} \right) = 200.$$

The first requirement has been satisfied, and we move to column 2. The lowest cost is $c_{32} = 0.20$; we set

$$x_{32} = \min \left(b_2, \frac{a_3}{d_{32}} \right) = \min \left(400, \frac{400}{0.40} \right) = 400,$$

and the second requirement is satisfied. In column 3, c_{23} is the lowest cost; we set $x_{23} = 500$ and satisfy the third requirement.

Column 4 presents more of a problem. The lowest cost is $c_{24} = 0.40$. However, we cannot set $x_{24} = 1000$ because there are not enough units of resource 2 to do this. We have used $0.30(500) = 150$ units of resource 2 in satisfying the requirement of column 3. This then leaves 350 units of resource 2. If we devote these 350 units to requirement 4, we have $x_{24} = 350/0.40 = 875$. Now all units of resource 2 have been used. However, we have not satisfied requirement 4. The next lowest cost in column 4 is $c_{14} = 0.50$. We have used $0.35(200) = 70$ units of resource 1 in satisfying the first requirement and thus have 130 units left. To satisfy requirement 4, we must set $x_{14} = 125$ so that $x_{14} + x_{24} = 1000$. This uses $0.50(125) = 62.5$ units of resource 1. All the requirements have been satisfied. However, $200 - 70 - 62.5 = 67.5$ units of resource 1 and $400 - 0.40(400) = 240$ units of resource 3 have not been used. Thus we have a solution with slack in resources 1 and 3. The values of the slack are entered in the table. We have found a unique feasible solution with exactly seven positive x_{ij}. Hence we have a nondegenerate basic feasible solution. The positive x_{ij} are the circled values in Table 9–17.

To determine whether the above solution is optimal, we must compute the $z_{ij} - c_{ij}$. This is done by solving the set of equations (9–47). For our case these equations are:

$$0.35u_1 + v_1 = 0.25, \quad 0.40u_3 + v_2 = 0.20, \quad 0.30u_2 + v_3 = 0.30,$$

$$0.40u_2 + v_4 = 0.40, \quad 0.50u_1 + v_4 = 0.50, \quad u_1 = u_3 = 0.$$

We immediately find $v_1 = 0.25$, $v_2 = 0.20$, $v_4 = 0.50$, $u_2 = -0.25$, $v_3 = 0.375$. The $z_{ij} - c_{ij} = d_{ij} u_i + v_j - c_{ij}$ can then be computed. They are listed in boldface type in Table 9–17.

TABLE 9–17

	P_1	P_2	P_3	P_4	Slack	a_i	u_i
R_1	0.25 / 0.35 — (200)	0.30 / 0.50 — −0.10	0.35 / 0.35 — +0.025	0.50 / 0.50 — (125)	0 / 1 — (67.5)	200	0
R_2	0.70 / 0.90 — −0.675	0.62 / 0.84 — −0.63	0.30 / 0.30 — (500)	0.40 / 0.40 — (875)	0 / 1 — −0.25	500	−0.25
R_3	0.40 / 0.80 — −0.15	0.20 / 0.40 — (400)	0.60 / 0.74 — −0.225	0.70 / 0.90 — −0.20	0 / 1 — (240)	400	0
b_j	200	400	500	1000			
v_j	0.25	0.20	0.375	0.50			

There is one positive $z_{ij} - c_{ij}$, namely $z_{13} - c_{13}$. Thus $\mathbf{p}_{13}$ should enter the basis. In order to determine the vector to leave the basis, the $y_{13}^{\alpha\beta}$ must be found. This is done by solving the system of equations (9–43). For this particular case, they become

$$0.35y_{13}^{11} + 0.50y_{13}^{14} + y_{13}^{s1} = 0.35, \qquad 0.30y_{13}^{23} + 0.40y_{13}^{24} = 0,$$

$$0.40y_{13}^{32} + y_{13}^{s3} = 0, \qquad y_{13}^{11} = 0, \qquad y_{13}^{32} = 0,$$

$$y_{13}^{23} = 1, \qquad y_{13}^{14} + y_{13}^{24} = 0.$$

Note that it is very easy to write down these equations. There is an equation for each row and each column (except the slack column). For example, to obtain the first equation above, we turn to the first row of Table 9–17. There are three cells of this row in the basic solution: (1, 1), (1, 4), (1, 5). Thus the left-hand side of the equation is $d_{11}y_{13}^{11} + d_{14}y_{13}^{14} + y_{13}^{s1}$; the right-hand side is d_{13} since the first component of $\mathbf{p}_{13}$ is d_{13}. The solution to these equations can be written down at once; it is

$$y_{13}^{11} = 0, \qquad y_{13}^{32} = 0,$$

$$y_{13}^{23} = 1, \qquad y_{13}^{s3} = 0,$$

$$y_{13}^{24} = -0.75, \qquad y_{13}^{14} = 0.75,$$

$$y_{13}^{s1} = -0.025.$$

Consider what happens if we attempt to evaluate the $y_{13}^{\alpha\beta}$ by means of the loop technique used for transportation problems. There is a unique loop connecting $\mathbf{p}_{13}$, $\mathbf{p}_{14}$, $\mathbf{p}_{24}$, $\mathbf{p}_{23}$. Thus we might attempt to write

$$\mathbf{p}_{13} = 0.35\mathbf{e}_1 + \mathbf{e}_6 = \frac{0.35}{0.50}(0.50\mathbf{e}_1 + \mathbf{e}_7)$$

$$- \frac{0.35}{0.50}(0.40\mathbf{e}_2 + \mathbf{e}_7) + \frac{0.35(0.40)}{0.50(0.30)}(0.30\mathbf{e}_2 + \mathbf{e}_6).$$

However, this does not work out, since on the left we have $\mathbf{e}_6$ and on the right $[0.35(0.40)/0.50(0.30)]\mathbf{e}_6$. Furthermore, there is no other vector in the basis which contains $\mathbf{e}_6$. Suppose that we traverse the loop in the other direction. Then we can write (note that now $\mathbf{e}_6$ is in $\mathbf{p}_{23}$)

$$\mathbf{p}_{13} = 0.35\mathbf{e}_1 + \mathbf{e}_6 = (0.30\mathbf{e}_2 + \mathbf{e}_6) - \frac{0.30}{0.40}(0.40\mathbf{e}_2 + \mathbf{e}_7)$$

$$+ \frac{0.30}{0.40}(0.50\mathbf{e}_1 + \mathbf{e}_7) - 0.025\mathbf{e}_1.$$

Here we have expressed $\mathbf{p}_{13}$ in terms of the basis vectors, and the $y_{13}^{\alpha\beta}$ are the same as above. However, to do this, we had to use the slack vector $\mathbf{e}_1$, which was not in the loop.

Only y_{13}^{23}, y_{13}^{14} are positive. The variable to leave is then found from

$$\frac{x_{qr}^B}{y_{13}^{qr}} = \theta = \min\left(\frac{x_{23}^B}{y_{13}^{23}} = \frac{500}{1}, \frac{x_{14}^B}{y_{13}^{14}} = \frac{125}{0.75}\right)$$

$$= 166.7 = \frac{x_{14}^B}{y_{13}^{14}}.$$

Thus x_{14} leaves the basis and is replaced by x_{13}. The new basic feasible solution can be found most quickly by adjusting the values in the tableau to obtain a new solution. We know that $\hat{x}_{13} = \theta = 166.7$. Hence to have the correct sum in column 3, it must be true that $\hat{x}_{23} = 333.3$. Then since $\hat{x}_{14} = 0$, we obtain $\hat{x}_{24} = 1000$. Now all that remains to be done is to adjust the slack. In the new solution, we are using $0.35(200) + 0.35(166.7) = 128.4$ units of resource 1. Thus $x_{s1} = 200 - 128.4 = 71.6$. For the second resource we should again obtain an exact balance. This is indeed true since the amount used of this resource is

$$0.30(333.3) + 0.40(1000) = 500,$$

and there is zero slack. Everything else remains unchanged.

The new basic feasible solution is given in Table 9–18. To obtain the $z_{ij} - c_{ij}$, we first determine the new u_α, v_β by solving the set of equations

TABLE 9–18

	P_1	P_2	P_3	P_4	Slack	a_i	u_i
R_1	0.25 (200) 0.35	0.30 −0.10 0.50	0.35 (166.7) 0.35	0.50 −0.034 0.50	0 (71.6) 1	200	0
R_2	0.70 −0.60 0.90	0.62 −0.56 0.84	0.30 (333.3) 0.30	0.40 (1000) 0.40	0 −0.167 1	500	−0.1667
R_3	0.40 −0.15 0.80	0.20 (400) 0.40	0.60 −0.25 0.74	0.70 −0.234 0.90	0 (240) 1	400	0
b_j	200	400	500	1000			
v_j	0.25	0.20	0.35	0.466			

(9–47) corresponding to the new solution. These equations are:

$$0.35u_1 + v_1 = 0.25, \quad 0.35u_1 + v_3 = 0.35, \quad u_1 = 0, \quad 0.30u_2 + v_3 = 0.30,$$

$$0.40u_2 + v_4 = 0.40, \quad 0.40u_3 + v_2 = 0.20, \quad u_3 = 0.$$

The solution is $u_1 = 0, v_1 = 0.25, v_3 = 0.35, u_2 = -0.1667, v_4 = 0.466,$ $u_3 = 0, v_2 = 0.20$.

The $z_{ij} - c_{ij}$ are then computed from (9–48); they are listed in Table 9–18. All $z_{ij} - c_{ij}$ are negative, and consequently, an optimal solution has been found. Since this problem can actually be solved by inspection, it is clear that we have indeed obtained an optimal solution.

REFERENCES

1. A. CHARNES and W. W. COOPER, "The Stepping-Stone Method of Explaining Linear Programming Calculations in Transportation Problems," *Management Science*, **1**, 1, 1954.

2. A. CHARNES and W. W. COOPER, "Management Models and Industrial Applications of Linear Programming," *Management Science*, **4**, 1, 1957.

3. J. B. DENNIS, "A High-Speed Computer Technique for the Transportation Problem," *J. Ass. for Computing Machinery*, April, 1958.

4. K. EISEMANN, "Simplified Treatment of Degeneracy in Transportation Problems," *Quart. of App. Math.*, **XIV**, 4, 1957.

5. A. R. FERGUSON, and G. B. DANTZIG, "The Allocation of Aircraft to Routes—An Example of Linear Programming under Uncertain Demand," *Management Science*, **3**, 1, 1956.

6. M. M. FLOOD, "On the Hitchcock Distribution Problem," *Pacific J. Math.* **3**, 2, 1953.

7. H. S. HOUTHAKKER, "On the Numerical Solution of the Transportation Problem," *Operations Research*, **3**, 2, 1955.

Houthakker presents a method for obtaining an initial solution to a transportation problem which is different from those discussed in this chapter. However, his method cannot be used too easily on digital computers.

8. T. C. KOOPMANS, ed., *Activity Analysis of Production and Allocation*. New York: Wiley, 1951.

In Chapter XXIII, Dantzig presents the original discussion of the simplex method as it applies to the transportation problem.

9. N. V. REINFELD and W. R. VOGEL, *Mathematical Programming*. Englewood Cliffs: Prentice-Hall, 1958.

10. M. A. SIMONNARD, "Transportation-Type Problems", Interim Technical Report No. 11, MIT Project, *Fundamental Investigations in Operations Research*, Jan., 1959.

PROBLEMS

9–1. Consider a transportation problem involving 4 origins and 6 destinations. Write out explicitly the matrix **A** of Eq. (9–7). By evaluating the determinant of the matrix whose columns are the vectors p_{21}, p_{22}, p_{12}, p_{13}, p_{33}, p_{34}, p_{44}, p_{45}, p_{46} show that these vectors are linearly independent and yield a set of basis vectors for the transportation problem. Express p_{16}, p_{41} in terms of the basis vectors, and write out the vectors explicitly.

9–2. Choose any 8th-order minor $|A_8|$ from matrix **A** of Problem 9–1 and show that $|A_8| = \pm 1, 0$.

9–3. Let **B** be the matrix of the basis vectors referred to in Problem 9–1. Show that every 9th-order minor of **B** is different from zero.

9–4. Solve the transportation problem for which the costs, origin availabilities, and destination requirements are given in the following tableau by the stepping-stone method and use the northwest-corner rule to obtain an initial feasible solution.

	D_1	D_2	D_3	D_4	D_5	D_6	a_i
O_1	1	2	1	4	5	2	30
O_2	3	3	2	1	4	3	50
O_3	4	2	5	9	6	2	75
O_4	3	1	7	3	4	6	20
b_j	20	40	30	10	50	25	175

9–5. Solve the preceding problem by means of the uv-method of computing the $z_{ij} - c_{ij}$.

9–6. Draw the basic tree for each tableau of Problem 9–4.

9–7. Solve Problem 9–4, using the row-minima technique to find an initial solution. Compare the number of iterations required to obtain an optimal solution with the number of iterations required in Problem 9–4.

9–8. Solve Problem 9–4, using the column-minima technique to find an initial solution. Compare the number of iterations required with that of Problem 9–4.

9–9. Solve Problem 9–4, using the matrix-minima technique to find an initial solution.

9–10. Solve Problem 9–4 by means of Vogel's method for finding an initial solution.

9–11. Solve the problem discussed in Section 9–8, using Table 9–11 for an initial solution.

9–12. Solve the problem discussed in Section 9–8, using Table 9–12 for an initial solution.

9–13. Solve the problem discussed in Section 9–8, using Table 9–13 for an initial solution.

9–14. Solve the problem discussed in Section 9–8, using Table 9–14 for an initial solution.

9–15. Solve the problem whose initial solution is given in Table 9–8. Carry along the ϵ's explicitly.

9–16. Solve the following transportation problem by the uv-method, using the northwest-corner rule. Do not introduce the ϵ's explicitly to remove the degeneracy problem. Simply keep track of the variables which are at a zero level in the basic solution.

	D_1	D_2	D_3	D_4	D_5	D_6	a_i
O_1	5	10	15	8	9	7	30
O_2	14	13	10	9	20	21	40
O_3	15	11	13	25	8	12	10
O_4	9	19	12	8	6	13	100
b_j	50	20	10	35	15	50	180

9–17. A company has three warehouses, numbered 1, 2, 3, containing 10,000, 5,000, and 16,000 units of its product. In the next month, 2,000; 1,000; 3,000; 4,500; 500; 600; 950 units must be shipped to seven retail outlets numbered

1, ..., 7. The unit cost of shipment from any warehouse to any retail outlet is contained in the following matrix. Find the minimum-cost shipping schedule.

	D_1	D_2	D_3	D_4	D_5	D_6	D_7
O_1	10	8	16	3	10	25	18
O_2	19	25	18	7	12	18	19
O_3	20	17	20	5	14	16	17

9–18. Solve the following transportation problem by the uv-method, using any one of the available methods for finding an initial solution.

	D_1	D_2	D_3	D_4	D_5	D_6	D_7	a_i
O_1	8	6	10	12	9	11	5	40
O_2	3	7	6	9	8	7	8	50
O_3	5	4	2	6	3	9	3	90
O_4	17	12	11	13	9	10	12	30
O_5	7	11	4	5	6	5	7	60
b_j	20	30	40	80	60	25	15	270

9–19. Solve the following transportation problem by the stepping-stone method; use any technique desired for obtaining an initial solution.

	D_1	D_2	D_3	D_4	a_i
O_1	2.67	−1.05	1.30	−2.00	45
O_2	1.45	−0.50	0.40	−0.05	30
O_3	3.00	2.00	1.50	1.40	30
b_j	25	15	40	25	105

9–20. Solve the following transportation problem by the uv-method, using any one of the techniques for obtaining an initial solution.

	D_1	D_2	D_3	D_4	a_i
O_1	5	3	6	2	19.3
O_2	4	7	9	1	37.4
O_3	3	4	7	5	34.3
b_j	16.3	18.2	30.7	25.8	91.0

9–21. Show that if $\mathbf{R}$ contains as columns the $m + n - 1$ basis vectors $\mathbf{p}_{\alpha\beta}^B$, then the set of equations (9–28) can be written $(\mathbf{u}, \mathbf{v})\mathbf{R} = \mathbf{c}_B$. Next show that if we set to zero one component of $(\mathbf{u}, \mathbf{v})$, say component k, and if $\mathbf{T}$ is the matrix formed from $\mathbf{R}$ by crossing out row k, then the remaining $m + n - 1$ components of $(\mathbf{u}, \mathbf{v})$ are given by $\mathbf{c}_B\mathbf{T}^{-1}$. Reconcile the fact that one of the components of $(\mathbf{u}, \mathbf{v})$ is arbitrary with the theory of the simplex method, where $\mathbf{c}_B\mathbf{B}^{-1}$ is uniquely determined. Hint: Let $\mathbf{B}$ be the corresponding basis matrix of order $m + n$ if the transportation problem was solved by the simplex method. Then $\mathbf{B}$ can be imagined to contain $\mathbf{R}$ in its first $m + n - 1$ columns and an artificial vector in the last column. Note that any artificial vector can be in the last column. Imagine that the price of the artificial vector is zero.

9–22. How is an optimal solution to a transportation problem changed if a constant λ is added to each cost in one row i of the transportation tableau? By how much is the optimal value of the objective function changed?

9–23. How is an optimal solution to a transportation problem changed if a constant λ is added to each cost in one column j of the transportation tableau? By how much is the optimal value of the objective function changed?

9–24. Consider the transportation problem

$$\sum_{j=1}^{n} x_{ij} \le a_i, \qquad i = 1, \ldots, m,$$

$$\sum_{i=1}^{m} x_{ij} \ge b_j, \qquad j = 1, \ldots, n,$$

$$\min z = \sum_{i,j} c_{ij}x_{ij}$$

for $x_{ij} \ge 0$. Assume that all $c_{ij} \ge 0$ and $\sum a_i \ge \sum b_j$. Prove that, in any optimal solution, the constraints $\sum_i x_{ij} \ge b_j$ will hold as strict equalities, i.e., no more than necessary will be shipped.

9–25. Suppose that we are maximizing z in Problem 9–24. Prove that, in any optimal solution, the constraints $\sum_j x_{ij} \leq a_i$ will hold as strict equalities. What is the physical interpretation of this result?

9–26. Consider the following transportation-type problem:

$$\sum_{j=1}^{n} x_{ij} \geq a_i, \qquad i = 1, \ldots, m,$$

$$\sum_{i=1}^{m} x_{ij} \geq b_j, \qquad j = 1, \ldots, n,$$

$$\min z = \sum_{i,j} c_{ij} x_{ij}.$$

For $c_{ij} \geq 0$ prove that, in an optimal solution, each of the first m constraints will hold as a strict equality if $\sum b_j > \sum a_i$, and each of the last n constraints will hold as a strict equality if $\sum a_i > \sum b_j$.

9–27. Consider the transportation-type problem

$$\sum_{j=1}^{n} x_{ij} \geq a_i, \qquad i = 1, \ldots, m,$$

$$\sum_{i=1}^{m} x_{ij} = b_j, \qquad j = 1, \ldots, n,$$

$$\max z = \sum_{i,j} c_{ij} x_{ij}$$

for $x_{ij} \geq 0$. Convert the constraints to a set of equations and introduce a new redundant equation so that $\sum a_i = \sum b_j$. Write out the matrix of the coefficients. Show that this matrix is unimodular.

9–28. How must the stepping-stone algorithm be modified to solve Problem 9–27? How can we obtain an initial basic feasible solution?

9–29. How must the uv-method be modified to become appliable to Problem 9–27?

9–30. Consider the transportation-type problem

$$\sum_{j=1}^{n} x_{ij} \leq a_i, \qquad i = 1, \ldots, m,$$

$$\sum_{i=1}^{m} x_{ij} \geq b_j, \qquad j = 1, \ldots, n,$$

$$\min z = \sum_{i,j} c_{ij} x_{ij}$$

for $x_{ij} \geq 0$. The c_{ij} may have any sign. Convert the constraints to a set of equations and introduce two additional equations so that $\sum a_i = \sum b_j$. Write out the matrix of the coefficients. Show that this matrix is unimodular.

9–31. How must the stepping-stone algorithm be modified to become applicable to Problem 9–30?

9–32. How must the uv-method be modified to treat Problem 9–30?

9–33. Consider the usual formulation of the transportation problem, that is, Eqs. 9–1 through 9–4. Suppose that certain x_{ij} are required to be zero. Show how to apply the stepping-stone or uv-methods to such a problem. Hint: Can one use a $-M$-trick here?

9–34. Show how to solve the linear programming problem

$$\sum_{j \geq i} x_{ij} \leq a_i, \qquad i = 1, \ldots, m,$$

$$\sum_{i \leq j} x_{ij} = b_j, \qquad j = 1, \ldots, n,$$

$$\min z = \sum_{i \leq j} c_{ij} x_{ij}$$

for non-negative x_{ij}.

9–35. Show how to incorporate artificial variables within the tableau format of Table 9–16 if they are needed to obtain an initial basic feasible solution to a generalized transportation problem. How are the $z_{ij} - c_{ij}$ computed when artificial vectors are in the basis?

9–36. How does degeneracy appear in the process of determining an initial basic feasible solution to a generalized transportation problem by means of one of the methods used to obtain basic solutions to transportation problems? Find a simple way of adding cells at a zero level to yield a degenerate basic feasible solution. What problems arise if one wishes to use a perturbation scheme which rigorously eliminates the possibility of degeneracy?

9–37. Solve the following generalized transportation problem: The upper number in each cell is the cost c_{ij}, and the lower number is d_{ij}. Assume that the objective function is to be minimized.

	P_1	P_2	P_3	P_4	P_5	Slack	a_i
R_1	2.4	1.5	3.4	0.95	3.0	0	200
	3.2	2.3	4.1	1.5	3.5	1	
R_2	0.75	0.90	1.2	1.0	1.2	0	100
	1.2	1.4	1.5	1.4	1.7	1	
R_3	3.5	1.4	2.3	2.4	4.0	0	600
	4.2	2.0	2.7	3.0	4.5	1	
b_j	50	40	80	150	210		

9–38. Under certain circumstances the techniques used to find initial basic feasible solutions to transportation problems will not work for generalized transportation problems. Suppose, for example, that the d_{ij} are inversely proportional to the c_{ij}. Thus the selection of a solution with the lowest c_{ij} may require more resources than are available, because the d_{ij} are largest for the small c_{ij}. However, there may be a feasible solution if activities with higher costs are used. How can one obtain an initial basic feasible solution in this case?

9–39. In Section 9–14, we presented an exact procedure for solving generalized transportation problems. Sometimes such problems can be solved approximately by scaling them so that all the coefficients are close to 1. Then we set all coefficients equal to 1 and use the transportation method as an approximation. The scaling is carried out by multiplying the constraints by a constant (which does not change the constraint) and by multiplying the activity vectors by some constant. (How does this affect the corresponding variable?) Discuss in detail how this scaling technique works, and indicate the conditions under which a generalized transportation problem can be reduced to a problem whose nonzero coefficients are all close to 1. Try to use the scaling technique on the example of Section 9–15.

*9–40. Discuss the way in which a digital computer might be used to solve a transportation problem by the uv-technique. Note that to determine the unique loop connecting the basis cells and the cell to enter the basis, the computer must be provided with a definite set of instructions for finding the loop. Develop such a set of instructions. Construct a flow chart for solving a transportation problem by the uv-method on a digital computer.

*9–41. Discuss the problems involved in developing a code for solving the generalized transportation problem on a digital computer.

9–42. For the tableau of Problem 9–4 assume that the origin availabilities are 50, 75, 75, 100, respectively, instead of the values shown. Add a slack column and solve the problem using the uv-method.

9–43. For the tableau of Problem 9–16 assume that the origin availabilities are 45, 70, 30, 100, respectively, instead of the values shown. Add a slack column and solve the problem using the uv-method.

9–44. For the tableau of Problem 9–18 assume that the origin availabilities are 60, 50, 120, 70, 60, respectively, instead of the values shown. Add a slack column and solve the problem using the uv-method.

9–45. For the tableau of Problem 9–4 assume that the b_j-values are 10, 15, 20, 10, 30, 20, respectively, instead of the values shown. Assume that the resulting tableau provides the data for a problem of the form given by Eq. (9–35). Add a surplus row to the tableau and solve the problem, using the uv-method.

9–46. For the tableau of Problem 9–18 assume that the b_j-values are 20, 10, 30, 50, 40, 15, 10, respectively, instead of the values shown. Assume that the resulting tableau provides the data for a problem of the form given by Eq. (9–35). Add a surplus row to the tableau and solve the problem using the uv-method.

---

* Starred problems assume that the reader has some familiarity with digital computers.

9–47. For the tableau given in Problem 9–18 assume that the a_i-values are 70, 50, 100, 50, 90, respectively, instead of the values shown. Assume that the resulting tableau provides data for a problem of the form given by Eq. (9–38), where the objective function is to be minimized. Add a slack column and a surplus row and solve the problem by the uv-method. Verify the results of Problem 9–24.

9–48. For the tableau given in Problem 9–19 assume that the a_i-values are 75, 40, 60, respectively, instead of the values shown. Assume that the resulting tableau provides data for a problem of the form given by Eq. (9–38), where the objective function is to be minimized. Add a slack column and a surplus row and solve the problem by the uv-method. Do the results of Problem 9–24 hold here?

9–49. A square matrix $\mathbf{B}$ is said to be triangular if $b_{ij} = 0$ when $i > j$, that is, all elements below the main diagonal are zero. A system of n equations in n unknowns $\mathbf{Bx} = \mathbf{b}$ is very easy to solve if $\mathbf{B}$ is nonsingular and triangular, for we have immediately $x_n = b_n/b_{nn}$. Then x_{n-1} can be found after substituting in the value of x_n, etc. The variables can be determined sequentially. For each of the tableaux given in Tables 9–2 through 9–6 write down the set of $m + n$ equations in $m + n - 1$ unknowns which determine the basic variables. After dropping any one of the redundant equations in each set, show that the resulting system of $m + n - 1$ equation in $m + n - 1$ unknowns can be arranged so that the matrix of the coefficients is triangular. For each of the tables referred to above, write down the set of equations which determine the u_i, v_j. After setting the value of any one of the u_i or v_j arbitrarily in each set of equations, show that the resulting system of $m + n - 1$ equation in $m + n - 1$ unknowns can be arranged so that the matrix of the coefficients is triangular.

9–50. Prove in general that for any transportation problem, the set of $m + n - 1$ equations in $m + n - 1$ unknowns which determine a basic solution can be arranged so that the matrix of the coefficients is triangular (see Problem 9–49). Prove the same result for the set of equations which determine the u_i, v_j. Hint: This requires that we show that one variable can be determined immediately and that this is also true for another variable in the resulting system of equations, after the value of the variable originally determined has been substituted back in. Use the type of analysis given on p. 302.

CHAPTER 10

NETWORK FLOWS

"The thought beneath so slight a film
Is more distinctly seen,—
As laces just reveal the surge,
Or mists the Apennine."

Emily Dickinson.

10–1 Theory of graphs. In Section 9–5 we introduced (without explicitly saying so) some material from the theory of graphs. In the last few decades, this subject has assumed an important place in the study of electrical networks and has even found its way into introductory texts on electrical engineering [8]. More recently, the theory of graphs has become of interest in economics and other fields, in connection with transportation networks and other flow problems. The computation of maximal flows in networks and the usefulness of this theory in solving linear programming problems of the transportation type will be the subject of this chapter. In order to introduce some terminology and definitions which will be useful in the development of this material, we shall first very briefly discuss some elementary topics in the theory of graphs.

GRAPH: *Consider a set of two or more different "points," with certain pairs of these points joined by one or more "lines." The resulting form is called a graph, and can be denoted by G.*

The "points" referred to in the above definition will be called *nodes, or vertices,* of the graph. What we here call nodes were the cells of the tableau in Section 9–5. A "line" joining two different nodes will be called a *branch, or edge,* of the graph. The nodes of the graph will be denoted by numbers, i.e., 1, 2, . . . We shall discuss only problems whose graphs contain a finite number of nodes. Any branch of a graph can be characterized by the pair of nodes which it joins. More than one branch may connect any two nodes. The two nodes joined by a branch are referred to as the end points of the branch. The degree of a node i is the number of branches of the graph which have node i as an end point. A node of degree 1 is called an extreme point of the graph. A branch one of whose end points has degree 1 is called a terminal branch.

Usually, the nodes of a graph are considered to be points in euclidean space, and the branches are straight lines or curves joining these points.

331

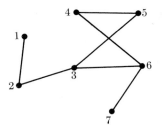

FIGURE 10–1

From the abstract point of view, however, a node can be any element whatever. A branch has only one characteristic: It defines two end points. Thus from the purely abstract point of view, the theory of graphs is the theory of combinatorial analysis. We shall always think of a graph as a set of nodes and branches which can be represented by some configuration drawn in a plane (for example, Fig. 10–1).

We can attribute a sense of direction to a branch by stating which node is to be considered the point of origin. Such a branch will be called *oriented*. When drawing a graph, we indicate the orientation of a branch by an arrowhead. An oriented branch with node i as the point of origin and node j as the point of termination can be represented algebraically by $\overrightarrow{(i, j)}$. If an orientation is assigned to each branch of a graph, the resulting graph is said to be oriented. If there are k branches in the graph, then it is possible to form 2^k oriented graphs. We shall use (i, j) to represent a nonoriented branch joining nodes i, j.

PATH: *A path joining nodes i, j is an ordered set of branches,*

$$(i, p), \ (p, q), \ (q, r), \ \ldots, \ (t, u), \ (u, j),$$

such that each node in the ordered set, with the possible exception of the first and last nodes, is the end point for two and only two branches in the set. The nodes i, j are called the extremity points of the path.

EXAMPLE: The following sets of branches form two different paths joining nodes 1, 4 in Fig. 10–1.

(a)   (1, 2), (2, 3), (3, 6), (6, 4),

(b)   (1, 2), (2, 3), (3, 5), (5, 4).

Intuitively, a path is a continuous broken line joining the extremity points. An oriented path is obtained from the path defined above if the branches are oriented such that the terminal point of one branch is the point of origin for the immediately succeeding branch.

LOOP: *If a path is defined so that $i = j$, i.e., the extremity points of the path are one and the same node, then the path is called a loop.*

CONNECTED GRAPH: *A graph G is said to be connected if there is a path in G joining any two nodes of the graph.*

If we remove from a connected graph G one of its extreme points and the corresponding terminal branch, the resulting graph G' is also connected. To prove this we note that any path in G which involves the extreme point removed must have the extreme point as one of its extremity points. Hence any path in G connecting two nodes of G' cannot involve the removed extreme point. Thus any path of G connecting two nodes of G' is also a path of G', and hence G' is connected.

TREE: *A tree is a connected graph which has no loops.*

A connected graph is a tree if and only if the path joining any two nodes is unique. If every path is unique, then there is no loop, for if there were a loop,

$$(i, p), \ (p, q), \ (q, r), \ldots, (t, u), \ (u, i),$$

there would be two distinct paths, (i, p), (p, q) and $(q, r), \ldots, (t, u)$, (u, i) joining the nodes i, q. On the other hand, if the graph is a tree, a path must be unique in every case, for if there were two distinct paths joining i, j, they could be combined to yield a loop.

It is easy to show that a tree always has at least two extreme points. To prove this choose any node i. If i is an extreme point, it is only necessary to show that there is at least one more extreme point. There is a branch joining i to another node, say j. Either j is an extreme point or there is a branch joining j to another node k, etc. Since we have only a finite number of nodes and no loops, this process must terminate at an extreme point different from i. If i is not an extreme point, then at least two branches lead from i to different nodes, say j and k. We can then follow along paths from j and k, and each of these must again terminate in an extreme point. Furthermore, the paths have no elements in common or a loop could be formed. Hence the two extreme points are different.

If a tree has N nodes, it has precisely $N - 1$ branches. This can be proved by induction. When $N = 2$ and there is no loop, then there can be only one branch joining the two nodes. Hence the result holds in this case. Suppose that the result holds for $N = n$. Consider a tree with $n + 1$ nodes. Let the number of branches be k. Locate an extreme point of this tree and remove this extreme point and the corresponding terminal edge. By the above proof, the resulting graph is connected and has no loops. Therefore it is a tree with n nodes. By hypothesis, it has $n - 1$ branches. Thus $k = n - 1 + 1 = n$, and the theorem holds for $N = n + 1$ if it holds for $N = n$. Hence, by induction, it holds for all integers $N \geq 2$.

These simple theorems should give the reader some feeling for the manner in which propositions in the theory of graphs can be proved.

It is often useful to imagine that some sort of flow (electric current, some fluid, goods, money, etc.) occurs in the branches of a graph.

NETWORK: *A network is a graph such that a flow can take place in the branches of the graph.*

A network may or may not be oriented. The orientation of any branch is now taken to be the direction of flow. If there is a limit to the magnitude of the flow in any branch of a network, then a *capacity restriction* is imposed on that branch. It is possible to have capacity restrictions on the nodes as well as on the branches. A node j is called a *source* if every branch which has this node as an end point is oriented in such a way that the flow in the branch moves away from j to another node. A node i is called a *sink* if every branch which has this node as an end point is oriented in such a way that the flow is from other nodes to i.

In a network, we assume that the branches are connected only at nodes. In Fig. 10–1 for example, the branches (4, 6), (3, 5) cross; however, it is assumed, that they are not interconnected, i.e., a flow in (4, 6) cannot enter (3, 5) at this point of intersection. In this particular case, we could have drawn the figure so that the branches would not intersect. When a network is drawn in a plane, we place no restrictions on the way its branches may cross one another. The understanding is, however, that they are connected only at nodes. In electrical engineering, it is sometimes necessary to be more specific and to assume that the network can be drawn so that the branches do not cross one another; i.e., it must be assumed that the network is topologically planar.

In the next section, we shall discuss the problem of finding maximal flows in connected networks containing one source and one sink. These results will be useful in the development of another algorithm for solving the transportation problem, which is even more efficient than that discussed in the preceding chapter.

10–2 Maximal flows in networks; intuitive approach. Consider a connected network consisting of a single source, a single sink, and some intermediate nodes. We shall assume that the network is oriented, and that there is a capacity restriction $d_{ij} \geq 0$ (which may be infinite) on each branch $(\overrightarrow{i, j})$. It will be assumed that there are no capacity restrictions on the nodes. All other cases of interest can be reduced to this case, and in some of the problems the reader will be asked to show how this can be done. A typical network is shown in Fig. 10–2. We wish to determine a procedure for computing the maximum possible flow from source to sink.

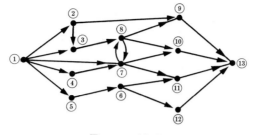

FIGURE 10–2

The flow in the networks to be considered may be flow of fluids, electricity, funds, automobiles, etc. The physical units of the flow may be cubic feet/sec, amperes, dollars per month, etc. In general, the flow will be a rate. We shall be interested in steady-state flows, i.e., flows which, in any branch, do not change with time. It is assumed that the flow in each branch is infinitely divisible, and that for a branch $(\overrightarrow{i, j})$ it can have any value x_{ij} satisfying $0 \leq x_{ij} \leq d_{ij}$. Furthermore, if there is a flow x_{ij} in branch $(\overrightarrow{i, j})$, then the flow in the branch can be increased by any amount up to a maximum of $g_{ij} = d_{ij} - x_{ij}$. It is also assumed that there is conservation of flow at any node other than the source and sink. That is, the flow into the node is equal to the flow out of the node.

Thus, in Fig. 10–2, if the flow through $(\overrightarrow{8, 10})$ is 2 and the flow through $(\overrightarrow{7, 10})$ is 1, then the flow in branch $(\overrightarrow{10, 13})$ is $2 + 1 = 3$.

A flow in a network is described by a set of non-negative numbers x_{ij} which give the flow from node i to node j through branch $(\overrightarrow{i, j})$. *A flow is said to be feasible if there is conservation of flow at every node except the source and sink, and if $0 \leq x_{ij} \leq d_{ij}$ for all i, j.* Any feasible flow determines a quantity z which is flowing from the source to the sink. *A feasible flow in a network is said to be maximal if the amount flowing from source to sink is finite, and if there is no other feasible flow which yields a larger flow from source to sink.* If there is no finite upper bound on the flow in some of the branches, it may turn out that the flow from source to sink can be made arbitrarily large.

Consider a given network and let any feasible flow be denoted by a set of x_{ij}. If the flow is feasible, it must satisfy the capacity restrictions and the conservation of flow at the nodes other than the source and sink. If there are N nodes in the network, we number the nodes so that 1 is the source and N the sink. In order to have conservation of flow at the nodes, it must be true that

$$\sum_k x_{ki} = \sum_r x_{ir}, \qquad i = 2, \dots, N - 1, \tag{10–1}$$

the sum being taken over all k for which there can be flow into i, and all r for which there can be flow out of i. These $N - 2$ constraints, together with the capacity constraints

$$0 \leq x_{ij} \leq d_{ij}, \qquad \text{all } i, j, \qquad (10\text{–}2)$$

represent the restrictions on the problem. In order to find the maximal flow, we must maximize the flow z from the source to the sink; i.e.,

$$z = \sum_s x_{1s}, \qquad (10\text{–}3)$$

the sum being taken over all branches leading from the source, subject to the constraints (10–1) and (10–2). Since we have assumed that no accumulation occurs, z must also be given by

$$z = \sum_q x_{qN}, \qquad (10\text{–}4)$$

the sum being taken over all branches leading to the sink. It follows that the problem of finding the maximal flow in a network is reducible to a linear programming problem. Hence, in theory, we have solved the problem. However, it is possible to develop a much more efficient computational procedure for finding maximal flows in networks.

Given a diagram of a network such as Fig. 10–2, and assuming that the capacity of each branch is labeled, intuition suggests the following technique for finding a maximal flow in the network. We begin at the source and move along branches of positive capacity until we determine a path from the source to the sink. We search this path for the branch with the smallest capacity $\bar{d}$ and set the flow in this path equal to $\bar{d}$. Then we decrease by $\bar{d}$ the capacity of each branch in the path and consider the resulting network. The capacity of any branch in the above path whose original capacity was $\bar{d}$ is now zero. We repeat the same operation for the new network, and continue until there is no path from the source to the sink such that each branch in the path has positive capacity. The maximal flow is then the sum of the flows in the paths which were obtained at each step.

Our intuitive idea is sound and will indeed yield a maximal flow, provided that we clear up one point. It is quite possible that we can find paths from the source to the sink such that one or more of the branches have a wrong orientation; i.e., a flow from the source to the sink would pass through these branches in the wrong direction. However, it may turn out that the flow in the network can be increased if we imagine that a flow imposed in the wrong direction decreases the flow in the proper direction. Our intuitive idea will work, provided we allow for the possibility that a flow may be imposed in the wrong direction on some branch if, for that branch, there is a flow in the proper direction. However, we never allow a net flow in the wrong direction.

The capacity d_{ij} for a flow in branch $\overrightarrow{(i,j)}$ will be assumed to refer to the net flow. We imagine that two flows, x'_{ij} and x'_{ji}, pass simultaneously in opposite directions through branch $\overrightarrow{(i,j)}$; the net flow is then

$$x_{ij} = x'_{ij} - x'_{ji} \geq 0, \qquad (10\text{–}5)$$

and must satisfy (10–2). The net flow is the only quantity of physical interest, but for mathematical reasons, we must allow for the fictitious flows in opposite directions. Given a value of x'_{ij}, then x'_{ji} must lie in the interval $0 \leq x'_{ji} \leq x'_{ij}$. This means that we cannot impose a flow in the wrong direction along a branch unless we have at least as great a flow in the proper direction. There cannot be a net flow in the wrong direction. If we are given a value of x'_{ji}, then x'_{ij} must satisfy $x'_{ji} \leq x'_{ij} \leq d_{ij} + x'_{ji}$.

There is no reason that there cannot be a provision for an actual physical flow in either direction between the nodes i, j of a network. On a diagram, this possibility is usually indicated by two directed branches $\overrightarrow{(i,j)}$, $\overrightarrow{(j,i)}$ [the branches $\overrightarrow{(7,8)}$, $\overrightarrow{(8,7)}$ in Fig. 10–2]. In this situation, d_{ij} and d_{ji} need not have the same value. When there can be an actual physical flow in both directions between node i, j, there exists a loop involving only these two nodes. We can note that a maximal flow never requires that both x_{ij}, x_{ji} be positive. To see this, let $\bar{d} = \min(x_{ij}, x_{ji})$ for any flow in the network. Consider the new variables $x_{ij} - \bar{d}$, $x_{ji} - \bar{d}$. One of these new variables will be zero. This change in variables does not in any way alter the flow from the source to the sink. All we did was to subtract the loop flow.

10–3. Maximal flows in networks; examples of the intuitive approach.

(1) Using the intuitive approach suggested above, let us determine the maximal flow in the network shown in Fig. 10–3. The capacities of the branches are shown, the node numbers are circled. We begin by finding a path from source to sink, i.e., from node 1 to node 6, in which each branch has a positive capacity. The path $\overrightarrow{(1,2)}$, $\overrightarrow{(2,4)}$, $\overrightarrow{(4,6)}$ is satisfactory. The minimum capacity among the branches is 4 for branch $\overrightarrow{(2,4)}$. We thus impose a flow of $\sigma_1 = 4$ along this path and decrease by 4 the capacity of each branch in the path. This yields the network in Fig. 10–4.

Let us next choose the path $\overrightarrow{(1,3)}$, $\overrightarrow{(3,4)}$, $\overrightarrow{(4,6)}$. The minimum capacity among the branches is 4 on branch $\overrightarrow{(4,6)}$. Thus we impose a flow of $\sigma_2 = 4$ along this path and reduce by 4 the capacity of each branch. This yields Fig. 10–5.

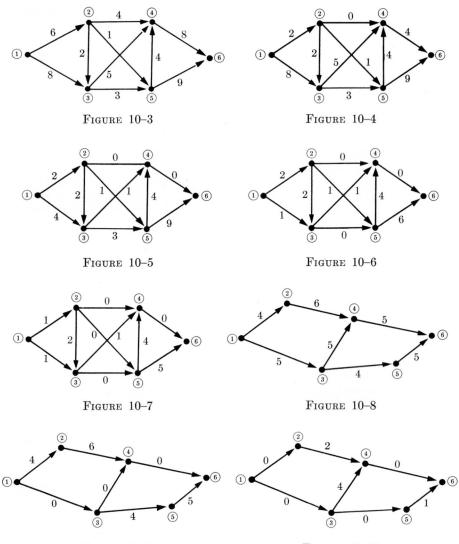

FIGURE 10–3

FIGURE 10–4

FIGURE 10–5

FIGURE 10–6

FIGURE 10–7

FIGURE 10–8

FIGURE 10–9

FIGURE 10–10

All the branches of the path $(\overrightarrow{1,3})$, $(\overrightarrow{3,5})$, $(\overrightarrow{5,6})$ have positive capacity. The minimum capacity is 3 for branch $(\overrightarrow{3,5})$. A flow of $\sigma_3 = 3$ is imposed on this path, and all the capacities are reduced by 3. This yields Fig. 10–6.

Every branch of the path $(\overrightarrow{1,2})$, $(\overrightarrow{2,5})$, $(\overrightarrow{5,6})$ has a positive capacity. The minimum capacity occurs for branch $(\overrightarrow{2,5})$ and is 1. A flow of $\sigma_4 = 1$ is imposed along this branch, and the capacity of each branch in the path is reduced by 1. This gives Fig. 10–7.

There is no path left along which we can impose a positive flow. For example, the path $(\overrightarrow{1, 3})$, $(\overrightarrow{3, 4})$, $(\overrightarrow{5, 4})$, $(\overrightarrow{5, 6})$ is not suitable; we cannot set x'_{45} to a positive value because $x'_{54} = 0$. Hence we must have a maximal flow, and it is given by $\sigma_1 + \sigma_2 + \sigma_3 + \sigma_4 = 4 + 4 + 3 + 1 = 12$. The flow in any branch $(\overrightarrow{i, j})$ is found by subtracting the capacity of that branch in Fig. 10–7 from the corresponding capacity in Fig. 10–3. Thus, for example, $x_{12} = 5$, $x_{13} = 7$. The sum of x_{12} and x_{13} should be the total flow, and indeed, it is. The reader might note that the set of branch flows yielding the maximal flow is not unique. For example, we can increase by 1 the flow along the path $(\overrightarrow{1, 3})$, $(\overrightarrow{3, 4})$, $(\overrightarrow{4, 6})$ and decrease by 1 the flow in the path $(\overrightarrow{1, 2})$, $(\overrightarrow{2, 4})$, $(\overrightarrow{4, 6})$, and the flow from the source to the sink is unchanged.

(2) Consider the network shown in Fig. 10–8. To find a maximal flow let us choose the path $(\overrightarrow{1, 3})$, $(\overrightarrow{3, 4})$, $(\overrightarrow{4, 6})$. The minimum capacity is 5; setting a flow of $\sigma_1 = 5$ in this path, we obtain the new capacity diagram of Fig. 10–9.

There is now no path from source to sink such that each branch has positive capacity, and the orientation of the branch is the same as the direction in which the path is traced. However, we do not have a maximal flow. Consider the path $(\overrightarrow{1, 2})$, $(\overrightarrow{2, 4})$, $(\overrightarrow{3, 4})$, $(\overrightarrow{3, 5})$, $(\overrightarrow{5, 6})$. Any flow in this path moves in the wrong direction along branch $(\overrightarrow{3, 4})$. However, since $x_{34} = 5$, we can impose a flow x'_{43} of as much as 5 in the wrong direction. The minimum capacity for the path is then 4. If a flow of $\sigma_2 = 4$ is imposed along this path, there remain the capacities shown in Fig. 10–10. The net flow in $(\overrightarrow{3, 4})$ is $x'_{34} - x'_{43} = 5 - 4 = 1$; hence the remaining capacity is 4.

Clearly the flow is now maximal and has the value $\sigma_1 + \sigma_2 = 9$. We note that $x_{12} = 4$, $x_{13} = 5$, $x_{24} = 4$, $x_{34} = 1$, $x_{46} = 5$, $x_{35} = 4$, $x_{56} = 4$. This illustrates a case where it is necessary to use the mathematical fiction of imposing a flow in the wrong direction. Note that the only result of imposing a fictitious flow in the wrong direction along $(\overrightarrow{3, 4})$ was that four units of flow from $(\overrightarrow{1, 3})$ were routed through $(\overrightarrow{3, 5})$ rather than through $(\overrightarrow{3, 4})$. The actual flow corresponding to the four units of flow in the wrong direction through $(\overrightarrow{3, 4})$ really went from $(\overrightarrow{2, 4})$ to $(\overrightarrow{4, 6})$ to make up the four units in $(\overrightarrow{4, 6})$ which were originally coming through $(\overrightarrow{3, 4})$.

Since, for complicated networks, the above procedure for finding the maximal flow is rather inconvenient, it is preferable to use a straightforward algebraic technique. Such a method can easily be developed from the above intuitive notions. The algebraic procedure can then be used to prove that the intuitive approach does indeed yield a maximal flow. In a complicated network, it is difficult to keep track of the branches which form the path from source to sink. Another time-consuming task is the search along the path for the branch with the smallest capacity. Both of these difficulties can be eliminated if a labeling process is used as we move from one node to the next. The procedure can be systematized in many ways. We shall present the method suggested by Ford and Fulkerson [4].

10–4 The labeling technique. Imagine that we have a network in which a flow may or may not exist. Assume that the capacity of each branch is known and that we have labeled the excess capacities of the branches. The excess capacities g_{ij} are defined in the following way. When a net flow is allowed from i to j but not from j to i, write $g_{ij} = d_{ij} - x_{ij} \geq 0$. This means that an additional flow of g_{ij} can be imposed through branch $\overrightarrow{(i,j)}$ from i to j. Furthermore, it is possible to impose a fictitious flow, up to x_{ij}, from j to i in a direction opposite to the orientation of the branch. Thus, write $g_{ji} = x_{ij} \geq 0$. When an actual physical flow is allowed from i to j and j to i, write $g_{ij} = d_{ij} - x_{ij} + x_{ji}$, $g_{ji} = d_{ji} - x_{ji} + x_{ij}$, so that g_{ij}, g_{ji} represent the combined excess capacities of the two branches in the respective directions.

To determine whether the flow can be increased, we begin at the source and consider all nodes which are joined to the source by branches of positive excess capacity. It will be supposed that the source is numbered 1. Let the index j refer to the nodes which are joined to the source by branches of positive excess capacity. On the diagram of the network, we label node j with two numbers (δ_j, γ_j), where $\delta_j = g_{1j}$ and $\gamma_j = 1$. The value of δ_j is the excess capacity from the source to node j. The value of γ_j indicates the node from which we came to label j; in our case, this node is the source. If in doing this we labeled the sink N, so that there is a branch of positive excess capacity from the source to the sink, we move to the final step (given below), which shows how to increase the flow.

Let us take up the case where the sink is not labeled at the first stage. For the set of nodes labeled at the first step, we choose the smallest index j. Then we investigate whether there are any unlabeled nodes which are joined to j by branches of positive excess capacity. If there are no such nodes, we move on to the next lowest index j and repeat the process. If some unlabeled nodes can be reached, then, using the general index k for these nodes, we label each as follows:

$$\delta_k = \min (g_{jk}, \delta_j), \qquad \gamma_k = j. \tag{10–6}$$

During this labeling process, we are not concerned about whether the orientation of the branch is in the direction of our move from j to k.

We only require that the branch have a positive excess capacity (with the conventions adopted above for a flow in the wrong direction) for flow from j to k. When two branches connect k, j so that a physical flow is allowed in either direction, we consider both branches simultaneously, that is, we consider the combined excess capacity of the two branches. The label δ_k on node k gives the minimum excess capacity of the two branches which form the path from the source to j to k. The label γ_k indicates the node from which we came to label k.

After having labeled all possible nodes k with the lowest index j, then, if the sink was not one of the nodes labeled k, we move on to the next lowest index and repeat the process. If the sink has been labeled, we jump to the final step given below. This process is continued until we have labeled all nodes that are connected by branches of positive capacity to the nodes j, or until we have labeled the sink.

At the third stage, we select from the set of nodes denoted by k the one with the lowest index. We then look for unlabeled nodes that are joined to this node by branches of positive excess capacity. Let these nodes be denoted by the general index q. We label nodes q in the same way as before, i.e.,

$$\delta_q = \min (g_{kq}, \delta_k), \qquad \gamma_q = k. \tag{10–7}$$

This process is repeated until, in a finite number of steps, we reach one of the two following states:

(1) No additional nodes can be labeled, and the sink is not labeled.

(2) The sink is labeled.

If we reach case 1, the existing flow is maximal. If we reach case 2, the existing flow can be increased. Our labeling procedure shows that δ_N, the label on the sink, is the amount by which the flow can be increased over the path we have followed in moving from the source to the sink. Since the second label on the nodes indicates the preceding node, it is easy to work backwards and trace the path.

Let us denote by $g_{\alpha\beta}$ the excess capacities of the branches in the path which led to labeling the sink (in the direction in which we move in going from source to sink). Then we consider the new network whose excess capacities are

$$\hat{g}_{\alpha\beta} = g_{\alpha\beta} - \delta_N, \qquad \hat{g}_{\beta\alpha} = g_{\beta\alpha} + \delta_N, \tag{10–8}$$

$$\hat{g}_{ij} = g_{ij} \quad \text{for branches not in the above path.} \tag{10–9}$$

Note that when the excess capacity in the direction from α to β is decreased, then that in the direction from β to α must be increased by the same amount. The entire labeling process is repeated for the new network.

After a finite number of steps, we must reach case 1, since δ_N is always strictly positive.* Then we can prove (Section 10–8) that the existing flow is optimal. The net flow in each (i, j)-branch is given by

$$x_{ij} = d_{ij} - g_{ij} = g_{ji} \tag{10–10}$$

when $d_{ji} = 0$, that is, when no net flow is allowed from j to i. When d_{ij}, d_{ji} are both positive and $d_{ij} - g_{ij} \geq 0$, set

$$x_{ij} = d_{ij} - g_{ij}, \qquad x_{ji} = 0; \tag{10–11}$$

if $d_{ji} - g_{ji} \geq 0$, set

$$x_{ji} = d_{ji} - g_{ji}, \qquad x_{ij} = 0. \tag{10–12}$$

Note that $d_{ij} - g_{ij}$, $d_{ji} - g_{ji}$ cannot both be positive since $d_{ij} - g_{ij} = x_{ij} - x_{ji}$.

The technique for finding a path from source to sink which results from the labeling process described here is somewhat different from that suggested in the previous section: we move out from the source and consider all possible paths at each step until the sink is labeled. In the previous section, we followed a single path as far as possible before backtracking to move out along another path. Both methods will yield a path with all branches having positive capacities, if such a path exists. The reader should also note that there is no inviolable rule requiring that one begin with the labeled node of lowest index at each stage. One could begin with any node. However, to avoid mistakes, it is desirable to follow a systematic procedure.

10–5 An example of the labeling process. The labeling process will be illustrated for the network shown in Fig. 10–11. The excess capacities are labeled on the branches.

At the first step, we find nodes joined to the source by branches of positive capacity, i.e., $g_{1j} > 0$. These are the nodes, 2, 3, 5. We label these nodes with the ordered pair of numbers (δ_j, γ_j), where $\delta_j = g_{1j}$ and $\gamma_j = 1$ since we came from the source. Thus node 2 is labeled $(1, 1)$. The first stage is now completed, and the sink has not been labeled. Next we select from the set just labeled the node with the lowest index, i.e., node 2. We find the nodes which are joined to node 2 by branches of positive excess capacity, i.e., 3, 7, 10. We ignore node 3, which has

---

* This assumes that a maximal flow exists. If the flow can be made arbitrarily large, then at some step, $\delta_N = \infty$, and case 1 is never reached.

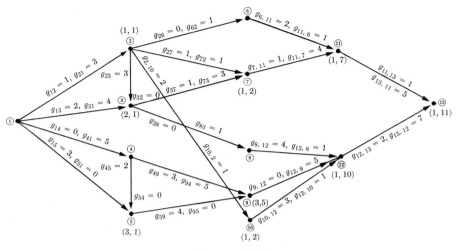

FIGURE 10–11

already been labeled. We then label nodes 7, 10. For example, for node 10,

$$\delta_{10} = \min(\delta_2, g_{2,\,10}) = \min(1, 2) = 1,$$

and $\gamma_{10} = 2$ since we came from node 2.

The sink is still unlabeled; hence we move on to the node with the next lowest index among those labeled at the first stage. This is node 3. No unlabeled nodes are joined to node 3 by branches of positive excess capacity, and we move on to node 5. Here we can label node 9. At this point, we have exhausted all nodes labeled at the first stage. During the second stage we labeled nodes 7, 9, 10. The sink remains unlabeled.

Beginning with the node of lowest index labeled at the second stage, i.e., node 7, we look for unlabeled nodes connected to node 7 by branches of positive excess capacity. We see that node 11 can be labeled. Moving out from node 9, we do not find any node to be labeled; moving from node 10, we can label node 12. The nodes labeled at stage two have been exhausted, and in stage three we have labeled nodes 11, 12. The sink was not labeled.

The node of lowest index labeled in stage three is 11. Now the sink is joined to node 11 by a branch of positive excess capacity. At this point, the labeling process stops. The flow in the network can be increased. The value of δ_{13} indicates that it can be increased by one unit along the path traced out in the move from source to sink. We can easily work backwards to find the path. The label on the sink shows that we came from node 11. From node 11 it is seen that we came from node 7. The label γ_j on node 7 shows that we came from node 2 which, of course, was preceded by the source. The path is $(\overrightarrow{1, 2})$, $(\overrightarrow{2, 7})$, $(\overrightarrow{7, 11})$, $(\overrightarrow{11, 13})$. To find the maximal flow in the network, we would repeat the whole process for the network having the excess capacities

$$\hat{g}_{12} = g_{12} - \delta_{13} = 1 - 1 = 0, \qquad \hat{g}_{21} = g_{21} + \delta_{13} = 3 + 1 = 4,$$

$$\hat{g}_{27} = 1 - 1 = 0, \qquad \hat{g}_{72} = 2, \qquad \hat{g}_{7,11} = 1 - 1 = 0,$$

$$\hat{g}_{11,7} = 4 + 1 = 5, \qquad \hat{g}_{11,13} = 1 - 1 = 0,$$

$$\hat{g}_{13,11} = 5 + 1 = 6, \qquad \hat{g}_{ij} = g_{ij} \qquad \text{for all other } i, j.$$

A maximal flow is achieved when the sink cannot be labeled.

10–6 The matrix solution. We can completely characterize any network without presenting a diagram. For a network of N nodes, we only need the Nth-order matrix of the capacities $\|d_{ij}\|$. From this matrix it is possible to draw a diagram of the network because the d_{ij} indicate which nodes are joined by branches and what the orientation of the branches is. When $d_{ij} > 0$, there is a branch from i to j which allows a net flow from i to j. If $d_{ij} = 0$, no net flow is allowed from i to j, and hence, as far as flow is concerned, there is no branch $(\overrightarrow{i, j})$. Of course, for a given network diagram, we can obtain different matrices $\|d_{ij}\|$, depending on how the nodes are numbered. The numbers appearing in these matrices will always be the same, but they can be changed around by numbering the nodes in different ways.

One can then compute the maximal flow in a network without ever using a diagram. The solution can be reached by constructing a series of excess capacity matrices $\|g_{ij}\|$. It is easy to perform the labeling process since only a $\|g_{ij}\|$-matrix and two additional columns giving δ_j, γ_j have to be used. The appropriate tableau format has the form shown in Table 10–1.

Given the excess capacities, the labels δ_j, γ_j are easily determined by means of the tableau form of Table 10–1. We begin in row 1 of the tableau and look for columns having $g_{1j} > 0$. For such columns, we set $\delta_j = g_{1j}$, $\gamma_j = 1$. Assuming that a value has not been assigned to δ_N at the first stage, we move on to the row of lowest index, say i, that was labeled at the first step (row 2, perhaps). In row i we look for $g_{ij} > 0$ for which row j has not been labeled. Then we set $\delta_j = \min(g_{ij}, \delta_i)$, $\gamma_j = i$. If no value was assigned to δ_N, we move on to the row (labeled at the first stage) with the second lowest index and repeat the procedure. We continue until a value is assigned to δ_N, or until all the rows labeled at the first stage have been exhausted.

If no value has been assigned to δ_N, and all rows labeled at the first stage are exhausted, we move on to the rows which received a label at

TABLE 10–1

TABLEAU FORM FOR COMPUTING MAXIMAL FLOWS IN NETWORKS

Nodes	1	2		j		N	Labels		Stage
1	$-$	g_{12}	$\ldots$	g_{1j}	$\ldots$	g_{1N}	δ	γ	
2	g_{21}	$-$	$\ldots$	g_{2j}	$\ldots$	g_{2N}	δ_2	γ_2	
$\vdots$									
i	g_{i1}	g_{i2}	$\ldots$	g_{ij}	$\ldots$	g_{iN}	δ_i	γ_i	
$\vdots$									
Total flow	g_{N1}	g_{N2}	$\ldots$	g_{Nj}	$\ldots$	$-$	δ_N	γ_N	

the second stage. We choose the row of lowest index and repeat the above process.

Thus, in a finite number of steps, we either assign a positive value to δ_N or we find it impossible to label δ_N. When δ_N is assigned a value, the flow can be increased. If δ_N cannot be assigned a value, the flow is maximal.

Suppose that we have assigned a value to δ_N. Let $\gamma_N = t$. We are ready to construct a new tableau. First we determine the $g_{\alpha\beta}$ in the path from source to sink. These elements are easily discovered in the tableau. The last row was reached from row t since $\gamma_N = t$. Thus the element g_{tN} in row t is one of those to be changed. Its new value is $\hat{g}_{tN} = g_{tN} - \delta_N$. Suppose that for row t, $\gamma_t = s$. The next element to be changed is then g_{st} in row s, and its new value is $\hat{g}_{st} = g_{st} - \delta_N$. If $\gamma_s = r$, the following element is g_{rs}, etc. One element in row 1 will also be changed. This completes the set of elements which are decreased in value by δ_N. For each element $g_{\alpha\beta}$ which is decreased by δ_N, the element $g_{\beta\alpha}$ is increased by δ_N (an increase in flow in one direction increases the excess capacity in the opposite direction). All other elements are unchanged in value. After the new tableau is constructed, the whole process is repeated. Since $\delta_N > 0$, we must, in a finite number of steps, reach the maximal flow (assuming that it exists), i.e., the condition under which a value cannot be assigned to δ_N.

For any network, d_{j1} and d_{Nj} are zero for all j since the flow is always away from the source and into the sink. Hence $g_{j1} = x_{1j}$, $g_{Nj} = x_{jN}$, and $\sum g_{j1} = \sum g_{Nj} =$ total flow in the network. Thus, to find the total flow in the network, we can add all the numbers in column 1 of Table 10–1, or we can add all the numbers in the last row of Table 10–1. The total flow is entered in the lower left-hand column of the tableau. It is convenient to number the rows and columns of the tableau as shown so that no counting has to be done in the labeling process, and to add a column indicating the stage at which the given row was labeled in order to eliminate the need to keep in mind which rows were labeled at the previous stage.

In every case, the x_{ij} for the maximal flow can be found from $x_{ij} = \max(d_{ij} - g_{ij}, 0)$, $i = 1, \ldots, N$, $j = 1, \ldots, N$. When d_{ij}, d_{ji} are not both positive, then $x_{ij} = g_{ji}$ if d_{ij} is positive. In such a case, it is helpful to number the nodes so that $i < j$. Then all g_{ji} lie below the principal diagonal of the tableau.

10–7 An example of the matrix solution. Let us find the maximal flow in the network of Fig. 10–3, using the tableau form rather than the diagram of the network. The initial tableau is given in Table 10–2. For this tableau, $g_{ij} = d_{ij}$ since $x_{ij} = 0$.

At stage 1, only δ_2, δ_3 can be assigned positive values. Beginning with row 2, positive values can be assigned to δ_4, δ_5. For example, $\delta_5 = \min(g_{25} = 1, \delta_2 = 6) = 1$. No value can be assigned to any additional δ_j by means of row 3. Thus at the end of the second stage, all rows but the last have been labeled. Moving to row 4, we see that

TABLE 10–2 — TABLEAU 1

Nodes	1	2	3	4	5	6	Labels		Stage
1	–	(6)	8	0	0	0	δ	γ	
2	[0]	–	2	(4)	1	0	6	1	1
3	0	0	–	5	3	0	8	1	1
4	0	[0]	0	–	0	(8)	4	2	2
5	0	0	0	4	–	9	1	2	2
0	0	0	0	[0]	0	–	4	4	3

$g_{46} > 0$ so that a value can be assigned to δ_6, and

$$\delta_6 = \min (g_{46} = 8, \delta_4 = 4) = 4.$$

Thus the flow can be increased by 4 along the traced path. To find the $g_{\alpha\beta}$ in this path, we begin by noting that node 6 was reached from node 4; hence we put a circle around g_{46}. By examining γ_4, the label on row 4, we see that it was reached from node 2, and we place a circle around g_{24} in row 2. Then γ_2 shows that node 2 was reached from node 1, and g_{12} is circled. We have reached the source, and the path is completed. In the next tableau, each of the circled elements is decreased by $\delta_6 = 4$. For each element $g_{\alpha\beta}$ decreased by δ_6, the element $g_{\beta\alpha}$ is increased by δ_6. We place a square around these elements in the tableau, as shown in Table 10–2. A new tableau is now constructed in which the circled elements of the previous tableau are decreased by $\delta_6 = 4$ and the elements enclosed by a square are increased by $\delta_6 = 4$. All these elements are unchanged in value. The new tableau is given in Table 10–3. The value of the flow is 4.

The entire procedure is repeated for the new tableau. The remaining tableaux are given in Tables 10–4 through 10–6. The reader might re-examine Figs. 10–3 through 10–7 and note that there is a tableau corresponding to each figure. However, the order is slightly different. The flow in each branch is found from $x_{ij} = \max (d_{ij} - g_{ij}, 0)$. The x_{ij} are the same as those obtained previously.

TABLE 10–3 — TABLEAU 2

Nodes	1	2	3	4	5	6	Labels		Stage
1	–	2	(8)	0	0	0	δ	γ	
2	4	–	2	0	1	0	2	1	1
3	[0]	0	–	(5)	3	0	8	1	1
4	0	4	[0]	–	0	(4)	5	3	2
5	0	0	0	4	–	9	1	2	2
4	0	0	0	[4]	0	–	4	4	3

TABLE 10–4 — TABLEAU 3

Nodes	1	2	3	4	5	6	Labels		Stage
1	–	②	4	0	0	0	δ	γ	
2	[4]	–	2	0	①	0	2	1	1
3	4	0	–	1	3	0	4	1	1
4	0	4	4	–	0	0	1	3	2
5	0	[0]	0	4	–	⑨	1	2	2
8	0	0	0	8	[0]	–	1	5	3

TABLE 10–5 — TABLEAU 4

Nodes	1	2	3	4	5	6	Labels		Stage
1	–	1	④	0	0	0	δ	γ	
2	5	–	2	0	0	0	1	1	1
3	[4]	0	–	1	③	0	4	1	1
4	0	4	4	–	0	0	1	3	2
5	0	1	[0]	4	–	⑧	3	3	2
9	0	0	0	8	[1]	–	3	5	3

TABLE 10–6 — TABLEAU 5

Nodes	1	2	3	4	5	6	Labels		Stage
1	–	1	1	0	0	0	δ	γ	
2	5	–	2	0	0	0	1	1	1
3	7	0	–	1	0	0	1	1	1
4	0	4	4	–	0	0	1	3	2
5	0	1	3	4	–	5			
12	0	0	0	8	4	–			

10–8 Proofs. As yet, we have not actually proved that the above technique does indeed yield a maximal flow. We now wish to carry out the proof. It is quite clear that by construction a feasible flow is obtained at each stage. The capacity restrictions are always satisfied, and there is conservation of flow at all nodes except the source and the sink. This latter property follows from the fact that when the flow is changed in any branch, it is changed in the entire series of branches which form a path from the source to the sink. It remains to prove that the final flow is maximal. We shall begin by defining a cut in a network.

CUT: *A cut in a network is a collection of oriented branches such that every oriented path from source to sink contains at least one branch in the cut.*

For any network, the number of different cuts is finite. If we sum the capacities of the branches in a cut, it is clear that a maximal flow cannot be greater than this sum, because the flow in every path is limited by the branch of lowest capacity, and every oriented path contains a branch of the cut.

Consider the final tableau that is obtained by means of the computational procedure described in Section 10–6. It is not possible to label the sink in this tableau. Denote by L the set of nodes which have been labeled and by U the set of nodes which cannot be labeled. Then $1 \in L^*$ and $N \in U$. Let us study the set W of all oriented branches $\overrightarrow{(i, j)}$ which join labeled nodes to unlabeled nodes, that is, $i \in L$, $j \in U$. For each

---

* The source can be considered to be in the set of labeled nodes by definition.

of these branches $g_{ij} = 0$, for otherwise node j could be labeled. This set of branches W is a cut in the network. If an oriented path from source to sink did not contain even one branch from W, every node in this path would have to be in L or every node would have to lie in U, because if the sets of nodes in L and in U were both nonempty, a branch of the path would be in W. However, $1 \in L$ and $N \in U$; this results in a contradiction.

Finally, let us show that the sum of the capacities of the branches in W is equal to the flow in the network. Note first of all that the manner in which the g_{ij} are defined determines that $d_{ij} - g_{ij} = -(d_{ji} - g_{ji})$. Because of the conservation of flow at any node other than a source or sink, Eq. (10–1) must hold. But $x_{ir} = d_{ir} - g_{ir}$, and $x_{ki} = d_{ki} - g_{ki} = -(d_{ik} - g_{ik})$ when a net flow is permitted in only one direction, and $x_{ij} - x_{ji} = d_{ij} - g_{ij}$ when a net flow is allowed in both directions. Hence (10–1) can be written for any node i which is not the source or sink as

$$\sum_{j=1,\ j\neq i}^{N} (d_{ij} - g_{ij}) = 0, \qquad i = 2, \dots, N - 1. \qquad (10\text{–}13)$$

When $i = 1$, that is, i is the source, then

$$\sum_{j=1,\ j\neq i}^{N} (d_{1j} - g_{1j}) = \sum_{j=2}^{N} x_{1j}, \qquad (10\text{–}14)$$

so that the summation is the total flow.

Consider

$$\sum_{i \in L} \sum_{j=1,\ j\neq i}^{N} (d_{ij} - g_{ij}),$$

the first summation being over the labeled nodes. Because the source is one of the labeled nodes we see that

$$\sum_{i \in L} \sum_{j=1,\ j\neq i}^{N} (d_{ij} - g_{ij}) = \sum_{j=2}^{N} x_{1j} = \text{total flow}. \qquad (10\text{–}15)$$

If $j \in L$ and $i \in L$, then $d_{ij} - g_{ij}$ and $d_{ji} - g_{ji}$ both appear in the summation and cancel each other. Hence all terms in the summation cancel for $j \in L$, and only terms for $j \in U$ appear. But when $j \in U$ and $i \in L$, then $g_{ij} = 0$. Consequently, (10–15) reduces to

$$\sum_{i \in L} \sum_{j \in U} d_{ij} = \text{total flow}. \qquad (10\text{–}16)$$

Recall that the set of all branches $\overrightarrow{(i, j)}$, $i \in L$, $j \in U$ form a cut in the network. Furthermore, the left-hand side of (10–16) is the sum of the capacities of the branches of this cut. We have already noted that the sum could not be smaller than the total flow in the network. Here we have a case where the sum of the capacities is equal to the total flow. Hence the flow must be maximal, and we have proved the validity of the computational procedure.

We have also proved another interesting result which is often referred to as the *max flow-min cut theorem*. If for each of the finite number of cuts that can be made in the network we find the total capacity of the cut, i.e., the sum of the capacities of the branches, then the smallest total capacity is equal to the maximal flow in the network.

10–9 A primal-dual algorithm for the transportation problem. In Section 8–12, we discussed a primal-dual algorithm for solving the general linear programming problem. The same algorithm can be used to solve transportation problems and, as expected, some considerable simplifications can be introduced. Perhaps the most important simplification is that each restricted primal becomes a problem of finding the maximal flow in a network, and hence the efficient procedure for finding maximal flows can be used instead of the simplex method. The algorithm to be considered, which is an adaption of the primal-dual algorithm for transportation problems, was developed by Ford and Fulkerson [4, 5].

When the primal-dual algorithm is applied to the transportation problem, it is unnecessary to annex the additional constraint which makes it easy to obtain a solution to the dual. We can find immediately a solution to the dual of a transportation problem without using this artifice. Recall that the dual of the transportation problem is

$$u_i + v_j \leq c_{ij}, \qquad i = 1, \ldots, m, \qquad j = 1, \ldots, n,$$

$$\max Z = \sum_{i=1}^{m} a_i u_i + \sum_{j=1}^{n} b_j v_j, \tag{10–17}$$

where the u_i, v_j are unrestricted in sign. If we select

$$u_i = \min_j c_{ij}, \qquad i = 1, \ldots, m,$$

$$v_j = \min_i [c_{ij} - u_i], \qquad j = 1, \ldots, n, \tag{10–18}$$

then these variables satisfy the dual constraints and are therefore a solution to the dual.

It will be recalled that when we start to apply the primal-dual algorithm, only artificial vectors are in the primal basis. When the artificial variables are driven to zero, the resulting basic feasible solution to the primal is optimal. For the transportation problem, these artificial variables do not need to be introduced explicitly. To see this, we note first that as long as any artificial variables are positive, not all primal constraints will be satisfied exactly by the positive legitimate variables. However, since the artificial variables are non-negative, the legitimate variables must satisfy

$$\sum_{j=1}^{n} x_{ij} \leq a_i, \qquad i = 1, \ldots, m,$$

$$\sum_{i=1}^{m} x_{ij} \leq b_j, \qquad j = 1, \ldots, n. \tag{10-19}$$

We wish to minimize the sum of the artificial variables, i.e., maximize the sum of the negatives of the artificial variables. However, the sum of the artificial variables is

$$\sum_{i=1}^{m} a_i + \sum_{j=1}^{n} b_j - 2 \sum_{i,j} x_{ij}.$$

Thus minimizing the sum of the artificial variables is equivalent to maximizing

$$\sum_{i,j} x_{ij}. \tag{10-20}$$

For any restricted primal, not all x_{ij} are allowed to be positive (in general). Let R be the set of indices ij such that the current solution to the dual satisfies the dual constraint ij as a strict equality. Then the set of primal variables Q which are allowed to be positive in the restricted primal is $Q = \{x_{ij} | ij \in R\}$. Because of this restriction, the equations (10-19) cannot always be satisfied as strict equalities when (10-20) is maximized. However, since we maintain $x_{ij} = 0$ when $u_i + v_j < c_{ij}$ (complementary slackness), we are sure that when a feasible solution to the primal is obtained, it will be optimal.

The problem of maximizing (10-20) subject to (10-19) with only x_{ij} in Q allowed to be positive can be solved as a network-flow problem. The appropriate network is shown in Fig. 10-12. We shall find it convenient to number the nodes as shown. Note that the directed branches $\overrightarrow{(i, j)}$ either have zero capacity (for those x_{ij} which must remain zero) or have no capacity restriction. Furthermore, observe that a net flow is allowed only from i to j and not from j to i. When the flow in the network is maximized, $\sum_{i,j} x_{ij}$ is maximized, subject to the constraints (10-19).

The usual transportation tableau rather than the tableau format of Table 10-1 can be used for maximizing the flow in Fig. 10-12. To see this, imagine that we place a circle inside those cells of the transportation tab-

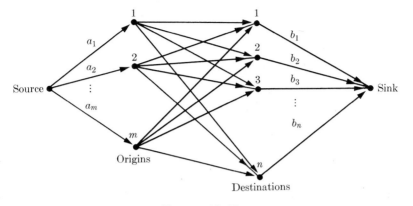

FIGURE 10–12

leau for which x_{ij} can be positive. Since there is no capacity restriction on such $\overrightarrow{(i,j)}$, one does not need to record the excess capacities. However, we may be able to move from j to i, that is, impose a flow in the wrong direction. The excess capacity g_{ji} of $\overrightarrow{(i,j)}$ is precisely x_{ij}. Hence, by recording the x_{ij} we simultaneously take care of all necessary information concerning capacities.

The transportation tableau is augmented by two additional columns and two additional rows. These are used for labeling the nodes in Fig. 10–12. Since the same number can appear on two different nodes, we must distinguish the labels of the origin nodes from the destination nodes. Let δ_i, γ_i be the labels on the origin nodes, and ξ_j, ρ_j the labels on the destination nodes. Define

$$x_s^i = a_i - \sum_{j=1}^{n} x_{ij}, \qquad i = 1, \ldots, m,$$

$$x_{sj} = b_j - \sum_{i=1}^{m} x_{ij}, \qquad j = 1, \ldots, n.$$

(10–21)

Then x_s^i is the excess capacity of the branch leading from the source to the origin node i, and x_{sj} is the excess capacity of the branch leading from destination node j to the sink. The column giving the a_i in the transportation tableau will now contain the x_s^i. Similarly, the row giving the b_j in the transportation tableau will be replaced by a row listing the x_{sj}.

Imagine now that we have some flow in the network of Fig. 10–12. We represent this flow in the transportation tableau by listing the positive x_{ij} values and by giving the x_s^i, x_{sj}. Note that positive x_{ij} must occur only in circled cells, i.e., in cells for which x_{ij} is allowed to be positive. We begin the labeling process by finding those rows of the tableau for which $x_s^i > 0$ (i.e., there is excess capacity in the branch leading from the source to i). For these rows, set $\delta_i = x_s^i$, $\gamma_i = s$ (we have come from the source). For the network under consideration, the sink cannot be labeled at the first stage.

Beginning with the labeled row of lowest index i, we look for columns j such that cell (i, j) will contain a circle (that is, x_{ij} can be positive). For each such j, we set $\xi_j = x_s^i$, $\rho_j = i$. The value of ρ_j tells us that we came from row i during the process of labeling column j. In labeling the columns, we only require that cell (i, j) be circled; we do not require that x_{ij} in the given flow be positive. If a column has been labeled such that $x_{sj} > 0$, we apply the procedure (discussed below) for modifying the flow. Otherwise, we move to the labeled row with the second lowest index (if there is such a row) and repeat the above procedure.

If, after examining all labeled rows, we find that no column with $x_{sj} > 0$ has been labeled, we begin the second stage by locating the labeled column with the lowest index j. Look for cells in this column for which $x_{ij} > 0$. If row i has not been labeled, we set $\delta_i = \min (\xi_j, x_{ij})$, $\gamma_i = j$. The value of γ_i indicates the column from which we came when labeling row i. Note that in going from j to i, we are moving in the wrong direction. If a flow is to be imposed in this direction, it must be true that $x_{ij} > 0$ since no net flow is allowed in the wrong direction. We repeat this process for each labeled column j.

From the rows of the tableau labeled at the second stage, we choose the one with the smallest index and look for unlabeled columns j containing a circle in the row i being considered. If there are such columns, we set $\xi_j = \delta_i$, $\rho_j = i$. This is done for each of the rows labeled at stage 2 until we label a column with $x_{sj} > 0$ or until the labeled rows are exhausted. If no column with $x_{sj} > 0$ is labeled at the third stage, we examine the columns labeled at the third stage for unlabeled rows having $x_{ij} > 0$, etc. Alternately labeling rows and columns, we continue until, in a finite number of steps, we reach one or the other of the following cases:

(1) No column with $x_{sj} > 0$ has been labeled, and it is not possible to label any additional rows or columns. In this case, the flow is maximal. Now there are again two alternatives:

$$\text{(a)} \quad \sum_{i=1}^{m} x_s^i = 0, \quad \text{that is} \quad \sum_{i,j} x_{ij} = \sum_{i=1}^{m} a_i;$$

$$\text{(b)} \quad \sum_{i=1}^{m} x_s^i > 0.$$

If we arrive at (1a), we have a feasible solution to the primal transportation problem. Since the solution is feasible, it is also optimal, and hence the problem has been solved. If we arrive at (1b), we have not yet obtained a feasible solution to the primal. In this case, a new solution to the dual is found by a method to be described below. This will release at least one new x_{ij} which can become positive. A new flow problem (restricted primal) is then solved.

(2) A column with $x_{sj} > 0$ is labeled. The flow in the network can be increased by

$$\sigma = \min (x_{sj}, \, \xi_j). \tag{10–22}$$

If $\rho_j = k$, we increase x_{kj} by σ, that is, $\hat{x}_{kj} = x_{kj} + \sigma$. Assuming that $\gamma_k = r$, we decrease x_{kr} by σ, that is, $\hat{x}_{kr} = x_{kr} - \sigma$. Then if $\rho_r = t$, we increase x_{tr} by σ, that is, $\hat{x}_{tr} = x_{tr} + \sigma$, etc. We alternately increase and decrease the branch flows until we come to a label $\gamma_w = s$, where s stands for the source label. A new tableau is constructed with the new values of the x_{ij}, and the labeling process is repeated. This iterative process is continued until we reach case (1).

Now we shall discuss the technique for obtaining a new solution to the dual when case (1b) is reached. Let I be the set of rows which were labeled in the last tableau (where it was impossible to increase the flow) and let J be the set of labeled columns in this tableau. Consider the number

$$h = \min_{\substack{i \in I \\ j \notin J}} (c_{ij} - u_i - v_j) > 0, \tag{10–23}$$

where the u_i, v_j are the values of the dual variables for the current solution to the dual. The number $h > 0$ because we consider only $j \notin J$; this means that the cell (i, j) does not contain a circle, and hence $u_i + v_j < c_{ij}$.

A new solution to the dual is then given by

$$
\begin{aligned}
\hat{u}_i &= u_i + h, & i \in I, \\
\hat{u}_i &= u_i, & i \notin I, \\
\hat{v}_j &= v_j - h, & j \in J, \\
\hat{v}_j &= v_j, & j \notin J.
\end{aligned}
\tag{10–24}
$$

We can see that this is indeed a solution by noting that for $i \notin I, j \notin J$, $\hat{u}_i = u_i$, $\hat{v}_j = v_j$; hence $\hat{u}_i + \hat{v}_j \leq c_{ij}$ since $u_i + v_j \leq c_{ij}$. For $i \in I$, $j \in J$, $\hat{u}_i = u_i + h$, $\hat{v}_j = v_j - h$; hence $\hat{u}_i + \hat{v}_j = u_i + v_j \leq c_{ij}$. For $i \notin I$, $j \in J$, $\hat{u}_i = u_i$, $\hat{v}_j = v_j - h$ and $\hat{u}_i + \hat{v}_j = u_i + v_j - h \leq c_{ij}$. Finally, for $i \in I, j \notin J$, $\hat{u}_i = u_i + h$, $\hat{v}_j = v_j$ and $\hat{u}_i + \hat{v}_j = u_i + v_j + h$. But by the manner in which h is chosen $\hat{u}_i + \hat{v}_j \leq c_{ij}$ from (10–23). Hence (10–24) does provide a solution to the dual.

This new solution to the dual is such that $\hat{u}_i + \hat{v}_j = c_{ij}$ for at least one $ij \notin R$; i.e., because of the manner in which h is selected, at least one x_{ij} which was previously required to be zero can now become positive. Denote the set of indices ij for which the minimum is taken on in (10–23) by st; then $\hat{u}_s + \hat{v}_t = c_{st}$. Any such $st \notin R$ since we consider only unlabeled columns in labeled rows. If $st \in R$, then cell (s, t) would contain a circle, and column t would be labeled.

It is also true that if $ij \in R$ and $x_{ij} > 0$ for the optimal solution to the restricted primal, then $\hat{u}_i + \hat{v}_j = c_{ij}$ for the new solution to the dual. This means that the new set of x_{ij} which is allowed to be positive includes all those x_{ij} which are positive in the optimal solution to the restricted primal. Hence in the new restricted primal problem, the maximal solution to the previous restricted primal problem can be used as an initial solution. The proof is immediate. For $x_{ij} > 0$ such that $i \notin I$, $j \notin J$, $\hat{u}_i + \hat{v}_j = u_i + v_j = c_{ij}$. Also for $x_{ij} > 0$ such that $i \in I$, $j \in J$, $\hat{u}_i + \hat{v}_j = u_i + v_j = c_{ij}$. There cannot be any $x_{ij} > 0$ with $i \in I$, $j \notin J$. Neither can there be any $x_{ij} > 0$ with $i \notin I$, $j \in J$ because in this case row i could be labeled.

The new value of the dual objective function $\hat{Z}$ is strictly greater than Z. Note that

$$\hat{Z} = \sum_{i \in I} a_i(u_i + h) + \sum_{j \in J} b_j(v_j - h) + \sum_{i \notin I} a_i u_i + \sum_{j \notin J} b_j v_j$$

$$= Z + h\left(\sum_{i \in I} a_i - \sum_{j \in J} b_j\right). \tag{10–25}$$

However, all i for which $x_s^i > 0$ must be in I; furthermore, for all $j \in J$,

$$\sum_{i \in I} x_{ij} = b_j.$$

If this were not true, the flow could be increased. Recall that for labeled j, either there is no circle in cell (i, j), or when there is, $x_{ij} = 0$ if $i \notin I$ (otherwise row i could be labeled). Then

$$\sum_{j \in J} \sum_{i \in I} x_{ij} = \sum_{j \in J} b_j.$$

But since $x_s^i > 0$ for at least one $i \in I$,

$$\sum_{i \in I} a_i > \sum_{j \in J} \sum_{i \in I} x_{ij}.$$

Hence

$$\sum_{i \in I} a_i - \sum_{j \in J} b_j > 0, \tag{10–26}$$

and $\hat{Z} > Z$; i.e., there is a strict increase in the dual objective function whenever a new solution to the dual is found.

The new solution to the dual gives a new set of dual constraints $\hat{R} = (ij|\hat{u}_i + \hat{v}_j = c_{ij})$ and a new set of x_{ij}, $\hat{Q} = (x_{ij}|ij \in \hat{R})$ which are allowed to be positive in the restricted primal. We then solve the new restricted primal problem, using the maximal solution to the previous restricted primal as an initial solution. Whenever we find a new solution to the dual, the value of the dual objective function is increased. Hence we must arrive at case (1a), i.e., at an optimal solution to the given transportation problem, in a finite number of steps.

10–10 Summary of primal-dual algorithm. Let us summarize the primal-dual algorithm discussed in the last section by presenting a step-by-step procedure for solving a transportation problem by means of this algorithm. All quantities of interest can be represented conveniently in the tableau form shown in Table 10–7. At first glance, the tableau form may seem exceptionally complicated, but we shall see shortly that it is not. We define ϕ_{ij}, ψ_{ij} to be

$$\phi_{ij} = c_{ij} - u_i, \qquad \psi_{ij} = c_{ij} - u_i - v_j \geq 0. \qquad (10\text{--}27)$$

The step-by-step procedure for solving the problem can be described as follows:

(1) Begin by constructing a tableau of the form shown in Table 10–7. At the start, only the values of the costs appear in this tableau. To obtain the initial solution to the dual, we search each row for the lowest cost. Then we set $u_i = \min c_{ij}$ for row i and enter the u_i-values in the first column of the tableau. At the same time, we place a circle inside those cells for which $u_i = c_{ij}$. For the columns j for which one or more circles appear we set $v_j = 0$. For the columns j for which no circle appears, we compute the ϕ_{ij} for each i and enter them into the tableau. Then we find $v_j = \min_i \phi_{ij}$ and list the remaining v_j-values. At the same time, we place a circle into those cells for which $v_j = \phi_{ij}$. Now we have an initial solution to the dual, and we have circles in those cells for which x_{ij} can be positive in the restricted primal. The ϕ_{ij} are computed for the sole purpose of obtaining the initial solution to the dual. They are never computed in succeeding tableaux.

(2) We are now ready to solve the restricted primal by the network-flow algorithm. Only the x_{ij} in cells containing circles can be positive. It is very easy to obtain an initial flow in the network, and hence there is no need to begin with all $x_{ij} = 0$. Starting in row 1 of the tableau, move to the first circled cell provided there is one. For this cell $(1, j)$, set $x_{1j} = \min (a_1, b_j)$. If $b_j < a_1$, move to the next circled cell, say

Table 10–7

Tableau Form for Primal-Dual Algorithm

		D_1		D_2		...		D_n		a_i x_s^i	δ_i	γ_i
	v_j / u_i	v_1		v_2		...		v_n				
O_1	u_1	c_{11}	ϕ_{11}	c_{12}	ϕ_{12}	...	c_{1n}	ϕ_{1n}		a_1 / x_s^1	δ_1	γ_1
		x_{11}	ψ_{11}	x_{12}	ψ_{12}		x_{1n}	ψ_{1n}				
O_2	u_2	c_{21}	ϕ_{21}	c_{22}	ϕ_{22}	...	c_{2n}	ϕ_{2n}		a_2 / x_s^2	δ_2	γ_2
		x_{21}	ψ_{21}	x_{22}	ψ_{22}		x_{2n}	ψ_{2n}				
$\vdots$	$\vdots$	$\vdots$		$\vdots$			$\vdots$			$\vdots$	$\vdots$	$\vdots$
O_m	u_m	c_{m1}	ϕ_{m1}	c_{m2}	ϕ_{m2}	...	c_{mn}	ϕ_{mn}		a_m / x_s^m	δ_m	γ_m
		x_{m1}	ψ_{m1}	x_{m2}	ψ_{m2}		x_{mn}	ψ_{mn}				
b_j / x_{sj}		b_1 / x_{s1}		b_2 / x_{s2}		...	b_n / x_{sn}			$\sum x_s^i$		
ξ_j		ξ_1		ξ_2		...	ξ_n					Labels
ρ_j		ρ_1		ρ_2		...	ρ_n					

$(1, k)$ in row 1, and set $x_{1k} = \min (a_1 - b_j, b_k)$ etc. This is continued until all that is available at origin 1 is used or until the destination requirements have been satisfied for each circled cell. Compute $x_s^1 = a_1 - \sum x_{1j}$ and enter its value in the x_s^1-column. Next move to row 2, and for the first circled cell $(2, r)$, set $x_{2r} = \min (b_r - x_{1r}, a_2)$, etc. In this way, we obtain an initial flow and the values of x_s^i. Next compute the x_{sj} for this flow and enter them in the appropriate row. If $\sum x_{sj} = 0$, move to step 6. If $\sum x_{sj} \neq 0$, move to step 3.

(3) The maximal flow is found next. For the rows with $x_s^i > 0$, set $\delta_i = x_s^i$, $\gamma_i = s$. In each labeled row look for circled cells. It is not necessary that in these cells $x_{ij} > 0$. For columns j containing a circled cell in a labeled row i, set $\xi_j = \delta_i$, $\rho_j = i$. Begin with the labeled row of

lowest index i. If a column for which $x_{sj} > 0$ has been labeled, go to step 4. If no column with $x_{sj} > 0$ has been labeled, look in the labeled columns for circled cells with $x_{ij} > 0$. When there are such cells in a row i which has not been labeled, set $\delta_i = \min(x_{ij}, \xi_j)$, $\gamma_i = j$. In the newly labeled set of rows look for circled cells in unlabeled columns. Set $\xi_j = \delta_i$, $\rho_j = i$. If no column was labeled with $x_{sj} > 0$, try to label additional rows, etc. This process can end in only two ways:

(a) It is not possible to label a column with $x_{sj} > 0$. In this case the flow is maximal. Compute $\xi = \sum x_{sj}$. If $\xi = 0$, go to step 6. If $\xi > 0$, go to step 5.

(b) A column with $x_{sj} > 0$ is labeled. In this case, go to step 4.

(4) Let k be the labeled column with $x_{sk} > 0$. In this case, the flow can be increased. A new tableau is constructed. We first fill in the x_{ij} whose values are changed. Let $\sigma = \min(\xi_k, x_{sk})$. Then if $\rho_k = u$, set $\hat{x}_{uk} = x_{uk} + \sigma$. If $\gamma_u = t$, then $\hat{x}_{ut} = x_{ut} - \sigma$; if $\rho_t = v$, then $\hat{x}_{vt} = x_{vt} + \sigma$, etc. The values of the x_{ij} in the path are alternately increased and decreased. For all other x_{ij}, $\hat{x}_{ij} = x_{ij}$. Note that the solution to the dual does not change during the construction of the new tableau. We are still optimizing the restricted primal. Return to step 3.

(5) When it is no longer possible to label a column with $x_{sj} > 0$, the flow is maximal, and we are ready to determine a new solution to the dual. Let I refer to the set of labeled rows and J to the set of labeled columns. Then for the $i \in I$, $j \notin J$, compute ψ_{ij} and enter the values in the tableau. Next find $h = \min \psi_{ij}$. A new solution to the dual is given by $\hat{u}_i = u_i + h$ for $i \in I$, $\hat{u}_i = u_i$, $i \notin I$, $\hat{v}_j = v_j - h$, $j \in J$, $\hat{v}_j = v_j$, $j \notin J$. A new tableau is constructed, and the new values of the dual variables are entered in the appropriate row and column. Circle all cells for which $\hat{u}_i + \hat{v}_j = c_{ij}$. Any cell in the preceding tableau with $x_{ij} > 0$ will contain a circle in the new tableau. At least one cell will be circled in the new tableau which was not circled in the preceding one. Enter the x_{ij}-values from the preceding tableau into the new tableau. The optimal solution for the preceding restricted primal can be used as the initial solution for the new restricted primal. Return to step 3.

(6) When in the restricted primal $\sum x_s^i = \sum x_{sj} = 0$, we have obtained a feasible solution to the given primal problem. Hence it is an optimal solution. The corresponding solution to the dual is also optimal. Frequently $\min z$ can be computed most easily from $\min z = \max Z = \sum a_i u_i + \sum b_j v_j$. The process must terminate in a finite number of steps because each time a new solution to the dual is found, $\hat{Z} > Z$.

10–11 The primal-dual algorithm; an example. The computational procedure of the primal-dual algorithm can be illustrated by applying it to the problem solved in Tables 9–2 through 9–6. The first tableau is shown in Table 10–8. We start the computation by obtaining the u_i for the initial solution to the dual. Beginning with row 1, we look for the lowest cost. It occurs in column 2 and is $c_{12} = 1$; hence we place a circle inside cell $(1, 2)$ and set $u_1 = 1$. In the second row, we find that the lowest cost occurs in columns 2, 3; we place a circle into cells $(2, 2)$, $(2, 3)$. Since the minimum cost is 2, we set $u_2 = 2$. Similarly, we find $u_3 = 1 = u_4$. Next the v_j are found. For each column containing a circle we set $v_j = 0$. Thus $v_2 = v_3 = v_4 = v_6 = 0$. For the remaining columns 1, 5, we compute the ϕ_{ij} and enter the values as shown. In each of these columns, we set $v_j = \min_i \phi_{ij}$ and place a circle into the cells where ϕ_{ij} assumes the minimum value. Thus we place a circle into cells $(1, 1)$, $(2, 1)$ of column 1, and $(1, 5)$, $(2, 5)$, $(4, 5)$ of column 5.

Having determined the x_{ij} which can become positive in the restricted primal, we are ready to solve the restricted primal. Beginning with row 1, we look for circled cells. Cell $(1, 1)$ is circled, and we set $x_{11} = \min (a_1, b_1) = \min (50, 30) = 30$. Twenty additional units are available at origin 1; hence we move to the next circled cell, $(1, 2)$, in row 1 and set $x_{12} = \min (a_1 - x_{11}, b_2) = \min (20, 50) = 20$. We have allocated all units available at the origin; thus we set $x_s^1 = 0$, $x_{s1} = 0$ and move to the second row. Cell $(2, 1)$ is circled, but the requirement of destination 1 has been satisfied. The next circled cell is $(2, 2)$; since 30 units are still needed at destination 2, we set $x_{22} = \min (30, a_2) = \min (30, 40) = 30$. There are 10 more units available at origin 2; so we move to cell $(2, 3)$ and set $x_{23} = 10$. Now no more units are available at origin 2; we set $x_s^2 = 0$, $x_{s2} = 0$ and move on to row 3. In row three, there is only one circled cell, $(3, 6)$. Thus we set $x_{36} = 11 = b_6$, $x_s^3 = 60 - 11 = 49$, and $x_{s6} = 0$. Finally, going to the first circled cell in row 4, we set $x_{44} = 31 = a_4$, $x_s^4 = 0$, $x_{s4} = 40 - 31 = 9$. Only 10 units have been shipped to destination 3; hence we set $x_{s3} = 20 - 10 = 10$. Similarly, $x_{s5} = 30$.

An initial flow has been found. We now begin the labeling process. Only one row has $x_s^i > 0$; it is row 3. We have $\delta_3 = x_s^3 = 49$, $\gamma_3 = s$. There is only one circled cell, $(3, 6)$, in row 3. Thus column 6 is the only one that can be labeled, and $\xi_6 = 49$, $\rho_6 = 3$. Now $x_{s6} = 0$, and no other rows can be labeled from column 6. Thus the flow is maximal. However, since $\sum x_s^i \neq 0$, we do not have a solution to the actual primal problem.

A new solution to the dual must be found. The set I of labeled rows contains only row 3, and the set of labeled columns J contains only column 6. For $i \in I, j \notin J$, we compute the ψ_{ij}, which are listed in row 3 of Table 10–8. The smallest ψ_{ij} is 1; thus $h = 1$. The new solution to the dual is given by $\hat{u}_3 = u_3 + 1 = 1 + 1 = 2$, $\hat{v}_6 = v_6 - 1 = 0 - 1 = -1$, $\hat{u}_i = u_i$, $i \neq 3$, $\hat{v}_j = v_j$, $j \neq 6$. The new solution to the dual is given in Table 10–9. The solution of Table 10–8 is filled in since it is the initial solution for the new restricted primal. There are two new cells, (3, 1), (3, 4), for which $\hat{u}_i + \hat{v}_j = c_{ij}$; hence these cells are circled. All the cells circled in Table 10–8 have $\hat{u}_i + \hat{v}_j = c_{ij}$ and are again circled. Table 10–9 then presents the initial tableau for the new restricted primal.

At the beginning of the labeling process, we note that only row 3 can be labeled. Now, however, columns 1, 4, 6 can be labeled. In addition $x_{sj} > 0$ for column 4. Thus the flow can be increased by $\sigma = \min(x_{s4}, \xi_4) = 9$. A new tableau (Table 10–10) is constructed. The value of the x_{ij} which changes is $\hat{x}_{34} = x_{34} + \sigma = 0 + 9 = 9$. The label on row 3 is s, so this is the only changed variable.

The labeling in Table 10–10 is more complicated. Columns 1, 4, 6 are labeled from row 3. All of these have $x_{sj} = 0$. Examination of column 1 shows that $x_{11} > 0$, and that row 1 is not labeled. Thus we can label row 1. From column 4 we can label row 4. Turning next to the newly labeled rows, we see that we can label column 2 which has $x_{s2} = 0$, and column 5 which has $x_{s5} = 30$. Here we have labeled a column with $x_{sj} > 0$. The flow can be increased by $\sigma = \min(x_{s5}, \xi_5) = 30$. A new tableau (Table 10–11) is constructed. First the values of the variables which change are computed. The three variables which must be changed by σ are easily found. From $\rho_5 = 1$, we know that x_{15} is increased by σ, that is, $\hat{x}_{15} = x_{15} + \sigma = 0 + 30 = 30$. Now from $\gamma_1 = 1$ we move to column 1, and x_{11} is decreased by σ, that is, $\hat{x}_{11} = x_{11} - \sigma = 30 - 30 = 0$. Since $\rho_1 = 3$, we move to row 3 and increase x_{31} by σ, that is, $\hat{x}_{31} = x_{31} + \sigma = 0 + 30 = 30$. The value $\gamma_3 = s$ tells us that no more variables are to be changed. The $+, -$ signs in Table 10–10 indicate how the appropriate variables are changed. All other variables remain unchanged.

The whole procedure is repeated in Table 10–11. The flow can be increased; this leads to Table 10–12. Here $\sum x_s^i = 0$, and hence we have a feasible and optimal solution to the given primal problem. This optimal solution is not the same as that obtained in Table 9–6. However, since $z_{ij} - c_{ij} = 0$ for cell (1, 5) of Table 9–6, it is immediately obvious that the present solution is simply an alternative optimal solution. Both methods require precisely the same number of tableaux, but the primal-dual algorithm considerably reduces the work necessary for computing each tableau. Note that a new solution to the dual had to be determined only once.

The above example indicates that the primal-dual algorithm developed in this section may require fewer computations in solving a transportation problem than the stepping-stone algorithm or the modification of this algorithm which uses the dual variables to evaluate the $z_{ij} - c_{ij}$. Ford and Fulkerson feel that the primal-dual algorithm may on the average

TABLE 10-8 — TABLEAU 1

u_i	v_j	D_1	D_2	D_3	D_4	D_5	D_6	a_i x_s^i	δ_i	γ_i
		1	0	0	0	1	0			
O_1	1	2 ⃞1 ㉚	1 ⃞1 ⑳	3 ⃞1	3 ⃞1	2 ⃞1 ◯	5 ⃞1	50 / 0		
O_2	2	3 ⃞1 ◯	2 ⃞2 ㉚	2 ⃞2 ⑩	4 ⃞1	3 ⃞1 ◯	4 ⃞1	40 / 0		
O_3	1	3 ⃞2	5 ⃞2	4 ⃞4 ⃞3	2 ⃞2 ㉛	4 ⃞3	1 ⃞1 ⑪	60 / 49	49	8
O_4	1	4 ⃞3 ⃞3	2 ⃞4	2 ⃞3	1 ⃞1 ⃞1	2 ⃞1 ◯	2 ⃞2	31 / 0		
b_j		30	50	20	40	30	11	181		
x_{sj}		0	0	10	9	30	0	49		
ξ_j							49			
ρ_j							3			

Labels

TABLE 10-9 — TABLEAU 2

u_i \ v_j	D_1 (1)	D_2 (0)	D_3 (0)	D_4 (0)	D_5 (1)	D_6 (-1)	x_s^i	δ_i	γ_i
O_1 (1)	2 ⃝30	1 ⃝20	3	3	2 ⃝ [0]	5	0		
O_2 (2)	3 ⃝ [0]	2 ⃝30	2 ⃝10	4	3 ⃝ [0]	4	0		
O_3 (2)	3 ⃝ [0]	5 [3]	4 [2]	2 ⃝ [0]	4 ⃝ [1]	1 ⃝11	49	49	∞
O_4 (1)	4	2	2 [2]	1 ⃝31 [9]	2 [0]	2	0		
x_{sj}	0	0	10	49	30	0	49		
ξ_j	49			49		49			Labels
ρ_j	3			3		3			

TABLE 10–10 — TABLEAU 3

v_j \ u_i		D_1	D_2	D_3	D_4	D_5	D_6	x_s^i	δ_i	γ_i
	$v_j \to$	1	0	0	0	1	−1			Labels
O_1	1	2 ⃝−30	1 ⃝20	3	3	2 ◯+	5	0	30	1
O_2	2	3 ◯	2 ⃝30	2 ⃝10	4	3 ◯	4	0		
O_3	2	3 ◯+	5	4	2 ⃝9	4 ◯	1 ⃝11	40	40	8
O_4	1	4	2	2	1 ⃝31	2 [30]	2	0	31	4
x_{sj}		0	0	10	0	30	0	40		
ξ_j		40	30	10	40	30	40			
ρ_j		3	1		3	1	3			

TABLE 10-11 — TABLEAU 4

u_i \ v_j	D_1	D_2	D_3	D_4	D_5	D_6	x_s^i	δ_i	γ_i
	1	0	0	0	1	−1			Labels
O_1 (1)	2 ◯	1 ⟨20⟩	3	3	2 ⟨30⟩	5	0	10	5
O_2 (2)	3 ◯	2 ⟨30⟩	2 ⟨10⟩	4	3 ◯	4	0	10	2
O_3 (2)	3 ⟨30⟩	5	4	2 ⟨9⟩	4	1 ⟨11⟩	10	10	8
O_4 (1)	4	2	2	1 ⟨31⟩	2 ◯	2	0	10	4
x_{sj}	0	0	10	0	0	0	10		
ξ_j	10	10	10	10	10	10			
ρ_j	3	1	2	3	4	3			

TABLE 10–12 — TABLEAU 5

u_i \ v_j	D_1 (1)	D_2 (0)	D_3 (0)	D_4 (0)	D_5 (1)	D_6 (−1)	x_s^i	δ_i	γ_i	Labels
O_1 (1)	2 ◯	1 ㉚	3	3	2 ⑳	5	0			
O_2 (2)	3 ◯	2 ⑳	2 ⑳	4	3 ◯	4	0			
O_3 (2)	3 ㉚	5	4	2 ⑲	4	1 ⑪	0			
O_4 (1)	4	2	2	1 ㉑	2 ⑩	2	0			
x_{sj}	0	0	0	0	0	0				
ξ_j										
ρ_j										

reduce the computational effort by as much as 50%. They base their opinion on experience gained in solving a number of small problems by means of both algorithms. No extensive studies using digital computers have been made as yet, so that no results are available for large-scale problems. Ford and Fulkerson think that the primal-dual algorithm will be even more efficient for large-scale problems. If these views are correct, the primal-dual algorithm should soon replace the standard stepping-stone algorithm for solving the transportation problem.

10–12 Personnel-assignment problems. Personnel-assignment problems are special types of transportation problems. In the simplest form, there are m personnel categories with a_i individuals available in category i, and n types of jobs are to be filled. A total of b_j individuals can be used in job type j. A given individual cannot be assigned to more than one job. Individuals in a given personnel category may not qualify for each of the n types of jobs. Let J_i denote the subset of jobs for which individuals in personnel category i qualify. It is desired to determine the assignment of individuals which fills the maximum number of jobs.

It is easy to formulate this problem mathematically. Let x_{ij} be the number of individuals in personnel category i assigned to job type j. Then the constraints on the problem are

$$\sum_{j=1}^{n} x_{ij} \leq a_i, \qquad i = 1, \ldots, m,$$

$$\sum_{i=1}^{m} x_{ij} \leq b_j, \qquad j = 1, \ldots, n, \qquad (10\text{--}28)$$

$$x_{ij} \geq 0, \qquad \text{all } i, j, \qquad x_{ij} = 0, \qquad j \notin J_i.$$

The x_{ij} must also be integers. We desire to maximize

$$z = \sum_{j=1}^{n} \sum_{i=1}^{m} x_{ij}. \qquad (10\text{--}29)$$

The reader will immediately recognize that this problem has the form of the restricted primal in the primal-dual algorithm and hence can be solved efficiently by means of the network-flow algorithm devised to solve the restricted primal.

In the general personnel-assignment problem, we again imagine that there are m personnel categories with a_i individuals in category i. There are n job types, and b_j individuals are needed in job type j. No individual can be assigned to more than one job, but any individual can be assigned to any job. However, individuals in different personnel categories may have different degrees of efficiency in the same job. Let r_{ij} measure the efficiency of an individual from personnel category i working on job type j. Assume that $\sum a_i = \sum b_j$ so that the number of individuals available is the same as the number of jobs to be filled. It is desired to find the assignment which will maximize the total efficiency. If x_{ij} is the number of individuals from personnel category i assigned to job type j, it will be assumed that the total efficiency is

$$z = \sum_{j=1}^{n} \sum_{i=1}^{m} r_{ij} x_{ij}. \tag{10-30}$$

Mathematically, we wish to find non-negative integers x_{ij} which maximize (10–30) and satisfy the constraints

$$\sum_{j=1}^{n} x_{ij} = a_i, \qquad i = 1, \ldots, m,$$

$$\sum_{i=1}^{m} x_{ij} = b_j, \qquad j = 1, \ldots, n. \tag{10-31}$$

This is nothing but the general transportation problem. It can be solved by any one of the methods discussed previously.

Interestingly enough, the motivation for using the primal-dual algorithm to solve transportation problems stemmed from Kuhn's work on personnel-assignment problems which had only one individual in each personnel category [10]. Ford and Fulkerson modified his algorithm for the more general case.

10–13 Transhipment problem. In our discussion of the transportation problem we have assumed that c_{ij} was the minimum cost of shipping one unit from origin i to destination j. If there were several routes from i to j, all routes were examined to find the one which yielded the lowest cost. When there are many routes from each i to each j, the task of determining the minimum-cost routes can be quite a problem. Here we wish to study transportation problems with many possible routes for shipping from i to j.

We shall begin by studying a very special type of transportation problem with many routes from each origin to each destination, called a transhipment problem. In a transhipment problem, we imagine that there is only a single direct route from i to j. In addition, however, it is possible for any given origin i to ship to any other origin i' over a unique route with a known unit cost of shipment, and similarly, every destination can ship to any other destination over a unique route with a known unit cost of shipment. The generalization of allowing origins to ship to other origins and destinations to ship to other destinations makes it possible to ship a unit from i to j over a number of different routes. For example, a unit could be shipped from i to j by first shipping from i to i', then from i' to j', then from j' to i'', and finally, from i'' to j. Note that we now permit shipment over the direct route from i to j in either direction. The unit cost of shipment over the direct route from i to j need not be the same as that from j to i.

Since any origin or destination can ship to any other origin or destination, we shall find it convenient to number the origins and destinations sequentially, beginning with the origins. Thus what we would have called destination j in the usual transportation problem will here be denoted by $m + j$. This renumbering is necessary to avoid confusion with respect to the subscripts.

In solving a transhipment problem, we wish to find the minimum-cost shipping schedule that will meet the destination requirements. The solution to this problem also allows us to determine the minimum-cost route for shipping from i to j. As usual, we shall denote by a_i the origin availabilities and by b_{m+j} the destination requirements (recall that depot j is now numbered $m + j$); we also suppose that $\sum a_i = \sum b_{m+j}$. Let x_{ik}, x_{ki} $(k = 1, \ldots, m + n, k \neq i)$ be the quantities shipped from origin i to k and from k to origin i, respectively; k may be another origin or destination. Similarly, let $x_{k,m+j}$, $x_{m+j,k}$ $(k = 1, \ldots, m + n, k \neq m + j)$ be the quantities shipped from k to destination j and from destination j to k, respectively.

The net quantity received at destination j (the total quantity received minus the quantity shipped to other origins or destinations) must be b_{m+j}. Similarly, if the destination requirements are to be met, the net amount shipped from origin i must be a_i. In order to meet these requirements, the following constraints must be satisfied:

$$\sum_{\substack{k=1 \\ k \neq i}}^{m+n} x_{ik} - \sum_{\substack{k=1 \\ k \neq i}}^{m+n} x_{ki} = a_i, \qquad i = 1, \ldots, m; \qquad (10\text{–}32)$$

$$\sum_{\substack{k=1 \\ k \neq m+j}}^{m+n} x_{k,m+j} - \sum_{\substack{k=1 \\ k \neq m+j}}^{m+n} x_{m+j,k} = b_{m+j}, \qquad j = 1, \ldots, n. \qquad (10\text{–}33)$$

If we take c_{st} to be the unit cost of shipping from s to t $(s, t = 1, \ldots, m + n; s \neq t)$, then we wish to find $x_{st} \geq 0$ which satisfy (10–32) and (10–33) and minimize

$$z = \sum_{s=1}^{m+n} \sum_{\substack{t=1 \\ s \neq t}}^{m+n} c_{st} x_{st}. \qquad (10\text{–}34)$$

Equations (10–32) through (10–34) show that the transhipment problem is a linear programming problem. It will be noted that if $\mathbf{p}_{st}$ is the activity vector for x_{st}, then $\mathbf{p}_{ts} = -\mathbf{p}_{st}$. Hence in any optimal basic solution x_{st} and x_{ts} cannot both be positive. This is, of course, intuitively obvious; we would never ship in opposite directions along the same route because costs could be reduced by making only the net shipment.

The transhipment problem (10–32) through (10–34) may easily be converted into the form of a standard transportation problem. First, we add to and subtract from each constraint s of (10–32) and (10–33) a variable x_{ss} with cost $c_{ss} = 0$. Then in (10–32) we set

$$x_{ii} + \sum_{\substack{k=1 \\ k \neq i}}^{m+n} x_{ki} = \theta, \qquad i = 1, \ldots, m, \qquad (10\text{--}35)$$

and in (10–33)

$$x_{m+j,m+j} + \sum_{\substack{k=1 \\ k \neq m+j}}^{m+n} x_{m+j,k} = \theta, \qquad j = 1, \ldots, n. \qquad (10\text{--}36)$$

The set of constraints (10–32), (10–33) therefore becomes

$$
\begin{aligned}
\sum_{k=1}^{m+n} x_{ik} &= a_i + \theta, & i &= 1, \ldots, m, \\
\sum_{k=1}^{m+n} x_{m+j,k} &= \theta, & j &= 1, \ldots, n, \\
\sum_{k=1}^{m+n} x_{ki} &= \theta, & i &= 1, \ldots, m, \\
\sum_{k=1}^{m+n} x_{k,m+j} &= b_{m+j} + \theta, & j &= 1, \ldots, n.
\end{aligned}
\qquad (10\text{--}37)
$$

For sufficiently large $\theta > 0$, the set of constraints (10–37) is equivalent to (10–32) and (10–33). Note that the variables x_{ss} take up the slack when θ is large. The set of constraints (10–37) can be rewritten

$$
\begin{aligned}
\sum_{t=1}^{m+n} x_{st} &= g_s, & s &= 1, \ldots, m+n, \\
\sum_{s=1}^{m+n} x_{st} &= h_t, & t &= 1, \ldots, m+n,
\end{aligned}
\qquad (10\text{--}38)
$$

where

$$g_s = a_s + \theta, \quad s = 1, \ldots, m; \quad g_s = \theta, \quad s = m + 1, \ldots, m + n,$$
$$h_t = \theta, \quad t = 1, \ldots, m; \quad h_t = b_t + \theta, \quad t = m + 1, \ldots, m + n.$$

The function to be optimized is

$$z = \sum_{s,t} c_{st} x_{st}. \tag{10–39}$$

The set (10–38), (10–39) represents a standard transportation problem with $m + n$ origins and $m + n$ destinations. This transportation problem is equivalent to the transhipment problem represented by (10–32) through (10–34). By solving the transportation problem we find the solution to the transhipment problem.

Note that θ can be interpreted as the size of a fictitious stockpile at each origin and destination which is large enough to take care of all transhipments. The total quantity shipped is $\sum a_i$, and hence θ need not be larger than this value. Similarly, the value of x_{ss} is the amount of the stockpile not used in transhipments. We shall leave the detailed proof of the equivalence of Eqs. (10–38), (10–39) and Eqs. (10–32) through (10–34) to the problems.

Since a transhipment problem is nothing but a transportation problem for which we do not compute in advance the minimum cost of shipping from i to j, we expect an optimal solution of the transhipment problem to have no more than $m + n - 1$ variables different from zero. When we solve the transhipment problem by the equivalent transportation problem, we note that this transportation problem can have $2(m + n) - 1$ variables different from zero. However, $m + n$ of these variables represent the remaining stockpiles, and hence there are no more than $m + n - 1$ variables of interest which are different from zero.

Given a solution to the transhipment problem, it is easy to find the minimum-cost routes to be used in the minimum-cost shipping schedule. When $x_{i,m+j} \neq 0$, then the direct route from i to j is used, and it is the lowest-cost route. When there are shipments from one origin to another and/or from one destination to another, it is only necessary to trace through the shipments to determine the lowest-cost paths.

EXAMPLE: Consider a simple transhipment problem involving two origins and two destinations. The origin availabilities are 4, 5, and the destination requirements are 3, 6. The transportation costs are indicated on the network shown in Fig. 10–13.

Let us first solve the problem as a transportation problem, using only the direct routes and ignoring the possibility of transhipment. Table 10–13

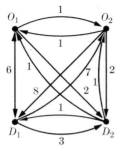

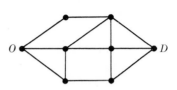

FIGURE 10–13   FIGURE 10–14

TABLE 10–13

	D_1	D_2	a_i
O_1	6 ③	2 ①	4
O_2	8 −2	2 ⑤	5
b_j	3	6	9

TABLE 10–14

	O_1	O_2	D_1	D_2	g_s
O_1	0 ⑨	1 −1	6 −3	2 ④	13
O_2	1 −1	0 ⑨	8 −5	2 ⑤	14
D_1	6 −9	7 −10	0 ⑨	3 −4	9
D_2	1 −3	1 −3	1 ③	0 ⑥	9
h_t	9	9	12	15	45

gives an optimal tableau for this problem. The minimum cost is 30. Next we solve the transhipment problem as an enlarged transportation problem. To find the origin and destination requirements, we take $\theta = a_1 + a_2 = 9$. Then $g_1 = a_1 + \theta = 13$, $g_2 = a_2 + \theta = 14$, $g_3 = g_4 = \theta = 9$; $h_1 = h_2 = \theta$, $h_3 = b_1 + \theta = 12$, $h_4 = b_2 + \theta = 15$. An optimal solution to the transhipment problem is given in Table 10–14. The minimum cost is 21. There is a reduction in cost because it is cheaper to ship everything to D_2, and then from D_2 to D_1, than to make any shipment from either origin directly to D_1.

In the more general case of a transportation problem with a number of routes other than transhipment routes from any given origin to any given destination, the simplest approach seems to be to find the lowest cost from each origin to each destination, and then to solve the standard transportation problem, using the lowest cost of shipment from each i to each j. It is interesting to note that the problem of finding the minimum cost route from a given origin to a given destination can be considered to be a transhipment problem. Suppose that an origin i is connected to a destination j, by a network of routes such as that shown in Fig. 10–14. We can imagine that a number is associated with each branch which represents the cost of shipping one unit along that branch. (When no branch connects two nodes i and j, we take the cost c_{ij} to be a very large number so that no shipment from i to j will be considered.) If we number the nodes so that the origin is 1 and the destination is N, we have a transhipment problem such that node 1 is an origin with availability 1, and node N is a destination with requirement 1. The intermediate nodes can be considered to be either origins or destinations with availabilities or requirements of 0. The solution of this transhipment problem yields the minimum cost of shipping one unit and the path of minimum cost. The basic ideas discussed in this section have been presented by Orden [11].

REFERENCES

1. C. BERGE, *Théorie des graphes et ses applications*. Paris: Dunod, 1958.

2. G. B. DANTZIG and D. R. FULKERSON, "On the Max Flow Min Cut Theorem of Networks," *RM*-1418-1, The RAND Corp., Jan., 1955.

3. L. R. FORD and D. R. FULKERSON, "Maximal Flow through a Network," *Can. J. Math.*, **8**, pp. 399–404, 1956, and *RM*-1400, The RAND Corp., Nov., 1954.

4. L. R. FORD and D. R. FULKERSON, "A Simple Algorithm for Finding Maximal Network Flows and an Application to the Hitchcock Problem, *Can. J. Math.*, **9**, pp. 210–218, 1957, and "*RM*-1604, The RAND Corp., Dec., 1955.

5. L. R. FORD and D. R. FULKERSON, "Solving the Transportation Problem," *Management Science*, **3**, 1, 1956.

6. D. R. FULKERSON and G. B. DANTZIG, "Computation of Maximal Flows in Networks," *RM*-**1489,** The RAND Corp., Apr., 1955.

7. D. GALE, "A Theorem on Flows in Networks," *RM*-**1737,** The RAND Corp., June, 1956.

8. E. A. GUILLEMIN, *Introductory Circuit Theory.* New York: Wiley, 1953.

Chapter 1 presents a very interesting discussion of networks from the point of view of electrical engineering.

9. D. KONIG, *Theorie der endlichen und unendlichen Graphen.* New York: Chelsea, 1950.

10. H. W. KUHN, "The Hungarian Method for the Assignment Problem," *Naval Research Logistics Quarterly*, **2**, 1, March, 1955.

11. A. ORDEN, "The Transhipment Problem," *Management Science*, **2,** 3, pp. 276–285, 1956.

PROBLEMS

10–1. Find a maximal flow in the following network, where the numbers associated with the branches are the capacities in the direction shown.

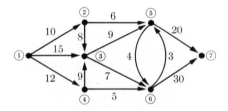

10–2. Find a maximal flow in the following network. The numbers associated with the branches are the capacities in the direction shown.

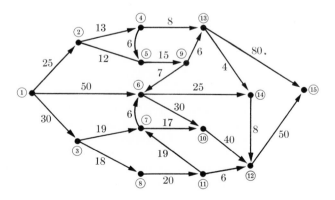

10–3. A network has the following capacitance matrix $\|d_{ij}\|$:

$$
\begin{pmatrix}
- & 12 & 19 & 8 & 0 & 0 & 0 & 0 \\
0 & - & 13 & 11 & 7 & 0 & 4 & 0 \\
0 & 0 & - & 12 & 9 & 0 & 0 & 1 \\
0 & 0 & 1 & - & 0 & 3 & 0 & 0 \\
0 & 0 & 0 & 1 & - & 2 & 3 & 5 \\
0 & 1 & 0 & 0 & 0 & - & 4 & 3 \\
0 & 0 & 0 & 0 & 0 & 0 & - & 2 \\
0 & 0 & 0 & 0 & 0 & 0 & 0 & -
\end{pmatrix}.
$$

Draw a diagram of the network. Using excess capacity matrices, find a maximal flow in the network.

10–4. Solve Problem 9–4 by the primal-dual algorithm.

10–5. Solve Problem 9–16 by the primal-dual algorithm.

10–6. Solve Problem 9–18 by the primal-dual algorithm.

10–7. Solve the following problem by the primal-dual algorithm:

	D_1	D_2	D_3	D_4	D_5	D_6	D_7	D_8	D_9	D_{10}	D_{11}	D_{12}	a_i
O_1	9	20	15	7	11	14	13	9	15	8	25	16	400
O_2	13	15	12	16	35	8	17	11	23	9	18	17	600
O_3	17	9	11	30	41	23	8	16	8	12	9	11	500
O_4	8	12	14	25	16	9	5	14	23	18	19	17	800
O_5	9	8	7	8	15	24	9	16	18	13	12	9	450
O_6	12	11	10	15	9	18	24	32	16	19	17	14	350
b_j	225	350	450	725	200	300	50	125	75	300	100	200	3100

10–8. Is degeneracy a problem in the primal-dual algorithm? Why or why not?

10–9. Is it certain that an optimal solution to a transportation problem obtained by the primal-dual algorithm will always be basic?

10–10. For the primal-dual algorithm, discuss the relation between the new solution [given by Eq. (10–24)] to the dual for transportation problems and the new solution [given by Eq. (8–100)] to the dual for the general linear programming problem.

10–11. What simplifications are introduced into the two types of personnel-assignment problems discussed in Section 10–12 when there is only one person in each personnel category?

10–12. Consider a network with capacity restrictions on the nodes. If d_i is the maximum allowable flow through node i, this means that $\sum_j x_{ji} \leq d_i$. Show how to reduce the problem to one in which there are no capacity restrictions on the nodes. Hint: Replace each capacitated node by two uncapacitated nodes joined by a single branch.

10–13. Show how to reduce a flow problem involving a number of sources and sinks to one in which there is only a single source and sink.

10–14. Show that for any $\theta \geq \sum a_i$, there is a one-to-one correspondence between the feasible solutions to (10–32) through (10–34) and (10–38), (10–39). Let $\mathbf{x}$ be an optimal solution to (10–32) through (10–34). Show that the corresponding solution to (10–38), (10–39) is also an optimal solution to (10–38), (10–39). Thus show the complete equivalence between the two problems.

10–15. Consider a transhipment problem. Let $Z(\theta)$ be the minimum cost for the equivalent transportation problem when θ is used to compute the origin availability and destination requirements. Prove that if $\theta_2 > \theta_1, Z(\theta_2) \leq Z(\theta_1)$.

10–16. Prove that for any transhipment problem, a value of $\theta > 0$ can be found such that all $x_{rr} > 0$ in any optimal solution to the equivalent transportation problem.

10–17. For any transhipment problem, show that if θ^* is large enough such that all $x_{rr} > 0$ for any optimal solution to the equivalent transportation problem and $Z(\theta)$ is the minimum cost for any θ, then $Z(\theta) = Z(\theta^*)$ if $\theta > \theta^*$. This means that after the stockpiles have become large enough, the minimum cost is independent of the size of the stockpile. From the results of Problems 10–14 and 10–15 deduce that an optimal solution to the equivalent transportation problem which has all $x_{rr} > 0$ is an optimal solution to the transhipment problem.

10–18. Find as many cuts as possible for the network shown in Problem 10–1. Find a cut such that the sum of its capacities gives the maximal flow.

10–19. Using a labeling procedure rather than the solution of a transhipment problem, develop an algorithm for finding the minimum-cost route through a network. Use this algorithm and the transhipment formulation to find the minimum cost of shipment and the minimum-cost path in the network below. Which method of solution is simpler? Are there any restrictions on your labeling algorithm?

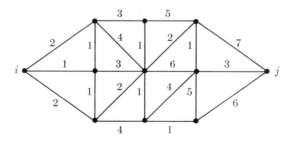

10–20. Consider a directed network and suppose that a number is associated with each branch. The number will be thought of as the time required to move through that branch. Develop a labeling procedure for finding the path through the network which requires the least time.

10–21. Show how the task of finding a least-time path in a network (discussed in Problem 10–20) can be solved as a transhipment problem.

10–22. For the network of Problem 10–1, assume that the numbers on the branches refer to the cost of shipping a unit along the corresponding branch. Find the minimum cost of shipping a unit from the source to the sink. Determine the minimum-cost path.

10–23. For the network of Problem 10–2, assume that the numbers on the branches refer to the time required to move through that branch. Find the minimum time required to move from the source to the sink. Determine the minimum-time path.

10–24. Consider a network which differs from the type discussed in this chapter only in that the branches are not oriented, i.e., a net flow in either direction along a branch is allowed, and the capacity is the same in both directions. Show how to find a maximal flow in such nonoriented networks. Is any change needed in the matrix method for finding maximal flows in oriented networks? Assume that the branches of the network shown in Fig. 10–3 are not oriented. Find a maximal flow for this assumption. How does the solution differ from that obtained in Section 10–3?

10–25. For the networks discussed in this chapter, show that if the capacity of every branch is a non-negative integer, then the maximal flow will also be a non-negative integer. Thus show that the primal-dual algorithm for the transportation problem will yield an optimal solution with integral values for the positive variables if the a_i, b_j are positive integers.

10–26. Find all cuts for the network shown in Fig. 10–3. Which cut corresponds to the optimal solution of Table 10–6? For this particular example, verify the theoretical results of Section 10–8.

10–27. Find a maximal flow in the network shown in Fig. 10–11.

10–28. When a new solution to the dual is found in the primal-dual algorithm for transportation problems, it will be true under certain circumstances that cells which contained circles in the previous flow problem (restricted primal) will no longer contain circles in the new flow problem. When does this happen?

10–29. Consider a personnel-assignment problem in which six individuals are to be assigned to six jobs in such a way as to maximize efficiency. Assume that the efficiencies are given by the first six rows and columns of the tableau shown in Problem 10–7 where the rows refer to individuals.

10–30. Develop the form of the primal-dual algorithm for transportation problems corresponding to the case where the objective function is to be maximized.

10–31. For any feasible flow in a network, show that there exists at least one set of oriented paths such that if an appropriate flow is imposed along each path, the sum of the flows in these paths gives the total flow in the network. Given a matrix of the net flows in each branch, devise an algorithm for finding such a set of oriented paths and the corresponding flows. Note that an oriented path implies that in moving from source to sink we never move along a branch in the wrong direction. Use this result to show why it was necessary to consider only oriented paths in Section 10–8.

10–32. Prove the validity of Eq. (10–26) by finding for the optimal solution to the flow problem the capacity of the cut described in Section 10–8. Hint: Show that the capacity of the cut is

$$\sum_{i \notin I} a_i + \sum_{j \in J} b_j.$$

10–33. Write down the dual of the linear programming problem given by Eqs. (10–1) through (10–3).

CHAPTER 11

SPECIAL TOPICS

"The time has come" the Walrus said,
"To talk of many things:
Of shoes—and ships—and sealing wax—
Of cabbages—and kings—
And why the sea is boiling hot—
And whether pigs have wings."

Lewis Carroll.

11–1 Introduction. In this chapter we shall consider a variety of special topics. Some of these deal with the possibility of simplifying the solution of linear programming problems in certain cases. Others deal with ways of making parameter variation analyses and sensitivity studies. We conclude the chapter by briefly discussing the relation between linear programming and zero-sum two-person games.

11–2 Postoptimality problems. Once some linear programming problem of practical interest has been solved, two situations may arise which require additional computations: (1) With practical problems, it often happens that we are not only interested in the solution to the given problem, but also desire to know how the solution will change if some of the parameters, such as the prices or the elements of the requirements vector, are changed. In other words, we wish to perform a sensitivity analysis and a parameter study.

(2) This situation is rather unpleasant, but it occurs nonetheless quite frequently. After solving the problem, we may discover that one or more of the prices were incorrect, one or more of the b_i were wrong, and perhaps a decimal point was misplaced in some of the a_{ij}. It may even turn out that some variable of interest or some constraint was omitted from the problem.

It is the purpose of the following sections to show how to keep to a minimum the additional computational effort required to take care of the above problems. In many cases, it is not necessary to solve the problem over again. A relatively small amount of work applied to the optimal solution will suffice. In other cases, however, there is no alternative but to go back to the beginning and re-solve the problem.

There are six specific problems which we shall discuss. These can be briefly stated as follows:

(1) How much can the price vector **c** be changed in some specified way before the optimal solution obtained will no longer be optimal?

(2) For a given change in **c**, how do we proceed to a new optimal solution if the original solution is no longer optimal?

(3) How much can the requirements vector **b** be changed in some specified way before the optimal solution will no longer be feasible?

(4) If a given change in **b** makes the optimal solution no longer feasible, how do we proceed to a new optimal solution?

(5) How can the addition of another variable (vector) be accounted for?

(6) How can the insertion of an additional constraint be incorporated into the system?

Changes in the matrix elements a_{ij} will be discussed in the problems at the end of this chapter. It is usually much more difficult to handle changes in the matrix elements than to deal with the problems listed under (1) through (4). This is especially true for a_{ij} in the optimal basix matrix.

11–3 Changing the price vector. We shall begin by considering problem (1). Assume that we have an optimal basic solution $\mathbf{x}_B = \mathbf{B}^{-1}\mathbf{b}$, $z = \mathbf{c}_B\mathbf{x}_B$ to the linear programming problem $\mathbf{Ax} = \mathbf{b}$, $\mathbf{x} \geq \mathbf{0}$, max $z = \mathbf{cx}$. It will be convenient to imagine that **c** is changed in the following way: We replace **c** by

$$\mathbf{c}^+ = \mathbf{c} + \phi\mathbf{f}, \qquad (11\text{–}1)$$

where **f** is some specified, but arbitrary vector, and ϕ is a non-negative scalar parameter. We wish to determine the largest value of ϕ for which the given optimal basic solution remains optimal.

If we denote by $z_j^+ - c_j^+$ the values of $z_j - c_j$ when **c** is replaced by $\mathbf{c}^+$, then the critical value of ϕ is such that any increase in ϕ would make one or more $z_j^+ - c_j^+$ negative. Now

$$z_j^+ - c_j^+ = (\mathbf{c}_B + \phi\mathbf{f}_B)\mathbf{y}_j - c_j - \phi f_j$$

$$= z_j - c_j + \phi(\mathbf{f}_B\mathbf{y}_j - f_j),$$

where $\mathbf{f}_B$ is the vector which contains the components of **f** corresponding to the components of **c** in $\mathbf{c}_B$. If all $\mathbf{f}_B\mathbf{y}_j - f_j$ are non-negative, then we can make ϕ arbitrarily large without destroying optimality. However, if one or more $\mathbf{f}_B\mathbf{y}_j - f_j$ are negative and $\phi \geq 0$ is large enough, then the corresponding $z_j^+ - c_j^+$ will become negative. The critical value

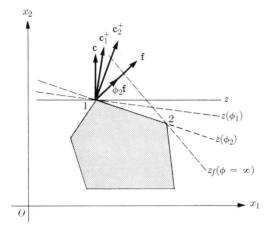

FIGURE 11–1

$\phi_c \geq 0$ is therefore given by

$$\phi_c = -\frac{z_k - c_k}{\mathbf{f}_B \mathbf{y}_k - f_k} = \min_j -\frac{z_j - c_j}{\mathbf{f}_B \mathbf{y}_j - f_j}, \qquad \mathbf{f}_B \mathbf{y}_j - f_j < 0, \quad (11\text{–}2)$$

or

$$\phi_c = \infty \qquad \text{if} \qquad \mathbf{f}_B \mathbf{y}_j - f_j \geq 0, \qquad \text{all } j.$$

If $\phi > \phi_c$, the current solution will not be optimal when $\mathbf{c}^+$ is the price vector.* The first vector to be inserted into the basis in order to maintain optimality as ϕ passes through ϕ_c is the $\mathbf{a}_k$ determined from (11–2) (or any one of the $\mathbf{a}_k$ if $\mathbf{a}_k$ is not unique) provided that an optimal solution exists for $\phi > \phi_c$.

The optimal value of $z = \mathbf{c}^+\mathbf{x} = \mathbf{cx} + \phi\mathbf{fx}$ varies continuously with ϕ. However, the optimal solution $\mathbf{x}$ varies discontinuously as we jump from one extreme point to an adjacent extreme point. This is illustrated geometrically in Fig. 11–1.

We start out with the optimal hyperplane denoted by z. Then a vector $\phi\mathbf{f}$ is added to the normal $\mathbf{c}$ to give a new hyperplane with normal $\mathbf{c}^+$. As ϕ is increased, the hyperplane becomes tilted, as shown. Extreme point 1 is still optimal when $\phi = \phi_c$. At this point, the hyperplane lies on one side of the convex polyhedron, and either extreme point 1 or extreme point 2 is optimal. When $\phi > \phi_c$, extreme point 2 becomes optimal instead of extreme point 1. Note that the solution $\mathbf{x}$ changed dis-

---

* In the event that the optimal solution is degenerate it may remain optimal for $\phi > \phi_c$, even though the optimality criterion is not satisfied. However, if we imagine that the problem is perturbed so that degeneracy does not occur, then the statement is strictly true.

continuously, while z changed continuously. For the example given, ϕ
can be increased arbitrarily, and extreme point 2 will remain optimal.
The limiting hyperplane is z_f which has $\mathbf{f}$ as a normal.

By means of the above procedure it is possible to determine the optimal
solutions for the whole range of ϕ. First ϕ_c is determined. The appropriate
vector is inserted to give a new solution which will be optimal for some
range of ϕ, $\phi_c \leq \phi \leq \phi'_c$. Then the next vector is inserted, etc.*

For problem (2) we imagine that $\mathbf{c}$ is replaced by $\mathbf{c}^+ = \mathbf{c} + \mathbf{f}$. The
new $z_j - c_j$ are

$$z_j^+ - c_j^+ = z_j - c_j + \mathbf{f}_B \mathbf{y}_j - f_j.$$

If one or more $z_j^+ - c_j^+ < 0$, it is only necessary to replace the $z_j - c_j$
by the $z_j^+ - c_j^+$ and to continue the simplex method. If the revised
simplex method is used, we must change the first row of $\mathbf{B}_1^{-1}$. Since
the new first row will be $(1, \mathbf{c}_B^+ \mathbf{B}^{-1})$, we must add $(0, \mathbf{f}_B \mathbf{B}^{-1})$ to the
first row of $\mathbf{B}_1^{-1}$ to obtain the appropriate new first row. In addition,
the first component of each $\mathbf{a}_j$ is changed from $-c_j$ to $-(c_j + f_j)$.

In the event that $\mathbf{f}$ introduces a radical change into $\mathbf{c}$, we have a completely different linear programming problem, and it may be better to
start from the beginning and solve the modified problem as if it were a
new one. However, if only a very small percentage of the c_j are changed,
it should be easier to continue from the optimal solution for the old c_j.

11–4 Changing the requirements vector. To solve problem (3), we
shall follow the approach used in Section 11–3 and replace $\mathbf{b}$ by

$$\mathbf{b}^* = \mathbf{b} + \theta \mathbf{r}, \tag{11–3}$$

where $\mathbf{r}$ is a specified, but arbitrary, vector and θ is a non-negative scalar.
We wish to find the largest θ for which the optimal basis matrix $\mathbf{B}$ yields
a feasible solution.

Consider

$$\mathbf{x}_B^* = \mathbf{B}^{-1} \mathbf{b}^* = \mathbf{B}^{-1} \mathbf{b} + \theta \mathbf{B}^{-1} \mathbf{r} = \mathbf{x}_B + \theta \mathbf{y}, \qquad \mathbf{y} = \mathbf{B}^{-1} \mathbf{r}, \tag{11–4}$$

where $\mathbf{x}_B$ is the given optimal basic feasible solution†. If all $y_i \geq 0$, θ

---

* We leave a discussion of some of the situations which can arise, such as
$\phi'_c = \phi_c$ and the appearance of unbounded solutions, to Problem 11–5.

† Note that here and in several of the following sections it is assumed that
$\mathbf{B}^{-1}$ is available. If the revised simplex method was used, $\mathbf{B}^{-1}$ is immediately
available. If the simplex method was used, $\mathbf{B}^{-1}$ will be available provided
any artificial vectors needed to initiate the computation were included as
columns in the tableaux and transformed at each iteration. Otherwise $\mathbf{B}^{-1}$
must be computed directly.

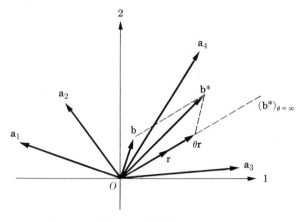

FIGURE 11–2

can be increased without limit, and $\mathbf{x}_B^*$ will be feasible and optimal. If one or more $y_i < 0$, the critical value θ_c (when the first x_{Bi}^* goes to zero) is

$$\theta_c = -\frac{x_{Bv}}{y_v} = \min_i \ -\frac{x_{Bi}}{y_i}, \qquad y_i < 0. \tag{11–5}$$

If $\theta > \theta_c$, the basis must be changed in order to maintain feasibility.

What vector should be inserted into the basis as θ passes through θ_c? Here we have an ideal application for the dual simplex algorithm. When θ becomes slightly greater than θ_c, we have a basic nonfeasible solution with all $z_j - c_j \geq 0$. The dual simplex algorithm immediately tells us that column v [v determined from (11–5)] should be removed, and (8–69) yields the vector (or if the minimum is not unique, any one of the vectors yielding the minimum) to be inserted. Proceeding in this way, we can, as θ is increased, develop a series of optimal bases.*

It may or may not be true that an optimal solution can be found for any $\theta \geq 0$. This depends on whether $\mathbf{r}$ lies in the convex polyhedral cone spanned by the activity vectors $\mathbf{a}_j$. If $\mathbf{r}$ is an element of the polyhedral cone, then $\mathbf{b}^*$ is always in the cone (by the convexity property), and there is always an optimal basic feasible solution (it is not possible to obtain an unbounded solution by changing $\mathbf{b}$— see Problem 11–17). The final basis for which θ can be increased arbitrarily without losing feasibility will correspond to an optimal solution where $\mathbf{r}$ is used as the requirements vector. Such a case is illustrated in Fig. 11–2.

When $\mathbf{r}$ is not an element of the cone spanned by the $\mathbf{a}_j$, a point will be reached where any further increase of θ will mean that there is no feasible solution. This will be signaled by the fact that all $y_{vj} \geq 0$ when column

* We leave a detailed discussion of this procedure for Problem 11–8.

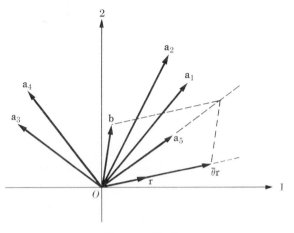

FIGURE 11–3

v is to be removed. Such a situation is illustrated in Fig. 11–3. The final optimal basis will contain $\mathbf{a}_5$. The largest value of θ for which there is a feasible solution is $\bar{\theta}$. At $\bar{\theta}$, x_5 is the only variable different from zero. One vector would presumably leave the basis if θ became larger than $\bar{\theta}$. However, there is no vector which could be inserted to yield a feasible solution.

In problem (4), we make an arbitrary change in $\mathbf{b}$, that is, we replace $\mathbf{b}$ by $\mathbf{b}^* = \mathbf{b} + \mathbf{r}$. The new basic solution is $\mathbf{x}_B^* = \mathbf{B}^{-1}\mathbf{b}^*$. If it is feasible, our task is finished. When one or more $x_{Bi}^* < 0$, we apply the dual simplex algorithm in order to find a new optimal solution, if such a solution exists. If $\mathbf{b}^*$ is radically different from $\mathbf{b}$, it may involve less work to solve the whole problem over again, with $\mathbf{b}^*$ as the requirements vector.

11–5 Adding variables or constraints. Problem (5), which involves the addition of a new variable, is easily handled. If the variable x_{n+1} with activity vector $\mathbf{a}_{n+1}$ and price c_{n+1} is annexed to the system, we compute

$$\mathbf{y}_{n+1} = \mathbf{B}^{-1}\mathbf{a}_{n+1}, \qquad z_{n+1} - c_{n+1} = \mathbf{c}_B\mathbf{y}_{n+1} - c_{n+1}, \qquad (11\text{–}6)$$

where $\mathbf{B}$ is the basis matrix for an optimal solution to the original problem. If $z_{n+1} - c_{n+1} \geq 0$, the present solution remains optimal. When $z_{n+1} - c_{n+1} < 0$, we proceed with the simplex method and insert $\mathbf{a}_{n+1}$ into the basis at the next step.

Finally, problem (6) is concerned with adding an additional constraint after an optimal solution has been found. A very important observation is to be made at this point: The additional constraint will either cause a decrease in $z_{\max}$ or leave it unchanged. We assume that the new constraint does not introduce any new variables which have nonzero prices. Hence we are maximizing the same z that we were maximizing before the new constraint was added. Assume that z can be increased by adding the new constraint. Note, however, that the new optimal solution satisfies the first m constraints as well as the new one and hence is a solution to the original problem. This contradicts the fact that we had an optimal solution to the original problem. Therefore, we can write in general

$$\max z_{m+1} \leq \max z_m, \tag{11–7}$$

where the subscript indicates the number of constraints. This analysis shows that if the optimal solution to the original problem satisfies the new constraint, it is also an optimal solution to the enlarged problem. If it does not satisfy the additional constraint, then a new optimal solution must be found.

An initial $(m + 1) \times (m + 1)$ basis matrix for the system with the additional constraint is

$$\mathbf{B}_1 = \begin{bmatrix} \mathbf{B} & \mathbf{0} \\ \boldsymbol{\gamma} & \pm 1 \end{bmatrix}, \qquad \mathbf{B}_1^{-1} = \begin{bmatrix} \mathbf{B}^{-1} & \mathbf{0} \\ \mp \boldsymbol{\gamma} \mathbf{B}^{-1} & \pm 1 \end{bmatrix}, \tag{11–8}$$

where $\mathbf{B}$ is the optimal basis for the original system. The last column is the slack, surplus, or artificial vector associated with the new constraint, and $\boldsymbol{\gamma}$ is a row vector containing the coefficients, in the new constraint, of the variables in the optimal basis $\mathbf{B}$. From our knowledge of the partitioned form of the inverse, we see that the $\mathbf{y}_j$ for the enlarged basis will be of the form $[\mathbf{y}_j, \alpha_i]$, and $\mathbf{y}_j = \mathbf{B}^{-1}\mathbf{a}_j$.

If the vector in the enlarged basis is a slack or surplus variable, its price is zero and it follows that the $z_j - c_j$ are unchanged. However, the slack or surplus variable is negative since the original optimal solution does not satisfy the new constraint. Consequently, the arrangement is such that the dual simplex algorithm may be applied to find an optimal solution.

The additional vector will be an artificial vector if the new constraint is an equality. If the artificial variable in the basic solution is negative, we can assign a price of zero to the artificial variable and use the dual simplex method to drive it out of the basis. If it is positive, we can assign to it a price of $-M$ and use the standard simplex method (note that, in this case, the $z_j - c_j$ do not remain unchanged).

When the new constraint radically alters the nature of the system, it may be more efficient to solve the whole problem over again. Similarly, if one wishes to add more than one or two new constraints which are not satisfied by the present optimal solution (these can be established by a quick check), it will be better to start at the beginning.

11–6 An example of parametric programming. To illustrate very simply the ideas of parametric programming, let us consider the first example of Section 4–11 (tableaux in Tables 4–2 through 4–4). This problem was also solved graphically in Chapter 1.

First we shall study a change in the price vector. The price vector is $\mathbf{c} = (5, 3, 0, 0)$. Let us find how far c_1 can be increased without destroying the optimality of the solution. We take $\mathbf{f} = (1, 0, 0, 0)$, and ϕ_c will be the allowable maximum increase in c_1. From (11–2),

$$\phi_c = \min_j - \frac{z_j - c_j}{\mathbf{f}_B \mathbf{y}_j - f_j}, \qquad \mathbf{f}_B \mathbf{y}_j - f_j < 0.$$

For the optimal basis, $\mathbf{f}_B = (0, 1)$ and $\mathbf{f}_B \mathbf{y}_3 - f_3 = -0.1053$, $\mathbf{f}_B \mathbf{y}_4 - f_4 = 0.2632$. Only one of these values is negative. Consequently,

$$\phi_c = - \frac{z_3 - c_3}{\mathbf{f}_B \mathbf{y}_3 - f_3} = \frac{0.2632}{0.1053} = 2.50.$$

If $c_1 > 7.50$, the basis matrix $(\mathbf{a}_2, \mathbf{a}_1)$ will no longer be optimal.

The vector to be inserted when ϕ passes through ϕ_c is $\mathbf{a}_3$. Then $\mathbf{a}_2$ is removed and we obtain Table 4–3; however, $\phi(\mathbf{f}_B \mathbf{y}_j - f_j)$ must be added to the $z_j - c_j$ of this table. For the new tableau, $\mathbf{f}_B = (0, 1)$, and

$$\mathbf{f}_B \mathbf{y}_2 - f_2 = 0.4, \qquad \mathbf{f}_B \mathbf{y}_4 - f_4 = 0.2.$$

Both values are positive, and hence the solution will remain optimal for arbitrarily large ϕ. This is clear from Fig. 1–1. An increase in c_1 tends to increase the slope of the hyperplane $z = \mathbf{cx}$. For $\phi > \phi_c$, the extreme point on the x_1-axis is optimal. As $\phi \to \infty$, $z = \mathbf{cx}$ approaches a vertical line. The extreme point on the x_1-axis will then remain optimal for arbitrarily large ϕ.

We shall consider next what happens when the second component of $\mathbf{b}$ is increased, i.e., when $\mathbf{b}$ is replaced by $\mathbf{b} + \theta \mathbf{e}_2$. To determine θ_c, the largest θ for which the optimal solution of Table 4–4 remains feasible, we first compute

$$\mathbf{y} = \mathbf{B}^{-1} \mathbf{e}_2 = \boldsymbol{\beta}_2 = [-0.1579, 0.2632].$$

The second column of $\mathbf{B}^{-1}$ is found under $\mathbf{a}_4$ in Table 4–4. According to (11–5),

$$\theta_c = \min_i - \frac{x_{Bi}}{y_i}, \qquad y_i < 0;$$

so

$$\theta_c = \frac{2.368}{0.1579} = 15.0,$$

since only $y_1 < 0$. Thus the second component of $\mathbf{b}$ can be increased to 25.0, and the given basic solution will remain feasible and optimal.

Using the dual simplex algorithm, we can find what the basis should be when θ passes through θ_c. The variable x_{B1} will become negative, and hence $\mathbf{a}_2$ will be removed. Only one y_{1j} not in the basis is negative. It is y_{14}, and thus $\mathbf{a}_4$ will enter the basis. Now we can see immediately that $\mathbf{b} + \theta\mathbf{e}_2$ will always be in the cone spanned by $\mathbf{a}_4 = \mathbf{e}_2$ and $\mathbf{a}_1$. Hence the new basis $(\mathbf{a}_4, \mathbf{a}_1)$ will be optimal for any $\theta > \theta_c$.

11–7 Upper and lower bounds. Frequently, a number of constraints in a linear programming problem will be of the especially simple form

$$0 \le x_j \le d_j. \tag{11–9}$$

These constraints are called upper bounds on the variables. Such constraints may, for example, represent sales restrictions (no more than a given amount of some product can be sold). In a transportation problem, they may represent upper limits on the amount that can be shipped over any given route. If there are many such constraints, and if they are treated in the conventional manner, they can rapidly build up the size of the basis. The special simplicity of these constraints allows us to hope that they can be handled without being explicitly introduced into the basis. This is indeed the case.

The system of constraints which do *not* contain the upper bounds will be denoted by

$$\mathbf{Ax} = \mathbf{b}, \qquad \mathbf{A} \text{ an } m \times n \text{ matrix.} \tag{11–10}$$

Assume that, in addition, each variable x_j has an upper $d_j > 0$ which may be infinite. Let $\mathbf{d} = [d_1, \ldots, d_n]$ and $\mathbf{x}_s = [x_{s1}, \ldots, x_{sn}]$, where x_{sj} is the slack variable needed to convert (11–9) into an equation. Then the set of constraints including the upper bounds can be written:

$$\begin{bmatrix} \mathbf{A} & \mathbf{0} \\ \mathbf{I}_n & \mathbf{I}_n \end{bmatrix} \begin{bmatrix} \mathbf{x} \\ \mathbf{x}_s \end{bmatrix} = \begin{bmatrix} \mathbf{b} \\ \mathbf{d} \end{bmatrix}, \qquad \mathbf{x} \ge \mathbf{0}, \quad \mathbf{x}_s \ge \mathbf{0}. \tag{11–11}$$

We shall denote by $\mathbf{a}_j^* = [\mathbf{a}_j, \mathbf{e}_j]$ the activity vector in (11–11) corresponding to x_j, and by $\mathbf{a}_{sj}^* = [\mathbf{0}, \mathbf{e}_j]$ the activity vector corresponding to the slack variable x_{sj}.

A basis matrix $\mathbf{B}_*$ for the constraints (11–11) contains $m + n$ vectors. Let us note that any such basis matrix cannot contain more than m vectors $\mathbf{a}_j^*$ whose variables are not at their upper bounds. To prove this, suppose on the contrary that there are $k > m$ such vectors. Then there must be k corresponding slack vectors since the variables are not at their upper bounds. Moreover, there must be $n - k$ additional vectors which will be $\mathbf{a}^*_{sj}$ if $x_j = 0$ or $\mathbf{a}^*_j$ if $x_j = d_j$. This gives in total $n + k > n + m$, which is a contradiction. Intuitively, the result just proved should be obvious. If no upper bounds exist, there cannot be more than m vectors in the basis. Hence, when upper bounds are added, we do not expect that, in the enlarged basis, there are more than m variables which are not at their upper bounds.

If there are $r < m$ vectors in $\mathbf{B}_*$ whose variables are not at their upper bounds, then there must be at least $m - r$ vectors in $\mathbf{B}_*$ whose variables are at their upper bounds (since there are only n slack vectors). In addition, there must be n other vectors in the basis which will be either slack vectors or legitimate vectors. If there are $k \geq m - r$ vectors in $\mathbf{B}_*$ whose variables are at their upper bounds, then there are $m + n - k - r$ slack variables in the basis. However, there are only $n - k$ variables which are not at their upper bounds. Hence $m - r$ of the slack vectors $\mathbf{a}^*_{sj}$ will be in the basis at a zero level; for these slack vectors $\mathbf{a}^*_j$ is also in the basis. Consequently, we can always arrange the vectors in $\mathbf{B}_*$ in such a way that the first m columns contain vectors $\mathbf{a}^*_j$ such that the vectors $\mathbf{a}_j$ form a basis $\mathbf{B}$ for (11–10). Columns $m + 1, \ldots, 2m$ of $\mathbf{B}_*$ contain slack vectors $\mathbf{a}_{sj}$ for the vectors in the first m columns of $\mathbf{B}_*$. If a vector $\mathbf{a}_j$ in one of the first m columns (say i) of $\mathbf{B}_*$ is in the basis at its upper bound, the corresponding slack vector $\mathbf{a}_{sj}$ will appear in column $m + i$ of $\mathbf{B}_*$ at a zero level. The remaining $n - m$ columns of $\mathbf{B}_*$ will contain either slack vectors or legitimate vectors in the basis at their upper bounds. Note that any basis $\mathbf{B}_*$ must contain $\mathbf{a}^*_j$ or $\mathbf{a}^*_{sj}$ (or both), $j = 1, \ldots, n$, since either x_j or x_{sj} must be positive because $d_j > 0$ for all j.

Thus, any basis matrix $\mathbf{B}_*$ for (11–11) can be written in partitioned form as

$$
\mathbf{B}_* = \begin{bmatrix} \mathbf{B} & 0 & \vdots & \mathbf{R} \\ \hline \mathbf{I}_m & & & \\ \hline & & \mathbf{I}_n & \\ 0 & & & \end{bmatrix}, \tag{11–12}
$$

where $\mathbf{B}$ is an $m \times m$ basis matrix for (11–10). We have included in the first m columns of $\mathbf{B}_*$ all vectors $\mathbf{a}^*_j$ whose variables are not at their upper bounds. If $r < m$ variables are not at their upper bounds, we also include in the first m columns of $\mathbf{B}_*$ those $m - r$ columns $\mathbf{a}^*_j$ whose variables are at their upper bounds, for which $\mathbf{a}_{sj}$ is also in the basis at a zero level. The remaining k vectors (if there are any) whose variables have attained their upper bounds are placed in the last k columns of $\mathbf{B}_*$. The constraints and columns can always be numbered so that the basis will have the form (11–12). Columns $m + 1, \ldots, 2m$ contain the slack vectors for the vectors in columns $1, \ldots, m$.

The inverse of $\mathbf{B}_*$ can easily be computed by the partitioning method of Chapter 2; it is

$$\mathbf{B}_*^{-1} = \begin{bmatrix} \mathbf{B}^{-1} & \mathbf{0} & \mathbf{0} & -\mathbf{B}^{-1}\mathbf{R} \\ \hline -\mathbf{B}^{-1} & \mathbf{I}_m & \mathbf{0} & \mathbf{B}^{-1}\mathbf{R} \\ \hline \mathbf{0} & \mathbf{0} & \mathbf{I}_{n-m-k} & \mathbf{0} \\ \hline \mathbf{0} & \mathbf{0} & \mathbf{0} & \mathbf{I}_k \end{bmatrix} \tag{11–13}$$

The partitioned form above will be most useful for our purposes.

We shall now show that one can carry out the simplex computations for the enlarged system by only using the tableau form for the constraints (11–10).

If $\mathbf{c}_B^*$ is the vector containing the costs for the vectors in $\mathbf{B}_*$, then

$$\mathbf{c}_B^* = (\mathbf{c}_B, \mathbf{0}, \mathbf{c}_R), \tag{11–14}$$

where $\mathbf{c}_B$ contains the prices of the $\mathbf{a}_j$ in $\mathbf{B}$, and $\mathbf{c}_R$ contains the prices of the $\mathbf{a}_j$ in $\mathbf{R}$. Then

$$\mathbf{c}_B^*\mathbf{B}_*^{-1} = (\mathbf{c}_B\mathbf{B}^{-1}, \mathbf{0}, \mathbf{c}_R - \mathbf{c}_B\mathbf{B}^{-1}\mathbf{R}). \tag{11–15}$$

For any vector $\mathbf{a}_j^*$ not in $\mathbf{B}_*$, we have

$$z_j^* - c_j = \mathbf{c}_B^*\mathbf{B}_*^{-1}\mathbf{a}_j^* - c_j = \mathbf{c}_B\mathbf{B}^{-1}\mathbf{a}_j - c_j = z_j - c_j, \tag{11–16}$$

since the 1 of the $\mathbf{e}_j$ in $\mathbf{a}_j^*$ enters a row such that the corresponding column of $\mathbf{c}_B^*\mathbf{B}_*^{-1}$ contains a zero. Thus, when $\mathbf{B}$ is the basis matrix for the constraints (11–10), $z_j^* - c_j$ for $\mathbf{a}_j^*$ is the same as $z_j - c_j$ for $\mathbf{a}_j$. For any slack vector $\mathbf{a}_{sj}^*$ not in the basis,

$$z_{sj}^* - c_{sj} = z_{sj}^* = \mathbf{c}_B^*\mathbf{B}_*^{-1}\mathbf{a}_{sj}^* = (\mathbf{c}_R - \mathbf{c}_B\mathbf{B}^{-1}\mathbf{R})\mathbf{e}_j = -(z_j - c_j), \tag{11–17}$$

since the 1 in $\mathbf{e}_j$ must appear in a row of $\mathbf{a}_{sj}^*$ corresponding to one of the last k columns of $\mathbf{B}_*$ because $\mathbf{a}_j^*$ must be in $\mathbf{B}_*$. Hence, when $\mathbf{B}$ is the basis matrix for the system (11–10), we can find the z_{sj}^* for a slack vector $\mathbf{a}_{sj}^*$ by simply taking the negative of $z_j - c_j$ for $\mathbf{a}_j$ (which is not in $\mathbf{B}$ since $\mathbf{a}_j^*$ appears in one of the last k columns of $\mathbf{B}_*$). Note that if $\mathbf{a}_j^*$ is not in the basis $\mathbf{B}_*$, $\mathbf{a}_{sj}^*$ is in the basis, and vice versa.

Next observe that when $\mathbf{a}_j^*$ is not in $\mathbf{B}_*$,

$$\mathbf{y}_j^* = \mathbf{B}_*^{-1}\mathbf{a}_j^* = [\mathbf{y}_j, -\mathbf{y}_j, \mathbf{e}_{j-m}], \quad \text{where } \mathbf{y}_j = \mathbf{B}^{-1}\mathbf{a}_j, \tag{11–18}$$

because the 1 in $\mathbf{e}_j$ does not appear in a row of $\mathbf{a}_j^*$ corresponding to one of the last k columns of $\mathbf{B}_*$. The vector $\mathbf{e}_{j-m}$ is a unit vector which has $n - m$ components with the 1 appearing in the $(j - m)$th component. Then if $\mathbf{a}_{sj}^*$ is not in $\mathbf{B}_*$, the 1 in $\mathbf{e}_j$ must appear in a row corresponding to the last k columns of $\mathbf{B}_*$, and

$$\mathbf{y}_{sj}^* = \mathbf{B}_*^{-1}\mathbf{a}_{sj}^* = [-\mathbf{y}_j, \mathbf{y}_j, \mathbf{e}_{n-m-r}], \qquad (11\text{–}19)$$

where $\mathbf{e}_{n-m-r}$ is a unit vector having $n - m$ components and $\mathbf{a}_j^*$ is in the rth column of $\mathbf{B}_*$ if we count from the right (not the left).

Let us now use (11–18) and (11–19) to discuss the problem of inserting a vector into $\mathbf{B}_*$. Equation (11–18) shows that $\mathbf{a}_j^*$ can only replace one of the first $2m$ columns of $\mathbf{B}_*$ or its own slack vector $\mathbf{a}_{sj}^*$. If it replaces its own slack vector, $\mathbf{a}_j^*$ enters the basis at its upper bound. Furthermore, since it can never go in at a value greater than its upper bound, a vector which enters at its upper bound can always be made to replace its slack vector rather than one of the vectors in the first $2m$ columns of $\mathbf{B}_*$. If $\mathbf{a}_j^*$ replaces one of the vectors in $\mathbf{B}$, then $\mathbf{a}_j^*$ enters the basis and replaces a vector whose variable is not at its upper bound (or a vector $\mathbf{a}_u^*$ which is at its upper bound, for which $\mathbf{a}_{su}^*$ is also in $\mathbf{B}_*$). If $\mathbf{a}_j^*$ replaces one of the slack vectors $\mathbf{a}_{su}^*$ in columns $m + 1, \ldots, 2m$ of $\mathbf{B}_*$, we know that one of the variables in the first m columns of $\mathbf{B}_*$ is now at its upper bound. This in turn implies that to maintain the form assigned to $\mathbf{B}_*$, we must rearrange the new basis so that $\mathbf{a}_j^*$ replaces the vector $\mathbf{a}_u^*$ (whose variable has reached its upper bound) in the first m columns of $\mathbf{B}_*$. This vector $\mathbf{a}_u^*$, whose variable is now at its upper bound, should be included among the last k columns of $\mathbf{B}_*$, and $\mathbf{a}_{su}^*$ leaves $\mathbf{B}_*$. Intuitively, $\mathbf{a}_j^*$ cannot replace one of the last k columns of $\mathbf{B}_*$ because, by assumption, the vectors in the last k columns have attained their upper bounds, and if $\mathbf{a}_j^*$ replaced such a vector, say $\mathbf{a}_r^*$, the resulting collection of vectors would not form a basis since $\mathbf{a}_{sr}^*$ would not be in the collection.

Equation (11–19) tells us that a slack vector $\mathbf{a}_{sj}^*$ may replace one of the first m columns of $\mathbf{B}_*$, one of the slack vectors in columns $m + 1, \ldots,$ $2m$, or $\mathbf{a}_j^*$. If $\mathbf{a}_{sj}^*$ replaces $\mathbf{a}_j^*$, then x_j goes from its upper bound to zero. When $\mathbf{a}_{sj}^*$ replaces one of the first m columns of $\mathbf{B}_*$, then that variable is driven to zero while at the same time x_j is reduced below its upper bound. This means that, to retain the hypothesized form of $\mathbf{B}_*$, $\mathbf{a}_j^*$ must be placed in the column earmarked for $\mathbf{a}_{sj}^*$ (since x_j is no longer at its upper bound); if $\mathbf{a}_{sj}^*$ was originally supposed to go into column r, it will now enter column $m + r$, while the slack vector in column $m + r$ is moved over into the set of slack vectors which are at their upper bounds. These transformations again yield a type of basis which is in agreement with our hypothesis. If $\mathbf{a}_{sj}^*$ replaces the slack vector in column $m + r$ of $\mathbf{B}_*$, x_j is reduced from its upper bound, and the variable corresponding to column r of $\mathbf{B}_*$ is now at its upper bound. Thus to keep the above type of basis unchanged, $\mathbf{a}_j^*$ must be moved to column r of the basis, while the vector in column r moves to the column originally occupied by $\mathbf{a}_j^*$.

Finally, let us compute the basic feasible solution $\mathbf{x}_B^*$ for the system (11–11):

$$\mathbf{x}_B^* = \mathbf{B}_*^{-1}[\mathbf{b}, \mathbf{d}] = [\mathbf{B}^{-1}\mathbf{b} - \mathbf{B}^{-1}\mathbf{R}\hat{\mathbf{d}}, \ \mathbf{d}_B - \mathbf{B}^{-1}\mathbf{b} + \mathbf{B}^{-1}\mathbf{R}\hat{\mathbf{d}}, \ \mathbf{d}^*, \ \hat{\mathbf{d}}],$$

$$(11\text{–}20)$$

where $\mathbf{d} = [\mathbf{d}_B, \mathbf{d}^*, \hat{\mathbf{d}}]$, and $\mathbf{d}_B$ contains the first m components of $\mathbf{d}$, that is, the upper bounds for the variables whose vectors are in the first m columns of $\mathbf{B}_*$, $\hat{\mathbf{d}}$ contains the upper bounds for the k vectors (which are at their upper bounds) in the last k columns of $\mathbf{B}_*$, and $\mathbf{d}^*$ contains the upper bounds for those slack variables in the basis which are at their upper bounds. Equation (11–20) shows that the variables corresponding to the last $n - m$ columns of $\mathbf{B}_*$ are indeed at their upper bounds. If $\mathbf{x}_B = \mathbf{B}^{-1}\mathbf{b} - \mathbf{B}^{-1}\mathbf{R}\hat{\mathbf{d}} = \mathbf{B}^{-1}\mathbf{b} - \sum d_j\mathbf{y}_j$, then

$$\mathbf{x}_B^* = [\mathbf{B}^{-1}\mathbf{b} - \sum d_j\mathbf{y}_j, \ \mathbf{d}_B - \mathbf{B}^{-1}\mathbf{b} + \sum d_j\mathbf{y}_j, \ \mathbf{d}^*, \ \hat{\mathbf{d}}]$$

$$= [\mathbf{x}_B, \ \mathbf{d}_B - \mathbf{x}_B, \ \mathbf{d}^*, \ \hat{\mathbf{d}}]. \qquad (11\text{–}21)$$

The sum $\sum d_j\mathbf{y}_j$ is taken over the j for which x_j is at its upper bound, and $\mathbf{a}_j^*$ appears in the last k columns of $\mathbf{B}_*$.

When $\mathbf{a}_v^*$ or $\mathbf{a}_{sv}^*$ is to enter the basis, the criterion for the vector to be removed from the basis can be written

$$\frac{x_{Bu}^*}{y_{uv}^*} = \min \left(\theta_1, \theta_2, d_v\right), \qquad (11\text{–}22)$$

where

$$\theta_1 = \min \frac{x_{Bi}}{\bar{y}_{iv}}, \quad \bar{y}_{iv} > 0, \qquad \theta_2 = \min \frac{d_{Bi} - x_{Bi}}{-\bar{y}_{iv}}, \quad \bar{y}_{iv} < 0;$$

$\bar{y}_{iv} = y_{iv}$, if $\mathbf{a}_v^*$ is to enter the basis and $\bar{y}_{i(sv)} = -y_{iv}$ if $\mathbf{a}_{sv}^*$ is to enter the basis. This follows from (11–18) and (11–19). Note that this computation can be carried out by using only the information in the tableau form appropriate to the constraints (11–10).

It should now be fairly clear how we can solve a linear programming problem $\mathbf{Ax} = \mathbf{b}, 0 \le \mathbf{x} \le \mathbf{d}, \max z = \mathbf{cx}$, without enlarging the basis to include the upper bounds. We only need to know which vectors are in the first m columns of $\mathbf{B}_*$, i.e., which $\mathbf{a}_j$ are in $\mathbf{B}$, and which variables are in the last k columns of $\mathbf{B}_*$, i.e., which variables have reached their upper bounds. All other necessary information is available if we have a tableau giving $\mathbf{x}_B = \mathbf{B}^{-1}\mathbf{b} - \sum d_j\mathbf{y}_j$, all $\mathbf{y}_j = \mathbf{B}^{-1}\mathbf{a}_j$ and all $z_j - c_j = \mathbf{c}_B\mathbf{y}_j - c_j$. We begin as if we were going to solve the linear programming problem $\mathbf{Ax} = \mathbf{b}$, $\mathbf{x} \geq \mathbf{0}$, max $z = \mathbf{cx}$. Initially, none of the variables is at its upper bound, and hence $\mathbf{x}_B = \mathbf{B}^{-1}\mathbf{b}$. The vector to enter the enlarged basis at the first iteration is computed from (11–22). If θ_1 is the minimum, then the vector enters column u of $\mathbf{B}$ and column u of $\mathbf{B}_*$. We continue as if there were no upper-bound constraints until a point is reached where θ_1 is no longer the minimum in (11–22).

If θ_1 is not the minimum in (11–22), then at the next iteration, one or more variables will reach their upper bounds. If the minimum in (11–22) is d_v, then the variable entering the enlarged basis $\mathbf{B}_*$ goes in at its upper bound and replaces the slack vector $\mathbf{a}_{vs}^*$. Looking back to (11–17), (11–19), and (11–22), one will see that all $\bar{y}_{i(sv)}$ for the slack vector $\mathbf{a}_{sv}^*$ removed from $\mathbf{B}_*$ will be contained in the column for $\mathbf{a}_j$ since $\bar{y}_{i(sv)} = -y_{iv}$. Furthermore, since $z_{sv} = c_v - z_v$, we simply change the sign of $z_v - c_v$ to obtain z_{sv}. It is better not to change the sign of $\mathbf{y}_v$ or $z_v - c_v$ in the tableau because this can later lead to confusion. To indicate that $\mathbf{a}_v^*$ is at its upper bound and is in the enlarged basis we place some sort of mark on the column corresponding to $\mathbf{a}_v$ in the tableau. During the entire process, $\mathbf{B}$ has not changed.

Although the vectors in $\mathbf{B}$ have not changed, a vector has entered $\mathbf{B}_*$ at its upper bound, and hence $\mathbf{x}_B$ must be changed. From (11–21), the new $\mathbf{x}_B$, which we shall denote by $\hat{\mathbf{x}}_B$, is

$$\hat{\mathbf{x}}_B = \mathbf{x}_B - d_v\mathbf{y}_v. \qquad (11\text{–}23)$$

Thus we subtract $d_v\mathbf{y}_v$ from $\mathbf{x}_B$ if $\mathbf{a}_v^*$ enters $\mathbf{B}_*$ at its upper bound and, of course, $\mathbf{y}_v$ is found in the tableau in the $\mathbf{a}_v$-column. After the above transformations are made, we again compute min $z_j - c_j$, $z_j - c_j < 0$. Note that, since $\mathbf{a}_v^*$ is in $\mathbf{B}_*$, $\mathbf{a}_{sv}$ is the vector not in $\mathbf{B}_*$; so we use $c_v - z_v$ rather than $z_v - c_v$; thus a different vector from $\mathbf{a}_{sv}^*$ will be selected to enter the enlarged basis.

Let us next consider what to do when the minimum in (11–22) is θ_2, and $\mathbf{a}_v^*$ should enter the enlarged basis and replace one of the slack vectors in columns $m + 1, \ldots, 2m$ of $\mathbf{B}_*$. This means that some vector $\mathbf{a}_w^*$ in one of the first m columns of $\mathbf{B}_*$ whose slack vector is to be replaced reaches its upper bound. We noted previously that the hypothesized form of $\mathbf{B}_*$ will be maintained if $\mathbf{a}_v^*$ replaces $\mathbf{a}_w^*$, and $\mathbf{a}_w^*$ is moved to one of the last k columns of $\mathbf{B}_*$. Hence if θ_2 shows that x_{Bu} reaches its upper bound, then $\mathbf{a}_v$ should replace column u of $\mathbf{B}$. If, on the introduction of $\mathbf{a}_v$, more than one x_{Bu} reach their upper bound, select any one of them and remove it from $\mathbf{B}$. Place a mark on the column corresponding to $\mathbf{a}_w$, the vector removed, to indicate that it is now at its upper bound. Then transform the tableau to obtain the $\mathbf{y}_j$, $\mathbf{x}_B$, $z_j - c_j$ appropriate to the new basis matrix $\mathbf{B}$.

Now we must subtract $d_w\mathbf{y}_w$ from $\mathbf{x}_B$ since x_w is at its upper bound. Note that, to obtain z_{sw} for $\mathbf{a}_{sw}^*$ (which has just left $\mathbf{B}_*$), we change the sign of $z_w - c_w$ ($z_w - c_w$ will be negative, even though $\mathbf{a}_w$ has just been removed from $\mathbf{B}$, because y_{uv} is negative; thus z_{sw} will be positive as desired).

It is quite possible that some variable x_q which is in $\mathbf{B}_*$ at its upper bound will recede from its upper bound at a subsequent iteration. This will be signaled by $\mathbf{a}_{sq}^*$ entering the basis. In the standard simplex tableau, this will be evidenced by the fact that the vector to enter the basis will be a column marked to indicate that the variable is at its upper bound. When the minimum in (11–22) is d_q, then $\mathbf{a}_{sq}^*$ replaces $\mathbf{a}_s^*$. The vectors in $\mathbf{B}$ do not change. We simply add $d_q\mathbf{y}_q$ to $\mathbf{x}_B$ since x_q has been driven to zero, remove the mark from column q, and go on.

If the minimum in (11–22) is θ_1, then to maintain the hypothesized form of $\mathbf{B}_*$, $\mathbf{a}_q^*$ rather than $\mathbf{a}_{sq}^*$ must replace the appropriate vector in $\mathbf{B}$. Hence, we carry out the transformation of the tableau and then add $d_q\mathbf{y}_q$ to $\mathbf{x}_B$, since x_q is no longer at its upper bound. Because $\mathbf{a}_q$ is in column r of $\mathbf{B}$, $\mathbf{y}_q = \mathbf{e}_r$, and we simply add d_q to x_{Br} (before d_q is added, x_{Br} is negative since $y_{rq} < 0$).

Finally, if the minimum in (11–22) is θ_2, some variable x_w in $\mathbf{B}$, say in column r, reaches its upper bound when $\mathbf{a}_{sq}^*$ is inserted into $\mathbf{B}_*$. Thus $\mathbf{a}_q^*$ should be placed in column r of $\mathbf{B}$, and the vector in column r should be included in the last k columns of $\mathbf{B}_*$, i.e., it should be removed from $\mathbf{B}$. We therefore insert $\mathbf{a}_q$ into $\mathbf{B}$, remove column r of $\mathbf{B}$, and transform to a new tableau. We place a mark in column $\mathbf{a}_w$ to indicate that x_w is at its upper bound. Then we add d_q to x_{Br} since x_q is no longer at its upper bound and, in addition, subtract $d_w\mathbf{y}_w$ from $\mathbf{x}_B$ since x_w is now at its upper bound.

We have explained above how we can handle upper bounds without enlarging the basis to include them. The rules we have presented are rather complicated at first reading and, no doubt, appear more complicated to the reader than they really are. It may be desirable to summarize the way in which the computations are carried out.

We wish to solve the problem $\mathbf{Ax} = \mathbf{b}$, $\mathbf{0} \le \mathbf{x} \le \mathbf{d}$, max $z = \mathbf{cx}$. To do this we use the tableau form for the problem $\mathbf{Ax} = \mathbf{b}$, $\mathbf{x} \ge \mathbf{0}$, max $z = \mathbf{cx}$ so that the upper bounds are not explicitly introduced. Let $\mathbf{B}$ be a basis matrix for $\mathbf{Ax} = \mathbf{b}$. Write, as usual, $\mathbf{y}_j = \mathbf{B}^{-1}\mathbf{a}_j$, $z_j - c_j = \mathbf{c}_B\mathbf{y}_j - c_j$. However, $\mathbf{x}_B$ is defined differently; we write $\mathbf{x}_B = \mathbf{B}^{-1}\mathbf{b} - \sum d_j\mathbf{y}_j$, where the sum $\sum d_j\mathbf{y}_j$ is taken over those variables which are at their upper bounds, but are not in $\mathbf{B}$. Of course, $\mathbf{x}_B$ gives the values of the variables in $\mathbf{B}$ which, together with the variables which are at their upper bounds, satisfy $\mathbf{Ax} = \mathbf{b}$. The computational procedure is as follows:

I. Compute $z_v^* - c_v = \min (z_j^* - c_j)$, $z_j^* - c_j < 0$, where $z_j^* - c_j = z_j - c_j$ if $x_j = 0$, and $z_j^* - c_j = c_j - z_j$ if $x_j = d_j$. If all $z_j^* - c_j \geq 0$, the solution is optimal, and we go to step III. Otherwise the vector $\mathbf{a}_v$ enters $\mathbf{B}$, or reaches its upper bound, or goes from its upper bound to zero at the next iteration. Go to step II.

II. Compute the minimum in Eq. (11–22). There are six cases to be distinguished:

(1) Assume x_v is not at its upper bound; if x_v is at its upper bound, this will be indicated by a mark on column $\mathbf{a}_v$. In this case, there are three alternatives:

(a) The minimum in (11–22) is θ_1, and column r of $\mathbf{B}$ is to be replaced. Insert $\mathbf{a}_v$ into column r of $\mathbf{B}$ and transform the tableau in the usual way. Return to step I.

(b) The minimum in (11–22) is θ_2, and the minimum is taken on for x_{Br} (if the minimum is not unique, choose any r for which the minimum value is taken on). Then $\mathbf{a}_v$ replaces column r of $\mathbf{B}$ which contains, say $\mathbf{a}_w$. Transform as usual to obtain a new tableau. Mark column $\mathbf{a}_w$ to indicate that x_w is at its upper bound. After transforming the tableau, subtract $d_w \mathbf{y}_w$ from the $\mathbf{x}_B$. Return to step I.

(c) The minimum in (11–22) is d_v. Mark the column v to indicate that x_v is at its upper bound. $\mathbf{B}$ is unchanged. Subtract $d_v \mathbf{y}_v$ from $\mathbf{x}_B$ and write these numbers in the $\mathbf{x}_B$-column. Return to step I.

(2) If x_v is at its upper bound as indicated by a mark in column v, we have the following possibilities:

(a) The minimum in (11–22) is θ_1, and column r of $\mathbf{B}$ is to be replaced. Transform the tableau as usual and add d_v to the new x_{Br}. Remove the mark from column v, indicating that x_v is no longer at its upper bound. Return to step I.

(b) The minimum in (11–22) is θ_2, and the minimum is taken on at $i = r$. Replace column r, say $\mathbf{a}_w$, by $\mathbf{a}_v$ and transform the tableau in the usual way. Remove the mark from column $\mathbf{a}_v$ and place a mark on column $\mathbf{a}_w$. Add d_v to x_{Br} and subtract $d_w \mathbf{y}_w$ from the $\mathbf{x}_B$ so obtained. Return to step I.

(c) The minimum in (11–22) is d_v. Remove the mark from column v and add $d_v \mathbf{y}_v$ to $\mathbf{x}_B$. Go to step I.

III. When all $z_j^* - c_j \geq 0$, an optimal solution has been obtained. The vector $\mathbf{x}_B$ gives the values of the x_j in $\mathbf{B}$. The marked columns have $x_j = d_j$.

Lower bounds are much easier to handle than upper bounds. They can be accounted for at the outset, and it is not necessary to worry about them thereafter. Assume that, along with other constraints, there are some additional constraints representing lower bounds on the variables. These lower bound constraints are of the form

$$0 \leq g_j \leq x_j. \tag{11-24}$$

Again it is unnecessary to increase the size of the basis to include constraints of this simple form.

Let us define the variables

$$\bar{x}_j = x_j - g_j \quad \text{or} \quad x_j = \bar{x}_j + g_j, \quad j = 1, \ldots, n. \tag{11-25}$$

Then $\bar{x}_j \geq 0$, and $x_j \mathbf{a}_j$ becomes $\bar{x}_j \mathbf{a}_j + g_j \mathbf{a}_j$. We now consider a new system for which the variables are $\bar{x}_j$. The matrix $\mathbf{A}$ of the coefficients for this system is the same as that for the original system. However $\mathbf{b}$ is replaced by

$$\mathbf{b} - \sum_{j=1}^{n} g_j \mathbf{a}_j. \tag{11-26}$$

Thus to convert a system $\mathbf{A}\mathbf{x} = \mathbf{b}$, $0 \leq \mathbf{g} \leq \mathbf{x}$, into a system without lower bounds, we treat the equivalent system

$$\mathbf{A}\bar{\mathbf{x}} = \mathbf{b} - \mathbf{A}\mathbf{g}, \quad \bar{\mathbf{x}} \geq \mathbf{0}, \quad \mathbf{x} = \bar{\mathbf{x}} + \mathbf{g}. \tag{11-27}$$

11–8 The capacitated transportation problem. It is much easier to treat upper bounds on the variables for a transportation problem than it is for the general linear programming problem. The primal-dual algorithm yields a very efficient way of handling transportation problems with bounded variables, i.e., so-called capacitated transportation problems. We shall now present the modification of the primal-dual algorithm which was developed by Ford and Fulkerson [7] to solve capacitated transportation problems.

Consider the capacitated transportation problem

$$\sum_{j=1}^{n} x_{ij} = a_i, \quad i = 1, \ldots, m,$$

$$\sum_{i=1}^{m} x_{ij} = b_j, \quad j = 1, \ldots, n,$$

$$0 \leq x_{ij} \leq d_{ij}, \quad \text{all } i, j,$$

$$\min z = \sum_{i,j} c_{ij} x_{ij}.$$

$$\tag{11-28}$$

As usual, we assume that $\sum_i a_i = \sum_j b_j$. It is no longer true, however, that this condition guarantees a feasible, and hence an optimal, solution.

Because of the upper bounds, there may not be any feasible solution. There does not seem to be any simple way of determining at the outset whether there is a feasible solution. Of course, the primal-dual algorithm will ultimately indicate whether or not a feasible solution exists.

To convert (11–28) into the form of the primal used in the primal-dual algorithm, $x_{ij} \leq d_{ij}$ is replaced by $x_{ij} + x_{ij}^s = d_{ij}$, where x_{ij}^s is a slack variable. Then the dual problem can be written

$$u_i + v_j + w_{ij} \leq c_{ij}, \qquad \text{all } i, j,$$

$$w_{ij} \leq 0, \tag{11–29}$$

$$\max Z = \sum_{i=1}^{m} a_i u_i + \sum_{j=1}^{n} b_j v_j + \sum_{i,j} d_{ij} w_{ij},$$

where the u_i, v_j are unrestricted in sign.

Consider now any solution to the dual problem (11–29); let R be the set of indices ij for which $u_i + v_j + w_{ij} = c_{ij}$ in the given solution to the dual. Also, let S be the set of indices ij for which $w_{ij} < 0$. As before, this solution to the dual defines a restricted primal problem for which each x_{ij}, $ij \in R$, is allowed to become positive, while all x_{ij}, $ij \notin R$, must remain zero. However, we now have the additional restriction that those x_{ij}^s, $ij \in S$, must be zero, i.e., for $ij \in S$, $x_{ij} = d_{ij}$. These conditions maintain complementary slackness so that $z = Z$, and consequently, when we have found a feasible solution to (11–28), it will be optimal.*

The restricted primal problem to be optimized (just as for the standard transportation problem) can be solved as a network flow-problem. It has the form [note that when the primal is written in the form (8–98) no artificial variables are needed on the upper bound constraints]:

$$\sum_j x_{ij} \leq a_i, \qquad i = 1, \ldots, m,$$

$$\sum_i x_{ij} \leq b_j, \qquad j = 1, \ldots, n,$$

$$0 \leq x_{ij} \leq d_{ij}, \qquad \text{all } i, j, \tag{11–30}$$

$$x_{ij} = 0, \quad ij \notin R, \qquad x_{ij} = d_{ij}, \quad ij \in S,$$

$$\max \sum_{i,j} x_{ij}.$$

---

* We assume that the solution to the dual has the property that if $ij \in S$, then $ij \in R$. If $ij \in S$ and $ij \notin R$, complementary slackness requires that $x_{ij} = 0$ and $x_{ij}^s = 0$. This would unnecessarily complicate the solution of the restricted primal. Fortunately, there is no difficulty in finding solutions and maintaining solutions such that if $ij \in S$, then $ij \in R$.

The appropriate flow network is again that of Fig. 10–12. However, the branch $(\overrightarrow{i, j})$ now has a capacity restriction d_{ij}. This network-flow problem can be solved by means of the tableau format of Table 10–7, provided that we change slightly the information contained in each cell. Now we must also have the d_{ij} (and

c_{ij}	d_{ij}
x_{ij}	w_{ij}

FIGURE 11–4

for the purpose of finding a new solution to the dual, the w_{ij}). Let us then replace each cell of Table 10–7 by a cell of the form shown in Fig. 11–4.

We no longer have room to carry along the equivalents of ϕ_{ij} and ψ_{ij}, although they are being used.

To begin the solution of the restricted primal, we set $x_{ij} = d_{ij}$ for $ij \in S$. It is desirable to place a mark in these cells to indicate that during the process of optimizing the restricted primal, the x_{ij}, $ij \in S$, must always be at their upper bound. For those rows and columns for which $ij \in S$, compute the x_{sj}, x^i_s in Table 10–7. Now place a circle in the cells for which $ij \in R$ but $ij \notin S$, and determine an initial flow (as described in step 2 of Section 10–10), taking account of the upper bounds on x_{ij}, i.e., no x_{ij} can be greater than its upper bound.

The labeling process used to determine whether the flow can be increased is almost identical to that used for the standard transportation problem. The only difference arises in labeling the columns. Suppose that row i has been labeled, and we are trying to find the columns which can be labeled from row i. We look for cells containing circles in row i, whose variables are not at their upper bounds. For these columns, we set

$$\xi_j = \min\,[d_{ij} - x_{ij},\ \gamma_i]. \tag{11–31}$$

When attempting to label new rows from labeled columns, we must also remember that we never consider marked cells which signify that these variables must remain at their upper bounds, i.e., we never impose a flow in the wrong direction through those branches whose variables must remain at their upper bounds. With these minor modifications, the procedure for maximizing the flow is precisely the same as for the standard transportation problem.

Once the restricted primal has been optimized, we compute $\zeta = \sum x^i_s$. If $\zeta = 0$, we have an optimal solution to the capacitated transportation problem. If on the other hand $\zeta > 0$, a new solution to the dual with $\hat{Z} > Z$ can be found.

Let us finally consider the determination of the new solution to the dual for the case where $\zeta > 0$. In the development of this algorithm, probably the most difficult task was to determine how a new solution to the dual could be obtained. For the tableau giving the optimal solution to the restricted primal, let I denote the set of labeled rows, and J the set of labeled columns. Then it is easy to show that

$$\hat{u}_i = \begin{cases} u_i + h, & i \in I, \\ u_i; & i \notin I; \end{cases} \qquad \hat{v}_j = \begin{cases} v_j - h, & j \in J, \\ v_j, & j \notin J; \end{cases}$$

$$\hat{w}_{ij} = \begin{cases} w_{ij} - h, & i \in I, \quad j \notin J, \quad \text{and} \quad ij \in R, \\ w_{ij} + h, & i \notin I, \quad j \in J, \quad \text{and} \quad ij \in S, \\ w_{ij}, & \text{all other} \quad i, j, \end{cases} \qquad (11\text{–}32)$$

is a solution to the dual provided that

$$h = \min \left[\min_{\substack{i \in I \\ j \notin J \\ ij \notin R}} (c_{ij} - u_i - v_j - w_{ij}), \min_{\substack{i \notin I \\ j \in J \\ ij \in S}} |w_{ij}| \right] > 0, \qquad (11\text{–}33)$$

or $h = \infty$ if there are no elements in the sets of (11–33). The reader is asked to prove this in Problem 11–22.

It is also true that the new solution to the dual is such that $\hat{Z} > Z$ and the increase in Z is proportional to h. Thus if $h = \infty$, the dual has an unbounded solution, and the primal has no feasible solution. The proof that $\hat{Z} > Z$ can be made in a way similar to that used in Section 10–9. It is slightly more difficult, however, and is left for Problem 11–24.

If h is finite, the new solution to the dual defines new sets R and S, which will be denoted by $\hat{R}$ and $\hat{S}$. From the manner in which h is chosen, it follows that $\hat{R}$ will contain at least one ij which was not in R, and/or at least one $ij \in S$ will not be in $\hat{S}$ (i.e. at least one primal variable will be allowed to recede from its upper bound). Thus a new restricted primal is obtained. It is not hard to show that the optimal solution to the previous restricted primal may be used as an initial solution to the new restricted primal. The reader is asked to prove this in Problem 11–23.

A suitable initial solution to the dual is

$$u_i = \min_j c_{ij}; \qquad v_j = \min_i (c_{ij} - u_i); \qquad w_{ij} = 0, \quad \text{all } i, j. \quad (11\text{–}34)$$

11–9 Secondary constraints. For a given linear programming problem, it may turn out that *a priori* considerations suggest that the respective slack or surplus variables of a certain group of inequality constraints will be different from zero in an optimal solution. Dantzig calls such constraints inactive. Active constraints are those which hold in equality form for an optimal solution. The constraints that are felt to be inactive will be called secondary constraints. They are in no way different from any other constraints in the problem except that they are expected to be inactive.

The above discussion leads us to predict that in an optimal basis the slack and surplus variables for the secondary constraints will appear at a positive level. Now suppose that before beginning the solution of the problem, we drop the secondary constraints. We then have a smaller number of constraints and hence a smaller basis. However, since we expect that the additional variables of a larger optimal basis which included the secondary constraints will be only slack or surplus variables for these secondary constraints, it should be true that the smaller basis will yield all the variables that are really needed.

After obtaining an optimal solution to the smaller problem, we use the optimal $\mathbf{x}$ and test whether the secondary constraints are indeed satisfied. If they are, then we know from Section 11–5 that $\mathbf{x}$ is an optimal solution to the problem which includes the secondary constraints. Consequently, we have finished our task.

On the other hand, if one or more of the slack or surplus variables of the secondary constraints are negative, some change must be made. If $\mathbf{B}$ is the optimal basis matrix for the system without the secondary constraints, then a basis for the enlarged system which includes the secondary constraints can be found by inserting the slack and surplus vectors of the secondary constraints as additional columns. This will give a new basis of the form

$$\begin{bmatrix} \mathbf{B} & \mathbf{0} & \mathbf{0} \\ \mathbf{R}_1 & \mathbf{I} & \mathbf{0} \\ \mathbf{R}_2 & \mathbf{0} & -\mathbf{I} \end{bmatrix}. \tag{11–35}$$

The slack vectors give the $\mathbf{I}$, and the surplus vectors the $-\mathbf{I}$ (of course, $\mathbf{I}$ and $-\mathbf{I}$ are not necessarily of the same size). The inverse of this basis is

$$\begin{bmatrix} \mathbf{B}^{-1} & \mathbf{0} & \mathbf{0} \\ -\mathbf{R}_1\mathbf{B}^{-1} & \mathbf{I} & \mathbf{0} \\ \mathbf{R}_2\mathbf{B}^{-1} & \mathbf{0} & -\mathbf{I} \end{bmatrix}. \tag{11–36}$$

Since the prices associated with the additional slack and surplus variables are zero, it is clear that the $z_j - c_j$ remain unchanged, and consequently the optimality criterion is satisfied for the enlarged system. Just as in Section 11–5, we are implicitly assuming that the secondary constraints do not contain any variables which did not appear in the optimized problem. We thus have, for the enlarged problem, a system where the optimality criteria are satisfied and some of the variables in the basis are negative. The dual simplex method can now be applied to obtain an optimal solution.

When these modifications are made, it is not necessary to add all the secondary constraints. If we feel that some secondary constraints which are not active for the optimal solution to the smaller problem will remain inactive, it is unnecessary to add them into the new basis. Clearly one must be very careful in choosing secondary constraints. If a fair number of secondary constraints turns out to be active, considerably more work may be required to find an optimal solution than if all constraints had been included originally.

11–10 The decomposition principle for linear programs. Often large linear programming problems are encountered in practice which have the structure

$$
\begin{bmatrix}
\mathbf{A}_1 & \mathbf{A}_2 & \mathbf{A}_3 \cdots \mathbf{A}_r \\
\mathbf{B}_1 & \mathbf{0} & \mathbf{0} \cdots \mathbf{0} \\
\mathbf{0} & \mathbf{B}_2 & \mathbf{0} \cdots \mathbf{0} \\
\mathbf{0} & \mathbf{0} & \mathbf{B}_3 \cdots \mathbf{0} \\
\vdots & & \vdots \\
\mathbf{0} & \mathbf{0} & \mathbf{0} \cdots \mathbf{B}_r
\end{bmatrix}
\begin{bmatrix}
\mathbf{x}_1 \\
\mathbf{x}_2 \\
\vdots \\
\vdots \\
\vdots \\
\mathbf{x}_r
\end{bmatrix}
=
\begin{bmatrix}
\mathbf{b}_0 \\
\mathbf{b}_1 \\
\vdots \\
\vdots \\
\vdots \\
\mathbf{b}_r
\end{bmatrix},
\qquad (11\text{–}37)
$$

$$
\mathbf{x}_j \geq \mathbf{0}, \qquad j = 1, \ldots, r,
$$

$$
\max z = \sum_{j=1}^{r} \mathbf{c}_j \mathbf{x}_j.
$$

We here wish to show how such a problem can be solved efficiently by means of a decomposition principle which requires the solution of a series of linear programming problems whose size is smaller than (11–37). The material to be discussed was developed by Dantzig and Wolfe [5, 6].

In (11–37) we shall suppose that $\mathbf{A}_j$ is $m_0 \times n_j$, $\mathbf{B}_j$ is $m_j \times n_j$, $\mathbf{x}_j$, $\mathbf{c}_j$ are vectors having n_j components, $\mathbf{b}_j$ is a vector having m_j components for $j = 1, \ldots, r$ and $\mathbf{b}_0$ is a vector having m_0 components. If each $\mathbf{A}_j = \mathbf{0}$, then (11–37) reduces to a set of r smaller linear programming problems of the form $\mathbf{B}_j \mathbf{x}_j = \mathbf{b}_j$, $\mathbf{x}_j \geq \mathbf{0}$, $\max z_j = \mathbf{c}_j \mathbf{x}_j$.

However, when not all $\mathbf{A}_j = \mathbf{0}$, the set of constraints $\sum_j \mathbf{A}_j \mathbf{x}_j = \mathbf{b}_0$ couples the system together, and it is not possible to optimize over a particular $\mathbf{x}_j$ independently of the other $\mathbf{x}_k$. Nonetheless, it is possible to optimize (11–37) without using a basis of size $\sum_{j=0}^{r} m_j$. We shall now study how this can be done.

The set of points $\mathbf{x}_j \geq \mathbf{0}$ which satisfies $\mathbf{B}_j \mathbf{x}_j = \mathbf{b}_j$ is a closed convex set with only a finite number of extreme points. If the set is strictly bounded, it is a polyhedron, and any point in the convex set can be represented as a convex combination of the extreme points. We shall assume this to be the case. Denote by $\mathbf{x}_{kj}^*$, the extreme points of the convex set of feasible solutions to $\mathbf{B}_j\mathbf{x}_j = \mathbf{b}_j$. We shall assume that there are h_j such extreme points. Then any feasible solution $\mathbf{x}_j \geq \mathbf{0}$ to $\mathbf{B}_j\mathbf{x}_j = \mathbf{b}_j$ can be written

$$\mathbf{x}_j = \sum_{k=1}^{h_j} \rho_{kj}\mathbf{x}_{kj}^*, \quad \rho_{kj} \geq 0, \quad k = 1, \ldots, h_j;$$

$$\sum_{k=1}^{h_j} \rho_{kj} = 1. \tag{11–38}$$

Furthermore, any $\mathbf{x}_j$ of the form (11–38) is automatically a feasible solution to $\mathbf{B}_j\mathbf{x}_j = \mathbf{b}_j$, since any convex combination of the extreme points will be an element of the convex set of feasible solutions.

Now consider the set of $\rho_{kj} \geq 0$ satisfying the constraints

$$\sum_{j=1}^{r} \sum_{k=1}^{h_j} \rho_{kj}\mathbf{A}_j\mathbf{x}_{kj}^* = \mathbf{b}_0,$$

$$\sum_{k=1}^{h_j} \rho_{kj} = 1, \quad j = 1, \ldots, r. \tag{11–39}$$

The set of constraints (11–39) is completely equivalent to the constraints (11–37). Every feasible solution to (11–37) determines a set of $\rho_{kj} \geq 0$ which satisfy (11–39), and every set of $\rho_{kj} \geq 0$ satisfying (11–39) determines a set of $\mathbf{x}_j \geq \mathbf{0}$ satisfying (11–37).* Thus the linear programming problem (11–37) is completely equivalent to the linear programming problem whose constraints are expressed by (11–39), and which seeks to maximize the objective function

$$z = \sum_{j=1}^{r} \sum_{k=1}^{h_j} \rho_{kj}\mathbf{c}_j\mathbf{x}_{kj}^*. \tag{11–40}$$

If we denote an optimal solution to (11–39) and (11–40) by ρ_{kj}^*, $k = 1, \ldots, h_j$; $j = 1, \ldots, r$, then an optimal solution to (11–37) is

$$\mathbf{x}_j = \sum_{k=1}^{h_j} \rho_{kj}^*\mathbf{x}_{kj}^*, \quad j = 1, \ldots, r. \tag{11–41}$$

---

* Observe that a set of $\rho_{kj} \geq 0$ satisfying (11–39) uniquely determines a set of $\mathbf{x}_j$ satisfying (11–37). However, a set of $\mathbf{x}_j$ satisfying (11–37) may not *uniquely* determine a set of $\rho_{kj} \geq 0$ satisfying (11–39); there will, however, be at least one such set of ρ_{kj}.

Let us write

$$\mathbf{d}_{kj} = \mathbf{A}_j \mathbf{x}_{kj}^*, \qquad f_{kj} = \mathbf{c}_j \mathbf{x}_{kj}^*, \qquad \text{all } j, k. \qquad (11\text{–}42)$$

Then (11–37) is equivalent to the linear programming problem:

$$\sum_{j=1}^{r} \sum_{k=1}^{h_j} \rho_{kj} \mathbf{d}_{kj} = \mathbf{b}_0,$$

$$\sum_{k=1}^{h_j} \rho_{kj} = 1, \qquad j = 1, \ldots, r,$$

$$\rho_{kj} \geq 0, \qquad \text{all } j, k, \qquad (11\text{–}43)$$

$$\max z = \sum_{j,k} f_{kj} \rho_{kj}.$$

The linear programming problem (11–43) has a great advantage over (11–37) in that it will, in general, have considerably fewer constraints, thus requiring a smaller basis matrix than (11–37). The problem in (11–37) has $\sum_{j=0}^{r} m_j$ constraints, while (11–43) has $m_0 + r$ constraints. However, (11–43) will usually involve many more variables, since the number of extreme points of the convex set of feasible solutions to $\mathbf{B}_j \mathbf{x}_j = \mathbf{b}_j$ will, in general, be considerably larger than the number of components in $\mathbf{x}_j$. There would be little advantage to the formulation (11–43) if it were necessary to compute every $\mathbf{d}_{kj}, f_{kj}$, that is, to generate every extreme point $\mathbf{x}_{kj}^*$, before the problem was solved. The above remark is especially pertinent if we recall that, for a linear programming problem which has many more variables than constraints, it is normally true that a large percentage of the vectors never enter the basis and hence are never needed.

Fortunately, it is possible to generate the $\mathbf{d}_{kj}, f_{kj}$ as they are used. Let us next study the application of the simplex method to (11–43) and, at the same time, see how to generate the $\mathbf{d}_{kj}, f_{kj}$. If the constraints of (11–43) are written in the form

$$\sum_{j=1}^{r} \sum_{k=1}^{h_j} \rho_{kj} \mathbf{q}_{kj} = \mathbf{b}, \qquad (11\text{–}44)$$

then $\mathbf{q}_{kj} = [\mathbf{d}_{kj}, \mathbf{e}_j]$, where $\mathbf{e}_j$ is the jth unit vector having r components, and $\mathbf{b} = [\mathbf{b}_0, \mathbf{1}']$, where $\mathbf{1}'$ is a sum vector having r components. Denote by $\mathbf{B}$ any basis matrix (of order $m_0 + r$) for (11–44), by $\boldsymbol{\rho}_B$ a vector containing the variables in the basis, and by $\mathbf{f}_B$ a vector containing the prices in the basis.

Suppose that we have a basic feasible solution $\rho_B = \mathbf{B}^{-1}\mathbf{b}$ to (11–44). Let $\boldsymbol{\sigma} = (\boldsymbol{\sigma}_1, \boldsymbol{\sigma}_2) = \mathbf{f}_B\mathbf{B}^{-1}$, where $\boldsymbol{\sigma}_1$ contains the first m_0 components of $\boldsymbol{\sigma}$, and $\boldsymbol{\sigma}_2$ contains the last r components of $\boldsymbol{\sigma}$. Then, by (11–42),

$$z_{kj} - f_{kj} = \mathbf{f}_B\mathbf{B}^{-1}\mathbf{q}_{kj} - f_{kj} = \boldsymbol{\sigma}_1\mathbf{d}_{kj} + \sigma_{2j} - f_{kj}$$

$$= (\boldsymbol{\sigma}_1\mathbf{A}_j - \mathbf{c}_j)\mathbf{x}_{kj}^* + \sigma_{2j}, \qquad (11\text{–}45)$$

where σ_{2j} is the jth component of $\boldsymbol{\sigma}_2$.

To determine whether the given basic feasible solution is optimal, we must compute min $(z_{kj} - f_{kj})$ over all k, j. If this minimum is non-negative, the given solution is optimal; otherwise more iterations are to be made. Now

$$\min_{\text{all } k,j} (z_{kj} - f_{kj}) = \min [\min_k (z_{k1} - f_{k1}), \min_k (z_{k2} - f_{k2}), \ldots,$$

$$\min_k (z_{kr} - f_{kr})]. \qquad (11\text{–}46)$$

Going back to (11–45), we see that, for a given j, $\min_k (z_{kj} - f_{kj})$ occurs at an extreme point of the convex set of feasible solutions to $\mathbf{B}_j\mathbf{x}_j = \mathbf{b}_j$. Consequently, since each extreme point $\mathbf{x}_{kj}^*$ is a basic feasible solution to $\mathbf{B}_j\mathbf{x}_j = \mathbf{b}_j$, $\min_k (z_{kj} - f_{kj})$ is σ_{2j} plus the optimal value of the objective function for the linear programming problem

$$\mathbf{B}_j\mathbf{x}_j = \mathbf{b}_j, \qquad \mathbf{x}_j \geq \mathbf{0}, \qquad \min Z_j = (\boldsymbol{\sigma}_1\mathbf{A}_j - \mathbf{c}_j)\mathbf{x}_j. \qquad (11\text{–}47)$$

Furthermore, an optimal basic solution to (11–47) gives an extreme point $\mathbf{x}_{kj}^*$ for which the corresponding $z_{kj} - f_{kj}$ has the smallest possible value over k. This $\mathbf{x}_{kj}^*$ can then be used to generate the corresponding $\mathbf{d}_{kj}, f_{kj}$ by means of (11–42) and $\mathbf{q}_{kj}$.

Thus to determine min $(z_{kj} - f_{kj})$ over all k, j, we solve r linear programming problems of the form (11–47). Writing Z_j^* for the optimal value of Z_j for the jth such problem, we compute $Z_j^* + \sigma_{2j}$, and

$$\min_{\text{all } k,j} (z_{kj} - f_{kj}) = \min_j (Z_j^* + \sigma_{2j}) = Z_s^* + \sigma_{2s}. \qquad (11\text{–}48)$$

Let $\mathbf{x}_{rs}^*$ be an optimal extreme point of (11–47) for $j = s$. Then if $\mathbf{d}_{rs} = \mathbf{A}_s\mathbf{x}_{rs}^*$ and $\mathbf{q}_{rs} = [\mathbf{d}_{rs}, \mathbf{e}_s]$, $\mathbf{q}_{rs}$ enters the basis at the next iteration, and the price associated with $\mathbf{q}_{rs}$ is $f_{rs} = \mathbf{c}_s\mathbf{x}_{rs}^*$. Thus we have generated the vector to enter the basis. We now return to the problem (11–43) and transform to obtain $\hat{\mathbf{B}}^{-1}$, $\hat{\boldsymbol{\sigma}}$, $\hat{\rho}_B$, the new values of $\mathbf{B}^{-1}$, $\boldsymbol{\sigma}$, ρ_B. The value $\hat{\boldsymbol{\sigma}}$ is used to determine a new set of objective functions for the linear programming problems (11–47). These r new problems are solved, and thus the next vector to enter the basis in (11–43) is found. This process is continued until an optimal solution is obtained. The theory of the simplex method guarantees that an optimal solution will be obtained in a finite number of steps (provided that degeneracy is treated properly).

The reader will recognize that the revised simplex method provides an efficient way to solve (11–43). To obtain an initial basic feasible solution, we use a Phase I in which we add r artificial variables ρ_{ai} and maximize the form $-\sum_i \rho_{ai}$. In solving the set of problems (11–47), one of the special computational algorithms may often be used to advantage. For example, the problems (11–47) may be transportation problems.

The restriction (made at the beginning of our discussion) requiring that the convex set of feasible solutions to $\mathbf{B}_j\mathbf{x}_j = \mathbf{b}_j$ must be a polyhedron is unnecessary. The generalization to the case where the convex set is unbounded is left to Problem 11–28.

The computational technique discussed here can also be used to solve generalized linear programming problems in which we wish to determine not only an optimal vector $\mathbf{x}$, but also optimal activity vectors $\mathbf{a}_j$. We suppose that the activity vector $\mathbf{a}_j$ may be freely chosen from the set of solutions to the inequalities $\mathbf{B}_j\mathbf{a}_j \le \mathbf{b}_j$. It will be assumed that the set of $\mathbf{a}_j$ satisfying these inequalities is a convex polyhedron K_j. Thus $\mathbf{a}_j$ can be freely chosen from the convex polyhedron K_j. That is, we wish to solve the linear programming problem

$$\sum_{j=1}^{r} x_j\mathbf{a}_j = \mathbf{b}, \qquad \mathbf{x} \ge \mathbf{0}, \qquad \max z = \mathbf{cx}, \qquad (11\text{–}49)$$

where the $\mathbf{a}_j$ are not specified, but instead must satisfy $\mathbf{B}_j\mathbf{a}_j \le \mathbf{b}_j$, $j = 1, \ldots, r$.

To cast this problem into the above form, let us denote the extreme points of the convex polyhedron representing the solutions to $\mathbf{B}_j\mathbf{a}_j \le \mathbf{b}_j$ by $\mathbf{a}_{kj}^*$, $k = 1, \ldots, h_j$. Each point $\mathbf{a}_j$ in the polyhedron can be written

$$\mathbf{a}_j = \sum_{k=1}^{h_j} \rho_{kj}\mathbf{a}_{kj}^*, \quad \rho_{kj} \ge 0, \quad k = 1, \ldots, h_j; \qquad \sum_{k=1}^{h_j} \rho_{kj} = 1, \quad (11\text{–}50)$$

and any such point is in the polyhedron. Then we obtain the equivalent linear programming problem:

$$\sum_{j=1}^{r} \sum_{k=1}^{h_j} x_j\rho_{kj}\mathbf{a}_{kj}^* = \mathbf{b}, \quad \mathbf{x} \ge \mathbf{0}, \quad \rho_{kj} \ge 0, \quad \text{all } k, j;$$

$$\sum_{k} \rho_{kj} = 1, \quad j = 1, \ldots, r,$$

$$\max z = \mathbf{cx}. \qquad (11\text{–}51)$$

Now note that

$$z = \sum_{j=1}^{r} c_j x_j = \sum_{j=1}^{r} \sum_{k=1}^{h_j} c_j\rho_{kj}x_j, \qquad (11\text{–}52)$$

since $\sum_k \rho_{kj} = 1$. Thus defining new variables $v_{kj} = \rho_{kj}x_j \geq 0$, we obtain the linear programming problem

$$\sum_{j,k} v_{kj}a^*_{kj} = \mathbf{b}, \quad v_{kj} \geq 0, \quad \text{all } k, j, \qquad \max z = \sum_{j,k} c_j v_{kj}. \quad (11\text{-}53)$$

If all the $\mathbf{a}^*_{kj}$ were known, the simplex method could be applied directly. Since they are not, the $\mathbf{a}^*_{kj}$ may be generated as needed by the decomposition principle described above. Once an optimal solution is obtained, it is easy to determine the x_j and ρ_{kj}. Let U_j denote the set of positive v_{kj} for a given j. Then

$$x_j = \sum_{k \in U_j} v_{kj}; \quad \text{or} \quad x_j = 0, \quad \text{and for} \quad x_j > 0,$$

$$\rho_{kj} = \frac{v_{kj}}{x_j}, \qquad k = 1, \ldots, h_j. \tag{11-54}$$

Finally, the optimal activity vectors to be used at a positive level are given by*

$$\mathbf{a}_j = \sum_{k \in U_j} \rho_{kj}\mathbf{a}^*_{kj}. \tag{11-55}$$

11-11 Summary of computational technique for the decomposition algorithm; example. It might be desirable to summarize in a step-by-step fashion how the decomposition principle is used to solve a linear programming problem of the form (11-37). We begin by imagining that the given problem is converted to the form (11-43), although initially none of the vectors $\mathbf{q}_{kj}$ or prices f_{kj} are explicitly available. These are generated as needed. The revised simplex method is used to solve (11-43) and, in general, a Phase I will be needed to obtain a basic feasible solution. In Phase I zero prices are assigned to all legitimate variables, and prices of -1 to the artificial variables. An initial tableau is constructed. For this tableau, $\mathbf{B} = \mathbf{I}$ (recall that $\mathbf{B}$ is of order $r + m_0$), $\boldsymbol{\rho}_B = \mathbf{b}$, $\boldsymbol{\sigma} = \mathbf{c}^*_B$. Now it is necessary to determine the first vector to enter the basis. Go to step (1).

(1) Compute $\boldsymbol{\sigma}_1\mathbf{A}_j$ and the linear form $Z_j = (\boldsymbol{\sigma}_1\mathbf{A}_j - \mathbf{c}_j)\mathbf{x}_j$, $j = 1, \ldots, r$. In Phase I, $\boldsymbol{\sigma}$ is contained† in the last $m_0 + r$ columns of the second row of $\mathbf{B}_2^{-1}$ and, in Phase II, in the last $m_0 + r$ columns of the first row of $\mathbf{B}_2^{-1}$.

---

* For j such that $x_j = 0$, the ρ_{kj} are undetermined, and for these j, any $\mathbf{a}_j$ in K_j will do; of course, only the $\mathbf{a}_j$ to be used at a positive level are of interest.

† Recall that superscripts or subscripts 2 identify vectors appropriate to Standard Form II of the revised simplex method.

Solve the set of linear programming problems

$$\mathbf{B}_j\mathbf{x}_j = \mathbf{b}_j, \quad \mathbf{x}_j \geq \mathbf{0}, \quad \min Z_j = (\sigma_1\mathbf{A}_j - \mathbf{c}_j)\mathbf{x}_j, \quad j = 1, \ldots, r,$$

and write

$$Z_j^* = \min Z_j. \tag{11--56}$$

Often these problems may be solved efficiently by means of some special algorithm, such as the network-flow algorithm. In the event that $\sigma_1\mathbf{A}_j - \mathbf{c}_j$ for this iteration of the main problem does not differ much from $\sigma_1\mathbf{A}_j - \mathbf{c}_j$ at the previous iteration (if there was one), it may be better to begin with the optimal solution to (11–56) for the previous iteration (where the prices were slightly different) than to solve the problem all over again. Go to step (2).

(2) Compute $Z_j^* + \sigma_{2j}, j = 1, \ldots, r$, and determine

$$Z_s^* + \sigma_{2s} = \min_j \, (Z_j^* + \sigma_{2j}). \tag{11--57}$$

There are two possibilities to consider:

(a) $Z_s^* + \sigma_{2s} \geq 0$. If this occurs in Phase I, go to step (4), and if it occurs in Phase II, go to step (5).

(b) $Z_s^* + \sigma_{2s} < 0$. Go to step (3).

(3) Let $\mathbf{x}_{rs}^*$ be an optimal solution to (11–56) for $j = s$. Compute $\mathbf{d}_{rs} = \mathbf{A}_s\mathbf{x}_{rs}^*, f_{rs} = \mathbf{c}_s\mathbf{x}_{rs}^*$, and $\mathbf{q}_{rs} = [\mathbf{d}_{rs}, \mathbf{e}_s]$. Calculate $\mathbf{y}_{rs}^{(2)} = \mathbf{B}_2^{-1}\mathbf{q}_{rs}^{(2)}$, where $\mathbf{q}_{rs}^{(2)} = [-f_{rs}, 0, \mathbf{q}_{rs}]$, and transform the tableau to obtain the new basic feasible solution to (11–43). In addition to the revised simplex tableau, maintain a table giving the $\mathbf{x}_{rs}^*$ in the basis. Return to step (1).

(4) When in Phase I, $Z_s^* + \sigma_{2s} \geq 0$ and $\Sigma\rho_{ai} = 0$, Phase I has terminated and Phase II begins. If $\Sigma\rho_{ai} < 0$, there is no feasible solution.

(5) When in Phase II, $Z_s^* + \sigma_{2s} \geq 0$, the current basic feasible solution to (11–43) is optimal. Using the table which gives the $\mathbf{x}_{rs}^*$ in the current basis, compute the optimal $\mathbf{x}_j$ from

$$\mathbf{x}_j = \sum_{i \in V_j} \rho_{Bi}\mathbf{x}_{Bi}^*, \tag{11--58}$$

where $\mathbf{x}_{Bi}^*$ is the $\mathbf{x}_{rs}^*$ for column i of $\mathbf{B}$ and V_j is the set of $\mathbf{x}_{rj}^*$, i.e., the set of extreme points with index j in the basis. In general, the size of problems for which the decomposition principle is especially valuable is such that they could not easily be solved by a straightforward application of the simplex method to (11–37), even if a large computer were used. After the decomposition principle is applied, the resulting problem will, in general, continue to be of such a magnitude that a large digital computer will be required to solve it.

EXAMPLE: Let us solve the linear programming problem

$$x_1 + 4x_2 + 5x_3 + 2x_4 \leq 7, \tag{11–59}$$

$$2x_1 + 3x_2 \leq 6, \tag{11–60}$$

$$5x_1 + x_2 \leq 5,$$

$$x_3 \leq 4,$$

$$x_4 \leq 3, \tag{11–61}$$

$$-3x_3 - 4x_4 \leq -12,$$

$$\mathbf{x} \geq \mathbf{0},$$

$$\max z = x_1 + 8x_2 + 5x_3 + 6x_4, \tag{11–62}$$

using the decomposition principle. The constraint (11–59) will be abbreviated to $\mathbf{Ax} \leq 7$, (11–60) will be abbreviated to $\mathbf{B_1x_1} \leq \mathbf{b_1}$, and (11–61) will be abbreviated to $\mathbf{B_2x_2} \leq \mathbf{b_2}$.

In solving any problem by means of the decomposition principle, one is faced at the outset with the decision as to how far the problem will be decomposed. The constraints for the above problem can be written

$$(a) \quad \begin{bmatrix} \mathbf{A} \\ \mathbf{B} \end{bmatrix} \mathbf{x} \leq \begin{bmatrix} 7 \\ \mathbf{b} \end{bmatrix}, \quad \mathbf{B} = \begin{bmatrix} \mathbf{B_1} & \mathbf{0} \\ \mathbf{0} & \mathbf{B_2} \end{bmatrix}, \quad \mathbf{b} = \begin{bmatrix} \mathbf{b_1} \\ \mathbf{b_2} \end{bmatrix}; \tag{11–63}$$

$$(b) \quad \begin{bmatrix} \mathbf{A_1} & \mathbf{A_2} \\ \mathbf{B_1} & \mathbf{0} \\ \mathbf{0} & \mathbf{B_2} \end{bmatrix} \begin{bmatrix} \mathbf{x_1} \\ \mathbf{x_2} \end{bmatrix} \leq \begin{bmatrix} 7 \\ \mathbf{b_1} \\ \mathbf{b_2} \end{bmatrix}. \tag{11–64}$$

If (b) is used, then there will be three constraints when the problem is converted to the form (11–43); if (a) is used, there will be two constraints. For (a) a single subproblem will have to be solved in order to determine the vector to enter the bases; the constraints for this problem have the form $\mathbf{Bx} \leq \mathbf{b}$. For (b) there are two subproblems whose constraints have the form $\mathbf{B_1x_1} \leq \mathbf{b_1}$, $\mathbf{B_2x_2} \leq \mathbf{b_2}$. However, $\mathbf{Bx} \leq \mathbf{b}$ is equivalent to the two sets of constraints $\mathbf{B_1x_1} \leq \mathbf{b_1}$, $\mathbf{B_2x_2} \leq \mathbf{b_2}$. Hence the effort required for solving the single subproblem for (a) is the same as that necessary for solving the two subproblems for (b). However, (a) has the advantage that the main problem (11–43) has only two constraints rather than three. Hence we shall use the form (a) in solving the problem. We leave for Problem 11–32 a discussion of the relative desirability of various degrees of decomposition in solving problems by means of the decomposition algorithm.

The example to be discussed differs from the standard form (11–37) in that inequality signs appear. The subproblem can easily be solved graphically. The convex sets of feasible solutions to (11–60) and (11–61) are shown in Figs. 11–5 and 11–6, respectively. It is thus unnecessary to add slack variables to convert (11–60) and (11–61) to equalities. However, we shall add a slack variable x_5 to convert (11–59) into an equation. Note that x_5 does not appear in (11–60) or (11–61).

Denote by $\mathbf{x}_k^*$ the extreme points of the convex set of feasible solutions to $\mathbf{Bx} \le \mathbf{b}$. The first two components of each $\mathbf{x}_k^*$ are the components of an extreme point of the convex set of feasible solutions to $\mathbf{B}_1\mathbf{x}_1 \le \mathbf{b}_1$ shown in Fig. 11–5, and the last two components of $\mathbf{x}_k^*$ are the components of an extreme point of the convex set of feasible solutions to $\mathbf{B}_2\mathbf{x}_2 \le \mathbf{b}_2$ shown in Fig. 11–6. Any feasible solution to $\mathbf{Bx} \le \mathbf{b}$ can then be written

$$\mathbf{x} = \sum_k \rho_k \mathbf{x}_k^*, \qquad \rho_k \ge 0, \qquad \text{all } k, \qquad \sum_k \rho_k = 1. \qquad (11\text{–}65)$$

If we write $d_k = \mathbf{Ax}_k^*$, $f_k = \mathbf{cx}_k^*$, Eqs. (11–59) through (11–62) are converted to the equivalent linear programming problem,

$$\sum_k d_k \rho_k + x_5 = 7,$$

$$\sum_k \rho_k = 1, \qquad\qquad\qquad (11\text{–}66)$$

$$\max z = \sum_k f_k \rho_k.$$

The slack variable x_5 appears unchanged in (11–66) because it does not appear in $\mathbf{Bx} \le \mathbf{b}$.

We shall solve (11–66) by the revised simplex method. Only one artificial variable, x_6, is needed to obtain an initial identity matrix because the activity vector corresponding to x_5 is $\mathbf{e}_1$. A Phase I is required to drive x_6 to zero. In Phase I we wish to maximize $-x_6$. For Standard Form II, the initial basis matrix is

$$\mathbf{B}_2 = \begin{bmatrix} 1 & 0 & 0 & 0 \\ 0 & 1 & 0 & 1 \\ 0 & 0 & 1 & 0 \\ 0 & 0 & 0 & 1 \end{bmatrix}, \quad \text{and} \quad \mathbf{B}_2^{-1} = \begin{bmatrix} 1 & 0 & 0 & 0 \\ 0 & 1 & 0 & -1 \\ 0 & 0 & 1 & 0 \\ 0 & 0 & 0 & 1 \end{bmatrix}.$$

Then $\boldsymbol{\sigma} = (0, -1) = (\sigma_1, \sigma_2)$. For this case, $(\sigma_1\mathbf{A} - \mathbf{c})\mathbf{x} = 0$ since $\sigma_1\mathbf{A} = \mathbf{0}$, which follows from $\sigma_1 = 0$, and $\mathbf{c} = \mathbf{0}$ because in Phase I the legitimate variables have a price of 0. Hence z_k^*, the value of $z_k - f_k$ for Phase I, is independent of $\mathbf{x}$, and we can choose any extreme point of the convex set of feasible solutions to $\mathbf{B}\mathbf{x} \leq \mathbf{b}$ to determine a vector for entry into the basis. Let us choose extreme point 1 of Fig. 11–5 and extreme point 3 of Fig. 11–6 so that the extreme point for the convex set of feasible solutions to $\mathbf{B}\mathbf{x} \leq \mathbf{b}$ is $\mathbf{x}_1^* = [0, 0, 0, 3]$. Consequently,

$$d_1 = \mathbf{A}\mathbf{x}_1^* = 6, \qquad f_1 = 18, \qquad \mathbf{q}_1^{(2)} = [-18, 0, 6, 1],$$

and

$$\mathbf{y}_1^{(2)} = \mathbf{B}_2^{-1}\mathbf{q}_1^{(2)} = [-18, -1, 6, 1].$$

The first tableau is shown in Table 11–1. It is seen that the artificial vector is removed at the first iteration, and Phase I ends. In Phase II, it is unnecessary to retain the constraint which maintains the artificial vectors at a zero level, and hence it is omitted in the remaining tableaux.

The new tableau is shown in Table 11–2. Here $\boldsymbol{\sigma} = (0, 18)$. Recall that we are now in Phase II and that the actual prices are being used. Again $\sigma_1 = 0$ and $\sigma_1\mathbf{A} = \mathbf{0}$, so that $(\sigma_1\mathbf{A} - \mathbf{c})\mathbf{x} = -\mathbf{c}\mathbf{x}$. Therefore, to generate the next vector to enter the basis, we must solve the linear

TABLE 11–1 — TABLEAU 1

$\boldsymbol{\beta}_1^{(2)}$	$\boldsymbol{\beta}_2^{(2)}$	$\boldsymbol{\beta}_3^{(2)}$	$\boldsymbol{\rho}_B^{(2)}$	$\mathbf{y}_k^{(2)}$
0	0	0	0	−18
1	0	−1	−1	−1
0	1	0	7	6
0	0	1	1	1

TABLE 11–2 — TABLEAU 2

$\boldsymbol{\beta}_1^{(1)}$	$\boldsymbol{\beta}_2^{(1)}$	$\boldsymbol{\rho}_B^{(1)}$	$\mathbf{y}_k^{(1)}$
0	18	18	−36
1	−6	1	28
0	1	1	1

TABLE 11–3 — TABLEAU 3

$\beta_1^{(1)}$	$\beta_2^{(1)}$	$\rho_B^{(1)}$	$y_k^{(1)}$
1.287	10.28	19.287	−5.72
0.0357	−0.2145	0.0357	0.284
−0.0357	1.2145	0.9643	0.716

TABLE 11–4 — TABLEAU 4

$\beta_1^{(1)}$	$\beta_2^{(1)}$	$\rho_B^{(1)}$	$y_k^{(1)}$
2.005	5.96	20.00	
0.1250	−0.755	0.1250	
−0.1250	1.756	0.875	

programming problem $\mathbf{Bx} \leq \mathbf{b}$, $\mathbf{x} \geq \mathbf{0}$, min $Z = -\mathbf{cx}$. Of course, minimizing $-\mathbf{cx}$ is equivalent to maximizing $\mathbf{cx}$. This linear programming problem decomposes into the following two problems: $\mathbf{B}_1\mathbf{x}_1 \leq \mathbf{b}_1$, $\mathbf{x}_1 \geq \mathbf{0}$, max $x_1 + 8x_2$; $\mathbf{B}_2\mathbf{x}_2 \leq \mathbf{b}_2$, $\mathbf{x}_2 \geq \mathbf{0}$, max $5x_3 + 6x_4$. These problems are easily solved graphically, and it is seen that the solution is $\mathbf{x}_2^* = [0, 2, 4, 3]$, $d_2 = 34$, $f_2 = 54$, $\mathbf{q}_2^{(1)} = [-54, 34, 1]$, $\mathbf{y}_2^{(1)} = [-36, 28, 1]$. From Table 11–2, it is seen that $\mathbf{q}_2^{(1)}$ drives x_5 to zero. The remaining tableaux are given in Tables 11–3 and 11–4. At the next solution of the subproblem, the optimal extreme point is $\mathbf{x}_3^* = [0, 2, 0, 3]$, since $(\sigma_1\mathbf{A} - \mathbf{c}) = (0.287, -2.85, 1.44, -3.43)$. Also $\mathbf{q}_3^{(1)} = [-34, 14, 1]$. Note that $\mathbf{q}_3^{(1)}$ replaces $\mathbf{q}_2^{(1)}$. For the final tableau, $\sigma = (2.005, 5.96)$ and $(\sigma_1\mathbf{A} - \mathbf{c}) = (1.005, 0.020, 5.025, -1.990)$. The solution to the subproblem yields $\mathbf{x}_1^* = [0, 0, 0, 3]$ as the optimal extreme point. However, the vector $\mathbf{q}_1^{(1)}$ corresponding to $\mathbf{x}_1^*$ is in the basis, and hence $z_1 - f_1 = 0$ and the solution is optimal.

From the optimal solution we note that $\rho_{B1} = 0.1250$ and $\rho_{B2} = 0.875$. Since $\mathbf{q}_3$ is in the first column and $\mathbf{q}_1$ in the second column of $\mathbf{B}$, an optimal $\mathbf{x}$ which solves (11–59) through (11–62) is $\mathbf{x} = \rho_{B1}\mathbf{x}_3^* + \rho_{B2}\mathbf{x}_1^*$ or $\mathbf{x} = 0.1250[0, 2, 0, 3] + 0.875[0, 0, 0, 3] = [0, 0.2500, 0, 3]$. Observe that $\mathbf{x}_1 = [0, 0.2500]$ is not an extreme point of the convex set of feasible

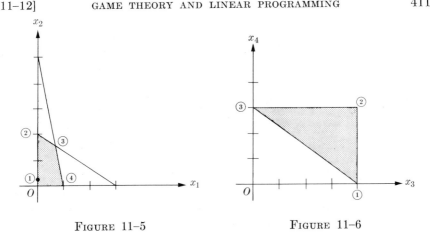

FIGURE 11–5   FIGURE 11–6

solutions to $\mathbf{B}_1\mathbf{x}_1 \leq \mathbf{b}$. Instead it is the point shown in Fig. 11–5. However, $\mathbf{x}_2 = [0, 3]$ is an extreme point of the convex set of feasible solutions to $\mathbf{B}_2\mathbf{x}_2 \leq \mathbf{b}_2$. It is extreme point 3 in Fig. 11–6.

For the example solved, it would not have been difficult to list all the extreme points of the convex set of feasible solutions to $\mathbf{Bx} \leq \mathbf{b}$, which would have made it possible to compute at the outset all the $\mathbf{q}_k$ and f_k, thus eliminating the need to solve the subproblem at each iteration. However, even for this simple problem, considerably more work would have been required if this procedure had been adopted.

11–12 Game theory and linear programming; introduction.   There is a close connection between linear programming problems and zero-sum two-person games. We shall investigate the connection in this and the following two sections. Let us begin by giving a very brief description of game theory.

Games of strategy deal with situations where there are conflicts of interest between two or more "persons." A game may be a parlor game, such as chess or bridge. More generally, games involve conflict situations in economic, social, political, or military activities. Games of strategy assume that players can influence the final outcome, and hence that the outcome is not controlled purely by chance. By a game we shall mean a set of rules for playing. These rules describe the moves, who makes moves, when they are made, what information is available to each of the players, what terminates a play of the game, etc. After the termination of one play of the game, we imagine that there are certain pay-offs to each participant (these are usually thought of as pay-offs in money). If the sum of the pay-offs to all participants at the end of the play is zero, then the game is called a zero-sum game. Two-person games, as the name implies, involve a conflict of interest between two "persons" (persons may be people, companies, countries, etc.). A zero-sum two-person game is one in which, at the end of a play, one person gains what the other person loses. We shall now restrict our attention to zero-sum two-person games.

The concept of a strategy is very important in game theory. We can imagine that one player writes on a sheet of paper what he will do under all possible circumstances at each move in a play of the game. In other words, he tells what he will do for each possible move the other player might make. This is called a strategy. For a game like chess it would be an exceedingly difficult task to write out such a set of specifications, but conceptually, it could be done. For each player there will be a number of different strategies (quite often a very large number). We shall assume that this number is finite. A set of strategies for a given player covers all possible alternative ways of carrying out a play of the game, each strategy taking into account all possible moves that the other player can make. The number of strategies available to each player does not need to be the same.

In two-person games, it is permissible for nature to make some of the moves (i.e., chance determines certain moves) so long as the players can influence the outcome. If nature does not make any moves and both players choose a strategy, the outcome of the game is strictly determined. We shall denote by a_{ij} the pay-off to player 1 if he chooses strategy i and player 2 chooses strategy j. When some of the moves are determined by chance, the outcome of the game is not strictly determined, and we can talk about the *expected* outcome only. If player 1 chooses strategy i and player 2 strategy j, the expected outcome is determined. The expected pay-off to player 1 will also be denoted by a_{ij}. Hence, when player 1 chooses strategy i and player 2 strategy j, a_{ij} represents the pay-off to player 1 if the game is strictly determined, or the expected pay-off if nature makes some of the moves; a_{ij} may be positive, negative, or zero.

If player 1 has m strategies and player 2 has n strategies, the pay-offs a_{ij} can be arranged into an $m \times n$ matrix

$$\mathbf{A} = \|a_{ij}\|. \tag{11-67}$$

The rows of this matrix refer to the strategies of player 1, and the columns to the strategies of player 2. Row i of $\mathbf{A}$ gives the pay-offs (or expected pay-offs) to player 1 if he uses strategy i. The pay-off depends, of course, on which strategy player 2 uses. $\mathbf{A}$ is called the pay-off matrix. When we have a list of strategies for each player and a pay-off matrix, then the game has been reduced to what is called its normal form.

Since the matrix $\mathbf{A}$ represents the pay-offs to player 1 (the pay-offs to player 2 are the negatives of these), then in terms of this matrix, player 1 is trying to win as much as possible, while player 2 is trying to prevent him from winning any more than possible. With this interpretation, we can refer to player 1 as the maximizing player. It will be assumed that each player knows his own strategies and the strategies available to his opponent. Furthermore, each player is assumed to be intelligent. This means that player 2 will do everything possible to cut down the winnings of player 1, and player 1 will do everything possible to get as much as possible.

Now if player 1 chooses strategy i, he is sure of getting

$$\min_j a_{ij},$$

no matter what player 2 does.* It then seems wise for player 1 to choose the strategy which gives the maximum of these minima, i.e.,

$$\max_i \min_j a_{ij}. \tag{11–68}$$

Player 2 is attempting to prevent player 1 from getting any more than necessary. If player 2 selects strategy j, he is sure that player 1 will not get more than

$$\max_i a_{ij},$$

no matter what player 1 does. It would then seem reasonable that player 2 attempts to minimize his maximum loss, i.e., select a strategy, using

$$\min_j \max_i a_{ij}. \tag{11–69}$$

If it turns out that there is an element (or elements) a_{rk} such that

$$a_{rk} = \max_i \min_j a_{ij} = \min_j \max_i a_{ij}, \tag{11–70}$$

the game is said to have a saddle point. In such a situation, the optimal strategy for player 1 is r and for player 2 is k. The reason that these strategies can be considered optimal from both players' viewpoints is that if player 2 chooses k, player 1 cannot get more than a_{rk}, and if player 1 chooses r, he is sure of getting at least a_{rk}.

Difficulties arise when

$$a_{rv} = \max_i \min_j a_{ij} < \min_j \max_i a_{ij} = a_{uk}. \tag{11–71}$$

Player 1 feels that he should be able to do better than a_{rv}, and player 2 feels that he should be able to cut the winnings of player 1 below a_{uk}. To

---

* If nature makes some of the moves, we should say that his expected winnings are at least min a_{ij}. We shall not continue to repeat this stipulation. However, the reader should keep it in mind.

resolve this problem, Von Neumann introduced the notion of a mixed strategy. The strategies considered up to the present are called pure strategies. One of these pure strategies is actually used by each player in a play of the game. Consider now the case where the player does not select the pure strategy he is going to use, but that the strategy is determined by a game of chance. Assume that for player 1 some chance device selects strategy i with probability $u_i \geq 0$, $\sum_{i=1}^{m} u_i = 1$, and for player 2 another game of chance selects strategy j with probability $v_j \geq 0$, $\sum_{j=1}^{n} v_j = 1$. In this way, chance devices determine the strategy each player will use, and neither knows what the other's strategy will be. In fact, a player does not know what his own strategy will be until it is determined by the chance device. The vector $\mathbf{u} \geq \mathbf{0}$, $\mathbf{1u} = 1$ (or equivalently $\mathbf{v}$), defines a mixed strategy, with u_i being the probability of choosing pure strategy i.

When each player decides to use mixed strategies, we can no longer be sure what the outcome of the game will be. It is only possible to speak of the expected winnings for player 1. If player 1 uses the mixed strategy defined by $\mathbf{u}$ and player 2 the mixed strategy defined by $\mathbf{v}$, the expected winnings for player 1 are

$$E(\mathbf{u}, \mathbf{v}) = \mathbf{u}'A\mathbf{v} = \sum_{i,j} u_i a_{ij} v_j. \qquad (11\text{--}72)$$

The reader should note at this point that uncertainty can creep into a game in two different ways. First, nature may make some of the moves. This introduces uncertainty, regardless of how the players choose the strategies they are going to use. Then the players may choose their strategies by a chance device. This introduces uncertainty into the game even if nature does not make any moves.

We have as yet said nothing about the determination of $\mathbf{u}$, $\mathbf{v}$. This is really the central problem in solving games. Player 1 wishes to find a $\mathbf{u}$ which maximizes his winnings (and here we must mean his expected winnings). For any $\mathbf{u}$ he chooses, he is sure his expected winnings will be at least

$$\min_{\mathbf{v}} E(\mathbf{u}, \mathbf{v}).$$

He then maximizes this expression over $\mathbf{u}$ so that his expected winnings are at least

$$M_1^* = \max_{\mathbf{u}} \min_{\mathbf{v}} E(\mathbf{u}, \mathbf{v}). \qquad (11\text{--}73)$$

Similarly, player 2 can be sure that the expected winnings of player 1 are not more than

$$M_2^* = \min_{\mathbf{v}} \max_{\mathbf{u}} E(\mathbf{u}, \mathbf{v}). \qquad (11\text{--}74)$$

If there exist vectors $\mathbf{u}^*$, $\mathbf{v}^*$ such that $M_1^* = M_2^*$, then we have what may be called a generalized saddle point, and in such a case player 1 should use the mixed strategy defined by $\mathbf{u}^*$, and player 2 the mixed strategy defined by $\mathbf{v}^*$. The expected winnings of player 1 are M_1^*, and this is called the value of the game. Interestingly enough, a $\mathbf{u}^*$ and a $\mathbf{v}^*$ always exist such that

$$M_1^* = \max_{\mathbf{u}} \min_{\mathbf{v}} E(\mathbf{u}, \mathbf{v}) = \min_{\mathbf{v}} \max_{\mathbf{u}} E(\mathbf{u}, \mathbf{v}) = M_2^*,$$

(11–75)

$$\mathbf{u}^* \geq \mathbf{0}, \quad \mathbf{1u}^* = 1; \quad \mathbf{v}^* \geq \mathbf{0}, \quad \mathbf{1v}^* = 1.$$

This is the fundamental theorem for two-person zero-sum games.

The fundamental theorem of two-person zero-sum games tells us that a solution in the above sense always exists. The problem of solving any two-person zero-sum game consists then in finding the mixed strategies described by $\mathbf{u}$, $\mathbf{v}$ and the "value" of the game $M^* = M_1^* = M_2^*$.

We shall not attempt to defend the procedure of using mixed strategies, nor shall we seek to justify it in any more detail. Having given this very brief summary of two-person zero-sum games, we now wish to show that the fundamental theorem follows directly from the duality theory of linear programming. It will also be shown that linear programming can be used to solve zero-sum two-person games, and conversely, linear programming problems can be solved as zero-sum two-person games.

11–13 Reduction of a game to a linear programming problem. John von Neumann was the first to show that a zero-sum two-person game in normal form can be solved as a linear programming problem. Let us see how this is done.

When player 1 uses the mixed strategy defined by $\mathbf{u} \geq \mathbf{0}$, $\mathbf{1u} = 1$, and player 2 uses pure strategy j, the expected winnings for player 1 are

$$\sum_{i=1}^{m} a_{ij} u_i.$$

Consequently, player 1 can be sure that his expected winnings will be at least M_1 if there exists a mixed strategy $\mathbf{u}$ such that

$$\sum_{i=1}^{m} a_{ij} u_i \geq M_1, \quad j = 1, \ldots, n.$$

(11–76)

Player 1 can never expect to win more than the largest value of M_1 for which there exists a $\mathbf{u} \geq \mathbf{0}$, $\mathbf{1u} = 1$, satisfying (11–76).

In matrix form (11–76) becomes

$$\mathbf{A'u} \geq M_1 \mathbf{1'}, \quad \mathbf{u} \geq \mathbf{0}, \quad \mathbf{1u} = 1.$$

(11–77)

Without loss of generality, we can assume $M_1 > 0$, because the nature of a game (i.e., the set of optimal mixed strategies) is unchanged when the same positive constant is added to each a_{ij}. This is to be proved in Problem 11–38. Let us then write

$$w_i = \frac{u_i}{M_1}, \qquad i = 1, \ldots, m; \qquad \text{then} \quad w_i \geq 0 \quad \text{since} \quad M_1 > 0.$$
$$(11\text{–}78)$$

Now (11–77) can be written

$$\mathbf{A}'\mathbf{w} \geq \mathbf{1}', \qquad \mathbf{w} \geq \mathbf{1},$$

$$\mathbf{1}\mathbf{w} = \frac{1}{M_1} = Z. \tag{11–79}$$

Here we have a linear programming problem. We wish to find a $\mathbf{w} \geq \mathbf{0}$ which satisfies the constraint inequalities, maximizes M_1, and therefore minimizes Z.

Following the type of reasoning used by player 1, player 2 is trying to find a $\mathbf{v} \geq \mathbf{0}$, $\mathbf{1}\mathbf{v} = 1$, which will give the smallest M_2 satisfying

$$\sum_{j=1}^{n} a_{ij}v_j \leq M_2, \qquad i = 1, \ldots, m. \tag{11–80}$$

In matrix form, this is

$$\mathbf{A}\mathbf{v} \leq M_2\mathbf{1}', \qquad \mathbf{v} \geq \mathbf{0}, \quad \mathbf{1}\mathbf{v} = 1. \tag{11–81}$$

If we introduce the variables x_j (and without loss of generality assume that $M_2 > 0$),

$$x_j = \frac{v_j}{M_2} \geq 0, \qquad j = 1, \ldots, n, \tag{11–82}$$

Eq. (11–81) becomes

$$\mathbf{A}\mathbf{x} \leq \mathbf{1}', \qquad \mathbf{x} \geq \mathbf{0},$$

$$\mathbf{1}\mathbf{x} = \frac{1}{M_2} = z. \tag{11–83}$$

This is also a linear programming problem for which we wish to find an $\mathbf{x} \geq \mathbf{0}$ which satisfies the constraint inequalities, minimizes M_2, and therefore maximizes z.

We can now make the very interesting observation that the linear programming problems for players 1 and 2 are dual linear programming problems. It will be noted that there are always feasible solutions $\mathbf{u}$, $\mathbf{v}$ since each player can use pure strategies. Furthermore, since there are

M_1, $M_2 > 0$, there exist feasible vectors $\mathbf{x}$, $\mathbf{w}$ for the primal and dual problems. This in turn means that the primal and hence the dual have optimal solutions. This follows from the fact that since there is a feasible solution, the primal (which can be either of the problems) has either an optimal or an unbounded solution. If it has an unbounded solution, the dual will have no solution, contradicting the fact that there is a feasible solution to the dual. Thus both problems have optimal solutions.

Hence it must be true that

$$\max z = \min Z, \tag{11–84}$$

or

$$M_2^* = \min M_2 = \max M_1 = M_1^*. \tag{11–85}$$

In this way we have proved the fundamental theorem of game theory. It follows directly from the duality theory of linear programming. To see more explicitly that we have proved the equivalent of (11–75), note that, because of the linearity with respect to $\mathbf{v}$, we have for a given $\mathbf{u}$,

$$\min_{\mathbf{v}} E(\mathbf{u}, \mathbf{v}) = \min [E(\mathbf{u}, \mathbf{e}_1), \ldots, E(\mathbf{u}, \mathbf{e}_n)], \tag{11–86}$$

where $\mathbf{e}_j$ means that player 2 is using pure strategy j. Then

$$M_1^* = \max_{\mathbf{u}} \min_{\mathbf{v}} E(\mathbf{u}, \mathbf{v}) \tag{11–87}$$

can be determined by finding the largest M_1 such that there exists a $\mathbf{u}$ satisfying

$$M_1 \leq E(\mathbf{u}, \mathbf{e}_j), \quad j = 1, \ldots, n, \quad \mathbf{u} \geq \mathbf{0}, \quad \mathbf{1u} = 1. \tag{11–88}$$

This is the same as Eq. (11–76).

Many different proofs of the fundamental theorem of game theory have been developed. The first was given by von Neumann in 1928. It was quite complicated and involved the use of Brouwer's fixed-point theorem. The first elementary proof was made by Ville in 1938. Other proofs have been presented by Nash; Gale, Kuhn, Tucker; Dantzig; Weyl; Shapley, Snow; and von Neumann and Morgenstern.

The task of solving any two-person zero-sum game involves finding the optimal strategies for each player and the value of the game. We have shown that such games can be solved by means of linear programming. Indeed, this is one of the most efficient methods for solving games. From our previous results we know that the optimal strategies need not be unique. However, the set of optimal strategies for each player forms a convex set. We also note that optimal mixed strategies $\mathbf{u}$, $\mathbf{v}$ need not have more than min (n, m) of the u_i, v_j different from zero.

11–14 Conversion of a linear programming problem to a game problem.
Here we shall show how to convert any linear programming problem into
a zero-sum two-person game in normal form. The discussion follows that
presented by Dantzig [2]. Consider the linear programming problem

$$\mathbf{Dx} \le \mathbf{d}, \qquad \mathbf{x} \ge \mathbf{0}, \qquad \max z = \mathbf{cx} \qquad (11\text{–}89)$$

and its dual

$$\mathbf{D'w} \ge \mathbf{c'}, \qquad \mathbf{w} \ge \mathbf{0}, \qquad \min Z = \mathbf{d'w}. \qquad (11\text{–}90)$$

From Section 8–3 we know that for feasible solutions $\mathbf{x}$, $\mathbf{w}$ to the primal
and dual,

$$\mathbf{cx} \le \mathbf{d'w}, \qquad \text{or} \qquad \mathbf{cx} - \mathbf{d'w} \le 0. \qquad (11\text{–}91)$$

Furthermore, when (11–89) has an optimal solution, then

$$\max z = \min Z. \qquad (11\text{–}92)$$

Consequently, if $\mathbf{x} \ge \mathbf{0}$, $\mathbf{w} \ge \mathbf{0}$ can be found which satisfy the constraints
in (11–89) and (11–90), respectively, and if

$$\mathbf{cx} - \mathbf{d'w} \ge 0, \qquad (11\text{–}93)$$

[this is the reverse of (11–91)], then we know that $\mathbf{x}$ is an optimal solution
to the primal and $\mathbf{w}$ an optimal solution to the dual.

We shall now introduce a new variable $t > 0$ and a new set of variables
$\mathbf{u}$, $\mathbf{v}$ defined by

$$\mathbf{x} = \frac{\mathbf{u}}{t}, \qquad \mathbf{w} = \frac{\mathbf{v}}{t}. \qquad (11\text{–}94)$$

In terms of these new variables, the constraints of (11–89) and (11–90)
become

$$\mathbf{Du} - t\mathbf{d} \le \mathbf{0},$$

$$\mathbf{D'v} - t\mathbf{c'} \ge \mathbf{0}. \qquad (11\text{–}95)$$

To these we append

$$\mathbf{cu} - \mathbf{d'v} \ge 0. \qquad (11\text{–}96)$$

For any $t > 0$, optimal solutions $\mathbf{x}$, $\mathbf{w}$ to the primal and dual, respectively,
can be transformed into variables $\mathbf{u}$, $\mathbf{v}$ which satisfy (11–95) and (11–96).
Conversely, if we can find $\mathbf{u} \ge \mathbf{0}$, $\mathbf{v} \ge \mathbf{0}$, $t > 0$ which satisfy (11–95)
and (11–96), then the $\mathbf{x}$, $\mathbf{w}$ computed according to (11–94) will be optimal
solutions to the primal and dual linear programming problems, respec-
tively. Since t can be arbitrary so long as $t > 0$, let us impose the additional restriction that

$$\mathbf{1u} + \mathbf{1v} + t = 1. \qquad (11\text{–}97)$$

Consider now the game for which the problem of player 1, when cast into the form (11–77), is

$$-\mathbf{Du} + t\mathbf{d} \geq M\mathbf{1}',$$

$$\mathbf{D'v} - t\mathbf{c}' \geq M\mathbf{1}',$$

$$\mathbf{cu} - \mathbf{d'v} \geq M,$$

$$[\mathbf{v}, \mathbf{u}, t] \geq \mathbf{0}, \; \mathbf{1}[\mathbf{v}, \mathbf{u}, t] = 1.$$

$$(11\text{–}98)$$

Here M is to be maximized, and $\max M = M^*$ is the value of the game. If $\max M = 0$, then a solution to (11–98) for $M = 0$ which has $t > 0$ yields optimal solutions to the primal and dual linear programming problems [by means of (11–94)].

Now (11–98) can be written in matrix form as

$$\begin{bmatrix} \mathbf{0} & -\mathbf{D} & \mathbf{d} \\ \mathbf{D'} & \mathbf{0} & -\mathbf{c}' \\ -\mathbf{d'} & \mathbf{c} & \mathbf{0} \end{bmatrix} \begin{bmatrix} \mathbf{v} \\ \mathbf{u} \\ t \end{bmatrix} \geq M\mathbf{1}'. \qquad (11\text{–}99)$$

When this is thought of as the problem of player 1, then this player wishes to find a mixed strategy defined by $\mathbf{y} = [\mathbf{v}, \mathbf{u}, t] \geq \mathbf{0}, \; \mathbf{1y} = 1$, which maximizes M. By (11–77) the pay-off matrix for this game is merely the transpose of the matrix in (11–99), i.e.,

$$\begin{bmatrix} \mathbf{0} & \mathbf{D} & -\mathbf{d} \\ -\mathbf{D'} & \mathbf{0} & \mathbf{c}' \\ \mathbf{d'} & -\mathbf{c} & \mathbf{0} \end{bmatrix}. \qquad (11\text{–}100)$$

Note that (11–100) is a skew-symmetric matrix. A game represented by a skew-symmetric pay-off matrix is called a symmetric game because the roles of players 1 and 2 can be interchanged without changing the pay-off matrix. From this it immediately follows that the value of the game $M^* = 0$ (the proof is left for Problem 11–35). Consequently, by means of (11–94) any optimal strategy $\mathbf{y} = [\mathbf{v}, \mathbf{u}, t], \; t > 0$, for player 1 will yield optimal solutions to the primal and dual linear programming problems (11–89) and (11–90). If $t = 0$ for every optimal strategy, we leave it for the reader to prove in Problem 11–39 that at least one of the primal and dual linear programming problems has no solution.

In this section, we have shown how game theory can be used to solve a linear programming problem. However, this is not an efficient way and it is never used in practice. Nevertheless, it is interesting to know that the possibility exists.

References

1. J. ABADIE, "Le principe de décomposition de Dantzig et Wolfe," *Revue Française de Recherche Opérationelle*, **4**, 2, 1960, 93–115.

2. G. B. DANTZIG, "A Proof of the Equivalence of the Programming Problem and the Game Problem," Chapter XX, *Activity Analyses of Production and Allocation*, Koopmans, ed. New York: Wiley, 1951.

3. G. B. DANTZIG, "Constructive Proof of the Min-Max Theorem," *RM*–1267–1, The RAND Corp., Dec., 1953.

4. G. B. DANTZIG, "Upper Bounds, Secondary Constraints, and Block Triangularity," *Econometrica*, **23**, 1955, 174–183; also *RM*–**1367,** The RAND Corp., Oct., 1954.

5. G. B. DANTZIG and P. WOLFE, "The Decomposition of Mathematical Programming Problems," *P*–**1818,** The RAND Corp., May 1959.

6. G. B. DANTZIG and P. WOLFE, "A Decomposition Principle for Linear Programs," *Operations Research*, **8**, 1; 1960, pp. 101–111, and *P*–**1544,** The RAND Corp., Nov., 1958, revised Nov., 1959, revised Dec., 1959.

7. L. R. FORD and D. R. FULKERSON, "A Primal-Dual Algorithm for the Capacitated Hitchcock Problem," *Naval Research Logistics Quarterly*, **4**, 1957, 47–54.

8. D. GALE, H. W. KUHN, and A. W. TUCKER, "Linear Programming and the Theory of Games," Chapter XIX, in *Activity Analyses of Production and Allocation*, Koopmans, ed. New York: Wiley, 1951.

9. S. I. GASS and T. L. SAATY, "The Parametric Objective Function, Part 1," *Operations Research*, **2**, 1954, 316–19.

10. S. I. GASS and T. L. SAATY, "The Parametric Objective Function (Part 2) —Generalization," *Operations Research*, **3**, 1955, 395–401.

11. S. I. GASS and T. L. SAATY, "The Computational Algorithm for the Parametric Objective Function," *Naval Research Logistics Quarterly*, **2**, 1955, 39–45.

12. A. S. MANNE, *Scheduling of Petroleum Refinery Operations*. Cambridge: Harvard University Press, 1956.
   Manne did some of the original work on parametric programming. It is presented in an appendix of Manne's book.

13. W. ORCHARD-HAYS, "Background, Development, and Extensions of the Revised Simplex Method," *RM*–**133,** The RAND Corp., April, 1954.

14. A. W. TUCKER, "Dual Systems of Homogeneous Linear Relations," *Linear Inequalities and Related Systems*, Kuhn and Tucker, eds. Princeton: Princeton University Press, 1956.

Problems

11–1. Consider the following tableau which presents an optimal solution to some linear programming problem:

c_B	Vectors in Basis	c_j **b**	2 $\mathbf{a}_1$	3 $\mathbf{a}_2$	1 $\mathbf{a}_3$	0 $\mathbf{a}_4$	0 $\mathbf{a}_5$
2	$\mathbf{a}_1$	1	1	0	0.5	4	−0.5
3	$\mathbf{a}_2$	2	0	1	1	−1	2
	$z_j - c_j$	8	0	0	3	5	5

How much can c_3 be increased before the present basic solution will no longer be optimal? Determine the sequence of optimal bases as c_3 is allowed to increase indefinitely.

11–2. For the tableau presented in Problem 11–1, find the largest value of ϕ for which the given basic solution is optimal if $\mathbf{c}$ is replaced by $\mathbf{c} + \phi\mathbf{f}$, $\mathbf{f} = (1, 2, 1, 0, 0)$. Determine the sequence of optimal bases as ϕ is allowed to increase indefinitely.

11–3. Assume that for the tableau presented in Problem 11–1, $\mathbf{a}_4$, $\mathbf{a}_5$ were, in that order, in the initial identity matrix basis. How much can b_1 be increased before the optimal solution is no longer feasible? Determine the sequence of optimal bases as b_1 is allowed to increase indefinitely. Will there always be a feasible basis?

11–4. Starting with the tableau presented in Problem 11–1 and with the assumption made in Problem 11–3, determine how much b_2 can be increased before the optimal solution is no longer feasible. Determine the sequence of optimal solutions as b_2 is allowed to increase indefinitely.

11–5. In Eq. (11–2) show that if the minimum is unique, then $\phi'_c > \phi_c$, that is, the new basic feasible solution is optimal over some interval of ϕ. On the other hand, if the minimum is not unique and $\mathbf{a}_k$ is chosen arbitrarily from among the tied values, then the new solution may be optimal only at ϕ_c, that is, $\phi'_c = \phi_c$. Is it possible to choose an $\mathbf{a}_k$ from among the tied values in such a way that $\phi'_c > \phi_c$? Consider as a special case that where ϕ_c in Eq. (11–2) is zero. Is it possible that, as ϕ is increased, the solution will become unbounded? How will this be signaled? If one begins with an optimal solution and reaches an unbounded solution, is it ever possible that an additional increase in ϕ will again lead to an optimal solution?

How much can each price be changed (increased and decreased) if all others are held constant and only a single price is changed at a time, before the given solution will no longer be optimal?

11–6. Consider the following tableau which presents an optimal solution to some linear programming problem. By how much can c_2 be changed (increased or decreased) before the current solution is no longer optimal?

| c_B | Vectors in Basis | b | c_j 2 | 4 | 1 | 3 | 2 | 0 | 0 | 0 |
			a_1	a_2	a_3	a_4	a_5	a_6	a_7	a_8
2	a_1	3	1	0	0	−1	0	0.5	0.2	−1
4	a_2	1	0	1	0	2	1	−1	0	0.5
1	a_3	7	0	0	1	−1	−2	5	−0.3	2
	$z_j - c_j$	17	0	0	0	2	0	2	0.1	2

11–7. For the tableau presented in Problem 11–6, assume that a_6, a_7, a_8 were in the initial identity matrix basis, in the order given. Determine how much each b_i can be increased and decreased before the optimal solution is no longer feasible. Each b_i is changed individually, while the others are held constant.

11–8. Show that if the minimum in (11–5) is unique, then there is an interval in θ over which the new solution is optimal. On the other hand, show that if the minimum is not unique and an arbitrary selection among the tied values is made for the variable to leave the basis, then the new solution may be optimal only at θ_c. Is it possible to make a choice among the tied values in such a way that the new solution will be optimal over some interval of θ? Discuss how the sequence of optimal solutions may be traced out as θ varies from 0 to ∞.

11–9. Consider the tableau presented in Problem 11–6. Would the optimal solution be altered if the activity vector [2, 0, 3] having a price of 5 were annexed to the system? Would the optimal solution be altered if, instead of the above vector, the activity [1, 1, 2] with a price of 7 were annexed to the original problem? If in either case the solution is no longer optimal, find the new optimal solution.

11–10. Consider the tableau presented in Problem 11–6. If the additional constraint

$$2x_1 + 3x_2 - x_3 + 2x_4 + 4x_5 \leq 5$$

were annexed to the system, would there be any change in the optimal solution? Suppose instead that the constraint

$$3x_1 + x_2 + 2x_3 + x_4 + 9x_5 \leq 19$$

were annexed to the system. If in either case the constraint is not satisfied, determine the new optimal solution (if there is one).

11–11. Show how to compute the extent to which a_{ij} can be changed before an optimal solution to $\mathbf{Ax} = \mathbf{b}$, $\mathbf{x} \geq \mathbf{0}$, max $z = \mathbf{cx}$ is no longer optimal. Assume $\mathbf{a}_j$ is not in the optimal basis. When an arbitrary change is made in a_{ij}, show what change is necessary to obtain a new optimal solution.

11–12. Answer Problem 11–11, assuming that $\mathbf{a}_j$ is in the optimal basis. Note that when $\mathbf{a}_j$ is in the basis, a change in a_{ij} may affect the nonsingularity of $\mathbf{B}$, the feasibility of the optimal solution, and the optimality, i.e., the $z_j - c_j$. Each of these cases must be considered separately. Note that it is rather difficult to make changes in a_{ij} when $\mathbf{a}_j$ appears in the optimal basis. If any such changes must be made, it is probably better to solve the entire problem all over again.

11–13. Given the linear programming problem $\mathbf{Ax} = \mathbf{b}$, $\mathbf{x} \geq \mathbf{0}$, max $z = \mathbf{cx}$. Let $\mathbf{x}^0$ be an optimal solution to this problem. Now imagine that the price vector $\mathbf{c}$ is replaced by a new vector $\mathbf{c}^*$. Assume that $\mathbf{x}^*$ is an optimal solution to the new problem (which has the same constraints as the given problem). Prove that $(\mathbf{c}^* - \mathbf{c})(\mathbf{x}^* - \mathbf{x}^0) \geq 0$. If only a single price c_j is changed, that is, $\mathbf{c}^* = \mathbf{c} + \phi \mathbf{e}_j$, what is the result of this reduction? Give an economic interpretation of this result. If price c_k is changed and all other prices remain constant, what (if anything) can be said about the change in x_j, $j \neq k$? Hint: $\mathbf{cx}^0 \geq \mathbf{cx}$; thus $\mathbf{cx}^0 \geq \mathbf{cx}^*$ or $\mathbf{c}(\mathbf{x}^0 - \mathbf{x}^*) \geq 0$. Also, $\mathbf{c}^*\mathbf{x}^* \geq \mathbf{c}^*\mathbf{x}$, so $\mathbf{c}^*\mathbf{x}^* \geq \mathbf{c}^*\mathbf{x}^0$.

11–14. If one had a computer program in which it was possible to parametrize only the requirements vector for a parameter study, could duality theory be used to take care of parametrizing the price vector? Would this be a feasible procedure?

11–15. Generalize the technique of parametrizing the price vector discussed in Section 11–3 to the case where ϕ can be positive and negative. In other words, show how to start out with a given optimal basic solution and determine the optimal solutions for all values of ϕ, or show that the solution is ultimately unbounded. Prove that as ϕ varies from $-\infty$ to ∞, there can be only a finite number of different optimal solutions. Show that for all $\phi \geq \phi^*$ for some $\phi^* > 0$, the optimal solution will remain unchanged (or the solution will be unbounded). Do the same when the requirements vector is parametrized and θ is allowed to vary from $-\infty$ to ∞.

11–16. Suppose that we have a basic feasible solution to a linear programming problem and that there exists a vector $\mathbf{a}_j$ not in the basis with $z_j - c_j < 0$ and $y_{ij} \leq 0$, all c_j, i.e., there is an unbounded solution. If we now attempt to change the price vector in the way discussed in Section 11–3, under what circumstances will it be possible to find a ϕ large enough so that an optimal solution exists?

11–17. Given an optimal basic solution to a linear programming problem. Can one obtain an unbounded solution by changing the requirements vector? What is the geometrical interpretation of this result? Hint: Is there a solution to the dual?

11–18. Prove that if a given basic feasible solution to some linear programming problem is optimal, the same basis vectors will yield an optimal solution for any requirements vector which lies in the cone spanned by these basis vectors.

SPECIAL TOPICS

11–19. Solve the following linear programming problem by means of the technique developed in Section 11–7:

$$2x_1 + 3x_2 - x_3 + 4x_4 + 2x_5 = 38,$$

$$x_1 + 4x_2 + 2x_3 - 5x_4 + 3x_5 \geq 7,$$

$$3x_1 - 2x_2 + 4x_3 + x_4 + x_5 = 24,$$

$$0 \leq x_1 \leq 4, \quad 0 \leq x_2 \leq 2, \quad x_3, \ x_4, \ x_5 \geq 0,$$

$$\max z = 6x_1 + 8x_2 + x_3 + 2x_4 + x_5.$$

11–20. Prove that if Eq. (11–34) is used to determine the initial solution to the dual, then the primal-dual algorithm for the capacitated transportation problem will never lead to a solution to the dual such that $ij \in S$, $ij \notin R$, which requires that $x_{ij} = x_{ij}^s = 0$ if complementary slackness is to be maintained.

11–21. Discuss the restricted primal and the determination of a new solution to dual if the initial solution to the dual is taken to be $u_i = v_j = w_{ij} = 0$, all i, j, in the primal-dual algorithm for the capacitated transportation problem. Assume that each $c_{ij} > 0$.

11–22. Show that in the primal-dual algorithm for the capacitated transportation problem, Eq. (11–32) is a new solution to the dual if Eq. (11–33) holds. Do this by considering all possibilities. Consider the sets $ij \notin R$; $ij \in S$; $ij \in R$, $ij \notin S$, together with the various combinations of labeled rows and columns. Be sure to consider also the constraints $w_{ij} \leq 0$. Show how the case $h = \infty$ follows from the nature of the new solution.

11–23. For the primal-dual algorithm as applied to the capacitated transportation problem, prove the following:

(a) If $i \notin I$ and $j \in J$, $ij \in R$, $ij \notin S$ in an optimal solution to a restricted primal problem, then $x_{ij} = 0$.

(b) If $i \in I$ and $j \notin J$, $ij \in R$, $ij \notin S$ in an optimal solution to a restricted primal problem, then $x_{ij} = d_{ij}$.

(c) If, after a new solution to the dual is obtained, $ij \in \hat{S}$, then $x_{ij} = d_{ij}$ in the optimal solution to the restricted primal which yielded the new solution to the dual.

(d) If, after a new solution to the dual is obtained, $ij \notin R$, then $x_{ij} = 0$ in the optimal solution to the restricted primal which yielded the new solution to the dual. Thus conclude that an optimal solution to the previous restricted primal will serve as an initial solution for the new restricted primal.

11–24. For the primal-dual algorithm as applied to the capacitated transportation problem, prove that the new solution to the dual given by Eqs. (11–32) and (11–33) increases the value of the dual objective function by

$$h\left[\sum_{i \in I} a_i - \sum_{j \in J} b_j + \sum_{\substack{i \notin I \\ j \in J \\ ij \in S}} d_{ij} - \sum_{\substack{i \in I \\ j \notin J \\ ij \in R}} d_{ij}\right] > 0.$$

Hint: Using the min cut-max flow theorem, show that the maximal flow in the network is

$$V = \sum_{\substack{i \notin I}} a_i - \sum_{\substack{i \notin I \\ ij \in S}} d_{ij} + \sum_{\substack{j \in J}} b_j - \sum_{\substack{j \in J \\ ij \in S}} d_{ij} + \sum_{\substack{i \in I, ij \in R \\ j \notin J, ij \notin S}} d_{ij} + \sum_{\substack{ij \in S}} d_{ij} < \sum_{i=1}^{m} a_i.$$

Thus

$$\sum_{\substack{i \in I}} a_i - \sum_{\substack{j \in J}} b_j - \sum_{\substack{ij \in S}} d_{ij} + \sum_{\substack{i \notin I \\ ij \in S}} d_{ij} + \sum_{\substack{j \in J \\ ij \in S}} d_{ij} - \sum_{\substack{i \in I, ij \in R \\ j \notin J, ij \notin S}} d_{ij} > 0.$$

Then use (proof?)

$$\sum_{\substack{ij \in S}} d_{ij} = \sum_{\substack{i \notin I \\ ij \in S}} d_{ij} + \sum_{\substack{j \in J \\ ij \in S}} d_{ij} + \sum_{\substack{i \in I \\ j \notin J \\ ij \in S}} d_{ij} - \sum_{\substack{i \notin I \\ j \in J \\ ij \in S}} d_{ij}.$$

11-25. Solve the following capacitated transportation problem. The upper numbers in each cell are the costs and the lower numbers are the upper bounds.

	D_1	D_2	D_3	D_4	D_5	a_i
O_1	25	35	20	15	40	50
	40	35	10	20	50	
O_2	18	24	25	18	10	75
	23	30	20	20	10	
O_3	10	20	30	20	20	35
	10	45	30	30	15	
O_4	5	10	25	25	25	100
	5	11	32	70	30	
b_j	60	50	50	75	25	

11-26. Consider the tableau presented in Problem 11-6. Assume that in solving the problem which led to the given tableau, the following constraints were originally considered to be secondary:

$$4x_1 + 2x_2 - 7x_3 + x_4 - 3x_5 \leq 10,$$
$$2x_1 + 4x_2 + 2x_3 + 6x_4 + 7x_5 \leq 15.$$

Does the optimal solution satisfy these constraints? If not, determine an optimal solution which does satisfy the secondary constraints.

11–27. Suppose that one has an optimal solution to some linear programming problem and it is desired to remove one of the constraints. Discuss the procedure for doing this.

11–28. Suppose that in using the decomposition principle to solve (11–37), we find that the problem $\mathbf{B}_j\mathbf{x}_j = \mathbf{b}_j$, $\mathbf{x}_j \geq 0$, min $Z_j = (\boldsymbol{\sigma}_1\mathbf{A}_j - \mathbf{c}_j)\mathbf{x}_j$ has an unbounded solution (this of course implies that the convex set of feasible solutions to $\mathbf{B}_j\mathbf{x}_j = \mathbf{b}_j$ is unbounded). Denote the columns of $\mathbf{B}_j$ by $\mathbf{g}_u$, a basis matrix by $\mathbf{H}$, and $\mathbf{H}^{-1}\mathbf{g}_u$ by $\mathbf{t}_u$. Assume that $\mathbf{g}_v$ was being considered for entry into the basis $\mathbf{H}$ when the unbounded solution was discovered, i.e., $t_{iv} \leq 0$, $i = 1, \ldots, m_j$, and that the insertion of $\mathbf{g}_v$ decreases the objective function. Then note that $\theta(\mathbf{g}_v - \sum_i t_{iv}\mathbf{h}_{Bi}) = 0$ for any θ where $\mathbf{h}_{Bi}$ are the columns in the basis. Insertion of $\mathbf{g}_v$ into the solution will yield for sufficiently large θ an arbitrarily small value of Z_j. Now let $\mathbf{a}_{Bi}(j)$ be the columns of $\mathbf{A}_j$ corresponding to the columns of $\mathbf{B}_j$ in the basis $\mathbf{H}$ and, similarly, let $c_{Bi}(j)$ be the prices of $\mathbf{c}_j$ corresponding to the columns of $\mathbf{B}_j$ in $\mathbf{H}$. Consider

$$\mathbf{d}_j = \theta[\mathbf{a}_v(j) - \sum_i t_{iv}\mathbf{a}_{Bi}(j)];$$

$$f_j = \theta[c_v(j) - \sum_i t_{iv}c_{Bi}(j)]$$

for any $\theta > 0$, and

$$\mathbf{q}_j = [\mathbf{d}_j, 0].$$

Show that if $\mathbf{q}_j$ enters the basis of the connecting problem [Eq. (11–43)] at a positive level, z will be increased. Also show that the increase in z is independent of θ; hence θ can be taken equal to 1, without loss of generality. Note that a zero appears in $\mathbf{q}_j$ in place of e_j since in this case there is no restriction on the level at which $\mathbf{q}_j$ may enter the basis (why?). Prove that with the above modification to take care of unbounded solutions, an optimal solution to (11–37) will be reached in a finite number of steps in all cases. How is the optimal $\mathbf{x}_j$ computed when there are vectors, such as $\mathbf{q}_j$ above, in the optimal basis for (11–43)? Prove that the final $\mathbf{x}_j$ is also independent of the choice of θ. Note that there will also be at least one extreme of the convex set of feasible solutions to $\mathbf{B}_j\mathbf{x}_j = \mathbf{b}_j$ in an optimal basic solution to (11–43), since the constraint $\sum \rho_{kj} = 1$ is present. Thus show that it is certain that the constraints $\mathbf{B}_j\mathbf{x}_j = \mathbf{b}_j$ will be satisfied.

11–29. Solve the example of Section 11–11, using the decomposition (b) of Eq. (11–64), i.e., the decomposition for which there are three constraints in Eq. (11–43) rather than two.

11–30. Solve the following linear programming problem, using the decomposition principle.

$$5x_1 + 3x_2 + 4x_3 + 2x_4 + 6x_5 \leq 20,$$

$$x_1 + 7x_2 \leq 8, \qquad 3x_3 + 9x_4 + 2x_5 \geq 4,$$

$$4x_1 + 2x_2 \leq 5, \qquad 2x_3 + x_4 + x_5 \leq 12, \qquad \text{all } x_j \geq 0,$$

$$\max z = 3x_1 + 4x_2 + 5x_3 + 4x_4 + 7x_5.$$

11–31. Discuss the use of the decomposition principle to treat linear programming problems with upper bounds on the variables. Hint: To what degree should the problem be decomposed?

11–32. Discuss the relative advantages and disadvantages of using various degrees of decomposition when employing the decomposition algorithm to solve a linear programming problem.

11–33. Discuss in detail how the vector $\mathbf{a}_{kj}^*$ which is to enter the basis is generated in generalized linear programming problems, where the activity vector $\mathbf{a}_j$ may be freely chosen from the convex polyhedron K_j.

11–34. Find a set of mixed strategies for each player which solves a game described by the following pay-off matrix:

$$\mathbf{A} = \begin{pmatrix} 3 & 5 & 0 & 9 & 6 \\ 2 & 6 & 8 & 1 & 2 \\ 1 & 7 & 4 & 9 & 3 \end{pmatrix}.$$

Determine the value of the game.

11–35. Prove that the value of a game with a skew-symmetric pay-off matrix is zero.

11–36. Prove that for any matrix $\mathbf{A}$

$$a_{rv} = \max_{i} \min_{j} a_{ij} \leq \min_{j} \max_{i} a_{ij} = a_{uk}.$$

11–37. Show that if a_{st}, a_{uv} are saddle points of the matrix $\mathbf{A}$, then a_{sv}, a_{ut} are also saddle points.

11–38. Prove that the set of optimal strategies for a game is not altered by adding a constant M to each a_{ij} in the pay-off matrix. How does the value of the game change?

11–39. For player 1, show that if every optimal strategy $\mathbf{y} = [\mathbf{v}, \mathbf{u}, t]$ applied to the game whose pay-off matrix is (11–100) has $t = 0$, then at least one of the primal and dual linear programming problems (11–89), (11–90) has no solution.

11–40 Prove rigorously that for the situation discussed in Section 11–3, z is a continuous function of ϕ.

11–41. Develop the theory of parameter variations and sensitivity analysis for transportation problems. What special restrictions must be placed on changes in the requirements vector in order to maintain the existence of feasible solutions?

11–42. For the optimal transportation tableau given in Table 9–6, by how much can c_{12} be changed (increased and decreased) if the basic solution shown is to remain optimal. Answer the same question for c_{34} and c_{42}.

11–43. In Eq. (11–12), prove that if $\mathbf{B}_*$ is nonsingular, then $\mathbf{B}$ must also be nonsingular. Hint: Note that the first m columns of $\mathbf{B}_*$ will be linearly independent regardless of what $\mathbf{B}$ is. However, the first $2m$ columns of $\mathbf{B}_*$ will be linearly dependent unless $\mathbf{B}$ is nonsingular.

11–44. With respect to the decomposition principle, how is it possible ever to have $\mathbf{x}_j = 0$ in an optimal solution if it must be true that $\sum \rho_{kj} = 1$.

11–45. If a problem involving upper bounds is solved by the method discussed in Section 11–7, how is the optimal value of z obtained from the information given in the tableau? Note that the optimal value of z is not to be found in the cell which normally contains the value of the objective function.

11–46. Consider the convex set of feasible solutions X to $\mathbf{Bx} \leq \mathbf{b}$, where $\mathbf{B}$, $\mathbf{b}$ are as defined in Eq. (11–63). Show that for any extreme point $\mathbf{x}^*$ of X the first two components of $\mathbf{x}^*$ are an extreme point of the convex set of feasible solutions to $\mathbf{B}_1\mathbf{x}_1 \leq \mathbf{b}$, and the last two components are an extreme point of the convex set of feasible solutions $\mathbf{B}_2\mathbf{x}_2 \leq \mathbf{b}_2$. Generalize this result to the case where $\mathbf{B}$ is of order n and can be partitioned so that the only non-null submatrices are square submatrices $\mathbf{B}_i$ of order m_i lying on the main diagonal.

11–47. For the optimal tableau given in Table 4–10, determine how much each price can be changed (increased or decreased) if the given basic solution is to remain optimal. Change only one price at a time. Cases where two or more prices are changed simultaneously need not be considered. Similarly, determine how much each b_i can be changed if the optimal solution is to remain feasible. What effects do these changes have on the optimal value of the objective function?

11–48. Start with the optimal tableau given in Table 4–4 and determine the optimal basic solutions (if they exist) for all values of b_1, that is, as b_1 varies from $-\infty$ to ∞. Plot the optimal values of the variables x_1, x_2 as a function of b_1.

11–49. For the situation discussed in Section 11–3, prove that as ϕ passes through ϕ_c, only a single vector in the basis needs to be changed in order to maintain optimality. In certain cases, of course, the new solution may be optimal only at ϕ_c. What is the geometric interpretation of this situation?

11–50. Using a perturbation technique, prove rigorously that if for the situation discussed in Problem 11–5, $\phi'_c = \phi_c$, a basis never need be repeated. Hint: Replace c_j by $c_j + \epsilon^j$.

11–51. What simplifications are introduced into the technique discussed in Section 11–7 if not all the variables have finite upper bounds?

11–52. Consider those postoptimality problems discussed in the text which require application of the dual simplex algorithm for making the necessary modifications. Suppose that the revised simplex method was used to solve the original problem. Imagine that $x_{Bu} < 0$ is to leave the basic solution. How does one obtain the y_{uj} needed in the dual simplex algorithm to determine the vector to enter the basis? Recall that when the revised simplex method is used, the $\mathbf{y}_j$ are not computed. Hint: It is possible to compute y_{uj} without computing all the components of $\mathbf{y}_j$.

CHAPTER 12

APPLICATIONS OF LINEAR PROGRAMMING TO INDUSTRIAL PROBLEMS

"If you would understand me go to the heights or watershore,
The nearest gnat is an explanation, and a drop or motion of waves a key,
The maul, the oar, the hand-saw, second my words."

Walt Whitman.

12–1 Introduction. Linear programming is a practical subject. In fact, the rapid development of the subject is a result of the many practical applications that have been found. In this chapter we wish to discuss applications of linear programming to certain problems arising in industry. We have chosen an approach which will show, in a general way, how linear programming can be applied to a number of specific areas of interest.

There exists an amazing variety of problems which lend themselves to solution by linear programming. It is important to keep in mind that for most of these problems, the linear programming model is only an approximate representation of the real world. However, the representation is often good enough to yield useful results. In any field of science or engineering, it is rare, indeed, to find a model which represents the real world exactly. The important question is whether the representation is accurate enough to provide valuable information. Naturally, one must not become overzealous and attempt to apply some model to situations where it is completely inapplicable, just because the model is available. This is true for linear programming as well as for anything else.

We shall begin the discussion by illustrating some ways in which the transportation algorithm can be applied. In industrial applications, the transportation method has been used to a much greater extent than the simplex algorithm. We shall see that a number of important problems which have nothing to do with transportation can be cast into the form of transportation problems.

12–2 The standard transportation problem. We have already mentioned on several occasions that the standard transportation problem seeks to minimize those costs incurred from shipping a uniform product available in given amounts at m origins to n destinations, where the amount at each destination is also specified. For example, a wholesaler in some hard-goods item has warehouses throughout the United States. Orders for

429

delivery in the coming month are received from retailers in all fifty states. It is desired to set up a shipping schedule for the coming month which will minimize the total shipping cost. The quantity of the item available in each warehouse is known.

The example just presented seems simple and straightforward. In practice, any number of difficulties may be encountered. Note, for example, that the cost of shipping from each warehouse to every retailer must be known. Frequently, one finds that a company does not have all this information. Consequently, it must be generated in its entirety before the problem can be solved. If several methods of transportation and a number of different routes are available for shipping from any warehouse to any retailer, it can be quite a task to find the (minimum) cost of shipping from each warehouse to each retailer. Furthermore, if the problem is to be solved at the beginning of each month, the shipping costs must be continually revised to take account of changes in shipping rates.

In using the transportation method, we must assume that the unit cost of transportation from a given warehouse to a given destination does not depend on the number of units shipped. This assumption would not be valid if there were any sizable fixed charges that are independent of the quantity shipped. Fortunately, however, the assumption that costs are proportional to the quantity shipped is frequently close enough to the actual situation so that no serious errors are introduced. Since railroads and truckers mix their loads, it is not necessary to fill an entire car or trailer.

It is important to note that for a problem involving, say, 15 origins and 500 destinations, the cost of collecting the data for the transportation costs can run into a considerable amount of money. After these data are available, the cost of solving the problem on a large-scale digital computer could be $1000 or more, since the solution may require up to two hours of computer time. This does not include the cost of punching and checking the cards which form the input data. Whether this expenditure is justified depends on the total transportation costs. Many corporations spend as much as 10 million dollars per year on transportation costs alone, and a saving of 2 or 3% would amount to $200,000 or $300,000 per year. Such potential savings attained with a very small percentage improvement easily justify the expenditure of a considerable amount of money for the application of linear programming to cases of this kind.

The task of obtaining the correct answer to a large transportation problem on a digital computer is not so easy as one might think. If there are 15 origins and 500 destinations, 7500 costs must be punched correctly into cards. A single incorrect punch will lead to an answer which is completely wrong. Extreme care must be used to be sure that the cards are correctly punched.   Sometimes a mistake is immediately evident when the final optimal solution is examined.   In other instances, however, it is not obvious.   Even when the mistake is found, something in the order of $1000 of computer time has been wasted since the problem must be rerun after the mistake is corrected.   If a number of runs are required before all mistakes are eliminated, the cost of solving the problem increases sharply.

It is hardly necessary to dwell on straightforward applications of the transportation method.   However, before going on, we shall present one final example.   A transportation problem which has received considerable attention from certain segments of industry and from military planners is the scheduling of marine tankers [5, 7].   Many tanker-allocation problems are very complicated and cannot be reduced to linear programming problems.   However, if appropriate assumptions are made, especially simple problems do become transportation problems.

One of the simplest examples of scheduling a fleet of marine tankers can be formulated as follows: The U.S. Navy has known numbers of empty tankers at various ports throughout the world.   It will be assumed that all tankers are identical.   In a given time, known numbers of tankers must be available at certain ports throughout the world for loading. How should the empty tankers be routed to ports where they are needed, to ensure that transportation costs are minimized?

The cost per day of operating an empty tanker on the high seas and its speed are assumed to be given.   From a knowledge of the distances between ports, it is possible to compute the cost of moving a tanker from any given port to any other port.   If any route leads through the Suez or Panama canals, the appropriate fee can be added to the cost. The problem of routing the tankers clearly requires nothing but a straightforward application of the transportation method.   Flood [7] has discussed a problem of this type.

12–3 Production allocation and transportation.   Many corporations today find that the production costs for a given product vary considerably among their different plants.   Newer plants have lower production costs than older plants.   An important problem facing management is that of scheduling production at the various plants in such a way as to minimize the total variable costs consisting of the variable production costs and transportation costs.

Suppose that a corporation has m plants throughout the United States or the world and n jobbing points to which the product is to be shipped. Let a_i be the yearly productive capacity of plant i and b_j be the amount demanded at jobbing point j for the coming year.   Let c_{ij} be the cost of shipping one unit of the product from plant i to jobbing point j, and

k_i the variable cost of producing one unit at plant i. Furthermore, let x_{ij} be the number of units produced in plant i for shipment to jobbing point j.

If precisely the amount demanded is to be produced, we wish to determine x_{ij} which minimize

$$z = \sum_{i,j} (c_{ij} + k_i)x_{ij}, \qquad (12\text{–}1)$$

subject to the constraints

$$\sum_j x_{ij} \leq a_i, \qquad i = 1, \ldots, m,$$

$$\sum_i x_{ij} = b_j, \qquad j = 1, \ldots, n \qquad (12\text{–}2)$$

$$x_{ij} \geq 0, \qquad \text{all} \quad i, j.$$

If we write

$$d_{ij} = c_{ij} + k_i, \qquad (12\text{–}3)$$

the problem is nothing but the standard transportation problem with costs d_{ij}.

In solving this problem, we determine the lowest-cost shipping schedule as well as the amount to be produced at each of the plants. The production X_i at plant i for the coming year will be

$$X_i = \sum_j x_{ij}, \qquad (12\text{–}4)$$

where the x_{ij} in (12–4) correspond to an optimal solution to (12–1) and (12–2). The optimal production-shipping schedule depends on both the manufacturing and shipping costs.

It is not always easy to determine the variable production costs with any great accuracy. There is usually some question as to which costs should be considered variable and which should be considered fixed. The cost of production is rarely directly proportional to the quantity produced over the entire range from zero production to maximum capacity. However, this proportionality can be assumed to provide frequently a reasonably good approximation over some limited range of production. Each k_i is determined for the range within which the particular plant is expected to operate. If the optimal solution shows that one or more of the plants should be operating at a level quite different from that for which the k_i were determined, it may be necessary to recompute the k_i for these new levels and re-solve the problem.

Note that if the variable costs of production are the same at each plant, we do not need to include the production costs when solving the problem. The optimal allocation will depend on transportation costs alone. Similarly, if there is no excess capacity in any of the plants, i.e., the total demand is precisely the sum of the plant capacities, it again is unnecessary to include the production costs even though they may vary from plant to plant.

The demands b_j for the coming year at the various jobbing points will, in general, be based on forecasts. Depending on the nature of the industry, it may or may not be possible to make accurate forecasts of the demand for the coming year. The worst case is that in which the total sales cannot be predicted accurately and it is also impossible to estimate accurately the percentage of sales to be expected at each jobbing point. If accurate forecasts cannot be made, the problem may have to be re-solved later in the year to take account of more recent data. In such circumstances, the problem may have to be solved on a quarterly or monthly basis rather than once a year. The decision depends on the nature of the industry. Some industries (e.g., food-processing industries) turn out their entire production during two or three months of the year. If their forecasts are bad, they have no opportunity to correct them. Other industries which produce the given item continuously through the year can alter schedules to a certain extent, depending on the nature of the industry.

It should be observed that, in general, an optimal solution for a lower total level of sales cannot be found by simply multiplying the optimal x_{ij} for a higher predicted sales level by some constant factor, because the plant which produces at capacity at the higher sales level should, perhaps, also do so at the lower sales level and ship to some of the jobbers that previously received deliveries from a different plant. In general, the decision on which plant should ship to which jobbers cannot be made independently of the level of total sales.

12–4 A case study. To illustrate the application discussed in the preceding section by a practical example, we shall briefly discuss a case study on which the author worked in cooperation with company personnel. No actual data or tableaux will be presented.

A large food processor with four plants in different sections of the United States produces a number of different food products. The study dealt only with a group of twenty packaged foods. Each plant makes all twenty products, and the product mix is about the same at all plants. Production costs vary considerably among the plants because some are more modern than others. There is also excess capacity in the four plants, i.e., the total productive capacity is greater than the present demand.

About 2500 jobbing points in the United States receive deliveries from these four plants. A plant in Canada and plants overseas take care of the foreign business; these were not considered in the study. The company also has some government business. All military orders are processed at one plant because it is the only one with special facilities for military packaging. The government business was not included in this study, and its total volume was subtracted from the total capacity of the plant where government orders are processed.

The United States is divided into seventy sales districts, which have been in existence for many years. Although it is not a strict requirement, the company has followed the policy of having all jobbers in a given sales district receive shipments from the same plant. Over the years, the traffic department has been at work, attempting to minimize transportation costs. In recent years, the disparity between processing costs at the various plants increased, and management became worried about two problems. First, they were not sure that the sales districts were assigned to the proper plants so that total variable costs were indeed minimized. Secondly, they wondered whether the present districts were any longer suitable. They wished to know how much could be saved if the restriction were relaxed that all jobbers in a sales district had to receive shipments from the same plant. In other words, they wondered what changes would take place if the cost minimization were based on shipping to jobbers rather than to sales districts. This information could be used to form new sales districts if the practice of shipping to all jobbers in a sales district from only a single plant were to be continued. These were the questions in the minds of management which led to the linear programming study.

The company was unique in that it had data for the cost of shipping from every plant to all 2500 jobbers. This information was readily available. Much of the shipping is done by rail. Two different sizes of cars are used. The cost of shipping depends on the size of the car. The company is not at liberty to use only the cheaper cars. It negotiates with the railroad for the percentage of each type of car to be used. These percentages are known, and they vary from jobber to jobber.

The nature of the processing operations is such that the variable costs can be made directly proportional to the amount produced over a rather wide range. These variable production costs were known (with moderate accuracy) for each of the twenty products. The basic unit of measurement is what the company calls an "equivalent case." The food products are actually packaged in a number of different sizes of containers, and hence some standard unit had to be used. Since the company internally deals in equivalent cases, it was decided to use the equivalent case as the fundamental unit in the analysis. The railroads base their charges on a weight basis, i.e., cost per 100 pounds. The traffic department kept the shipping costs in units of cost per 100 pounds. It was therefore necessary to convert these costs to an equivalent-case basis.

Each plant is set up to produce all twenty products in roughly fixed proportions. The product mix can be varied somewhat at each plant. However, it was expected that there would be little variation in the product mix from plant to plant because the consumer demand was about the same in all sections of the country. Furthermore, the production costs are such that if one plant has favorable production costs for one product, it has favorable production costs for all products. This observation, together with the fact that accounting costs and other internal problems increase considerably if a jobber receives different products from different plants, led to the restriction that all twenty products in the proper product mix must be shipped from one plant to a given jobber.

The problem of proper assignment of sales districts was studied first. Since there are only four plants, it is clear that an optimal solution will require that no more than four districts be supplied from two or more plants. Thus practically every sales district will be supplied by one and only one plant. This fits in well with the established company policy of assigning each sales district to one plant.

An examination of the sales data per sales district showed that the product mix shipped did not vary much from district to district. Consequently, it was possible to compute for each plant a variable production cost which was a weighted average of the cost for each of the products. The weighted average was based on the product mix which was known to apply to all sales districts. These production costs were therefore independent of the sales district to which the products were to be shipped.

The sales-district problem was solved by using the sales figures of the preceding year to compute the demand for each district. This was done so that it could be determined whether an optimal shipping schedule had been used. The transportation method requires that there exist only one shipping cost to each sales district. In actuality, shipping costs varied within a sales district, depending on the jobber to which the products were shipped. To determine an average cost of shipping to a sales district from a particular plant, the demand of each jobber (in equivalent cases) was multiplied by the cost of shipment; these values were summed over all jobbers in the district and divided by the total cases shipped to the district. This provided an average cost per case. The variable processing cost at plant i was added to the average transportation cost of shipping one equivalent case from plant i to district j. This yielded the average total variable cost of producing one equivalent case of the proper product mix and shipping it to district j. Finally, the plant capacities (in equivalent cases) were determined for the given product mix.

The company owned a small digital computer, and the problem was solved on this computer by means of a transportation-method deck which was available for that computer. The computation time was one-half hour.

The same problem was also solved on the IBM 704 computer to test the program that was to be used for solving the larger problem. The computation time on the IBM 704 was four minutes.

The optimal solution was quite interesting: About 10% of the seventy districts were assigned to a plant different from that of their current assignment. The saving per year was about $150,000. In reality, the saving was a very small fraction of the total variable cost of about 25 million dollars per year. This shows that the traffic department had been quite successful in developing optimal shipping schedules. However, considerable savings, although a very small fraction of the total, were overlooked.

Work on the jobber problem was begun next. For this problem, each jobber was considered to be a separate destination; the jobbers were no longer aggregated into sales districts. Hence the problem had about 2,500 destinations and 4 origins. A problem of this size can be solved only on the largest digital computers. Since the company computer was not large enough, it was decided to solve the problem on an IBM 704 which has a memory capacity for 32,000 words.

Although a good approximation was achieved by assuming that the product mix was essentially the same for the various sales districts, it was known that this assumption did not hold for individual jobbing points. In some cases, there were considerable variations in the product mix. It was decided that this initial study did not warrant the very considerable amount of work required by an analysis of the product mix at each of the 2,500 jobbing points and the computation of a variable production cost for each point. Instead, only a few jobbing points corresponding to the large cities were analyzed, and, according to their individual product mixes, a variable production cost was computed for each point. These few jobbers, however, represented a large fraction of the company's total business. The production costs for the remaining jobbers were assumed to be the same as those used for the small problem.

The company's small digital computer was used to compute the total variable costs. The data were programmed in such a way that the small computer actually punched the cards (in proper format) that were to be used as the input data cards for the transportation program on the IBM 704. This reduced considerably the number of possible errors which may occur in punching the slightly over 2,500 cards needed for input data. To save time, the data were loaded into the IBM 704 from tape; however, to put the information on tape, it must first be put on cards.

The large problem was run off on the IBM 704; about two hours of machine time were required to reach an optimal solution. The results were quite interesting. Large additional savings were expected, but did not materialize. The optimal solution yielded a cost which was only about $50,000 below the optimal solution for the sales-district problem.

For this reason, management decided not to revise the sales districts radically. Instead, they chose to keep essentially the existing sales-district subdivision and use the optimal solution to the small problem as a basis for reallocation. Although the solution to the large problem did not lead to substantial additional savings, it was well worth the effort since it did point out that a revision of the sales districts would not result in any considerable cost reduction.

12–5 Machine-assignment problems. The transportation method has been used with considerable success to solve certain types of machine-assignment problems. Consider a shop which produces a variety of different parts, usually to order. Assume that the shop is divided into several different departments. Each department contains a number of machines of the same general type, i.e., lathes, presses, or milling machines. However, not all the machines in a department are identical; they may differ in age, size, or other characteristics, and hence be more suitable for making one type of product than another.

At the beginning of each week, the foreman of every department knows how much work is to be done in his department for the coming week (except for unexpected rush orders). He is faced with the task of assigning the work to the various machines in his department in such a way that production costs will be minimized. The cost of the operations on any one product depends on which machine does the work (it will be assumed that, in any department, none of the products need to be processed by more than one machine).

We shall imagine that there are m machines (or machine types) and n products (or jobs). Let d_{ij} be the time required to process one unit of product j on machine i, x_{ij} the number of units of j produced on machine i in the coming time period, a_i the time available on machine i, b_j the number of units of j which must be completed, and c_{ij} the cost of processing one unit of product j on machine i. The machine-assignment problem thus reduces to finding non-negative x_{ij} which satisfy the constraints

$$\sum_{j=1}^{n} d_{ij}x_{ij} \leq a_i, \qquad i = 1, \ldots, m,$$

$$\sum_{i=1}^{m} x_{ij} = b_j, \qquad j = 1, \ldots, n,$$

(12–5)

and minimize the cost

$$z = \sum_{i,j} c_{ij}x_{ij}.$$

The machine-assignment problem formulated above has the form of the generalized transportation problem studied in Section 9–14. There we developed a generalized uv-algorithm which requires considerably fewer computations than would be needed in a direct application of the simplex method. Recall that unlike the standard transportation problem, optimal basic solutions to (12–5) need not have integral values. If the number of units to be produced is so small that a solution which does not yield integral values of the x_{ij} is worthless, then some technique for solving linear programming problems in integers must be used. This requirement really converts the linear programming problem to a special type of nonlinear programming problem. We shall not attempt to discuss the solutions to such problems here.

Under certain circumstances, the generalized transportation problem (12–5) can be reduced to a standard transportation problem. It is always desirable to make such a reduction whenever possible, since it considerably simplifies the task of solving the problem. We shall consider one case in which (12–5) can be reduced to a transportation problem.

Let us suppose that the products to be processed have the property that the ratio of the times required to process one unit of a given product on any two different machines is the same for all products. Then select any machine, say, machine m, and call it the standard machine (to which all other machines will be compared). Thus, by the above assumption, $d_{ij}/d_{mj} = \alpha_i$, and the same α_i is obtained for every j. Now we can write

$$\sum_{j=1}^{n} d_{ij}x_{ij} = \sum_{j=1}^{n} \left(\frac{d_{ij}}{d_{mj}}\right)(d_{mj}x_{ij}) = \alpha_i \sum_{j=1}^{n}(d_{mj}x_{ij}) \le a_i, \quad (12\text{--}6)$$

or if

$$y_{ij} = d_{mj}x_{ij}, \qquad a'_i = \frac{a_i}{\alpha_i},$$

(12–6) becomes

$$\sum_{j=1}^{n} y_{ij} \le a'_i, \qquad i = 1, \ldots, m. \tag{12--7a}$$

However, multiplying $\sum_i x_{ij} = b_j$ by d_{mj}, we obtain

$$\sum_{i=1}^{m} d_{mj}x_{ij} = d_{mj}b_j,$$

or

$$\sum_{i=1}^{m} y_{ij} = b'_j, \qquad j = 1, \ldots, n, \tag{12--7b}$$

where $b'_j = d_{mj}b_j$. Finally z can be written:

$$z = \sum_{i,j} f_{ij}y_{ij}, \tag{12-7c}$$

where $f_{ij} = c_{ij}/d_{mj}$. It will be observed that a'_i is the number of standard machine hours available on machine i, b'_j is the quantity of product j which must be produced in the dimensions of standard machine hours, y_{ij} is the number of standard machine hours devoted to making product j on machine i, and f_{ij} is the cost per standard machine hour of processing product j. Equations (12–7a) through (12–7c) represent a standard transportation problem in the variables y_{ij}. To convert to the number of units of product j to be produced on machine i, we use $x_{ij} = y_{ij}/d_{mj}$.

Now we shall consider another case which turns out to be identical to the one just examined. Let us suppose that the ratio of times required to process one unit of any two different products on any given machine is the same for all machines. Then select any product, say, product n, and call it the standard product. Thus, by the above assumption, $d_{ij}/d_{in} = \beta_j$ and is independent of i. Then, if we write

$$w_{ij} = \beta_j x_{ij}, \qquad a''_i = \frac{a_i}{d_{in}}, \qquad b''_j = \beta_j b_j, \qquad g_{ij} = \frac{c_{ij}}{\beta_j}, \tag{12-8}$$

(12–5) reduces to

$$\sum_{j=1}^{n} w_{ij} \le a''_i, \qquad i = 1, \ldots, m,$$

$$\sum_{i=1}^{m} w_{ij} = b''_j, \qquad j = 1, \ldots, n,$$

$$z = \sum_{i,j} g_{ij}w_{ij},$$

which is a standard transportation problem. Problem 12–13 asks the reader to provide a physical interpretation for the quantities introduced in (12–8). We leave it for the reader to show that if $d_{ij}/d_{mj} = \alpha_i$ is independent of j, then $d_{ij}/d_{in} = \beta_j$ is independent of i and vice versa, so that if the substitution (12–6) reduces a problem to a transportation problem the substitution (12–8) will also reduce it to a transportation problem, and vice versa.

12–6 Regular-time and overtime production. The problem of scheduling regular and overtime production can sometimes be solved with the help of the transportation method. Suppose that the manufacturer of a single product knows or can estimate what the demand for this product will be for n future time periods. These time periods may be days, weeks, or months. He wishes to schedule production over these next n time periods in such a way as to minimize the total variable costs.

We shall assume that the product under consideration can be inventoried, if necessary, for as many as n time periods. There will be a cost associated with keeping one unit of the production in inventory for one time period.

In some circumstances, overtime production may be used to advantage and, in others, it ought to be avoided. For example, it might be known that if production were scheduled to follow exactly the demand pattern, considerable overtime would be needed in certain future time periods of especially heavy demand. On the other hand, certain quantities of the product could be produced on regular time in slack periods and inventoried until the demand exceeded regular-time production. The problem is to schedule production so that storage charges are balanced against overtime charges in such a way as to minimize the total variable cost. In another case, it may be advantageous to schedule overtime production in certain periods and build up inventory even when demand is low, because the cost of production may be considerably lower in certain periods than in others, perhaps because raw-material prices show seasonal fluctuations, etc.

We shall begin with a general formulation of the production-scheduling problem for a single product. Pertinent costs are: The cost c_i of producing one unit in time period i on regular time, the cost d_i of producing one unit in time period i on overtime, and the cost f_i of storing one unit in inventory for time period i. The production scheduler has to determine the schedule which minimizes the sum of production and storage costs.

Let x_{ij} be the number of units of the product produced on regular time in period i for sale in period j, and y_{ij} be the number of units produced on overtime in period i for sale in period j. We shall consider a_i to be the number of units which can be produced in time period i on regular time, and a'_i the number of units which can be produced in time period i on overtime (a'_i does not include the units which can be produced on regular time). Finally, let b_j be the number of units demanded in time period j. We wish to find the x_{ij} and y_{ij} which satisfy the production constraints, meet the demand requirements, and minimize the total variable cost.

To formulate the problem mathematically, we begin by noting that the units produced in period i must be sold in period i or during a later period. Thus the production constraints take the form

$$\sum_{j=i}^{n} x_{ij} \leq a_i, \quad i = 1, \ldots, n; \quad \sum_{j=i}^{n} y_{ij} \leq a'_i, \quad i = 1, \ldots, n.$$

$$(12\text{-}9)$$

Any units sold in period j must have been produced in period j or during an earlier period. Thus the demand constraints take the form

$$\sum_{i=1}^{j} x_{ij} + \sum_{i=1}^{j} y_{ij} = b_j, \qquad j = 1, \ldots, n. \qquad (12\text{–}10)$$

We wish to find $x_{ij} \geq 0$, $y_{ij} \geq 0$ which minimize the total variable cost

$$z = \sum_{i=1}^{n} \sum_{j=i}^{n} c_i x_{ij} + \sum_{i=1}^{n} \sum_{j=i}^{n} d_i y_{ij}$$

$$+ \sum_{j=2}^{n} \sum_{i=1}^{j-1} \left\{ \sum_{k=i}^{j-1} f_k \right\} (x_{ij} + y_{ij}). \qquad (12\text{–}11)$$

To see that this is the total variable cost, note that $\sum_{j=i}^{n} c_i x_{ij}$ is the cost of producing on regular time in period i. The total cost of producing on regular time is the sum over all time periods. The cost of storage for x_{ij} units made in period i on regular time and sold in period j is $(f_i + f_{i+1} + \cdots + f_{j-1})x_{ij}$. We assume that no storage charges are incurred during the selling period. To find the storage charges for all units sold in period j, we must sum $(\sum_{k=i}^{j-1} f_k)(x_{ij} + y_{ij})$ from $i = 1$ to $i = j - 1$. Finally, the total storage charges are found by summing over all j.

The problem described by (12–9) through (12–11) is a transportation problem. To see this more clearly, let us write

$$x_{n+i,j} = y_{ij}, \qquad \text{all } i, j,$$

$$a_{n+i} = a'_i, \qquad i = 1, \ldots, n, \qquad (12\text{–}12)$$

and

$$c_{ij} = c_i + \sum_{k=i}^{j-1} f_k, \qquad i < j, \qquad c_{jj} = c_j, \qquad j = 1, \ldots, n,$$

$$c_{ij} = M, \qquad i > j, \qquad i \leq n, \qquad j = 1, \ldots, n - 1,$$

$$\qquad (12\text{–}13)$$

$$c_{n+i,j} = d_i + \sum_{k=i}^{j-1} f_k, \qquad i < j, \qquad c_{n+j,j} = d_j, \qquad j = 1, \ldots, n,$$

$$c_{n+i,j} = M, \qquad i > j, \qquad j = 1, \ldots, n - 1.$$

We take M to be a large positive number so that the corresponding x_{ij} will be zero in an optimal solution. In this form we have a transportation problem with $2n$ origins and $n + 1$ destinations.

TABLE 12-1

TABLEAU FOR REGULAR AND OVERTIME SCHEDULING

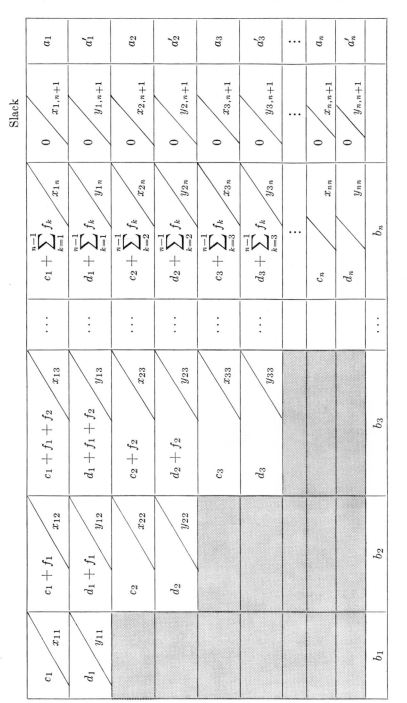

The fact that Eqs. (12–9) through (12–11) represent a transportation problem is more easily seen if we set up a tableau. In terms of the notation of (12–9) through (12–11), we obtain the tableau shown in Table 12–1. The last column gives the slack.

Table 12–1 is interesting in that only about half the tableau is needed. None of the cells below the main diagonal need to be used.

It is quite clear that the problem has no solution unless

$$\sum_{k=1}^{j} (a_k + a_k') \geq \sum_{k=1}^{j} b_k, \qquad j = 1, \ldots, n.$$

We shall assume that this condition is always satisfied.

Note that it is very easy to determine the cost which is to be entered into each cell; it consists of the production cost plus the storage costs for the total number of periods during which the item is stored.

Having formulated the problem in fairly general terms, we shall now concentrate our attention on an important special case. Assume that all costs are independent of the time period, i.e., $c_i = c$, $d_i = d$, $f_i = f$, $i = 1, \ldots, n$. Then the function to be minimized becomes:

$$z = c \sum_{i=1}^{n} \sum_{j=i}^{n} x_{ij} + d \sum_{i=1}^{n} \sum_{j=i}^{n} y_{ij} + f \sum_{j=2}^{n} \sum_{i=1}^{j-1} (j - i)(x_{ij} + y_{ij}). \qquad (12\text{–}14)$$

Suppose that the demand for each of the next ten time periods is represented by the solid dots in Fig. 12–1, and the amount which can be pro-

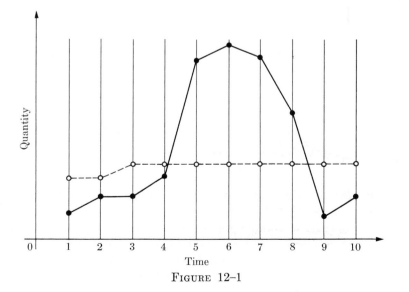

FIGURE 12–1

duced on regular time in each of the time periods by the open dots. For some of the time periods, the demand exceeds the regular-time capacity. Therefore to meet the demand, either the entire excess demand must be made on overtime (if this can be done) or some units must be made in previous time periods and inventoried to help meet the excess demand.

The nature of the minimum-cost schedule depends on the relative values of the difference between overtime and regular-time production, $d - c$, and the cost of storage per period for one unit f. When f is small compared to $d - c$, it will be cheaper to produce on regular time in periods when the demand is smaller than the regular-time capacity in order to build up an inventory for the periods when demand is greater than regular-time capacity, so that overtime work can be kept to a minimum. On the other hand, if f is roughly the same as or greater than $d - c$, overtime will be used to produce items when demand exceeds supply, although these items could have been produced on regular time in preceding periods. The transportation method enables us to determine the optimal combination of regular-time production, overtime production, and storage charges, i.e., the combination yielding minimum costs.

As has been pointed out by Johnson [10], it is remarkably easy to find optimal solutions to the types of scheduling problems described above. No simplex iterations are required; an optimal solution can be obtained immediately without iterations. In fact, if we use the column-minima method for finding an initial basic feasible solution to a transportation problem, the resulting solution is optimal, provided we begin the technique with column 1, i.e., with the first time period. The fact that the column-minima solution is optimal is almost obvious. We ask the reader to prove it in Problem 12–8.

In general, production would not be scheduled in advance for some given number of time periods, say ten weeks, and then forgotten until the end of this period. The ten weeks would be used as a planning horizon, and computations would be made each week to account for new orders, cancelled orders, etc., that is, each week a new production schedule would be devised for the next ten weeks. One schedules ten weeks in advance, although only the plans for the first week will actually be used, because demands in the distant future can influence the production in the coming week. In other words, we may find that some items should perhaps be produced in the coming week and be inventoried for delivery five weeks hence. By means of this procedure, future production can be adjusted according to the numbers of units in inventory at the time of computation.

The technique described above can be generalized to the case where the same production facilities are used to make a number of different products. Here we deal in units of time rather than in the number of units of each product. Suppose that the plant produces m different items. Let r_j^k be the units of product k for which there is a demand in period j, and

t_k be the time required to produce one unit of product k. Then $b_j^k = t_k r_j^k$ is the total production time which must be devoted to the units of product k for which there is a demand in period j. Assume that a_i hours are available for regular-time production, and a_i' hours for overtime production in period i. Take x_{ij}^k to be the hours of regular-time production in period i devoted to the manufacture of product k to meet the demands arising in period j, and y_{ij}^k be the corresponding overtime production. Finally, suppose that c_k is the cost of producing one unit of product k on regular time, d_k the cost of producing one unit of product k on overtime, and f_k the storage cost for one unit of product k for one time period.

We then wish to find non-negative x_{ij}^k, y_{ij}^k which satisfy

$$\sum_{k=1}^{m} \sum_{j=i}^{n} x_{ij}^k \le a_i, \qquad i = 1, \ldots, n,$$

$$\sum_{k=1}^{m} \sum_{j=i}^{n} y_{ij}^k \le a_i', \qquad i = 1, \ldots, n, \tag{12–15}$$

$$\sum_{i=1}^{j} (x_{ij}^k + y_{ij}^k) = b_j^k, \qquad k = 1, \ldots, m, \qquad j = 1, \ldots, n, \tag{12–16}$$

and minimize

$$z = \sum_{k=1}^{m} \sum_{i=1}^{n} \sum_{j=i}^{n} c_k x_{ij}^k + \sum_{k=1}^{m} \sum_{i=1}^{n} \sum_{j=i}^{n} d_k y_{ij}^k$$

$$+ \sum_{k=1}^{m} f_k \sum_{j=2}^{n} \sum_{i=1}^{j} (j - i)(x_{ij}^k + y_{ij}^k). \tag{12–17}$$

Here again we have a transportation problem, with the equivalent of $2n$ origins and $mn + 1$ destinations. The general structure of the tableau is shown in Fig. 12–2. The cells in the shaded areas are not used. As usual, we assume that set-up times and costs are negligible.

In this multiproduct case, it is important that the total production time be a realistic measure of the availability of productive capacity. If the products require a number of operations, such as work on different machines, then we must assume that all products require the same operations and in the same proportions on the various machines. In other words, one product cannot require a great deal of time in department 1 and almost no time in department 5, while another product requires almost no time in department 1 but a great deal of time in department 5. We must essentially assume that such variations among the products are minor and that the time required to create these variations is not a limiting factor. If we are concerned with more than a single product, the initial solution obtained by the column-minima method is not necessarily optimal.

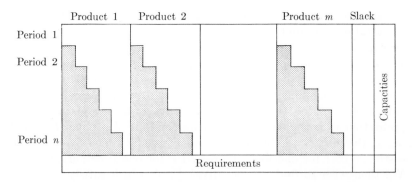

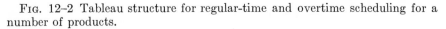

Fig. 12-2 Tableau structure for regular-time and overtime scheduling for a number of products.

EXAMPLE: Consider a scheduling problem involving two products and two time periods. The costs, requirements, and the capacities on regular time and overtime are shown in Table 12-2. The cost of storage is included in the costs for products made in period 1 for sale in period 2.

An initial solution is easily obtained by inspection (see Table 12-2). Since it was degenerate, one slack cell was added at a zero level to yield a basic solution. There is one cell with $z_{ij} - c_{ij} > 0$. The new tableau is shown in Table 12-3. The nonzero values of the variables have not changed. Only the location of the zero-level variable has been changed.

TABLE 12-2 — TABLEAU 1

Time period 1	2 / ⑩ / —2	3 / ⑤	3 / —2	5 / —1	0 / 15
	4 / —1	5 / —3	4 / ③	6 / —2	0 / ⑫ / 15
Time period 2		2 / ⑮		3 / +1	0 / ⓪ / 15
		4 / —2		4 / ⑫	0 / ③ / 15
	10	15	8	12	15 / 60

TABLE 12–3 — TABLEAU 2

2 ⃞ (10)	3 ⃞ −1	3 ⃞ (5)	5 ⃞ −2	0 ⃞ −1	15
4 ⃞ −1	5 ⃞ −2	4 ⃞ (3)	6 ⃞ −2	0 ⃞ (12)	15
	2 ⃞ (15)		3 ⃞ (0)	0 ⃞ −1	15
	4 ⃞ −1		4 ⃞ (12)	0 ⃞ (3)	15
10	15	8	12	15	60

The optimality criterion is now satisfied. Thus the original schedule was optimal.

12–7 Optimal product mix and activity levels. We now wish to consider practical problems which, when formulated, become general linear programming problems rather than transportation-type problems, and have to be solved by the simplex algorithm or by one of the other general algorithms. In studying machine-assignment problems, we have assumed thus far that the number of units of each item to be produced was specified, and we were only concerned with assigning production to machines in a single department. This approach was suitable for a job shop, for example, where the orders for the coming period are available, and where the relative demands for the various products can change considerably from one period to the next.

Now we wish to study a slightly different situation. We shall again consider a company which makes a number of products. However, we shall assume that production is essentially continuous. We can imagine that a number of different operations are required to produce the product. These may be operations on different machines in a textile mill or the passage of crude oil through different units in a refinery. We can also allow for the possibility that each product can be made in a number of different ways. In this case, we shall not assume that the product mix is given; instead we wish to determine the product mix which will maximize profits. In addition, we wish to determine which process or combination of processes should be used to produce each product.

To be concrete, let us suppose that the production of each product involves a sequence of operations on different machines. In general, a given machine can be used in the production of several different products. We shall assume that a number of different combinations of machines can be used to produce a given product. For each way of producing a given product, we set down the sequence of machines used. Denote by x_j the amount of variable j produced per week; variable j refers to a given product produced by a given process. Since it is possible that several different processes can be used to produce a single product, several different x_j can refer to the same product. Let a_{ij} be the time required on machine i to produce one unit of the product corresponding to variable x_j when the particular production process characterized by this variable is used. Let b_i be the total time per week available on machine i. Then, if there are m machine types and set-up times are negligible, the $x_j \geq 0$ must satisfy the constraints

$$\sum_{j=1}^{n} a_{ij} x_j \leq b_i, \qquad i = 1, \ldots, m. \qquad (12\text{–}18)$$

The number of variables, n, is the sum of the number of possible production processes for each item.

In addition to the machine-time restrictions, there may be other constraints, such as sales constraints. For example, it may be known that no more than a certain amount of each product can be sold, and that at least a certain amount of each product must be made to fill out the line. These constraints take the form

$$\sum x_j \leq d, \qquad (12\text{–}19)$$

$$\sum x_j \geq f. \qquad (12\text{–}20)$$

The summations are taken over all variables which refer to the same product.

Let c_j be the profit made on the sale of one unit of variable j, that is, on the sale of one unit of a given product made by a particular process. We then wish to determine $x_j \geq 0$ which satisfy the constraints (12–18) through (12–20) and which maximize the function

$$z = \sum_{j=1}^{n} c_j x_j. \qquad (12\text{–}21)$$

When we have solved this problem, we have determined the loading on each machine type, the total amount of each product to be produced, and what fraction of each product should be produced by each of the possible processes. Clearly the solution to such a problem provides a great deal of information.

EXAMPLE: A small company makes three different products, 1, 2, 3. Each product requires work on two different machine types A, B. The shop has two varieties of type A machines which we shall designate by A_1, A_2 and three varieties of type B machines, B_1, B_2, B_3. Product 1 can be made on any of the type A and type B machines. Product 2 can be made on any variety of type A machines, but must be processed on machines B_1 of type B. Finally, product 3 can be made only on machines A_2 of type A and machines B_2 of type B.

The time in minutes required by one unit of each product on each variety of machine is given in Table 12–4, along with the total minutes of machine time available per week and the cost per week of running the machines at full capacity. The cost of raw materials for one unit of each product and its selling price are given in the last two rows of the table. We shall assume that the cost of running the machines is directly propor-

TABLE 12–4 — DATA FOR EXAMPLE

	Product			Total time available per week (minutes)	Cost at full capacity
	1	2	3		
A_1	5	10	—	6,000	300
A_2	7	9	12	10,000	321
B_1	6	8	—	4,000	250
B_2	4	—	11	7,000	783
B_3	7	—	—	4,000	200
Material cost	0.25	0.35	0.50		
Selling price	1.25	2.00	2.80		

tional to the operating time and that this cost includes all other costs, aside from raw-materials cost (we shall ignore advertising costs, etc.).

Product 1 can be produced in six different ways represented by the following combinations of machines: (A_1, B_1), (A_1, B_2), (A_1, B_3), (A_2, B_1), (A_2, B_2), (A_2, B_3). Let $x_1, \ldots, x_6$ denote the respective number of units of product 1 produced per week by each of these six processes. Product 2 can be made in two ways represented by the combinations of machines (A_1, B_1), (A_2, B_1). Let x_7 be the number of units of product 2 produced per week by process (A_1, B_1), and let x_8 be the number produced by process (A_2, B_1). Product 3 can be produced in only one way, i.e., on the combination of machines (A_2, B_2). Take x_9 to be the units of product 3 produced per week.

Next we shall formulate the machine-capacity constraints. There are five varieties of machines, and hence there will be five such constraints. A process of production, or an activity, is one way of producing one product. Each of the variables defined above refers to a different activity. There are nine activities in all. For activity j, let a_{ij} be the time required for one unit on machine variety i. Activity vector $\mathbf{a}_j = [a_{1j}, a_{2j}, a_{3j}, a_{4j}, a_{5j}]$ gives the times required on each variety of machines to produce one unit. Only two of the a_{ij}-values will differ from zero. For example, activity 1 refers to producing product 1 on the (A_1, B_1) combination of machines. Thus $\mathbf{a}_1 = [5, 0, 6, 0, 0]$ since five minutes are required on machine variety A_1 and six minutes on machine variety B_1 to produce one unit of product 1. The other activity vectors can be written down immediately. They are:

$$\mathbf{a}_2 = [5, 0, 0, 4, 0], \qquad \mathbf{a}_3 = [5, 0, 0, 0, 7],$$
$$\mathbf{a}_4 = [0, 7, 6, 0, 0], \qquad \mathbf{a}_5 = [0, 7, 0, 4, 0],$$
$$\mathbf{a}_6 = [0, 7, 0, 0, 7], \qquad \mathbf{a}_7 = [10, 0, 8, 0, 0],$$
$$\mathbf{a}_8 = [0, 9, 8, 0, 0], \qquad \mathbf{a}_9 = [0, 12, 0, 11, 0].$$

The machine-capacity constraints then have the form $\sum_{j=1}^{9} x_j \mathbf{a}_j \leq \mathbf{b}$. Written out in detail, they are

$$5x_1 + 5x_2 + 5x_3 \qquad\qquad + 10x_7 \qquad\qquad \leq 6{,}000,$$
$$7x_4 + 7x_5 + 7x_6 \qquad + 9x_8 + 12x_9 \leq 10{,}000,$$
$$6x_1 \qquad\qquad + 6x_4 \qquad\qquad + 8x_7 + 8x_8 \qquad \leq 4{,}000,$$
$$4x_2 \qquad\qquad + 4x_5 \qquad\qquad + 11x_9 \leq 7{,}000,$$
$$7x_3 \qquad\qquad + 7x_6 \qquad\qquad \leq 4{,}000.$$

In addition to these, there may be some sales constraints. Suppose, for example, that no more than 800 units per week of product 1 could be sold. This constraint would have the form

$$x_1 + x_2 + x_3 + x_4 + x_5 + x_6 \leq 800$$

since the first six activities refer to the production of product 1.

The final task is that of computing the unit profits to be used in the objective function. We shall illustrate the computation for activity 1, which describes the production of product 1 on machines (A_1, B_1). The cost on A_1 of producing one unit is $(5/6000)(300) = 0.25$. The cost on B_1 is $(6/4000)(250) = 0.375$. The raw material cost for one unit is 0.25. Thus the total variable cost of one unit is 0.875. The selling price is 1.25, so that the unit profit $c_1 = 0.375$. The unit profits for the other activities are computed in the same way. They are: $c_2 = 0.300$, $c_3 = 0.400$, $c_4 = 0.400$, $c_5 = 0.325$, $c_6 = 0.425$, $c_7 = 0.650$, $c_8 = 0.861$, $c_9 = 0.672$. We wish to determine $x_j \geq 0$ satisfying the constraints which maximize

$$z = 0.375x_1 + 0.300x_2 + 0.400x_3 + 0.400x_4 + 0.325x_5$$
$$+0.425x_6 + 0.650x_7 + 0.861x_8 + 0.672x_9.$$

We have shown how to formulate the problem. It will be noted that a rather small-scale problem can yield a rather large linear programming problem. If a large number of products can be made in many ways and requires numerous operations, the resulting linear programming problem can become quite large when sales restrictions and other constraints are included.

The author assisted company personnel in solving one practical problem of the type considered in this section, which was concerned with the operation of a textile mill. This particular mill made blankets. A number of blankets of different qualities and sizes were produced. Any given blanket required operations on a number of different machines. Furthermore, certain blankets could be produced on more than a single combination of machines, i.e., by several different activities. In addition, there were maximum and minimum sales restrictions on some of the blankets. Including the sales restrictions, the problem involved about 35 constraints and 50 variables.

The problem was solved by including first all sales restrictions, then only the maximum sales restrictions, and finally only the minimum sales restrictions. The company executives were quite interested in the results. However, the results were not too clear-cut, since considerable difficulties in obtaining data, especially costs and prices, made it impossible to ascertain just how much operations could be improved. (For example, the company had a different selling price for almost every customer.)

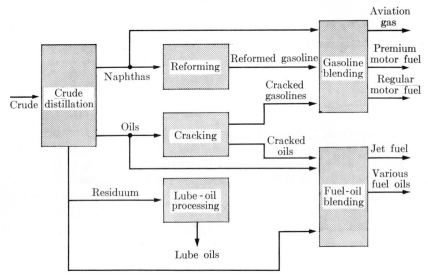

FIGURE 12–3

12–8 Petroleum-refinery operations. In recent years, many petroleum companies have made efforts to optimize refinery operations by means of linear programming. In this section we shall describe briefly how such a problem can be attacked. The problem of optimizing refinery operations is extremely complicated, and we can do no more than present the barest outline of the procedure.

The refining operation begins with the atmospheric distillation of crude petroleum. The distillation yields a number of different products (fractions), such as naphthas, straight-run oils, and bottoms. These fractions can be routed to a number of different units for further treatment or sent directly to blending of final products. For example, the straight-run oils may be sent to a catalytic cracking unit to break down the long-chain hydrocarbons, and the naphthas may be sent to a catalytic reformer. A partial flow chart of a refinery operation is shown in Fig. 12–3. In any actual refinery there are many more fractions at each stage and also more stages. However, Fig. 12–3 will suffice for our purposes.

Many final refinery products, such as gasolines, are formed by blending a number of different refinery streams. A product of given quality can be obtained from many different blends. There is a number of different decisions to be made in order to determine the final mix of refinery products. First, a refinery often receives several different types of crude oil, and it must be decided which crude or mix of crudes should be run. Once this decision is made, the output of the crude-distillation unit is essentially determined. Next one must decide what fraction of the outputs of crude distillation should go directly to blending and what fraction should go to successive conversion operations (cracking, etc.). Finally, at the blending stage, it has to be decided how to blend the various streams.

In addition to determining the routing of the various streams, decisions have to be made on the operating conditions of a number of the units. It is possible to change the composition of the output of some units by changing some variables, such as temperature, pressure, and the so-called reflux ratio (parts of some of the outputs are recycled into the unit). We shall assume that the operating conditions for each unit are fixed. This means that once the input to the unit is specified, the various outputs are also determined. No attempt will be made to optimize the operating conditions of the various units. We shall concern ourselves only with the optimal allocations of the streams to the various units.

The constraints fall naturally into several categories. First, there are the constraints representing the availability of the various crudes. Then there are the constraints on the equipment capacity, which limit the volumetric throughput in the various units. Next there are material-balance equations which relate the input into any one unit and the various output streams from the unit. Finally, there are the constraints representing the final products requirements.

Let us return to the simplified, hypothetical refinery for which the flow chart is given in Fig. 12–3. We shall formulate the constraints by beginning with the crude and by following the various streams through the refinery. All variables will be assumed to be measured in the dimensions of barrels per day (bbl/day). A refinery may use ten or more different crudes. For simplicity, assume that our refinery uses two crudes which differ somewhat in chemical composition. Such differences can have an important influence on the quantities and types of final products which can be made. Let the daily availabilities of these two crudes be θ_1, θ_2 (these availabilities may change from week to week), and let x_1, x_2 be the bbl/day actually used. Then

$$0 \le x_1 \le \theta_1, \qquad 0 \le x_2 \le \theta_2. \tag{12–22}$$

The crude-distillation unit will have a capacity limitation on the quantity of crude it can handle per day. If no more than A barrels per day of crude can be sent to crude distillation, then we must have

$$x_1 + x_2 \le A. \tag{12–23}$$

Now we are ready to study the output of the crude distillation unit.

The naphtha stream of Fig. 12–3 will, in reality, be a number of different streams. Suppose that our refinery produces light, medium, and heavy naphthas. One barrel of crude i ($i = 1, 2$) yields a_{1i} barrels of light naphthas, a_{2i} barrels of medium naphthas, and a_{3i} barrels of heavy naphthas. Thus if y_1, y_2, y_3 are the barrels per day of light, medium, and heavy naphthas produced, we have

$$y_1 = a_{11}x_1 + a_{12}x_2, \qquad y_2 = a_{21}x_1 + a_{22}x_2, \qquad y_3 = a_{31}x_1 + a_{32}x_2.$$
$$(12\text{--}24)$$

Each naphtha stream is split into two streams: one goes to gasoline blending, and the other to reforming. Let y_j^b be the bbl/day of naphtha, grade j, routed to blending, and y_j^r the bbl/day routed to reforming. Thus

$$y_j = y_j^b + y_j^r, \qquad j = 1, 2, 3. \qquad (12\text{--}25)$$

We can eliminate the y_j and reduce the number of constraints by three if we substitute (12–25) into (12–24). This gives

$$y_j^b + y_j^r - a_{j1}x_1 - a_{j2}x_2 = 0, \qquad j = 1, 2, 3. \qquad (12\text{--}26)$$

Let us next consider the streams from crude distillation which are labeled oils in Fig. 12–3. Assume that there are only two such streams, light oil (oil 1) and heavy oil (oil 2). One barrel of crude i ($i = 1, 2$) yields b_{1i} barrels of light oil and b_{2i} barrels of heavy oil. If u_j^b, u_j^c are the bbls/day of oil j ($j = 1, 2$) which are routed to fuel-oil blending and cracking, respectively, then

$$u_j^b + u_j^c - b_{j1}x_1 - b_{j2}x_2 = 0, \qquad j = 1, 2, \qquad (12\text{--}27)$$

represents the material balances on the light and heavy oils.

For the hypothetical refinery under consideration, the residuum stream of Fig. 12–3 is a single stream. One barrel of crude i ($i = 1, 2$) yields d_i barrels of residuum. If v_b bbl/day of residuum are routed directly to fuel-oil blending and v_d to lube-oil processing, then the material balance on the residuum stream is:

$$v_b + v_d - d_1x_1 - d_2x_2 = 0. \qquad (12\text{--}28)$$

Material balances have now been written for all the streams emanating from crude distillation. We next turn our attention to the intermediate operations of reforming and cracking. The total daily input to the reformer is $y_1^r + y_2^r + y_3^r$. Let B be the maximum number of bbl/day of input which the reformer can handle. Then

$$y_1^r + y_2^r + y_3^r \leq B. \qquad (12\text{--}29)$$

This takes care of the capacity constraint on the reformer. Next the reformer material balances must be formulated.

We shall imagine that only a single gasoline stream is produced by the reformer. One barrel of naphtha j sent to the reformer yields f_j barrels of reformed gasoline. Thus, if w is the output in bbl/day of reformed gasoline, there is only a single material balance equation for the reformer, namely,

$$w - f_1 y_1^r - f_2 y_2^r - f_3 y_3^r = 0. \tag{12–30}$$

Consider now the cracking unit; this cracker yields only one cracked gasoline stream and one cracked oil stream. One barrel of oil j sent to the cracking unit produces g_j barrels of cracked gasoline and h_j barrels of cracked oil. If r bbl/day of cracked gasoline and s bbl/day of cracked oil are produced, then the material-balance equations for cracked gasoline and oil are respectively

$$r - g_1 u_1^c - g_2 u_2^c = 0, \tag{12–31}$$

$$s - h_1 u_1^c - h_2 u_2^c = 0. \tag{12–32}$$

If D is the capacity of the cracking unit, then it must be true that

$$u_1^c + u_2^c \leq D. \tag{12–33}$$

We have now formulated all the constraints which apply to the cracking unit.

For our hypothetical refinery, there is only one stream into the lube-oil processing unit. Assume that only one type of lube oil is produced, and that one barrel of residuum yields k barrels of lube oil. If q bbl/day of lube oil are produced, then the lube-oil material balance becomes

$$q - k v_d = 0. \tag{12–34}$$

The capacity of the lube-oil processing unit is E bbl/day of input. Then the capacity constraint is

$$v_d \leq E. \tag{12–35}$$

There may or may not be restrictions on the quantity of lube-oil output. Suppose that the refinery can sell all the lube oil it produces, but that it must supply at least δ bbl/day. This yields the additional constraint

$$q \geq \delta. \tag{12–36}$$

At last we are ready to move to the final stage and write the constraints for the blending of the various final products. In practice, various quality restrictions are imposed on the final gasoline products. We shall simplify matters by assuming that for each gasoline, there is only a single octane requirement to be satisfied. It is required that aviation, premium, and regular gasolines have octane numbers of at least p_1, p_2, p_3, respectively. Let m_j^n ($j = 1, 2, 3$) be the octane numbers of the three naphthas, m_r the octane number of reformed gasoline, and m_c the octane number of cracked gasoline. It will be assumed that the octane numbers of the various components blend linearly by volume.

Denote by y_j^{ba}, y_j^{bp}, y_j^{br}, $j = 1, 2, 3$, the bbl/day of naphtha j blended into aviation, premium, and regular gasolines, respectively. Similarly, w^a, w^p, w^r will denote the bbl/day of reformed gasoline, and r^a, r^p, r^r will denote the bbl/day of cracked gasoline blended into aviation, premium, and regular gasolines, respectively. The material balances for all components then read

$$y_j^{ba} + y_j^{bp} + y_j^{br} - y_j^b = 0, \qquad j = 1, 2, 3, \qquad (12\text{--}37)$$

$$w^a + w^p + w^r - w = 0, \qquad (12\text{--}38)$$

$$r^a + r^p + r^r - r = 0. \qquad (12\text{--}39)$$

Equations (12–37) through (12–39) can be used to eliminate the y_j^b, w, r in the previous constraints, thus eliminating the need for constraints (12–37) through (12–39).

The total bbl/day of aviation fuel produced will be $y_1^{ba} + y_2^{ba} + y_3^{ba} + w^a + r^a$. Thus, the octane constraint for aviation gasoline becomes:*

$$m_1^n y_1^{ba} + m_2^n y_2^{ba} + m_3^n y_3^{ba} + m_r w^a + m_c r^a$$

$$\geq p_1(y_1^{ba} + y_2^{ba} + y_3^{ba} + w^a + r^a). \quad (12\text{--}40)$$

This can be rearranged to read

$$(p_1 - m_1^n)y_1^{ba} + (p_1 - m_2^n)y_2^{ba} + (p_1 - m_3^n)y_3^{ba}$$

$$+ (p_1 - m_r)w^a + (p_1 - m_c)r^a \leq 0. \quad (12\text{--}41)$$

Similarly, the octane constraints for premium and regular motor fuels are:

$$(p_2 - m_1^n)y_1^{bp} + (p_2 - m_2^n)y_2^{bp} + (p_2 - m_3^n)y_3^{bp}$$

$$+ (p_2 - m_r)w^p + (p_2 - m_c)r^p \leq 0; \quad (12\text{--}42)$$

$$(p_3 - m_1^n)y_1^{br} + (p_3 - m_2^n)y_2^{br} + (p_3 - m_3^n)y_3^{br}$$

$$+ (p_3 - m_r)w^r + (p_3 - m_c)r^r \leq 0. \quad (12\text{--}43)$$

---

* If this inequality is not obvious to the reader, he will find its detailed derivation in the following section.

In addition to the octane requirements on gasoline, there may also be constraints on the quantities produced. A typical constraint, for example, requires that the premium motor fuel be a given fraction γ of the output of regular motor fuel. This constraint has the form

$$y_1^{bp} + y_2^{bp} + y_3^{bp} + w^p + r^p - \gamma y_1^{br} - \gamma y_2^{br} - \gamma y_3^{br} - \gamma w^r - \gamma r^r = 0.$$

$$(12\text{–}44)$$

We have yet to discuss the subject of fuel-oil blending. Suppose that the refinery produces one jet fuel and one other fuel oil. Let s^j, s^f be the bbl/day of cracked oil, u_1^{bj}, u_1^{bf} the bbl/day of light oil, u_2^{bj}, u_2^{bf} the bbl/day of heavy oil, and v_b^j, v_b^f the bbl/day of residuum blended for jet fuel and fuel oil, respectively. We then have the following material-balance equations:

$$s^j + s^f - s = 0, \qquad (12\text{–}45)$$

$$u_1^{bj} + u_1^{bf} - u_1^b = 0, \qquad u_2^{bj} + u_2^{bf} - u_2^b = 0, \qquad (12\text{–}46)$$

$$v_b^j + v_b^f - v_b = 0. \qquad (12\text{–}47)$$

These equations could, of course, be used to eliminate u_1^b, u_2^b, s, v_b in the preceding constraints.

A limit on the vapor pressure is the only quality constraint we shall impose on the jet fuel. The upper limit to the vapor pressure is to be ϕ. If q_1, q_2, q_c, q_r are the vapor pressures of the light, heavy, cracked, and residuum oils, respectively, then the vapor pressure constraint can be written

$$q_1 u_1^{bj} + q_2 u_2^{bj} + q_c s^j + q_r v_b^j \leq \phi(u_1^{bj} + u_2^{bj} + s^j + v_b^j),$$

or

$$(12\text{–}48)$$

$$(\phi - q_1)u_1^{bj} + (\phi - q_2)u_2^{bj} + (\phi - q_c)s^j + (\phi - q_r)v_b^j \geq 0,$$

provided we assume that the vapor pressures of the constituents blend linearly by volume. In addition to this constraint, constraints on the boiling range and aromatic content of the jet fuel are often imposed in practice.

No particular quality specifications will be given for the fuel oil. However, we require that the various components be blended in fixed proportions. Expressing the quantity of all other components as a certain fraction of the light oil used, we obtain the following set of constraints:

$$u_2^{bf} - \psi_2 u_1^{bf} = 0, \qquad s^f - \psi_c u_1^{bf} = 0, \qquad v_b^f - \psi_r u_1^{bf} = 0. \quad (12\text{–}49)$$

In addition, there may be maximum and minimum limitations on the output of fuel oil.

We have finally completed the task of formulating the constraints for our oversimplified, hypothetical refinery. All the variables must, of course, be non-negative. Although many simplifications were introduced, the number of constraints is considerable. Any attempt to represent realistically the operations of an actual refinery can easily lead to 150 or 200 constraints, and thus to a very large linear programming problem. It should be noted that one must be careful in imposing quantity constraints on the final products, since their output cannot be arbitrarily specified. For example, it is not possible to produce only fuel oil and no gasolines, or vice versa. This fact has presented some problems for the petroleum industry. For example: To produce enough fuel oil to meet the winter's demand, it is sometimes necessary to produce more gasoline than is really needed; this, of course, leads to excessively large stocks of gasolines.

We have not yet discussed the objective function we wish to maximize. If arbitrary quantities of any final product could be sold, then no upper limits would have to be placed on the output of any product, and we would maximize the function

$$Z = c_a(y_1^{ba} + y_2^{ba} + y_3^{ba} + w^a + r^a) + c_p(y_1^{bp} + y_2^{bp} + y_3^{bp} + w^p + r^p)$$

$$+ c_r(y_1^{br} + y_2^{br} + y_3^{br} + w^r + r^r) + c_j(u_1^{bj} + u_2^{bj} + s^j + v_b^j)$$

$$+ c_f(u_1^{bf} + u_2^{bf} + s^f + v_b^f) + c_u q, \tag{12–50}$$

where c_a, c_p, c_r, c_j, c_f, c_u are the profits per barrel of aviation, premium, and regular gasolines, jet fuel, fuel oil, and lube oils, respectively.

However, as has been noted above, the demand for one product (such as fuel oil) may require that another product be produced in a larger quantity than can be sold immediately. Hence, profits may be maximized by minimizing the quantity of gasoline produced in the course of processing a given amount of fuel oil. Or, if gasoline is in demand, we may wish to minimize the production of fuel oil for a given gasoline-production rate. Thus we see that it is not always simple to decide what the objective function should be.

Alan Manne [12] has made an interesting study of the refining industry as a whole, along the lines presented in this section. He wished to determine the maximum jet-fuel production on the basis of a given output quota for certain other products.

12–9 Blending problems. We shall now discuss the application of linear programming to so-called blending problems. In the preceding section, we encountered some excellent examples of blending problems. We noted that many of the final refinery products were formed by blending a number of different refinery streams. In general, blending problems refer to situations where a number of components are mixed together to yield one or more products. Usually, there are restrictions on the available quantities of raw materials, restrictions on the quality of the products, and perhaps restrictions on the quantities of the products to be produced. However, there are usually infinitely many different ways in which the raw materials can be blended to form the final products while satisfying the various constraints. It is desired to carry out the blending operation so that some given objective function will be optimized.

The petroleum industry does not provide the only example of blending operations. In the manufacture of paints, and even in the manufacture of ice cream, blending problems are encountered. Similarly, blending problems exist in the steel industry. As an example, consider the determination of the charge for a blast furnace. Several varieties of ore, along with scrap steel, limestone, and coke, are mixed together to form the charge. Many blends are possible. The optimal blend depends on what the objectives are.

Linear programming forms a natural technique for optimizing blending operations provided that the various quantities of interest blend linearly. It is by no means true that all physical quantities blend linearly, and hence if linear programming is applied in a case of nonlinear blending, it will yield only an approximate answer. In many instances, however, the assumption of linearity has given answers which were good enough to make linear programming a very useful tool for studying blending operations.

We shall begin with a discussion of the blending of motor gasolines. Gasoline blending is a very important problem because a small percentage improvement in operations could mean millions of dollars to the oil companies. Many of the larger oil companies have been using linear programming for some time to solve their blending problems. Some have claimed that substantial amounts of money were saved by means of linear programming. Gasoline-blending problems alone, even if divorced from the operations of the refinery as a whole, can lead to quite large linear programming problems. One oil company has worked with a gasoline-blending problem involving eighty constraints. It required more than two hours of time on the IBM 704 to reach an optimal solution.

Any motor fuel must satisfy a number of quality requirements. Impurities, such as sulfur, must not exceed a given concentration, the vapor pressure (referred to in the industry as the Reid vapor pressure) must be within a certain range, and the octane number must equal or exceed some minimum value.

Most of these requirements are met by measures which are independent of the blending operation. For example, some impurities are controlled by the proper selection of crudes, while other impurities are eliminated by chemical treatment. The vapor pressure of the motor fuel is often adjusted by adding butane to the fuel. The raw refinery stocks are passed through a debutanizer to reduce their vapor pressure for easy storage. The butane is added after the fuels have been blended. In the winter, more butane is added than during the summer, so that ignition will be rapid in cold weather. Tetraethyl lead is usually also added to motor fuels. Since this is a very dangerous substance, it is not added to the blended fuels until they are ready to be shipped. The only quality restriction which remains to be taken care of in the blending operation is the octane number.*

The quality requirement on the octane number refers to more than a single restriction. Gasoline is a mixture of a number of hydrocarbons. When gasoline is heated, it will begin to vaporize. Initially, the vapor will contain the lighter hydrocarbons (those with a smaller number of carbon atoms). With continued heating, the composition of the vapor and liquid changes; furthermore, the boiling point of the liquid increases as it becomes more concentrated in the heavier hydrocarbons. Thus, specification of the boiling point specifies the liquid composition.

For any one gasoline, the minimum octane number is usually specified for several boiling ranges. Although the refineries attempt to obtain one octane number for all boiling ranges, this cannot be done exactly. A single octane number is desirable for the following reasons: When the mixture of gas and air is inserted into the cylinder of an engine, it is partially vaporized. Unfortunately, the composition of the liquid and vapor may vary from cylinder to cylinder. If the octane number of the liquid-vapor mixture in the various cylinders varies considerably, the tendency of the engine to knock is aggravated.

Let us turn to the details of the blending problem. Assume that three refinery streams 1, 2, 3 are blended to form regular, r, and premium, p, motor fuel. The availabilities of the refinery streams 1, 2, 3 are known to be A_1, A_2, A_3 bbl/day, respectively. Suppose the minimum octane numbers of regular and premium gas are to be δ_1, γ_1, respectively, in the 250–300°F boiling range. The corresponding octane numbers in the 350–400°F boiling range are to be δ_2, γ_2. Let ϵ_{j1} be the octane number of refinery stream j in the 250–300°F boiling range, and ϵ_{j2} be the octane number of stream j in the 350–400°F boiling range.

We shall imagine that the refinery under consideration is a small Gulf Coast refinery which produces only premium and regular motor fuels—

---

* The quantity of tetraethyl lead added to motor fuels has an important bearing on the antiknock performance of the final fuel, and sometimes it is desirable to include it as one of the components to be blended. We shall assume that the quantity of tetraethyl lead to be added is fixed; and we shall not consider it in the blending problem.

no aviation gasoline. However, it can sell the refinery streams at prices of c_1, c_2, c_3 per barrel, respectively. The selling prices (tank-wagon price) of premium and regular gasolines are c_p and c_r, respectively. The refinery is under contract to blend at least R bbl/day of regular gasoline. The amount of premium gasoline is always a fixed fraction, f, of the amount of regular gasoline. The refinery can sell all regular and premium gasolines it produces. We wish to determine how the raw stocks should be blended to form the motor fuels and, in addition, how much of each motor fuel ought to be made in order to maximize profits.

Denote by $x_{pj} \geq 0$, $j = 1$, 2, 3 the bbl/day of raw stock j used to blend premium gasoline, and by $x_{rj} \geq 0$, $j = 1$, 2, 3 the bbl/day of raw stock j used to blend regular gasoline. The constraints on the availabilities of the raw stocks read

$$x_{pj} + x_{rj} \leq A_j, \qquad j = 1, 2, 3. \tag{12–51}$$

At least R bbl/day of regular gasoline must be produced. Therefore

$$x_{r1} + x_{r2} + x_{r3} \geq R. \tag{12–52}$$

To write (12–52), we must assume that the volumes are strictly additive. This is a very good approximation. The amount of premium fuel produced must be a fixed fraction of the regular fuel. Thus

$$x_{p1} + x_{p2} + x_{p3} - fx_{r1} - fx_{r2} - fx_{r3} = 0. \tag{12–53}$$

We now come to the octane constraints. In reality, octane numbers do not blend linearly. This is especially true when aromatic hydrocarbons are added. However, over limited regions, the linearity assumption is a good approximation. According to this hypothesis, each constituent contributes to the octane number of the mixture an amount equal to the product of its octane number and its fraction of the total volume of the mixture; for example, the volume fraction of j in regular gasoline is $x_{rj}/(x_{r1} + x_{r2} + x_{r3})$. Thus, at 250–300°F the octane constraint for regular gas is:

$$\epsilon_{11} \frac{x_{r1}}{x_{r1} + x_{r2} + x_{r3}} + \epsilon_{21} \frac{x_{r2}}{x_{r1} + x_{r2} + x_{r3}} + \epsilon_{31} \frac{x_{r3}}{x_{r1} + x_{r2} + x_{r3}} \geq \delta_1,$$

or

$$\epsilon_{11}x_{r1} + \epsilon_{21}x_{r2} + \epsilon_{31}x_{r3} \geq \delta_1(x_{r1} + x_{r2} + x_{r3}), \tag{12–54}$$

or

$$(\delta_1 - \epsilon_{11})x_{r1} + (\delta_1 - \epsilon_{21})x_{r2} + (\delta_1 - \epsilon_{31})x_{r3} \leq 0.$$

The remaining octane-number constraints are:

$$(\gamma_1 - \epsilon_{11})x_{p1} + (\gamma_1 - \epsilon_{21})x_{p2} + (\gamma_1 - \epsilon_{31})x_{p3} \le 0, \quad (12\text{--}55)$$

$$(\delta_2 - \epsilon_{12})x_{r1} + (\delta_2 - \epsilon_{22})x_{r2} + (\delta_2 - \epsilon_{32})x_{r3} \le 0, \quad (12\text{--}56)$$

$$(\gamma_2 - \epsilon_{12})x_{p1} + (\gamma_2 - \epsilon_{22})x_{p2} + (\gamma_2 - \epsilon_{32})x_{p3} \le 0. \quad (12\text{--}57)$$

The constraints have been formulated. Now we shall discuss the objective function. Since we assume that a fixed amount of each raw stock is produced each day, and since the entire output is sold, the costs are fixed and do not enter into the optimization. Thus the function to be optimized is

$$z' = c_p(x_{p1} + x_{p2} + x_{p3}) + c_r(x_{r1} + x_{r2} + x_{r3}) + c_1(A_1 - x_{p1} - x_{r1})$$

$$+ c_2(A_2 - x_{p2} - x_{r2}) + c_3(A_3 - x_{p3} - x_{r3}).$$

Equivalently, we wish to maximize

$$z = (c_p - c_1)x_{p1} + (c_p - c_2)x_{p2} + (c_p - c_3)x_{p3} + (c_r - c_1)x_{r1}$$

$$+ (c_r - c_2)x_{r2} + (c_r - c_3)x_{r3}. \quad (12\text{--}58)$$

The solution to the blending problem not only tells us how the raw stocks should be blended, but in addition, it indicates how much of each gasoline will be blended, and therefore what quantities of raw stocks will be sold directly. It may amuse the reader to know that the refineries do not completely trust these blending computations. They will often test the gasolines in octane engines to see whether they do indeed satisfy the octane requirements.

Diet problems form another interesting class of blending problems. Dieticians tell us that a balanced diet must contain certain quantities of nutrients, such as calories, minerals, and vitamins. Suppose that we are asked to determine from a given number of foods the lowest-cost diet which satisfies the minimum requirements for a balanced diet. Assume that n foods are available, and that there are m nutrients which, in given minimum amounts, must be supplied by the diet.

Let a_{ij} be the number of units of nutrient i in one unit of food j. Furthermore, imagine that x_j units of food j are to be used per day, and that the diet must supply at least b_i units of nutrient i per day. Denote by c_j the cost of one unit of food j. We shall assume that if x_j units of food j are eaten, $a_{ij}x_j$ units of nutrient i are provided. In addition, we imagine that the amount of nutrient i obtained by eating several foods is the sum of the amounts of nutrient i in each of the foods eaten. Then the $x_j \ge 0$, $j = 1, \ldots, n$ which provide a minimum-cost diet are an optimal solution to the linear programming problem

$$\sum_{j=1}^{n} a_{ij}x_j \geq b_i, \qquad i = 1, \ldots, m, \qquad \min z = \sum_{j=1}^{n} c_j x_j. \quad (12\text{–}59)$$

It should be noted that the diet problem, as formulated, does not provide for any variations in the diet. The same mixture must be eaten day in and day out. Furthermore, it does not take into consideration whether the diet is at all palatable. Finally, there are no constraints that place an upper limit on the quantity of any nutrient provided by the diet. It may be desirable to include upper limits on the nutrients so that the consumer of the diet would not get too many carbohydrates, for example.

As indicated in Chapter 1, Stigler was probably the first to find a minimum-cost diet. He did not use linear programming. Later Dantzig and Laderman solved the same problem by the use of linear programming. Needless to say, the diet was not one that anybody would care to eat for any length of time. However, it showed that in terms of 1939 prices, a person could have a balanced diet for the remarkably small sum of about $40 per year.

Minimum-cost diets have been applied in practice by farmers and ranchers for feeding various kinds of livestock. Other potential fields of application are space exploration and nuclear submarines, where the goal is to minimize the weight of food needed for an adequate diet rather than to minimize cost.

References

1. J. N. Boles, "Linear Programming and Farm Management Analysis," *J. Farm Econ.*, **37**, 1–24, 1955.

2. E. H. Bowman, "Production Scheduling by the Transportation Method of Linear Programming," *Operations Research*, **4**, 100–103, 1956.

3. A. Charnes, W. W. Cooper, and B. Mellon, "Blending Aviation Gasolines," *Econometrica*, **20**, 135–159, 1952.

4. A. Charnes and W. W. Cooper, "Management Models and Industrial Applications of Linear Programming," *Management Science*, **4**, 1, 1957.

5. G. B. Dantzig and D. R. Fulkerson, "Minimizing the Number of Tankers to Meet a Fixed Schedule," *Nav. Res. Log. Quart.*, **1**, 217–222, 1954.

6. K. Eisemann, "The Trim Problem," *Management Science*, **3**, 279–284, 1957.

7. M. M. Flood, "Application of Transportation Theory to Scheduling a Military Tanker Fleet," *Operations Research*, **2**, 150–162, 1954.

8. P. Gunther, "Use of Linear Programming in Capital Budgeting," *Operations Research*, **2**, 219–224, 1954.

9. A. Henderson and R. Schlaifer, "Mathematical Programming," *Harvard Business Review*, **32**, 73–100, 1954.

10. S. M. JOHNSON, "Sequential Production Planning over Time at Minimum Cost," *Management Science*, **3**, 4, 1957.

11. H. C. MACKENZIE, "The Linear Programming Approach to Production Planning," *Scottish J. of Polit. Econ.*, **4**, 29–45, 1956.

12. A. MANNE, "A Linear Programming Model of the U. S. Petroleum Refining Industry," *RM*-**1757**, The RAND Corp., July, 1956.

13. A. MANNE, *Scheduling of Petroleum Refinery Operations*, Harvard Economic Studies, vol. 48. Cambridge: Harvard University Press, 1956.

14. A. E. PAULL, "Linear Programming: A Key to Optimum Newsprint Production," *Pulp and Paper Magazine of Canada*, **57**, 85–90, 1956.

15. E. D. STANLEY, D. P. HONIG, and L. GAINEN, "Linear Programming in Bid Evaluation," *Nav. Res. Log. Quart.*, **1**, 48–54, 1954.

16. G. H. SYMONDS, *Linear Programming: The Solution of Refinery Problems*. New York: Esso Standard Oil Company, 1955.

17. S. VAJDA, *Readings in Linear Programming*. New York: Wiley, 1958.

PROBLEMS

12–1. A dog-food manufacturer has three plants which ship to six major distribution points. The tableau below contains the shipping costs per case and the plant capacities and predicted demands for the coming year in millions of cases. The variable production costs per case at the plants are: (1) 0.85, (2) 0.94, (3) 0.72. Determine the minimum cost production-shipping schedule.

	1	2	3	4	5	6	a_i
1	0.26	0.30	0.54	0.41	0.20	0.37	2.2
2	0.45	0.35	0.30	0.50	0.32	0.41	3.4
3	0.53	0.40	0.41	0.20	0.35	0.25	1.8
b_j	0.85	0.75	0.42	0.58	1.02	0.92	

12–2. Prove that if the variable production costs are the same at every plant, one can obtain an optimal production-shipping schedule, using transportation costs only.

12–3. Prove that if every plant must be operated at capacity, then one can obtain an optimal shipping schedule, using transportation cost only, even though variable production costs differ from plant to plant.

12–4. A farmer has 100 acres which can be used for growing wheat or corn. The yield is 60 bushels per acre per year of wheat or 95 bushels of corn. Any fraction of the 100 acres can be devoted to growing wheat or corn. Labor requirements are 4 hours per acre per year, plus 0.15 hour per bushel of wheat and 0.70 hour per bushel of corn. Cost of seed, fertilizer, etc., is 20 cents per bushel of wheat and 12 cents per bushel of corn. Wheat can be sold for $1.75 per bushel, and corn for $0.95 per bushel. Wheat can be bought for $2.50 per bushel, and corn for $1.50 per bushel.

In addition, the farmer may raise pigs and/or poultry. The farmer sells the pigs or poultry when they reach the age of one year. A pig sells for $40. He measures the poultry in terms of one "pig equivalent" (the number of chickens needed to bring in $40 at the time of sale). One pig requires 25 bushels of wheat or 20 bushels of corn, plus 25 hours of labor and 25 square feet of floor space. An equivalent amount of poultry requires 25 bushels of corn or 10 bushels of wheat, 40 hours of labor, and 15 square feet of floor space.

The farmer has 10,000 square feet of floor space. He has available per year 2,000 hours of his own time and another 2,000 hours from his family. He can hire labor at $1.50 per hour. However, for each hour of hired labor, 0.15 hour of the farmer's time is required for supervision. How much land should be devoted to corn and how much to wheat, and in addition, how many pigs and/or poultry should be raised to maximize the farmer's profits.

12–5. A caterer has undertaken a contract for a series of dinners to be given by an exclusive New York Club. There will be n dinners, one on each of n successive days. The caterer must purchase napkins especially for these dinners because the Club has requested a special type of napkin which has not been used before and will not be used again. On day k, $k = 1, \ldots, n$, a_k dinners will be served, and hence a_k napkins will be needed. Two types of laundry service are available to the caterer. Regular service takes p days (if the laundry is sent at the end of day k, it can be used again on day $k + p$), and the costs are β cents per napkin. A faster service takes $q < p$ days and costs $\gamma > \beta$ cents per napkin. New napkins cost α cents each. The caterer would like to minimize the costs associated with purchasing and laundering napkins. The problem of deciding how many napkins to buy, and of determining the number of napkins to be sent to the regular and to the fast laundry service each day is to be formulated as a linear programming problem. Show that the problem, called the caterer problem, can be solved by the transportation method (Jacobs, W. W., "The Caterer Problem," *Nav. Res. Log. Quart.* **1,** 1954). Hint: Let x_i be the number of napkins used on day i which have never been laundered before. Let y_{ij} be the number of napkins soiled on day i which are sent to the regular laundry service to be used again on day j. Take t_i to be the number of soiled napkins not sent to the laundry on day i. There are no costs associated with maintaining inventories of laundered or soiled napkins. What will be the value of y_{ij} when $j < i + p$? Will it ever be profitable not to send some soiled napkins to the laundry on day i, but to send them later on, say, day j? Sketch the structure of the transportation-type tableau.

12–6. Solve Problem 12–5 for the special case where $a_1 = 100$, $a_2 = 200$, $a_3 = 300$, $a_4 = 400$, $a_5 = 200$, $a_6 = 100$, $\alpha = 1.00$, $\beta = 0.05$, $\gamma = 0.10$, $p = 4$, $q = 2$.

12–7. Generalize the regular-time versus overtime production-scheduling problem discussed in Section 12–6 to the case where an initial inventory of α units of the product is available and where, in addition, the final inventory at the end of the nth time period is to be β. Hint: Add a row to represent the initial inventory allocated to the requirement of each time period.

12–8. Prove that for the scheduling problem of a single product discussed in Section 12–6, the column-minima technique for determining an initial basic feasible solution yields an optimal solution. Hint: Let α be the difference between the costs in rows r and s, $r > s$, in column k. What is the difference between the costs in rows r and s in column q, $q > k$?

12–9. Show that for production-scheduling problems of the type discussed in Section 12–6, the column-minima solution is optimal even if the manufacturing costs are nonlinear, provided $c_i(x'') \geq c_i(x')$ if $x'' > x'$ [$c_i(x)$ is the cost of producing x units in time period i].

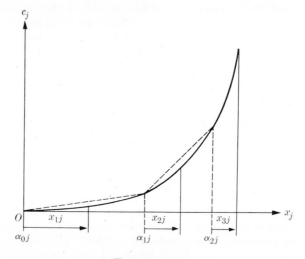

FIGURE 12–4

12–10. Consider the following nonlinear programming problem: Determine an $\mathbf{x} \geq \mathbf{0}$ which minimizes $z = \sum_{j=1}^{n} c_j(x_j)$ and satisfies the constraints $\mathbf{Ax} = \mathbf{b}$. Show that, to an arbitrary degree of accuracy, this problem can be reduced to a linear programming problem, provided that $c_j(x_j)$, $j = 1, \ldots, n$, is a continuous function of x_j, $d^2c_j/dx_j^2 \geq 0$, and $c_j(0) = 0$. Hint: Note that each c_j is a function of x_j only. By assumption, each c_j-curve is similar to that shown in Fig. 12–4. Use the points α_{1j}, α_{2j}, α_{3j}, ... to divide the x_j-axis into a set of intervals. Then define a set of variables x_{ij} such that $0 \leq x_{ij} \leq \alpha_{ij} - \alpha_{i-1,j}$, with the additional provision that $x_{kj} = 0$ unless all x_{ij} are at their upper bounds when $i < k$. With these assumptions, $x_j = \sum_i x_{ij}$. Now in the interval $\alpha_{i-1,j} \leq x_j \leq \alpha_{ij}$ write $c_j(x_j) = \gamma_{i1}x_{ij} + \gamma_{i2}$, where γ_{i1}, γ_{i2} are chosen so that $c_j(\alpha_{i-1,j}) = \gamma_{i2}$, $c_j(\alpha_{ij}) = \gamma_{i1}(\alpha_{ij} - \alpha_{i-1,j}) + \gamma_{i2}$. Set up the programming problem in terms of the variables x_{ij}. Show that it is a linear programming problem. Also show that it follows automatically that an optimal solution has the property $x_{kj} = 0$ unless all x_{ij} are at their upper bounds when $i < k$. Why is it necessary to require that $c_j(0) = 0$ for all j?

12–11. For the coming month, a domestic airline is faced with the problem of allocating available aircraft to its various routes. There are n different routes in all, and the expected demand in numbers of passengers wishing to make a one-way trip over route j will be denoted by b_j. To simplify the problem we shall suppose that if the plane makes one or more intermediate stops before the final destination, and if someone gets off at an intermediate stop, this person is replaced by another passenger boarding the plane. Thus the demand represents one-way trips from the origin to the final destination. The airline has m different types of planes. A plane of type i flying route j can carry d_{ij} passengers. Some planes may not fly certain routes and are not to be considered for allocation to these routes. If a plane of type i is used, the profit per passenger on route j will be taken to be p_{ij}. Assume that a_i planes of type i will be available for service in the coming month. We wish to determine the allocation of planes to routes which will maximize profits for the coming month. Set up the problem as a linear programming problem. To set up the model, what implicit assumptions have to be made about the nature of the demand?

12–12. Generalize the model developed in the previous problem to include first-class and tourist flights. Assume that the expected demands on the various routes for both first-class and tourist flights are given. Suppose that a given flight will not mix first-class and tourist passengers.

12–13. Provide a physical interpretation for each of the variables introduced in Eq. (12–8).

12–14. For the production-transportation problem discussed in Section 12–3, what problems are created by inventories carried at the manufacturers and jobbers? How can inventories be accounted for in the model?

12–15. A small Gulf Coast refinery blends five raw stocks to produce two grades of motor fuel, A and B. The number of barrels per day (bbl/day) of each raw stock available, the octane numbers and the cost per barrel are given in the following table:

Stock	Octane number	bbl/day	cost/bbl
1	70	2000	0.80
2	80	4000	0.90
3	85	4000	0.95
4	90	5000	1.15
5	99	3000	2.00

The octane number of motor fuel A must be at least 95, and that of motor fuel B at least 85. Assume that a contract requires that at least 8000 bbl/day of motor fuel B must be blended. However, the refinery can sell its entire output of fuels A and B. Motor fuel A is sold to distributors at \$3.75 per bbl and motor fuel

TABLE 12-5

Job	Number of pieces in job	Production time (Hours per piece)					Cost (Dollars per piece)					Selling price Dollars per piece
		Machine					Machine					
		1	2	3	4	5	1	2	3	4	5	
1	50	0.50	0.75	0.90	0.80	0.60	2.00	2.50	2.75	2.45	2.30	5.00
2	100	0.75	1.125	1.35	1.20	0.90	3.25	3.50	3.75	3.50	2.85	10.00
3	150	0.40	0.60	0.72	0.64	0.48	1.85	2.00	2.25	2.00	1.75	8.00
4	200	0.30	0.45	0.54	0.48	0.36	2.10	2.30	2.50	2.25	2.00	6.50
5	125	1.25	1.875	2.25	2.00	1.50	5.20	6.00	7.50	8.00	7.00	14.00
6	75	0.60	0.90	1.08	0.96	0.72	9.10	9.50	11.20	10.00	9.80	20.00
Total hours available in coming month		120	140	120	110	150						

B at \$2.85 per bbl. All raw stocks not blended into motor fuel with an octane number of 90 or more are sold for use in aviation gasolines at \$2.75 per bbl, and those of octane number 85 or less are sold at \$1.25 per bbl for use in fuel oils. In order to maximize daily profits, how much of each motor fuel should be made and how should the raw stocks be blended? Is it really necessary to know the cost per barrel of each stream?

12–16. Discuss the problems of obtaining data for any practical application of linear programming. Consider the effects of errors in estimating various parameters and the costs of obtaining the data.

12–17. For the coming month, the foreman of the lathe department in a small machine shop must schedule six jobs on five lathes. The pertinent data are provided in Table 12–5. No job requires time on more than one machine. The costs shown include raw material costs. Set up the problem as a linear programming problem and solve it.

12–18. In machine-loading problems, it sometimes turns out that tooling up for a job is a rather costly operation, and hence it is not desirable to split jobs (i.e., have more than a single machine work on a job) if this can be avoided. Develop an approximate method for assigning jobs to machines for the case where jobs are not split, in order to minimize costs. Try to find such a solution to Problem 12–17. How does the cost of your solution compare with that for the optimal solution to Problem 12–17, where splitting is allowed? Use the costs given in Problem 12–17. Hint: For the general procedure compute the total cost, including setup costs for doing each job on every machine where it can be processed. Then compute for each job and each machine the difference between the cost on the given machine and the machine that does the job at lowest cost. Enter these numbers in a transportation-type tableau along with the times required to complete the entire job. First assign jobs to machines which can do the jobs at least cost; then transfer jobs from overloaded machines.

12–19. In practice, when machine loading must be done once a week or more often, it may be difficult to solve exactly the suitable linear programming problem, especially in a small company which does not own a computer. Try to develop some approximate procedures for solving machine-loading problems, which require very little computation and which can be carried out quickly. Hint: See preceding problem.

12–20. Solve the example in Section 12–7. In solving the problem, ignore the sales constraint on product 1. How does the optimal solution change when this sales constraint is included? It is expected that in the near future competition will force the selling price of product 3 down to \$2.30. How will the optimal solution (including the sales constraint) change if this happens? How much can the selling price of product 3 be decreased without changing the optimality of the original solution?

12–21. A manufacturer of metal office equipment makes desks, chairs, cabinets, and bookcases. The work is carried out in three departments: (1) metal stamping, (2) assembly, (3) finishing. The pertinent data are presented in the table below. The times are printed in boldface type, while the cost incurred for one unit in each department is in lower-case Roman type.

Department	Desk	Chair	Cabinet	Bookcase	Hours per week available
Stamping	3 15	1.5 8	2 12	2 12	800
Assembly	10 30	6 18	8 24	7 21	1200
Finishing	10 35	8 28	8 25	7 21	800
Selling price	175	95	145	130	

Finishing work can also be subcontracted to an outside firm at a 30% increase in the cost of finishing. What should the rate of production of each of the items be in order to maximize weekly profits if no restrictions are placed on the number of any item to be made. What is the optimal product mix if one chair is to be made for each desk? How much could weekly profits be increased by a 10% increase in the capacity of the finishing department? What is the optimal product mix if it is necessary to make at least one cabinet and one bookcase for every three desks produced (assume that one chair is made for each desk)?

12-22. Consider a firm which manufactures m different products, using common productive facilities. Each product may, for example, require operations on several different machines. Assume that there is a number of different ways to make each product. Furthermore, assume that each product can be inventoried. An attempt is being made to schedule production for n future time periods. The demands for the individual products vary widely from period to period. Suppose that the demand for each product can be forecast for each of the coming periods. The selling prices of the products may fluctuate from period to period, as may the costs of raw materials. Assume that the cost of carrying each item in stock for one period is known. Set up the linear programming problem which will determine how much of each product should be made in each period and which activities should be used to produce them. Sketch the structure of the matrix. What might be an efficient procedure for solving such a problem? Can you provide an example of one or more industries where such a problem has practical significance?

12-23. A food processor has m farms, n plants, and k jobbers. Let us consider one product, say, tomato soup. Tomatoes can be grown at all m farms; however, the cost of growing them varies from farm to farm. Take f_i to be the cost per bushel at farm i. Any farm can ship to any plant, and any plant may ship to any jobber. Let c_{ij} be the cost of shipping one bushel of tomatoes from farm i to plant j, and let d_{jk} be the cost of shipping one case of tomato soup from plant j to jobber k. Assume that β bushels of tomatoes make one case of soup. The variable cost of making one case of soup at plant j is ρ_j, and the capacity of the plant for tomato soup is T_j cases. Take b_k to be the number of cases of tomato soup required at jobber k for the coming year and let a_i be the maximum number of bushels of tomatoes which can be grown at farm i. Set up the linear programming problem whose solution minimizes the cost of growing, processing, and transportation, and which meets the jobber requirements for tomato soup. Can you devise an efficient computational scheme for solving this problem? Can you list other industries where a problem of this type is relevant?

12–24. Discuss how the decomposition principle could be used to solve problems of the type illustrated in the example of Section 12–7. Under what circumstances would the example of Section 12–7 be a generalized transportation problem?

12–25. Set down the structure of the constraints for the gasoline-blending problem discussed in Section 12–9. How could the decomposition principle be used to solve such problems? Under what circumstances would a gasoline-blending problem be reducible to a generalized transportation problem?

12–26. Formulate the regular-time and overtime production scheduling problem of Section 12–6 in a different way, using as variables the total quantities produced in any period on regular and overtime and the inventories at the beginning of each period. In terms of these variables, is it so obvious that the problem is a transportation problem?

12–27. A speculator operates a large silo for storing corn. In the real world, he will not know what the selling price or the purchase price of corn will be in future periods. His success will depend on how well he can predict these values. Instead of this real-world situation, consider the simple case where he knows (or can predict very accurately) the prices for which he can buy and sell corn in each of n future time periods. Let R be the capacity of the silo in bushels and let d_i be the cost per bushel in period i and f_i the selling price per bushel in period i. Assume that anything bought in period i cannot be sold until period $i + 1$ or a later period, i.e., assume that corn purchased in period i does not reach the silo until the end of period i. Take x_i, y_i to be the quantities bought and sold in period i. Formulate as a linear programming problem the problem of determining how much to buy and sell in each of the coming n periods so as to maximize profits. Assume that at the beginning of the first period K bushels of corn are in the silo. Also assume that there are no inventory-carrying charges. Show that an optimal solution will have $x_i = 0$, or $R - K$, or R and that $y_i = 0$, or R, or K for all i. Devise a simple way of solving the problem which does not involve linear programming. This problem is often referred to as the warehouse problem.

12–28. Solve the warehouse problem formulated in Problem 12–27 for 10 time periods during which, beginning with the first period, the selling prices per bushel are 2.10, 2.50, 2.75, 2.80, 2.85, 2.65, 2.55, 2.30, 2.20, 2.40, and costs per bushel are 2.45, 2.50, 2.35, 2.20, 2.00, 1.80, 2.00, 2.20, 2.30, 2.40. The silo capacity is 100,000 bushels, and at the beginning of the first period 40,000 bushels are in the silo.

12–29. Would the nature of the optimal solution to Problem 12–27 be changed if inventory-carrying charges were added?

12–30. Generalize the situation discussed in Problem 12–27 to a warehouse which can stock n different items. Formulate as a linear programming problem the question of determining how much to buy and sell of each item each period in order to maximize profits. What can be said about the nature of an optimal solution? This problem is discussed in A. Charnes and W. W. Cooper, "Generalizations of the Warehouse Problem," *Operational Research Quart.*, **6**, 1955.

12–31. Consider the refinery problem formulated in Section 12–8. Assume that the daily availabilities of crudes 1 and 2 are 20,000 and 30,000 bbl/day, respectively. The capacity limitation on crude distillation is 45,000 bbl/day. One barrel of crude 1 yields 0.10, 0.20, 0.20 bbl of light, medium, and heavy naphthas, and crude 2 yields 0.15, 0.25, 0.18 bbl of the same naphthas. One barrel of crude 1 yields 0.12 and 0.20 bbl of light and heavy oils, respectively, and crude 2 yields 0.08 and 0.19 bbl of the same oils. Crudes 1 and 2 yield 0.13 and 0.18 bbl, respectively, of residuum. The reformer capacity is 10,000 bbl/day, and the capacity of the catalytic cracker is 8000 bbl/day. On passing through the reformer, one barrel each of light, medium, and heavy naphthas yields 0.60, 0.52, 0.45 bbl, respectively, of reformed gasoline. On passing through the cracking unit, one barrel of light oil yields 0.28 bbl of cracked gasoline and 0.68 bbl of cracked oil, while one barrel of heavy oil yields 0.20 and 0.75 bbl of cracked gasoline and cracked oil, respectively. On passing through lube-oil processing, one barrel of residuum yields 0.45 bbl of lube oil. The capacity of the lube oil processor is 1000 bbl/day. The refinery must supply at least 500 bbl/day of lube oil. The octane numbers of light, medium, and heavy naphthas are 90, 80, 70, respectively, while the octane number of reformed gasoline is 115, and that of cracked gasoline is 105. The octane number of aviation gasoline must be at least 107, while those of premium and regular motor fuels must be at least 94 and 84, respectively. The output of premium motor fuel is to be 0.45 times that of regular motor fuel. The vapor pressure of jet fuel must not be greater than 2 psi (pounds per square inch). The vapor pressures of light, heavy, cracked, and residuum oils are respectively 2.0, 1.2, 2.5, 0.1 psi. In the blending of fuel oil, $\psi_2 = 0.3, \psi_c = 0.4$, $\psi_r = 0.1$ in Eq. (12–49). On a large sheet of paper write down the constraints for the refinery problem. Also write down the matrix of the coefficients. If the reader has access to a small digital computer, he will find it instructive to solve this problem by trying different sorts of objective functions such as those discussed in the text. It is also interesting to study the changes resulting from an increase in the capacity of either the reformer or the cracking units. Finally, it is interesting to note what happens when one attempts to specify the output of several streams, such as aviation gas and fuel oil.

12–32. An international petroleum company has m refineries and r crude-producing regions throughout the world. Each refinery and each producing region is close to a seaport. Tankers transport crude from the fields to the refineries. Different fields produce different types of crude. These are used at the various refineries in different proportions, depending on the type of equipment available at a given refinery. It is desired to schedule tankers for delivering crude to the refineries. The time span to be considered is the coming year. Each refinery presents a schedule of requirements. The schedule specifies the quantities of crudes wanted and the delivery date to be aimed for. To simplify the problem it will be assumed that all tankers are of the same size, and that refineries always order quantities of crude in integral multiples of a tanker's capacity. Thus the full load of any tanker will be discharged at only one refinery. After a tanker discharges its load, it can go to any port to pick up more crude, provided it can reach this port and from there a refinery in time to meet the refinery's schedule. We wish to determine the minimum number of tankers that will meet the scheduled demands at the refineries. Assume that the time required to sail from any given loading point to a refinery is known and is not subject to any uncertainty. Set up the problem as a linear programming problem and show that it is a transportation problem. Assume that tankers can begin at any loading port at any time desired and can end their runs at any refinery. How does the problem change if the tankers must end up in specified ports? Hint: Arrange the demands at the refineries in order of increasing time, without taking into account which refinery is making the demand. Thus on day 29, refinery 1 may want a tanker load from field 3 and a tanker load from field 6, and the next time a demand occurs is on day 33 when refinery 4 may want a tanker load from field 4. In this way, one obtains a time sequence of N demands which must be met. Thus the ith demand specifies that a total of k tanker loads from perhaps several different fields must arrive at refinery s on a given day. Assume that once a tanker is loaded it immediately sails for the refinery where it is to unload, and the time required to make the trip is that referred to above. From this observation it is seen that the refinery demand schedule can be used to set up a loading schedule at the loading ports similar to the demand schedule at the refineries (simply by deducting the sailing time to the refineries plus loading time). The jth loading item in this time-sequenced schedule will indicate that a total of w tankers must be available at port p for loading on a given day for delivery to perhaps several different refineries. Now consider the scheduling problem. A tanker which has just unloaded at a given refinery can be sent to any loading port if it can arrive there, load, and reach some other refinery in the required time. Then let x_{ij} be the number of tankers available at the time and refinery associated with the ith demand which are sent to the port associated with loading item j to be loaded at the day required by item j. For the sake of conceptual simplicity, assume that tankers immediately leave the refinery on unloading and arrive at the loading points on the day required. If the time required to sail to the loading port is less than the time available, assume that the tanker remains at sea for this additional time. Note that the number of tankers used will be the sum of the slack variables at each of the destinations (loading items j), provided that tankers can be made available at any loading port and at any point in time desired. Hence, what are the prices? Similarly, slack at the origins indicates that a tanker ends its run there. This type of problem is discussed in [5].

12-33. Solve the tanker allocation problem formulated in Problem 12-32, using the following data for three refineries and producing fields. In the requirements matrix, the light-face numbers give the days on which a given refinery wishes tankers to arrive from a given field, and the boldface numbers specify the number of tanker loads desired. Assume that loading and unloading take a day. Tankers may start at any loading port at any time and end at any refinery. Sketch graphically the optimal routing for each tanker.

Requirements

Field Refinery	1			2			3		
1	18	41	120	41	160	220	120	180	250
	2	2	5	3	2	2	1	2	3
2	35	72	200	55	96	240	40	200	290
	3	1	2	2	1	3	1	3	2
3	40	190		190	230		75	145	220
	2	4		1	2		2	1	1

Sailing times (days)

Field Refinery	1	2	3
1	12	16	6
2	14	8	10
3	19	3	12

12–34. A painting contractor has been awarded the job of finishing a large, newly constructed office building. He is attempting to determine the minimum-cost paint blend which will meet all specifications. He has three grades of paint, P_1, P_2, P_3, and two types of thinner, T_1, T_2, which can be blended together. The first requirement to be met concerns coverage. The final blend must be such that only a single coat of paint will be needed. The contractor recognizes that the coverage depends on the viscosity of the paint. From previous experience, he decides that any blend whose final viscosity is at least 350 centipoise (cp) will do. The next requirement has to do with the "brilliance" of the finished job. This is a quantitative way of measuring reflectivity of the surface. The brilliance depends on the number of grams per gallon of a certain constituent X in the final blend. For suitable brilliance, the final blend should contain between 10 and 25 grams of X per gallon. Another characteristic of importance is the drying time. If the paint dries too slowly, a lot of dirt will become imbedded in the surface. If it dries too fast, it will later crack and peel off. The drying time depends on the vapor pressure of the final blend. The contractor knows that for a proper drying time, the vapor pressure should be between 2 and 4 pounds per square inch (psi). The final specification concerns the "lasting quality" of the paint, i.e., it should remain in good condition for a certain length of time without fading. This quality can be measured by the number of grams per gallon of a certain constituent Y in the final blend. The final blend should contain at least 550 grams of Y per gallon. A table listing the characteristics of the individual constituents which can be blended is presented below. Set up the problem of determining the optimal blend as a linear programming problem. Assume that all quantities of interest blend linearly by volume, and that the total number of gallons of paint required to do the job will be independent of the blend used. Solve the problem.

	P_1	P_2	P_3	T_1	T_2
Cost (dollars per gallon)	7.00	5.50	4.20	3.30	2.00
Viscosity (cp)	800	600	400	2	20
X-content (grams per gallon)	20	50	10	0	0
Y-content (grams per gallon)	1500	1000	500	0	0
Vapor pressure (psi)	0.3	0.6	0.9	12.0	8.0

12–35. Solve the problem formulated in Section 1–3. How much can each of the profits be changed if the solution obtained is to remain optimal?

12–36. Consider the problem of scheduling regular and overtime production of a certain item for the next year, on a month-by-month basis. The costs of producing one unit on regular time and overtime are \$3 and \$4, respectively, for months 1, 2, 3 and 7, 8, 9, and \$2 and \$2.50, respectively, for months 4, 5, 6, and 10, 11, 12. The cost of storing one unit for one month is \$0.50. The initial inventory is 50 units, and it is desired to have 50 units in inventory at the end of the year. The regular and overtime capacities (in units per month) are 500 and 200, respectively. The monthly demands are expected to be 400, 600, 500, 800, 800, 700, 600, 800, 600, 700, 600, 800, in the order given. How should production be scheduled so as to minimize costs?

CHAPTER 13

APPLICATIONS OF LINEAR PROGRAMMING TO ECONOMIC THEORY

*"I have found you an argument: but I am
not obliged to find you an understanding."*

Dr. Samuel Johnson.

13–1 Introduction. Almost all applications of linear programming are somehow connected with economics. The difference between the material in this chapter and that of the preceding chapter lies in the emphasis. Chapter 12 emphasized practical industrial applications; now we shall concentrate on the applications of linear programming to economic theory. The dividing line between the material presented in the two chapters is rather fine. Some of the material which will be discussed here, such as the interpretation of dual problems, has potentially useful applications in industry. Similarly, the material on input-output analysis and its generalizations is considered by government agencies (where it is used) to be a practical application, although it does not find direct applications in industry.

13–2 Theory of the firm; classical approach. The theory of the firm has long been a subject of study in economics. Interest has centered about the problems of determining the level at which a firm should operate (i.e., how much should be produced) and of determining the optimal combination of resources to carry out production. The criterion used to solve these problems is the maximization of the rate of profit (say yearly profit).

The case most frequently studied is that of pure competition. Pure competition implies that a large number of firms makes the same product, and that no firm can influence the market price. A firm selling in a perfectly competitive market can sell any quantity at the given market price. For the moment, we shall limit our attention to a firm which produces a single good and markets it under pure competition.

Let p be the market price for one unit of the firm's product. If q units per year are produced, the firm will receive a revenue $R(q) = pq$. Note that p is independent of q. To determine the firm's yearly profit on producing q units per year we must know the cost of production. The economist assumes that the yearly cost of production, $C(q)$, is known for all q.

He assumes that the cost function is based on the most efficient technological process of production, so that $C(q)$ is a unique single-valued function of q. The rate of profit, $\Pi(q)$, associated with a production rate q is then

$$\Pi(q) = R(q) - C(q). \tag{13–1}$$

The firm wishes to maximize its profits for the year. Then if $\Pi(q)$ is differentiable, the calculus tells us that the production per year, $q^* \geq 0$, which maximizes the profit rate is a solution to the equation

$$\frac{d\Pi}{dq} = \frac{dR}{dq} - \frac{dC}{dq} = p - \frac{dC}{dq} = 0, \tag{13–2}$$

or $q^* = 0$, or $q^* = \infty$. It is almost always assumed that the q which maximizes Π will satisfy (13–2). In the language of economics, (13–2) says that the firm continues production until the marginal cost dC/dq is equal to the price.

There may be more than one q which satisfies (13–2). In general, however, economists make the assumption that only one of these will yield a non-negative profit. This q^* is then the production rate which maximizes the profit rate. Note that q^* will be a function of the market price p. A value of q^* can be found for each p. The function $q^*(p)$ is the supply curve for the firm. For any given market price, it shows how much the firm will produce in order to maximize its profits for the year.

The above analysis has treated only part of the problem. It is also of interest to know how much of each factor of production the firm will use when it maximizes its profits. Assume that there are n factors, such as labor, raw materials, capital equipment, etc., which can be used in the production of the good. Furthermore, we shall assume that pure competition also exists in the factor markets, so that the price w_i of one unit of any factor is a constant independent of the quantity purchased. If y_i units per year of factor i are used, the cost of production is

$$C = \sum_{i=1}^{n} w_i y_i + K, \tag{13–3}$$

where K is a fixed cost independent of the level of production.

In order to relate the output to the quantities of factors used in production, economists assume the existence of a production function $q = \phi(y_1, \ldots, y_n)$ which, for any set of y_i, gives the maximum amount that can be produced by means of these quantities of the factors of production. Economists assume that this function is given, and that the production process will be such that it is always satisfied. Then if factor

i is used at a level y_i, the yearly profit of the firm is

$$\Pi = p\phi(y_1, \ldots, y_n) - \sum_{i=1}^{n} w_i y_i - K. \tag{13-4}$$

The profit rate can now be considered to be a function of n variables, the y_i.

Calculus tells us that the set of y_i which maximize Π should satisfy the set of n equations

$$\frac{\partial \Pi}{\partial y_i} = p \frac{\partial \phi}{\partial y_i} - w_i = 0, \qquad i = 1, \ldots, n, \tag{13-5}$$

provided that each optimal y_i lies in the interval $0 < y_i < \infty$. These equations can be rewritten in the form

$$p = \frac{w_i}{\partial \phi / \partial y_i} = \frac{w_i}{\partial q / \partial y_i}, \qquad i = 1, \ldots, n. \tag{13-6}$$

In the language of economics, (13-6) states that each factor of production is used until the point is reached where its price divided by its marginal physical product is equal to the price of the product. Quite possibly one or more of the y_i will be zero when Π is maximized; that is, the absolute maximum of Π may lie on the boundary of the region $y_i \geq 0$, $i = 1, \ldots, n$, over which the y_i may vary. For such cases, we have equations like (13-5) only for those factors which are used at a positive level. To determine the absolute maximum of (13-4), we must find, in addition to the solution of (13-5), the relative maxima of (13-4) for all combinations of one or more $y_i = 0$, and select the solution yielding the largest value of Π.

Economists often assume that (13-6) defines a set of functions,

$$y_i = g_i(w_1, \ldots, w_n, p), \qquad i = 1, \ldots, n, \tag{13-7}$$

which are the demand functions for the factors of production. The demand for any factor of production is, in general, dependent on the prices of all the factors of production and the price of the product. Intuitively, the existence of (13-7) means that Eqs. (13-6) can be solved explicitly for the y_i.

It should be noted that, for the above analysis to be meaningful, the production function must be continuous and capable of being differentiated everywhere. This is a strong assumption. Of course, from the practical point of view, the determination of a production function is often extremely difficult.

In the above derivation, we have been a little vague in indicating whether there were certain factors of production, such as the size of the plant, that were not allowed to vary. The above analysis assumes that everything can vary, and hence it also determines the size of the firm. However, where the plant size is fixed, the same sort of analysis can also be applied in the short run. Formally, the same equations are obtained. Only the nature of the production function and the number of variable factors change. For the short run, there is an upper limit on the productive capacity, and thus the optimal production rate may not satisfy (13–2); instead it may be an end point, i.e., the maximum possible production.

In the theory of pure competition it is usually assumed that any one firm never makes more than a single product unless there are joint products, in which case one item cannot be made without producing one or more other goods. If a single firm did produce more than one good, the production of each good would be treated as if it were made by a different firm, although the same production facilities were used to produce all products. This can be done because of the assumption that each factor of production can be varied continuously so that there is no need to be concerned about the fact that machines, etc., come only in certain discrete, or "quantized," sizes. It is imagined that a machine of precisely the required capacity is always available and that its price is proportional to its capacity (or, more generally, to some function of its capacity).

Let us examine the case of joint products, where a single firm must produce all joint products. However, by varying the mix of factors of production, it may be able to alter the mix of the joint products. Assume that there are m joint products. Let q_j be the yearly production of product j and y_i be the rate at which factor i with price w_i is used in the production.

For each product it will be imagined that there exists a production function

$$q_j = \phi_j(y_1, \ldots, y_n), \tag{13–8}$$

so that once the mix of the factors of production is specified, the rate of production of each good is uniquely determined. Then for any set of y_i, the firm's yearly profit is

$$\Pi = \sum_{j=1}^{m} p_j \phi_j(y_1, \ldots, y_n) - \sum_{i=1}^{n} w_i y_i - K. \tag{13–9}$$

The set of y_i which maximizes the profit should then satisfy the set of equations

$$\sum_{j=1}^{m} p_j \frac{\partial \phi_j}{\partial y_i} - w_i = 0, \qquad i = 1, \ldots, n, \tag{13–10}$$

provided that the optimal value of each y_i lies in the range $0 < y_i < \infty$.

If one or more y_i should be zero, (13–10) applies only to those which are positive. These equations determine the rate at which each factor is to be used. The production functions enable one to determine the rate at which each product should be produced in order to maximize the firm's profit rate.

Having given a brief survey of the theory of the firm under pure competition, we shall next consider the monopolistic case. Here it is assumed that the firm either controls a sufficiently large share of the market or has a product which is sufficiently differentiated from those of other firms that it can set the price. Furthermore, the sales volume will depend only on that price. For any given price p, consumers will purchase at a rate $q(p)$. The function $q(p)$ is called the demand curve for the product. Here the firm has to face the problem of determining the price p such that if the production rate is equal to the rate of demand at that price, the profit rate will be maximized. The yearly profit will then be a function of the price p.

As before, we assume the existence of a cost function $C(q)$. If the price is p, $q(p)$ units will be produced because precisely $q(p)$ units can be sold. The yearly profit is

$$\Pi(p) = pq(p) - C[q(p)]. \tag{13–11}$$

The price p^* which maximizes the profit rate should satisfy the equation

$$\frac{d\Pi}{dp} = 0 = p\frac{dq}{dp} + q - \frac{dC}{dq}\frac{dq}{dp} = 0. \tag{13–12}$$

The production rate which maximizes the profit rate is then $q(p^*)$. To obtain (13–12) we must assume that the demand and cost functions are differentiable.

It should be noted that, unlike in the case of pure competition, there is no supply curve in the monopolistic case. The firm is free to set the selling price, and there is only one price that maximizes yearly profits. Thus the supply curve is a single point. The firm will not consider any price other than that which maximizes the profit rate.

We have yet to consider the oligopolistic case, where a relatively small number of firms produces goods which are close substitutes. Each firm is free to choose the selling price of its product. Now, however, the demand for a given firm's product is a function not only of the price of that particular product, but also of the prices of all other substitute products.

Here we have encountered a case where the criterion of profit maximization does not lead to a uniquely determined solution. No firm can maximize its profit independently of what the other firms do. The final result depends on the strategies followed by the various firms. A solution can be obtained if it is assumed, for example, that the firms act in such a way as to maximize the total profit of all firms. A different result may be obtained for each different strategy.

To terminate this brief survey of the classical approach to the theory of the firm, several points are worth noting. First, since the approach is essentially static, and since no interaction exists between producers and consumers, the maximization of the profit rate at each instant of time is equivalent to maximizing the total profit over all time. Secondly, in the case of pure competition, the production of a finite, determinate quantity depends on the assumption that the marginal cost of production increases when q is larger than some given value, i.e., costs are not directly proportional to the quantity produced, for example.

13-3 Linear programming and the firm. Linear programming provides a much more practical approach to the theory of the firm than does classical analysis, which is based on the assumption that a firm produces just a single good. The linear programming model makes it possible to be more realistic and to permit the firm to produce a number of products which jointly use the production facilities. This approach is more realistic because it allows recognition of the fact that various types of productive resources are available only in certain discrete sizes, so that it may be necessary for a firm to produce a number of products in order to make best use of the productive facilities and thereby maximize profits.

Linear programming typically treats the firm from a strictly short-run point of view. Production facilities are assumed to be fixed. These limited production facilities limit the total quantities of the various items which can be produced. In addition, of course, there may be limits on the quantities available of the various raw materials.

Instead of dealing with the notion of a production function which is everywhere continuous and differentiable, linear programming starts at a more basic level with various processes of production. Suppose that there are m factors of production (resources) whose supply is limited. For a given process of production, let a_{ij} units of resource i be required to produce one unit of good j. The vector $\mathbf{a}_j = [a_{1j}, \ldots, a_{mj}]$ tells how much of each resource is required to make one unit of good j. Previously, we have referred to a process of production as an activity and to the vector $\mathbf{a}_j$ as an activity vector. This is the accepted terminology in economics.

The linear programming model assumes that the number of activities for making a given good is finite. This is different from the classical approach. The concept of a production function allowed for an infinite number of ways to produce a product. If we produce x_j units of good j (j refers to a given good produced by a given production process), x_j is called the level at which activity j is operated. In the linear programming model, the firm chooses the level at which each activity is to be operated in such a way that profits will be maximized. The various activities imply a certain type of production function for any one good. Let us examine the nature of this production function in a little more detail.

For a given output $\bar{q}$, the classical production function $\bar{q} = \phi(y_1, \ldots, y_n)$ implied that any point in the non-negative orthant on this surface in E^n gives a set of inputs which, when properly used, will yield $\bar{q}$ units of the good. Linear programming, however, is not so general. Let the subscript k refer to those activities which can be used to produce a given good. Then if activity k is operated at a level x_k, any set of $x_k \geq 0$ such that

$$\bar{q} = \sum x_k \tag{13–13}$$

will yield the required amount of the product. If $\mathbf{y} = [y_1, \ldots, y_m]$ is a vector giving the quantities of the resources needed to produce $\bar{q}$, then

$$\mathbf{y} = \sum x_k \mathbf{a}_k. \tag{13–14}$$

The $\mathbf{y}$ computed from (13–14) for any set of x_k satisfying (13–13) will do.

If we write $\mathbf{y}^* = [\mathbf{y}, \bar{q}]$, $\mathbf{a}_k^* = [\mathbf{a}_k, 1]$, Eqs. (13–13) and (13–14) can be combined to read

$$\mathbf{y}^* = \sum x_k \mathbf{a}_k^*, \qquad \text{all } x_k \geq 0. \tag{13–15}$$

The set of points $\mathbf{y}^*$ satisfying (13–15) forms the convex polyhedral cone generated by the $\mathbf{a}_k^*$. Let b_i be the maximum amount of resource i available in the time period under consideration. Then if $\mathbf{b} = [b_1, \ldots, b_m]$, any $\mathbf{y}^*$ given by (13–15) for which $\mathbf{y} \leq \mathbf{b}$ is an allowable point on the production function. Thus the production function is the collection of all points $\mathbf{y}^*$ in the convex polyhedral cone generated by the $\mathbf{a}_k^*$ for which $\mathbf{y} \leq \mathbf{b}$. This production function does not have the continuity and differentiability properties postulated for the classical models.

For a firm selling under pure competition, the linear programming problem whose solution yields the levels at which each activity should be operated to maximize profits will have the form

$$\mathbf{Ax} \leq \mathbf{b}, \qquad \mathbf{x} \geq \mathbf{0}, \qquad \max z = \mathbf{cx}. \tag{13–16}$$

All inequalities will be of the form $\leq$ because the constraints represent limitations on the available resources. Since the firm can sell its entire output at the prevailing market price, no constraints on the quantities produced appear. Each c_j represents the profit on one unit of the good made by activity j.

We know that an optimal solution to (13–16) need not have more than m of the $x_j > 0$. This means that the firm can maximize its profits, using only m of the activities. The remaining activities will not be used at all. It may of course be true that an optimal solution will require that a given product be produced by two or more activities. For any optimal solution, $z_j - c_j \geq 0$ for all j. Now $c_j - z_j$ can be interpreted as the increase in profit made possible by producing one additional unit of j and adjusting the levels of the other basic activities so as to obtain a feasible solution. Thus, provided that degeneracy is eliminated, a basic feasible solution is optimal if it is not possible to increase the profit by inserting into the basic solution any activity not in the solution. These fundamental theorems of linear programming are the equivalents of Eqs. (13-2) and (13-6) for the classical approach.

Our discussion of refinery operations in Chapter 12 showed that linear programming can be used in industries where there are joint products and where the product mix can be varied by changing the nature of the process. Constraints on the quantities to be produced can also be handled without difficulty. However, linear programming cannot handle the details of the monopolistic case, where the quantity which can be sold depends upon the price. Such a situation leads to a nonlinear programming problem. Of course, linear programming cannot help solve the oligopolistic case either. In practice, linear programming has been applied to both monopolistic and oligopolistic industries. However, the prices are then usually assumed to be constants, and the demand is made independent of prices.

It is important to note that if pure competition is treated by linear programming, it is necessary to assume that the profit from any one product is directly proportional to the quantity produced. If marginal costs change with the level of production, the objective function will not be linear, and we must solve a nonlinear programming problem. Thus, if we drop the assumption of pure competition or if the marginal costs change with the level of production,* we leave the realm of linear programming.

13-4 Economic interpretation of dual linear programming problems. In the preceding section, it was shown that for a firm with constant marginal costs, selling in purely competitive markets, and having only a finite number of activities, the problem of determining the level at which each activity should be operated in order to maximize profits is a linear programming problem of the form

$$\mathbf{Ax} \leq \mathbf{b}, \qquad \mathbf{x} \geq \mathbf{0}, \qquad \max z = \mathbf{cx}. \qquad (13\text{-}17)$$

There is a constraint for each resource in limited supply.

---

* See, however, Problem 12-10.

The physical dimensions of the variables x_j will be the units of some good produced for some given time period. The dimensions of the b_i are units of resource i available in a given time period, viz., machine hours per week. The a_{ij} then have the dimensions of units of resource i per unit of good j.

Consider now the dual of (13–17). It is

$$\mathbf{A'w} \geq \mathbf{c'}, \qquad \mathbf{w} \geq \mathbf{0}, \qquad \min Z = \mathbf{b'w}. \tag{13–18}$$

Since the dimensions of the c_j are dollars per unit of good j, $a_{ij}w_i$ must have the dimensions of dollars per unit of good j. But the dimensions of a_{ij} are units of resource i per unit of good j. Thus the dimensions of w_i must be dollars per unit of resource i.

To each resource i there corresponds a dual variable w_i which, by its dimensions, is a price, or cost, or value to be associated with one unit of resource i. Suppose that we assign a value w_i to resource i. Then $Z = \mathbf{b'w}$ is the total value of the available resources. The jth dual constraint reads $\sum_{i=1}^{m} a_{ij}w_i \geq c_j$. But $\sum_{i=1}^{m} a_{ij}w_i$ is the value of the resources used in making one unit of product j. The dual problem determines the w_i so that the total value of the resources is minimized, and the value of the resources used in producing one unit of j is at least as great as the profit received from selling one unit of j.

The dual variables w_i are sometimes referred to as imputed values or shadow prices for the resources. Note that the dual variables have nothing to do with the actual costs of the resources. The c_j are profits, and thus the actual costs of the resources never appear. Instead the dual variables provide, in a certain sense, a way of measuring the contribution to the profit c_j of each resource i. Let us see why this is so. Recall that if $x_j > 0$ is in an optimal solution to (13–17), then by complementary slackness $\sum_{i=1}^{m} a_{ij}w_i = c_j$ so that for the activities used, the value of the resources used to produce one unit of j is precisely equal to the profit. We know also that if in an optimal solution to (13–17), the ith constraint is a strict inequality (the corresponding slack variable is positive) so that not all of resource i is used, then $w_i = 0$, and the cost or value of that resource is 0. Such a resource is a free good.

The valuation of the resources by means of the w_i is thus an opportunity-cost valuation. To see this more clearly, recall that for optimal solutions to the primal and dual problems, $z = \mathbf{cx} = Z = \mathbf{b'w}$. The maximum profit is equal to the minimum value of the resources. Now if it were possible to increase or decrease the amount available of resource i by one unit without changing the solution to the dual, the maximum profit would be increased or decreased by w_i. This is the basis for the opportunity-cost interpretation. Of course, if we actually change b_i to $b_i + 1$, the profit will not, in general, increase by w_i because the entire optimal solution changes. However, when z is being maximized, w_i is a measure of the rate of change of z with respect to b_i. When a resource is not fully utilized in an optimal solution, z will not change if the availability of the resource is changed slightly. Hence w_i for this resource should be zero. The complementary slackness principle ensures that this will, indeed, be the case.

The dual variables have potential applications in cost accounting. Consider a large decentralized corporation which is broken down into a number of departments. Each department may make several products. In addition, there may exist a number of different activities for making a single product. These various departments jointly use manufacturing facilities and other services or resources which are in limited supply. Suppose that the chief executive officer has obtained an optimal solution to the linear programming problem for the entire corporation, and therefore knows which activities should be used and what their level should be.

Top management wishes to make sure that the department managers select the proper activities. However, this selection process should originate with the department managers and not come about as a result of directives from top management. Suppose that to each resource which is in short supply we assign the cost w_i, where w_i is the ith dual variable obtained from the optimal solution to the corporate problem referred to above. For each unit of resource i, a department manager must pay w_i (regardless of the actual cost of i). Then the cost of one unit of good i produced by activity j is $\sum a_{ij}w_i = z_j$. We now suppose that the department manager is paid c_j for each unit, c_j being the unit profit on j. If $z_j > c_j$, the department manager will find that his department is losing money when activity j is operated at a positive level. Consequently, the manager will be forced to avoid using activity j. He can find no activities for which $z_j < c_j$, and hence will automatically seek out activities for which $z_j = c_j$, i.e., activities that *should* be operated at a positive level. There remains the problem of getting the managers to operate these activities at the correct level. This cannot be done by means of the above costing procedure, and hence another approach must be used. For a unique, nondegenerate optimum, the activities for which $z_j = c_j$ form a basis. Thus only one thing can happen, i.e., the resources are not fully utilized. If the resources are utilized to the fullest extent possible, the activities must operate at the correct level. Thus it is only necessary to ensure that the available resources are used, and the production pattern will be optimal. When there are alternative optima, it is still true that the solution will be optimal if the resources are utilized to the fullest extent possible. In this case, however, the manager's optimal solution may not be basic.

An economic interpretation of the dual variables is possible for other types of problems. Consider the diet problem discussed in the last section of Chapter 12. In its simplest form, this problem can be written

$$\mathbf{Ax} \geq \mathbf{b}, \qquad \mathbf{x} \geq \mathbf{0},$$

$$\min z = \mathbf{cx}.$$

Each constraint says that at least a certain amount of some nutrient must be consumed. The dual problem is

$$\mathbf{A'w} \leq \mathbf{c'}, \qquad \mathbf{w} \geq \mathbf{0},$$

$$\max Z = \mathbf{b'w}.$$

The dual variable w_i has the dimensions of dollars per unit of nutrient i and can be interpreted as the value of one unit of nutrient i.

The jth constraint of the dual problem reads: $\sum_{i=1}^{m} a_{ij} w_i \leq c_j$. But $\sum_{i=1}^{m} a_{ij} w_i$ is the value of the nutrients in one unit of food j. The dual problem thus determines the w_i in such a way that the imputed value of the minimal diet is maximized, subject to the constraints that the value of the nutrients in one unit of each food is less than or equal to the cost of the food. As expected, an optimal diet uses only foods for which the value of the nutrients is equal to the cost.

The dual variables in the transportation problem can easily be interpreted as prices also. To do this, it is convenient to formulate the primal problem so that the dual variables are non-negative. We write the primal as

$$-\sum_{j=1}^{n} x_{ij} \geq -a_i, \qquad i = 1, \ldots, m,$$

$$\sum_{i=1}^{m} x_{ij} \geq b_j, \qquad j = 1, \ldots, n, \qquad (13\text{--}19)$$

$$\min z = \mathbf{cx}.$$

If $\sum a_i = \sum b_j$, it is clear that the strict equalities must hold for any feasible solution.

The dual of (13–19) is

$$v_j - u_i \leq c_{ij}, \qquad \text{all } i, j,$$

$$\max Z = \mathbf{bv} - \mathbf{au}, \qquad (13\text{--}20)$$

and the dual variables are non-negative. If we write the dual constraints as $v_j \leq c_{ij} + u_i$, each u_i can be interpreted as the f.o.b. value of the product at origin i, and v_j as its value after delivery at destination j. The dual prices are determined in such a way that the value at destination j is never greater than the value at origin i plus transportation cost from i to j. In an optimal solution, only those routes are used for which $v_j = c_{ij} + u_i$.

13–5 Input-output analysis. We now turn from the study of an individual firm to the study of an economy, which involves the interactions of a number of industries.

A very interesting and important model of interacting industries (frequently called input-output analysis) was developed by Professor Wassily Leontief in the early 1930's. Since its introduction, a great deal of theoretical development and some testing have taken place, so that it ranks today as one of the most important models of an economy.

Leontief imagines that the economy consists of a number of interacting industries. Each industry produces a single good and uses only one process of production to make this good. In fact, an industry can be thought of as a process of production. To produce its good a given industry needs as inputs goods made by other industries, labor, and perhaps other inputs from outside the system. Each industry must produce enough to supply the needs of other industries and to meet the external (exogenous or net) demand. The external demand includes consumer demand and may also include government demand and foreign trade.

We shall suppose that there are n industries in our hypothetical economy. For a given time period (say one year) let y_{ij} be the amount of good i (from industry i) needed by industry j. Also let b_i be the exogenous demand for good i. The total amount x_i which industry i must produce to meet exactly the demands is

$$x_i = \sum_{j=1}^{n} y_{ij} + b_i, \qquad i = 1, \ldots, n. \qquad (13\text{–}21)$$

Next we must relate the inputs of y_{ij} to the output x_j for each industry j. This means that we must develop the production functions. Leontief assumed a very simple type of production function. He supposed that the required input of any factor was directly proportional to the production, i.e.,

$$y_{ij} = a_{ij}x_j, \qquad \text{all } i, j, \qquad (13\text{–}22)$$

where the a_{ij} are constants. Thus the factors of production are used in fixed proportions. Furthermore, there are no decreasing returns to scale.

When (13–22) is substituted into (13–21), we obtain

$$x_i = \sum_{j=1}^{n} a_{ij} x_j + b_i, \qquad i = 1, \ldots, n, \qquad (13\text{–}23)$$

or

$$\sum_{j=1}^{n} (\delta_{ij} - a_{ij}) x_j = b_i, \qquad i = 1, \ldots, n,$$

or

$$(\mathbf{I} - \mathbf{A})\mathbf{x} = \mathbf{b}, \qquad (13\text{–}24)$$

where $\mathbf{A} = \|a_{ij}\|$, $\mathbf{x} = [x_1, \ldots, x_n]$, $\mathbf{b} = [b_1, \ldots, b_n]$. If the exogenous demands represented by $\mathbf{b}$ are given, then (13–24) is a set of n simultaneous linear equations to be solved for the amounts x_i which must be produced to meet these demands. For a meaningful system we expect that there is a unique solution. Later we shall see that, under all normal circumstances, $r(\mathbf{I} - \mathbf{A}) = n$. It is also necessary that each x_i be nonnegative. It will be shown that this also follows automatically for all meaningful economies.

The a_{ij} are the technological coefficients which describe the nature of the economy. The dimensions of the a_{ij} depend on the dimensions in which the y_{ij}, x_j are measured. The natural dimensions of x_j are units of product j, and similarly, the natural dimensions of y_{ij} are units of product i. In such a case, the dimensions of a_{ij} are units of product i per unit of product j. Frequently, the x_j, y_{ij} are given in monetary units so that x_j, y_{ij} have dollar values. Then the dimensions of a_{ij} are dollars of i per dollar of j.

If we have an economy of the type postulated by the Leontief input-output system, the a_{ij} can be computed as follows: We choose a given time interval, say, one year. A table is constructed which lists in row i the amount of product i sold to industry j, $j = 1, \ldots, n$, and the exogenous consumer demand. In general, the entries will be in dollar terms although the natural dimensions may also be used. By summing row i, we find the total output x_i of industry i for the period under consideration. Such a tableau is shown in schematic form in Table 13–1. Each a_{ij} is found by dividing y_{ij} by x_j (not x_i).* The Leontief system is static and does not provide for technological improvement or other factors which would cause the a_{ij} to change with time.

---

* Here we assume that everything used by industry j is produced in the period under consideration, and that all of the production of industry i is used. In attempting to apply input-output analysis to the real world, we must be careful to account for changes in stocks, i.e. inventories.

TABLE 13–1

Industry	1 2 $\cdots$ n	Exogenous demand	x_i
1	y_{11} y_{12} $\cdots$ y_{1n}	b_1	x_1
2	y_{21} y_{22} $\cdots$ y_{2n}	b_2	x_2
$\vdots$			$\vdots$
n	y_{n1} y_{n2} $\cdots$ y_{nn}	b_n	x_n

If the inverse of $\mathbf{I} - \mathbf{A}$ exists, then (13–24) may be solved, and the unique solution is given by

$$\mathbf{x} = (\mathbf{I} - \mathbf{A})^{-1}\mathbf{b}. \tag{13–25}$$

Denoting the elements of $(\mathbf{I} - \mathbf{A})^{-1}$ by α_{ij}, we can write

$$x_i = \sum_{j=1}^{n} \alpha_{ij} b_j, \qquad i = 1, \ldots, n. \tag{13–26}$$

Equation (13–26) says that the gross output of product i required to meet the net demands depends linearly on these net demands.

The net demands are often referred to as a bill of goods. If the columns of $\mathbf{A}$ are denoted by $\mathbf{a}_j$, then there exists an $\mathbf{x} \geq \mathbf{0}$ satisfying (13–24) provided that $\mathbf{b}$ lies in the convex polyhedral cone spanned by the vectors $\mathbf{e}_j - \mathbf{a}_j$, $j = 1, \ldots, n$. A bill of goods $\mathbf{b}$ will be called producible if there exists an $\mathbf{x} \geq \mathbf{0}$ satisfying (13–24). The only type of bill of goods which is of economic interest must satisfy $\mathbf{b} \geq \mathbf{0}$ and $\mathbf{b} \neq \mathbf{0}$, i.e., at least one $b_i > 0$. The reason for this is that $\mathbf{b}$ includes consumer demand, and hence all b_i cannot be zero. Later we shall consider a modified model in which $\mathbf{b}$ can be $\mathbf{0}$. Thus, in order that there exist at least one producible bill of goods for an economy whose technological matrix is $\mathbf{A}$, it must be true that the intersection of the convex polyhedral cone C generated by the $\mathbf{e}_j - \mathbf{a}_j$ and the non-negative orthant of E^n contains at least one point $\mathbf{w} \in C$ such that $\mathbf{w} \geq \mathbf{0}$, $\mathbf{w} \neq \mathbf{0}$. Then $\mathbf{w}$ will be a producible bill of goods, as will any point $\mathbf{b} = \lambda\mathbf{w}$, $\lambda > 0$. The set of all producible bills of goods is the intersection of C and the non-negative orthant of E^n.

It is often assumed that labor is the only primary factor used in an economy described by a Leontief model, i.e., the only productive factor which is not produced by the economy. For the economy described by (13–24), assume that $a_{0j}x_j$ units of labor are needed to produce x_j units of good j; a_{0j} is a constant. Given a set of x_j, the total labor requirement is then $\sum_{j=1}^{n} a_{0j}x_j = \mathbf{a}_0\mathbf{x}$, $\mathbf{a}_0 = (a_{01}, \ldots, a_{0n})$. It is easy to compute the labor necessary to produce any final bill of goods $\mathbf{b}$ since the gross production required to meet this bill of goods is $\mathbf{x} = (\mathbf{I} - \mathbf{A})^{-1}\mathbf{b}$. The labor needed to produce $\mathbf{b}$ is $[\mathbf{a}_0(\mathbf{I} - \mathbf{A})^{-1}]\mathbf{b}$.

Suppose that there is an upper limit z to the labor available in the economy. For $\mathbf{b}$ to be produced, it is necessary that

$$[\mathbf{a}_0(\mathbf{I} - \mathbf{A})^{-1}]\mathbf{b} \leq z. \tag{13-27}$$

Thus when labor is a limited resource, the set of producible bills of goods for an economy with a technology matrix $\mathbf{A}$ is the intersection of three sets: C, the half-space (13–27), and the non-negative orthant of E^n.

13–6 Prices in a Leontief system. Nothing has been said so far about prices in our hypothetical economy. Let p_j be the unit price of good j. Then if the a_{ij} are measured in their natural dimensions, $a_{ij}p_i$ is the cost of the a_{ij} units of good i required to make one unit of good j. The cost of goods $1, \ldots, n$ needed to make one unit of good j is $\sum_{i=1}^{n} a_{ij}p_i$. We shall call the difference between the price of good j and this cost the "value added" by industry j in producing good j. Denote the value added by r_j. Then, by definition,

$$p_j - \sum_{i=1}^{n} a_{ij}p_i = r_j, \qquad j = 1, \ldots, n, \tag{13-28}$$

or in matrix form

$$(\mathbf{I} - \mathbf{A})'\mathbf{p} = \mathbf{r}, \tag{13-29}$$

where $\mathbf{p} = [p_1, \ldots, p_n]$, $\mathbf{r} = [r_1, \ldots, r_n]$. Now if $\mathbf{I} - \mathbf{A}$ is nonsingular, so is $(\mathbf{I} - \mathbf{A})'$. Hence if we know the value added by each industry, it is possible to obtain unique values for the prices in the economy. Recalling that the inverse of the transpose is the transpose of the inverse, and using (13–26), we can write

$$p_j = \sum_{i=1}^{n} \alpha_{ij}r_i, \qquad j = 1, \ldots, n. \tag{13-30}$$

The value added can be broken down into labor costs and other factors (such as profit). Imagine that only a single wage rate, w, exists in our economy. Then if a_{0j} units of labor are required to produce one unit of product j, the labor cost for one unit of product j is $a_{0j}w$, and hence r_j can be written

$$r_j = a_{0j}w + s_j, \tag{13-31}$$

where s_j refers to the value added other than labor.

Let us consider an economy in which labor is the only primary factor. Suppose that we wish to determine a set of accounting prices which reflect only labor costs in the value added (no profits, etc.). These may be thought of as the prices which would exist if the economy operated under pure competition and in a state of long-run equilibrium. Then $\mathbf{r} = w\mathbf{a}_0'$, and from (13–29),

$$\mathbf{p}' = w\mathbf{a}_0(\mathbf{I} - \mathbf{A})^{-1}. \tag{13–32}$$

If the y_{ij}, x_j are measured in monetary terms, they include the prices. Denoting by a_{ij}^n, a_{ij}^c the technological coefficients in their natural and monetary dimensions, respectively, we see that

$$a_{ij}^n = \left(\frac{p_j}{p_i}\right) a_{ij}^c. \tag{13–33}$$

Since we expect $\sum_{i=1}^n p_i a_{ij}^n < p_j$ because there must be labor costs in the production of good j, it follows that $a_{ij}^c \geq 0$, and $\sum_{i=1}^n a_{ij}^c < 1$.

The duality of prices and quantities in a Leontief system should be apparent to the reader. It is instructive to examine this aspect in more detail. Consider the linear programming problem

$$(\mathbf{I} - \mathbf{A})\mathbf{x} \geq \mathbf{b}, \qquad \mathbf{x} \geq \mathbf{0}, \qquad \min z = \mathbf{a}_0\mathbf{x}. \tag{13–34}$$

This problem seeks to minimize labor requirements while producing at least the bill of goods $\mathbf{b}$. The unique optimal solution is given by (13–25), with the minimum labor requirement being $\mathbf{a}_0(\mathbf{I} - \mathbf{A})^{-1}\mathbf{b}$. Thus the Leontief model can be considered to be a very simple linear programming problem. Now the dual of (13–34) is

$$(\mathbf{I} - \mathbf{A})'\mathbf{w} \leq \mathbf{a}_0', \qquad \mathbf{w} \geq \mathbf{0}, \qquad \max Z = \mathbf{b}'\mathbf{w}. \tag{13–35}$$

The unique optimal solution to the problem is $\mathbf{w} = (\mathbf{I} - \mathbf{A}')^{-1}\mathbf{a}_0'$. From (13–32), $\mathbf{w} = \mathbf{p}/w$, so that, once the wage rate is known, the dual of (13–35) determines the prices in the economy provided the value added is entirely due to labor. Hence, the problem of determining the prices in a Leontief economy can also be considered to be a linear programming problem. It is the dual of the problem which determines the quantities to be produced.

Duality theory shows that if the bill of goods $\mathbf{b}$ is producible, then there exists a set of non-negative prices for the economy. Since these prices are independent of $\mathbf{b}$, it also follows from duality theory that the same prices will apply for all producible bills of goods.

The duality of quantities and prices can also be interpreted in terms of convex cones. The prices in the economy are given by (13–32). Hence,

$$\mathbf{p}'\mathbf{b} = w\mathbf{a}_0'(\mathbf{I} - \mathbf{A})^{-1}(\mathbf{I} - \mathbf{A})\mathbf{x} = w\mathbf{a}_0\mathbf{x} > 0, \tag{13–36}$$

provided **b** is producible and $w > 0$. If **b** is producible, it lies in the convex polyhedral cone C spanned by the columns of $\mathbf{I} - \mathbf{A}$. But by (13–36) **p** is an element of C^+, the cone polar to C. Now a theorem on convex cones (Chapter 2) states: If C contains no vector $\mathbf{y} < \mathbf{0}$, C^+ contains a $\mathbf{y} \geq \mathbf{0}$, $\mathbf{y} \neq \mathbf{0}$. We do not expect the cone C spanned by the columns of $\mathbf{I} - \mathbf{A}$ to contain a $\mathbf{b} < \mathbf{0}$, for this would mean that negative net amounts could be produced, although the gross amounts are non-negative. Thus we expect C^+ to contain a $\mathbf{p} \geq \mathbf{0}$, and hence we see from the properties of cones and from the duality theory of linear programming that there should be a set of non-negative prices for the economy.

13–7 Other properties of the Leontief system. In Chapter 2 we noted that if $\lim_{k \to \infty} \mathbf{A}^k = \mathbf{0}$, then

$$(\mathbf{I} - \mathbf{A})^{-1} = \sum_{k=0}^{\infty} \mathbf{A}^k = \mathbf{I} + \mathbf{A} + \mathbf{A}^2 + \cdots . \tag{13–37}$$

In the preceding section, we saw that if monetary units are used, then it is always to be expected that $\sum_i a_{ij}^c < 1$ for all j. Furthermore, it was shown in Chapter 2 that if this condition holds for non-negative a_{ij}^c, then the expansion (13–37) is valid, and we can write $\mathbf{x} = (\mathbf{I} - \mathbf{A})^{-1}\mathbf{b}$ as

$$\mathbf{x} = \mathbf{b} + \mathbf{Ab} + \mathbf{A}^2\mathbf{b} + \cdots . \tag{13–38}$$

When the a_{ij} are expressed in their natural dimensions, there is no reason why $\sum_i a_{ij}^n < 1$ should be expected to hold. However, we suspect that the existence of the power-series form of the inverse should be independent of the dimensions used, and hence (13–38) should hold also when natural dimensions are used. There is an interesting physical interpretation of the power-series expansion which shows that the expansion should always be valid. Equation (13–38) is nothing more than a mathematical representation of the fact that the gross production can be thought of in the following way: First, the gross production must consist of the final bill of goods **b**. To turn out **b**, each industry i must produce an additional quantity $\sum_j a_{ij}b_j$ to be used in the production of **b** by industry i and other industries, i.e., **Ab** must be made in addition to **b**. However, to produce the amount **Ab**, an additional quantity $\mathbf{A}(\mathbf{Ab}) = \mathbf{A}^2\mathbf{b}$ must be produced. To produce $\mathbf{A}^2\mathbf{b}$ requires an additional output $\mathbf{A}^3\mathbf{b}$, etc. Thus the total required production is (13–38).

Under all normal circumstances, $\mathbf{A}^k\mathbf{b} \to \mathbf{0}$ for any **b** or $\mathbf{A}^k \to \mathbf{0}$ as $k \to \infty$, that is, we always expect the series (13–38) to converge. This will be true if less than one unit of good j is required in total by all industries to produce one unit of good j. For example, suppose that there were only two industries, steel and coal. If the first industry is taken to be coal, then consider the first component of (13–38). The first component of $\mathbf{b}$ is the consumer demand for coal. The first component of $\mathbf{d} = \mathbf{Ab}$ is the coal needed to mine b_1 units of coal and to make b_2 units of steel. The first component of $\mathbf{A}^2\mathbf{b}$ is the coal needed to mine d_1 units of coal (needed to mine b_1 units of coal and to make b_2 units of steel) and to make d_2 units of steel (needed to mine b_1 units of coal and to make b_2 units of steel), etc. The series will converge if only a finite amount of coal is needed to produce b_1 units of coal and b_2 units of steel for consumer demand; the same is true for the required quantities of steel. These conditions should always hold, and therefore, we should always be able to write (13–37).

The series expansion (13–37) reveals some other points of interest. Since $a_{ij} \geq 0$ for all i, j, irrespective of the dimensions used, we see that every element of $(\mathbf{I} - \mathbf{A})^{-1}$ will be non-negative for a Leontief system. This in turn means that for any $\mathbf{b} \geq \mathbf{0}, \mathbf{x} \geq \mathbf{0}$. Hence the convex polyhedral cone C spanned by the columns of $\mathbf{I} - \mathbf{A}$ must contain the entire non-negative orthant of E^n. In other words, any bill of goods is producible if the labor supply is unlimited. If z is the upper limit to the labor supply, then any bill of goods satisfying $\mathbf{a}_0(\mathbf{I} - \mathbf{A})^{-1}\mathbf{b} \leq z$ is producible.

Our above discussion may leave the impression that a Leontief economy requires all factors of production to be used in fixed proportions, and does not permit possible substitutions. However, this is not the case. Professor Samuelson was the first to make the interesting observation that if there is only one primary factor, labor, then the Leontief economy is compatible with the notion of substitutability. Although substitution is physically possible, it will never be observed because it is ruled out by the following economic considerations: If the only value added is the cost of labor, then only the wage rate can be freely varied. The prices of the goods are directly proportional to the wage rate, but the price ratios p_i/p_j are invariant and do not depend on the wage rate. Thus if the wage rate goes up, a shift from labor to machines will not occur because the increase in the wage rate also increases the price of machines.

We shall not prove rigorously that substitution, although physically possible, is ruled out. Several proofs may be found in Koopman's work [3].

13–8 The aggregation problem. In any attempt to apply a Leontief system to a real economy, we are immediately faced with a number of problems, in particular, with the question of aggregation. For an economic system such as the U.S. economy, there are thousands of different activities which, in a Leontief model, could be considered to be industries. The task of collecting the data needed to estimate the technological coefficients for an economy of several thousand industries would be monumental. Furthermore, even if the data could be collected, none of the computers available today could solve the resulting system of equations. Thus, to apply the Leontief model to a real economy, it is always necessary to aggregate a number of activities into a single industry.

The problem of aggregation is very difficult, and no definitive treatment of the subject has yet been given. Here we shall do no more than indicate the nature of the problem. It should be immediately obvious that the method of aggregation can have an important bearing on the answers obtained from a Leontief model. Three of the most frequent criteria used for aggregation are: (1) substitutability, (2) complementarity, and (3) similarity of production functions. If the first criterion were adopted, we would aggregate products which are close substitutes. According to the second principle, we would aggregate products that complement one another and are used in roughly fixed proportions. According to the third criterion, we would aggregate items requiring essentially the same type of production process. None of the above techniques provide a foolproof method of aggregation because it is almost impossible to find perfect substitutes, exact complements, or identical production functions.

Let us study briefly what happens to the system of equations (13–24) if we aggregate a set of industries. To simplify the discussion, we assume that all quantities are measured in monetary terms. Suppose that we decide to aggregate the industries $m, m+1, \ldots, n$ into a single industry. If $\hat{b}_m$ is the net demand for this single industry, then

$$\hat{b}_m = \sum_{i=m}^{n} b_i. \tag{13–39}$$

The sales from aggregated industry m to any other industry j will be denoted by $\hat{y}_{mj}$, and

$$\hat{y}_{mj} = \sum_{i=m}^{n} y_{ij}. \tag{13–40}$$

Similarly, if $\hat{y}_{im}$ represents the sales from industry i to the aggregated industry m, then

$$\hat{y}_{im} = \sum_{j=m}^{n} y_{ij}. \tag{13–41}$$

If, for the period under consideration, the gross sales of industry j are denoted by x_j, and $\hat{x}_m$ denotes the gross sales of the aggregated industry, then

$$\hat{x}_m = \sum_{j=m}^{n} x_j. \tag{13–42}$$

The new technological coefficients associated with the aggregated industry are

$$\hat{a}^c_{mj} = \frac{\hat{y}_{mj}}{x_j} = \frac{1}{x_j} \sum_{i=m}^n y_{ij} = \sum_{i=m}^n a^c_{ij}, \qquad j = 1, \ldots, m-1, \qquad (13\text{--}43)$$

and

$$\hat{a}^c_{im} = \frac{\hat{y}_{im}}{\hat{x}_m} = \frac{\sum_{j=m}^n y_{ij}}{\sum_{j=m}^n x_j} = \sum_{j=m}^n a^c_{ij} \frac{x_j}{\sum_{j=m}^n x_j}, \qquad i = 0, \ldots, m. \qquad (13\text{--}44)$$

Unfortunately, the $\hat{a}^c_{im}$ are not independent of the bill of goods. Hence, if these coefficients are determined under one set of conditions, it does not follow that they will remain valid for a different bill of goods.

If the aggregated industries have precisely the same production functions so that $a^c_{ij} = a^c_{ik}$, j, $k = m, \ldots, n$, then the $\hat{a}^c_{im}$ are indeed constants, and $\hat{a}^c_{im} = a^c_{im}$. Furthermore, if the aggregated industries are exactly complementary so that $x_j = \beta_j x_n$, $j = m, \ldots, n-1$, then the $\hat{a}^c_{im}$ are again constants since

$$\hat{a}^c_{im} = \left(1 + \sum_{i=m}^{n-1} \beta_j\right)^{-1} \left(a^c_{in} + \sum_{i=m}^{n-1} a^c_{ij} \beta_j\right).$$

However, if the industries are exact substitutes for one another, but the production functions are not identical, it does not follow that the $\hat{a}^c_{im}$ will be constant unless some specification is made as to the proportions in which the various substitutes will be used.

13–9 Decomposable systems. Several interesting features of a Leontief economy often become immediately obvious if we draw a graph representing the flows in the economy. The nodes refer to the industries. If $a_{ij} > 0$, we draw an oriented branch from i to j. The number of branches joining i and j may be 2, 1, or 0. In the event that $a_{ij} > 0$, and $a_{ji} > 0$, there will be two oriented branches (in opposite directions) joining i and j. Industry j buys directly from industry i if the network contains the oriented branch $(\overrightarrow{i, j})$. We say that j buys indirectly from i if there is an oriented path from i to j containing two or more branches in the path. An industry j buys indirectly from i if it buys from one or more industries that are supplied directly or indirectly from i. Industry j may buy both directly and indirectly from i. An industry j does not buy either directly or indirectly from i if there is no oriented path leading from i to j.

An economy is said to be indecomposable if each industry buys directly or indirectly from all other industries; otherwise the economy is called decomposable. In an indecomposable economy, a change in the net requirement for product j will be felt throughout the entire economy; i.e., if there is an increase in the net demand for product j, while the demand for all other products remains unchanged, then a strict increase must occur in the gross production of every product since industry j, which must increase its gross production, directly or indirectly uses products from all other industries. Hence, every industry must increase its gross production.

For any indecomposable economy, we can make an additional observation concerning the matrix $\|\alpha_{ij}\| = (\mathbf{I} - \mathbf{A})^{-1}$. Recall that $\mathbf{x}$ is given by (13–25). If $\mathbf{b}$ is replaced by $\mathbf{b} + \lambda \mathbf{e}_j$ and the new gross production is $\mathbf{x} + \Delta \mathbf{x}$, then $\mathbf{x} + \Delta \mathbf{x} = \|\alpha_{ij}\|(\mathbf{b} + \lambda \mathbf{e}_j)$ or $\Delta \mathbf{x} = \lambda \|\alpha_{ij}\| \mathbf{e}_j$. Hence $\Delta \mathbf{x} = \lambda \boldsymbol{\alpha}_j$, $\boldsymbol{\alpha}_j = [\alpha_{1j}, \ldots, \alpha_{nj}]$. We noted in the above paragraph that if $\lambda > 0$, $\Delta \mathbf{x} > 0$, and therefore $\boldsymbol{\alpha}_j > 0$, $j = 1, \ldots, n$. This shows that for an indecomposable economy, each element of $(\mathbf{I} - \mathbf{A})^{-1}$ is strictly positive.

Let us next study briefly decomposable economies. Suppose that an economy is represented by a graph, such as that shown in Fig. 13–1. The graph for this economy decomposes into three disjoint graphs which are not connected. If we number the industries as shown, the technology matrix $\mathbf{A}$ for this economy can be written:

$$\mathbf{A} = \begin{bmatrix} \mathbf{A}_1 & \mathbf{0} & \mathbf{0} \\ \mathbf{0} & \mathbf{A}_2 & \mathbf{0} \\ \mathbf{0} & \mathbf{0} & \mathbf{A}_3 \end{bmatrix}; \quad \mathbf{A}_1 = \begin{bmatrix} a_{11} & a_{12} \\ a_{21} & a_{22} \end{bmatrix};$$

$$\mathbf{A}_2 = \begin{bmatrix} a_{33} & a_{34} \\ a_{43} & a_{44} \end{bmatrix}; \quad \mathbf{A}_3 = \begin{bmatrix} a_{55} & a_{56} & a_{57} \\ a_{65} & a_{66} & a_{67} \\ a_{75} & a_{76} & a_{77} \end{bmatrix}.$$

Industries 1 and 2 neither buy from nor sell to the remaining industries. The same holds true for industries 3, 4 and 5, 6, 7. Such an economy can be viewed as three separate economies, that is, $(\mathbf{I} - \mathbf{A})\mathbf{x} = \mathbf{b}$ breaks down into $(\mathbf{I} - \mathbf{A}_1)\mathbf{x}_1 = \mathbf{b}_1$, $(\mathbf{I} - \mathbf{A}_2)\mathbf{x}_2 = \mathbf{b}_2$, $(\mathbf{I} - \mathbf{A}_3)\mathbf{x}_3 = \mathbf{b}_3$. An economy is called completely decomposable if the technology matrix can be written

$$\mathbf{A} = \begin{bmatrix} \mathbf{A}_1 & \mathbf{0} & \cdots & \mathbf{0} \\ \mathbf{0} & \mathbf{A}_2 & \cdots & \mathbf{0} \\ \vdots & & & \vdots \\ \mathbf{0} & \mathbf{0} & \cdots & \mathbf{A}_m \end{bmatrix}, \tag{13–45}$$

where $m \geq 2$. Such an economy can be treated as m separate economies. When the graph of an economy is drawn, it is immediately obvious whether or not it is completely decomposable.

We wish to note that if the industries had been numbered differently in Fig. 13–1, the technology matrix would not have had the form (13–45).

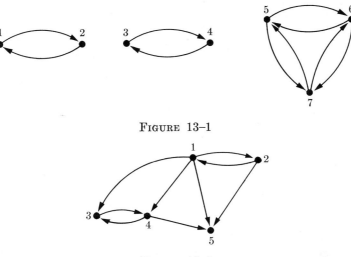

FIGURE 13–1

FIGURE 13–2

Observe that if in the graph of an economy the numbering of nodes i and j is interchanged, then rows i, j and columns i, j of the technology matrix are also interchanged. Thus an economy represented by a matrix $\mathbf{A}$ is completely decomposable if the matrix $\mathbf{A}$ can be cast into the form (13–45) by a series of interchanges of columns and corresponding rows.

Now consider the economy whose graph is given in Fig. 13–2. This economy has a peculiar feature: Although the graph is connected, certain groups of industries are joined to other industries only by a one-way link, i.e., they buy from these other industries, but do not sell to them. The industries in such an economy can be divided into groups so that every industry in group k directly or indirectly buys from every other industry in group k, but all industries in group k sell to industries in other groups only when the outside group has an index greater than k. The industries in Fig. 13–2 have been numbered so that they fall into three groups: (a) Industries 1, 2 in group 1 sell to each other, to industries 3, 4 in group 2, and industry 5 in group 3; (b) industries 3, 4 sell only to each other and to industry 5; (c) industry 5 does not sell to any other industry. This economy is decomposable, but not completely decomposable. The technology matrix $\mathbf{A}$ (Fig. 13–2) has the form

$$
\mathbf{A} = \begin{bmatrix}
a_{11} & a_{12} & a_{13} & a_{14} & a_{15} \\
a_{21} & a_{22} & 0 & 0 & a_{25} \\
0 & 0 & a_{33} & a_{34} & 0 \\
0 & 0 & a_{43} & a_{44} & a_{45} \\
0 & 0 & 0 & 0 & a_{55}
\end{bmatrix} = \begin{bmatrix}
\mathbf{A}_{11} & \mathbf{A}_{12} & \mathbf{A}_{13} \\
\mathbf{0} & \mathbf{A}_{22} & \mathbf{A}_{23} \\
\mathbf{0} & \mathbf{0} & \mathbf{A}_{33}
\end{bmatrix}.
$$

In a decomposable economy, it is not true that every industry buys directly or indirectly from every other industry. Hence the industries of a decomposable economy can be divided into groups such that each industry in a group buys directly or indirectly from all other industries in the group, but every industry in any group k can sell to an industry in another group only if the other group has an index greater than k. This means that if the industries are properly numbered, the technology matrix will have the triangular form

$$
\mathbf{A} = \begin{bmatrix} \mathbf{A}_{11} & \mathbf{A}_{12} \cdots \mathbf{A}_{1k} \\ \mathbf{0} & \mathbf{A}_{22} \cdots \mathbf{A}_{2k} \\ \vdots & \vdots \\ \mathbf{0} & \mathbf{0} \cdots \mathbf{A}_{kk} \end{bmatrix}, \tag{13-46}
$$

and the submatrices $\mathbf{A}_{ii}$ are square and cannot be written in the form (13–46). Note that a completely decomposable economy is a special case of the general form of the decomposable economy here described. If a decomposable economy whose matrix is given by (13–46) is not completely decomposable, then it must be true that for every index j, there is either at least one submatrix $\mathbf{A}_{ij} \neq \mathbf{0}$, $i < j$, or at least one submatrix $\mathbf{A}_{ji} \neq \mathbf{0}$ for $i > j$.

Note that if the industries in a decomposable economy are not numbered properly, the matrix $\mathbf{A}$ will not have the form (13–46). In mathematical terms, an economy is decomposable if by interchanging columns and also interchanging the corresponding rows we can cast the technology matrix into the form (13–46), with the submatrices $\mathbf{A}_{ii}$ being square.

The properties of economies which are decomposable and have technology matrices of the form (13–46) are somewhat different from those of indecomposable economies. Suppose that b_i in the bill of goods $\mathbf{b}$ is increased. Imagine that if $\mathbf{A}$ is partitioned as in (13–46), i falls in group k. Because every industry in group k directly or indirectly sells to all other industries in group k, every x_j in group k must increase. However, since industries in group k do not buy from industries in groups with an index greater than k, the x_j for industries in such groups will remain unchanged when b_i is increased. The x_j in some group r with an index smaller than k may or may not increase, depending on whether one or more industries in group k buy from one or more industries in group r.

The above information gives us some indication of the nature of $(\mathbf{I} - \mathbf{A})^{-1}$. It shows that if $(\mathbf{I} - \mathbf{A})^{-1}$ is partitioned in the same way as $\mathbf{A}$, all elements below the main diagonal vanish, and $(\mathbf{I} - \mathbf{A})^{-1}$ also has a triangular structure. This follows because a change of b_i in group k does not change x_j if x_j is in a group with an index greater than k. If

Λ_{rs} are the submatrices of $(\mathbf{I} - \mathbf{A})^{-1}$, then the elements of each Λ_{kk} are all positive because an increase in any one b_i of group k increases every x_j of group k. We know that the elements of Λ_{rs}, $s > r$, will be non-negative. However, some Λ_{rs} may be null matrices. But if one element of Λ_{rs} is positive, all elements will be positive for the following reason: If a change in some b_i in group s has the effect of changing one x_j in group r, it must cause a change in every x_j in group r because every industry in group r buys from all other industries in group r. This requires that each element of Λ_{rs} be positive (why?).

13–10 The closed Leontief model. In our previous discussions, labor was treated as a primary factor, and the purchases by consumers were assumed to be given as the bill of goods or part of the bill of goods. Suppose that we wish to study the effects of a change in the level of foreign trade or in government spending. Such changes will induce a change in the amount of labor required in the system, which in turn will presumably cause a change in consumer demand. Hence consumer demand will not be independent of changes in the level of foreign trade or of government spending.

To account for such changes we must relate consumer demand to the amount of labor used in the economy. This is done by treating labor as if it were another industry. In earlier sections, we have assumed that if activity j is operated at a level x_j, then $a_{0j}x_j$ units of labor are used. There is no external demand for labor. Hence if x_0 is the total labor requirement, the labor balance equation reads

$$x_0 - \sum_{j=1}^{n} a_{0j}x_j = 0. \tag{13–47}$$

We then assume that the consumer demand y_{i0} for product i is

$$y_{i0} = a_{i0}x_0, \qquad i = 1, \ldots, n. \tag{13–48}$$

The consumer demand for each product i is directly proportional to the total amount of labor employed.

Let $\hat{\mathbf{b}}$ be the bill of goods required for foreign trade and government orders. Write $\hat{\mathbf{a}}_0 = [a_{10}, \ldots, a_{n0}]$. The system of equations which determine $\mathbf{x}$, x_0 is then

$$\begin{bmatrix} 1 & -\mathbf{a}_0 \\ -\hat{\mathbf{a}}_0 & \mathbf{I} - \mathbf{A} \end{bmatrix} \begin{bmatrix} x_0 \\ \mathbf{x} \end{bmatrix} = \begin{bmatrix} 0 \\ \hat{\mathbf{b}} \end{bmatrix}. \tag{13–49}$$

This is a system of $n + 1$ equations in $n + 1$ unknowns. The solution determines the gross amount of each product to be made to meet consumer demands and exogenous demands. It also determines the amount of labor to be employed. It can be used to study changes in $\hat{\mathbf{b}}$ because it accounts for the change that takes place in consumer demand as the total amount of employed labor is changed.

Suppose now that we consider a completely closed system. No foreign trade exists, and government activities are either ignored or treated as an industry. Then (13–49) becomes

$$\begin{bmatrix} 1 & -\mathbf{a}_0 \\ -\hat{\mathbf{a}}_0 & \mathbf{I} - \mathbf{A} \end{bmatrix} \begin{bmatrix} x_0 \\ \mathbf{x} \end{bmatrix} = \mathbf{0}. \tag{13–50}$$

In order that there be solutions other than the trivial solution, it is necessary that

$$\begin{vmatrix} 1 & -\mathbf{a}_0 \\ -\hat{\mathbf{a}}_0 & \mathbf{I} - \mathbf{A} \end{vmatrix} = 0. \tag{13–51}$$

When (13–51) holds, there will always be solutions with not all $x_j = 0$. The solution to (13–50) does not determine the actual values of the variables. It determines them up to a constant multiple since $r(\mathbf{I} - \mathbf{A}) = n$. This is to be expected for a closed system. Whatever the level of employment, just enough will be produced to meet consumer demand.

At this point, we must stop to examine the difference between (13–49) and (13–50). In order to solve (13–49), the matrix of the coefficients must be nonsingular. However, in (13–50) we require that the matrix of the coefficients must be singular. Clearly, these matrices which were written in identical form must be different. The difference lies in public consumption. In a closed economy, the public always consumes precisely what the economy produces, and it is impossible to meet an exogenous demand. For the economy described by (13–49) public consumption is always at least a little less than the total output. Hence if we move from (13–49) to (13–50), the vector $\hat{\mathbf{a}}_0$ must change. This vector is all that needs to change.

Equation (13–49) has another surprising feature. It says that if $\hat{\mathbf{b}} = \mathbf{0}$, then $x_0 = 0$, $\mathbf{x} = \mathbf{0}$, that is, the economy does not produce anything if there are no exogenous demands. This is not realistic. The economy should be capable of operating at some level with not all $x_i = 0$ to support consumer demand. The difficulty lies in the fact that a matrix is either singular or nonsingular. For Eq. (13–49) to behave realistically as $\hat{\mathbf{b}}$ approaches $\mathbf{0}$, it is necessary to drop the assumption that the a_{0j} are constants, and to permit the a_{0j} to change as $\hat{\mathbf{b}}$ approaches $\mathbf{0}$ in such a way that the matrix of the coefficients becomes singular when $\mathbf{b} = \mathbf{0}$.

The above paragraph has shown that the a_{0j} cannot be expected to remain constant over wider ranges of x_0. In fact, it is not reasonable to expect any of the technological coefficients a_{ij} to remain constant over wide ranges of variation of x_j. It is only for a relatively small range of variation of the variables that one may expect the assumption of constant technological coefficients to be even an approximate representation of reality.

13–11 Practical uses for input-output models.

A great deal of effort has been devoted to the task of representing the American economy by input-output models. Most of this work has been done by government agencies, such as the Bureau of Labor Statistics and the Air Force. The model lends itself naturally to future planning; in fact, the main interest in the model derives from its suitability for planning purposes. For example, it is of interest to study employment levels and the gross production required to meet various specified bills of goods (consumption included). Of particular interest is the problem of deciding whether in times of war a bill of goods containing heavy demands by the military can be met with the available productive capacities and labor force.

It is also useful to study whether serious unemployment may result from a change-over to a peace-time economy.

The model for prices is also interesting. It is possible to study how an increase in the wage rate of steel workers will change prices throughout the whole economy if the assumption is made that the entire cost of the increase is passed on by increased prices. The general form of the price equations (13–29) is used in this case. It is not necessary to assume that the wage rate is the same throughout the whole economy or that the only value added is due to labor; it is only necessary to change the value added for one industry and to note the effects of this on the prices of all goods.

13–12 Alternative activities.

Our preceding discussions were based on the hypothesis that only a single industry (i.e., a single production process) makes a given product. Let us drop this assumption and imagine that several industries are capable of making the same product. We retain, however, the assumption that a given industry makes no more than one product. We shall denote by $\mathbf{e}_j - \mathbf{a}_j^s$, $s = 1, \ldots, r(j)$, the activity vectors for the industries which produce product j, and by x_j^s the levels at which these activities are operated. If $\mathbf{b}$ is the bill of goods, then the $x_j^s \geq 0$ must satisfy

$$\sum_{j=1}^{n} \sum_{s=1}^{r(j)} (\mathbf{e}_j - \mathbf{a}_j^s) x_j^s = \mathbf{b}. \tag{13–52}$$

Since there are now more variables than equations, the x_j^s cannot be determined without some additional requirements. If we also wish to minimize a linear objective function:

$$z = \sum_{j=1}^{n} \sum_{s=1}^{r(j)} c_j^s x_j^s, \tag{13-53}$$

then we have a linear programming problem which provides a way of selecting the industries which will operate at a positive level.

There are n equations in the set of constraints (13–52), and therefore an optimal solution never need have more than n nonzero x_j^s. If each $b_i > 0$, then an optimal solution must contain at least one industry which turns out product j, $j = 1, \ldots, n$. Since there are only n activities in the basis, an optimal solution will be such that one and only one industry produces each product.

Now if all industries are legitimate, we expect that for any $\mathbf{b} > \mathbf{0}$, every combination of n industries, with precisely one industry for each product, should yield a basic feasible solution to (13–52), i.e., should be able to produce the requisite amounts to meet the bill of goods. Let us suppose that we have some basic feasible solution which is not optimal. If the activity vector $\mathbf{e}_j - \mathbf{a}_j^s$ is to enter the basis at the next iteration, it must replace the activity vector in the basis which produces product j. No computation is required to determine which vector should leave the basis. This in turn yields the interesting result that the set of optimal solutions is independent of the bill of goods $\mathbf{b}$, since, in the simplex method, $\mathbf{b}$ has no influence on the vector to enter the basis; it only affects the vector to be removed.

Here we have shown that the Leontief model can be generalized to include alternative production processes. The activities to be used are chosen by minimizing some linear objective function.

Dantzig [1] has developed a short-cut technique for solving the linear programming problem (13–52), (13–53) for a decomposable economy. Let us assume that the technology matrix including the alternative activities has the form (13–46).* Dantzig calls such matrices block triangular. It will be assumed that all industries which produce a given good have the same structure so that if one industry which produces good j appears in $\mathbf{A}_{11}$, all industries producing j appear in $\mathbf{A}_{11}$.

We know that any basis matrix will contain one and only one activity vector for each good. Thus the basis matrices will also have a block-triangular form. From Section 13–9, we know that the inverse of any basis will also have a block-triangular form so that we can write the

_____

* Here the $\mathbf{A}_{ii}$ need not be square, however, since there can be alternative activities.

inverse of any basis $\mathbf{B}$ as

$$\mathbf{B}^{-1} = \begin{bmatrix} \boldsymbol{\Lambda}_{11} & \boldsymbol{\Lambda}_{12} \cdots \boldsymbol{\Lambda}_{1k} \\ 0 & \boldsymbol{\Lambda}_{22} \cdots \boldsymbol{\Lambda}_{2k} \\ \vdots & \vdots \\ 0 & 0 \cdots \boldsymbol{\Lambda}_{kk} \end{bmatrix}. \tag{13–54}$$

If $\mathbf{B}_{ij}$ is the submatrix in $\mathbf{B}$ corresponding to $\boldsymbol{\Lambda}_{ij}$ in $\mathbf{B}^{-1}$, the multiplication $\mathbf{B}\mathbf{B}^{-1}$ shows that $\boldsymbol{\Lambda}_{ii} = \mathbf{B}_{ii}^{-1}$, $i = 1, \ldots, k$.

Let $\mathbf{c}_B$ contain the prices in the basis; $\mathbf{c}_B$ will be partitioned in the same way as the rows of $\mathbf{B}^{-1}$, so that

$$\mathbf{c}_B = (\mathbf{c}_{B1}, \mathbf{c}_{B2}, \ldots, \mathbf{c}_{Bk}). \tag{13–55}$$

If in (13–46) $\mathbf{A}_{11}$ is $m_1 \times n_1$, then any activity vector in the first n_1 columns of $\mathbf{A}$ can be written in partitioned form as

$$\mathbf{e}_j - \mathbf{a}_j = [\mathbf{f}_j, 0, \ldots, 0]. \tag{13–56}$$

Assuming that $\mathbf{A}_{22}$ is $m_2 \times n_2$, we can write any activity vector in columns $n_1 + 1, \ldots, n_1 + n_2$ in the partitioned form

$$\mathbf{e}_j - \mathbf{a}_j = [\mathbf{f}_j, \mathbf{g}_j, 0, \ldots, 0]. \tag{13–57}$$

The same can be done for the remaining columns of $\mathbf{A}$.

Now consider $z_j - c_j = \mathbf{c}_B \mathbf{B}^{-1}(\mathbf{e}_j - \mathbf{a}_j)$ for any activity vector in the first n_1 columns of $\mathbf{A}$. By Eqs. (13–54) through (13–56), we have

$$z_j - c_j = \mathbf{c}_{B1}\mathbf{B}_{11}^{-1}\mathbf{f}_j - c_j. \tag{13–58}$$

Note that $z_j - c_j$ is completely independent of any activities other than the first n_1 activities. Thus the optimal set of activities for the first m_1 columns of $\mathbf{B}$ can be determined independently of the remaining columns of $\mathbf{B}$. No activity vector other than one of the first n_1 activity vectors in $\mathbf{A}$ will appear in the first m_1 columns of $\mathbf{B}$. To carry out the computation, $\mathbf{B}^{-1}$ is not needed; only $\mathbf{B}_{11}^{-1}$ is required.

Let us continue and see whether it is possible to optimize the columns $m_1 + 1, \ldots, m_2$ of $\mathbf{B}$ in the same way. For an activity vector in columns $n_1 + 1, \ldots, n_2$ of $\mathbf{A}$,

$$z_j - c_j = (\mathbf{c}_{B1}\mathbf{B}_{11}^{-1}, \mathbf{c}_{B1}\boldsymbol{\Lambda}_{12} + \mathbf{c}_{B2}\mathbf{B}_{22}^{-1})[\mathbf{f}_j, \mathbf{g}_j] - c_j. \tag{13–59}$$

We evaluate $\boldsymbol{\Lambda}_{12}$ by considering the product $\mathbf{B}\mathbf{B}^{-1}$. This gives

$$\mathbf{B}_{11}\boldsymbol{\Lambda}_{12} + \mathbf{B}_{12}\boldsymbol{\Lambda}_{22} = 0,$$

or
$$\mathbf{A}_{12} = -\mathbf{B}_{11}^{-1}\mathbf{B}_{12}\mathbf{B}_{22}^{-1}. \tag{13-60}$$

Substituting this result into (13–59), we obtain

$$z_j - c_j = (\mathbf{c}_{B2} - \mathbf{c}_{B1}\mathbf{B}_{11}^{-1}\mathbf{B}_{12})\mathbf{B}_{22}^{-1}\mathbf{g}_j - (c_j - \mathbf{c}_{B1}\mathbf{B}_{11}^{-1}\mathbf{f}_j),$$

or

$$z_j - c_j = \hat{\mathbf{c}}_{B2}\mathbf{B}_{22}^{-1}\mathbf{g}_j - \hat{c}_j, \tag{13-61}$$

where

$$\hat{\mathbf{c}}_{B2} = (\mathbf{c}_{B2} - \mathbf{c}_{B1}\mathbf{B}_{11}^{-1}\mathbf{B}_{12}); \qquad \hat{c}_j = c_j - \mathbf{c}_{B1}\mathbf{B}_{11}^{-1}\mathbf{f}_j.$$

Thus the columns $m_1 + 1, \ldots, m_2$ of $\mathbf{B}$ can also be optimized independently of the remaining columns. We only need to compute $\mathbf{B}_{22}^{-1}$. Equation (13–61) has the same form as (13–58) except that the prices must be modified. These prices depend on the first m_1 columns of $\mathbf{B}$ which we assume to be optimized.

Continuing in this way, we obtain the optimal solution to the entire linear programming problem by block optimization. The amount of work needed to solve the problems by Dantzig's short-cut method is considerably less than that required by a direct application of the simplex method.

13–13 Dynamic Leontief models. The Leontief economies studied thus far were static, and time did not appear. Leontief-type models have been generalized to include dynamic behavior. These generalizations will be briefly discussed in this section.

We shall be concerned with the state of the economy at different points in time. It will be assumed that some time period (a month or year, perhaps) is chosen, and the change in the economy from one time period to the next will be determined. As before, we assume that there are n industries. Each industry produces only one product and uses only a single process of production.

It will be convenient to measure all quantities in monetary terms. Let $y_{ij}(k)$ be the amount of good i bought by industry j in time period k, and let $x_j(k)$ be the gross production of good j in time period k. Then Leontief assumes that the inputs are related to the outputs by

$$y_{ij}(k) = a_{ij}x_j(k), \qquad \text{all } i, j, k, \tag{13-62}$$

where a_{ij} is a constant which does not depend on the time period under consideration.

The dynamic model also considers capital stocks. Let $s_{ij}(k)$ be the capital stock of good i held by industry j at the beginning of time period k.

Leontief assumes that the $s_{ij}(k)$, $i = 1, \ldots, n$, needed to support the production of j will be proportional to the amount of good j produced in time period k, i.e.,

$$s_{ij}(k) = d_{ij}x_j(k), \qquad \text{all } i, j, k, \tag{13-63}$$

where the $d_{ij} \geq 0$ are independent of the time period (of course, some of the d_{ij} may be zero). The total capital stock $s_i(k)$ of good i held by the entire economy (exclusive of consumers and other exogenous users of product i) is

$$s_i(k) = \sum_{j=1}^{n} s_{ij}(k) = \sum_{j=1}^{n} d_{ij}x_j(k), \qquad i = 1, \ldots, n. \tag{13-64}$$

Then $\Delta s_i(k) = s_i(k + 1) - s_i(k)$, which is the change in the capital stock of product i from the beginning of time period k to the end of this time period, must be produced by industry i in time period k. Leontief assumes that $\Delta s_i(k) \geq 0$, $i = 1, \ldots, n$, so that for the whole economy, there is never disinvestment in any capital stock, i.e., there is no depletion of productive capacity. Some of the individual $s_{ij}(k)$ may decrease, but $s_i(k)$ can never decrease.

Take $b_i(k)$ to be the exogenous demand for product i in time period k. Leontief assumes that the gross production for each industry in each time period exactly meets the total demands for the product, i.e.,

$$x_i(k) = \sum_{j=1}^{n} a_{ij}x_j(k) + \Delta s_i(k) + b_i(k), \qquad i = 1, \ldots, n, \tag{13-65}$$

and

$$\Delta s_i(k) = \sum_{j=1}^{n} d_{ij}[x_j(k + 1) - x_j(k)], \qquad i = 1, \ldots, n. \tag{13-66}$$

Now define

$$\mathbf{A} = \|a_{ij}\|, \qquad \mathbf{D} = \|d_{ij}\|, \qquad \mathbf{b}_k = [b_1(k), \ldots, b_n(k)],$$

$$\mathbf{x}_k = [x_1(k), \ldots, x_n(k)], \qquad \mathbf{s}_k = [s_1(k), \ldots, s_n(k)].$$

In matrix form, the dynamic Leontief model can then be summarized as

$$(\mathbf{I} - \mathbf{A})\mathbf{x}_k - \mathbf{D}\mathbf{x}_{k+1} + \mathbf{D}\mathbf{x}_k = \mathbf{b}_k, \tag{13-67}$$

$$\mathbf{s}_k = \mathbf{D}\mathbf{x}_k. \tag{13-68}$$

The matrix $\mathbf{D}$ is assumed to be nonsingular. The set of equations (13-67) is a set of n linear first-order difference equations.

If we are given the $\mathbf{b}_k$ for all k, an initial gross-production vector $\mathbf{x}_0$, and initial stocks $\mathbf{s}_0 = \mathbf{D}\mathbf{x}_0$, then the behavior of the entire economy is determined for all future times since

$$\mathbf{x}_{k+1} = \mathbf{x}_k + \mathbf{D}^{-1}(\mathbf{I} - \mathbf{A})\mathbf{x}_k - \mathbf{D}^{-1}\mathbf{b}_k. \qquad (13\text{-}69)$$

It does not follow that the economy, starting from an arbitrary $\mathbf{x}_0$, can always meet the bills of goods $\mathbf{b}_k$ and also maintain $\Delta\mathbf{s}_k > 0$. In fact, it may be necessary for both $\Delta\mathbf{s}_k$ and $\mathbf{s}_k$ to become negative in order to satisfy the two requirements. Leontief avoided this problem by making the d_{ij} nonlinear, i.e., the d_{ij} changed values when any $\Delta x_j(k) = x_j(k+1) - x_j(k)$ changed sign. This introduced a new type of behavior into the system, which is sometimes referred to as the relaxation phenomenon. A discussion of this subject would take us too far afield. However, the reader can find a study of the two-variable case in an article by Georgescu-Roegen [3].

Leontief based his development on a continuous change in time rather than on discrete time periods. Consequently, he dealt with production rates rather than amounts produced in a given time period, and obtained a set of first-order differential equations rather than difference equations. The differential-equation and difference-equation models do have the same qualitative behavior.

We can easily convert the deterministic, dynamic Leontief model to a form which requires that a linear programming problem be solved at each time step. Suppose that we replace (13–65) by

$$\mathbf{x}_k \geq \mathbf{A}\mathbf{x}_k + \Delta\mathbf{s}_k + \mathbf{b}_k, \qquad \text{all } k. \qquad (13\text{-}70)$$

The strict inequality can hold for one or more industries only if their output is so large that it cannot be used. We also write (13–64) as

$$\mathbf{s}_k \geq \mathbf{D}\mathbf{x}_k, \qquad \text{all } k. \qquad (13\text{-}71)$$

The inequality simply means that the capital stock may not be used at full capacity in the production for the given period, i.e., excess capacity can exist.

If we are given $\mathbf{s}_k$ and wish to determine $\mathbf{x}_k$ and $\Delta\mathbf{s}_k + \mathbf{b}_k$ which maximize some linear form $z = \mathbf{c}\,(\Delta\mathbf{s}_k + \mathbf{b}_k)$, then we have the linear programming problem

$$(\mathbf{I} - \mathbf{A})\mathbf{x}_k - (\Delta\mathbf{s}_k + \mathbf{b}_k) \geq \mathbf{0},$$

$$\mathbf{D}\mathbf{x}_k \leq \mathbf{s}_k,$$

$$\mathbf{x}_k \geq \mathbf{0}, \qquad \Delta\mathbf{s}_k + \mathbf{b}_k \geq \mathbf{0}, \qquad (13\text{-}72)$$

$$\max z = \mathbf{c}(\Delta\mathbf{s}_k + \mathbf{b}_k).$$

In this problem, $\mathbf{b}_k$ is not specified. For a given $\mathbf{b}_k$, the $\Delta\mathbf{s}_k$ obtained from the optimal solution to (13–72) may or may not satisfy $\Delta\mathbf{s}_k \geq \mathbf{0}$. However, there will be at least one $\mathbf{b}_k$ (perhaps $\mathbf{b}_k = \mathbf{0}$) for which $\Delta\mathbf{s}_k \geq \mathbf{0}$. In solving this linear programming problem, we maximize the growth of the economy in some way. The vector $\mathbf{c}$ determines the manner in which the growth is being maximized.

In addition to the above alternatives, there are many other ways of obtaining dynamic Leontief-type models. We shall terminate our presentation by considering a model suggested by Wagner [5]. We assume that n industries produce m products. More than a single industry may produce a given product. As usual, however, no industry produces more than a single product. Let $\mathbf{A}$ be the technology matrix for the economy. It will be assumed to be independent of time so that there is no technological improvement. Take $\mathbf{x}_k$ to be the gross production vector for period k, and let $\mathbf{s}_k$ be a vector representing the stocks of the various products available at the end of time period k. These stocks represent quantities produced, but not used, by the end of time period k. We do not say who holds these stocks. The bill of goods for period k will be written $\mathbf{b}_k$. We shall also assume that limits are imposed on the productive capacity, that is, $\mathbf{x}_k \leq \mathbf{q}_k$. However, $\mathbf{q}_k$ can change from period to period because some of the gross production is used to build more productive capacity. Assume that an increase of the productive capacity of industry j by an amount r_j requires an amount $d_{ij}r_j$ of product i. Let $\mathbf{D} = \|d_{ij}\|$, and $\mathbf{r}_k$ be a vector containing the increases in productive capacity built in period k. Imagine that this increase in productive capacity cannot be used until period $k + 1$.

If $\mathbf{q}_0$ represents the initial productive capacities and $\mathbf{b}_k, \mathbf{r}_k, \mathbf{s}_k, \mathbf{s}_{k-1}$ are given for time period k, then $\mathbf{x}_k \geq \mathbf{0}$ must satisfy

$$(\mathbf{I} - \mathbf{A})\mathbf{x}_k = \mathbf{s}_k - \mathbf{s}_{k-1} + \mathbf{D}\mathbf{r}_k + \mathbf{b}_k, \qquad (13\text{–}73)$$

$$\mathbf{x}_k \leq \mathbf{q}_0 + \sum_{j=1}^{k-1} \mathbf{r}_j. \qquad (13\text{–}74)$$

It may or may not be true that the $\mathbf{x}_k$ determined from (13–73) satisfies (13–74).

Suppose that we are interested only in a total of n time periods and that we wish to maximize $z = \mathbf{c}\mathbf{q}_n = \mathbf{c}[\mathbf{q}_0 + \sum_{j=1}^{n-1} \mathbf{r}_j]$, that is, some linear combination of the productive capacities for the final time period. At the same time, we must satisfy each bill of goods $\mathbf{b}_k, k = 1, \ldots, n$, if this is possible. Assume that we are given the initial productive capacities and inventories $\mathbf{q}_0, \mathbf{s}_0$, respectively. Then the problem is to determine the $\mathbf{x}_k, \mathbf{r}_k, k = 1, \ldots, n$, which maximize z. This means that we must solve the linear programming problem

$$(\mathbf{I} - \mathbf{A})\mathbf{x}_k = \mathbf{s}_k - \mathbf{s}_{k-1} + \mathbf{Dr}_k + \mathbf{b}_k, \qquad k = 1, \ldots, n,$$

$$\mathbf{x}_k \leq \mathbf{q}_0 + \sum_{j=1}^{k-1} \mathbf{r}_j,$$

$$\mathbf{x}_k \geq \mathbf{0}, \qquad \mathbf{r}_k \geq \mathbf{0}, \qquad (13\text{--}75)$$

$$\max z = \mathbf{c}\left[\sum_{j=1}^{n-1} \mathbf{r}_j\right].$$

Since upper bounds limit the capacities, it is quite possible that, in an optimal solution, more than a single industry will produce any given product. This may be true in one time period or all time periods.

It is much more difficult to represent the dynamic behavior of an economy than it is to study the static behavior over a relatively short time period. The attempts made to generalize Leontief models so that they will cover dynamic behavior illustrate this difficulty. Many new problems are encountered, and many more assumptions are needed. The models discussed here do not present a very adequate description of the real world since they omit consideration of many important factors, such as technological improvement, etc. However, as varieties of dynamic models, they are of interest in theoretical economics.

REFERENCES

1. G. DANTZIG, "Optimal Solution of a Dynamic Leontief Model with Substitution," *RM*-1281-1, The RAND Corporation, March 1955.

2. R. DORFMAN, P. SAMUELSON, and R. SOLOW, *Linear Programming and Economic Analysis*. New York: McGraw-Hill, 1958.

The entire text is devoted to applications of linear programming to economics. The mathematics is elementary, but the economic reasoning is advanced. Much of the material covered in this chapter is to be found and more–especially on the subject of economic growth and optimal paths for growth.

3. T. C. KOOPMANS, ed., *Activity Analysis of Production and Allocation*. New York: Wiley, 1951.

4. O. MORGENSTERN, ed., *Economic Activity Analysis*. New York: Wiley, 1954.

Almost the entire work is devoted to static input-output models.

5. H. M. WAGNER, "A Linear Programming Solution to Dynamic Leontief Type Models," *Management Science*, **3**, 3, 1957, 234–254.

PROBLEMS

13–1. Consider a firm which produces a single good and operates under pure competition. If q is the production rate, the firm incurs costs at the rate of

$$C(q) = 0.003(q - 50)^3 + 25.$$

The market price for the firm's product is $p = 10$. What production rate maximizes the firm's profit rate? What is the maximum profit rate? On a single graph, plot the marginal and average cost curves as well as the marginal revenue curves. On another graph, plot $R(q) = pq$, $C(q)$, $\Pi(q) = R - C$. What is the equation for the firm's supply curve?

13–2. A manufacturer of a single good buys and sells in competitive markets. There are two factors of production. If x_1, x_2 are the rates at which these factors are used, the production rate q is related to x_1, x_2 by the production function

$$q = x_1^\alpha x_2^\beta.$$

Costs are incurred at the rate

$$C = w_1 x_1 + w_2 x_2 + k.$$

If p is the market price of the good, find the production rate which maximizes the profit rate. Also, find the demand functions for the factors of production.

13–3. The demand curve for a good produced by a monopolist is

$$q = -200p + 1000,$$

where p is the price and q the rate of demand at this price. If the monopolist produces at a rate q, he incurs costs at a rate of

$$C = 10^{-4}(q - 100)^3 + 250.$$

Find the production rate which maximizes the profit rate. Also, find the price which should be charged to maximize the profit rate. Plot the profit, revenue, and cost curves as a function of q. If $\hat{p}$ is the price which maximizes the profit rate, what production rate would maximize the profit rate if the manufacturer sold in a competitive market with market price $\hat{p}$? What would be the profit rate? How do you explain the result obtained?

13–4. Assume that a firm which makes joint products buys and sells under pure competition. Show how the formulation given in Section 13–2 for joint products accounts for changes in some process variable, such as temperature or pressure, which can change the mix of the joint products. Hint: An increase in the temperature of some unit may require a larger electrical load on the heating coils, or an increase in the pressure on a unit may require more work from the pumps.

13–5. Consider the set of equations (13–5). Write these as

$$f_i(x_1, \ldots, x_n, w_1, \ldots, w_n, p) = 0, \qquad i = 1, \ldots, n.$$

Choose a particular w_i, say w_k. Show how to compute $\partial x_i/\partial w_k$, $i = 1, \ldots, n$. Under what condition is it possible to obtain a unique solution for these partial derivatives?

13–6. In Section 13–3, we have defined an activity as a process of production yielding only a single product. Show how to generalize the analysis so that an activity may involve the production of several products, i.e., joint products. Hint: Let the variable λ_j be the level at which the activity $\mathbf{a}_j$ is operated. Then $\mathbf{a}_j\lambda_j$ gives the amount of the resources used when $\mathbf{a}_j$ is operated at the level λ_j. Let $b_{ij}\lambda_j$ be the amount of good i produced when the activity is operated at level λ_j. What price should be used for λ_j?

13–7. A farmer can use three activities at any level: The first produces 1000 hogs by means of 30 man-months of labor, 50 acres of land, and 200 tons of corn. The second produces 100 tons of corn, using 20 man-months of labor and 100 acres of land. The third produces 500 hogs and 200 tons of corn, using 40 man-months of labor and 130 acres of land. Corn can be bought or sold at \$100/ton, and hogs can be sold at \$30 each. The farmer has available 50 man-months of labor and 150 acres of land. At what level should each activity be operated in order to maximize profits?

13–8. Consider an economy consisting of two industries whose technology matrix in terms of natural units is

$$\mathbf{A} = \begin{bmatrix} 0.05 & 0.25 \\ 0.15 & 0.20 \end{bmatrix}.$$

How much should each industry produce to meet the bill of goods $\mathbf{b} = [20, 50]$?

13–9. Given the technology matrix of Problem 13–8, how much of good 1 must be used to produce 80 units of good 1 and 10 units of good 2? How much of good 2 is needed?

13–10. For the technology matrix of Problem 13–8, find the prices of the goods if the values added per unit are 0.50 for good 1 and 0.32 for good 2. An increase in wages increases the value added per unit in industry 1 to 0.60. If the entire cost is passed on, what are the new prices for both goods?

13–11. Use the prices determined in the first part of Problem 13–10 to convert the technology matrix of Problem 13–8 to monetary units.

13–12. A hypothetical economy consists of three industries: agriculture, autos, and chemicals. The distribution of the output of each industry during the past year is shown in Table 13–2. Compute the technology matrix $\mathbf{A}$ in natural units and $(\mathbf{I} - \mathbf{A})^{-1}$.

13–13. For the economy described in Problem 13–12, assume that labor is the only primary factor and that the wage rate is \$1.50 per hour. The labor hours are: 5×10^4 per million pounds of chemicals, 8.2×10^6 per million autos, and 6×10^5 per million carloads of agricultural products. Compute the prices which prevail in the economy if profits are neglected. Compute the technology matrix in monetary units.

13–14. For the economy presented in Problem 13–12, find how the output will change if exports of chemicals increase from 1 to 2 million pounds per year.

TABLE 13–2

	Chem- icals	Autos	Agri- culture	Con- sumers	Foreign trade
Chemicals (millions of lbs)	5	1	10	2	1
Autos (millions of vehicles)	0.01	0.01	0.05	4	0.02
Agriculture (millions of carloads)	2	0.2	0.5	10	0.7

Take account of the fact that consumer expenditure will change. Use the information on labor requirements given in Problem 13–13.

13–15. Write the form of the technology matrix (if possible, in decomposed form) for an economy which can be represented by the graph in Fig. 13–3.

13–16. A hypothetical economy consists of three industries: (1) agriculture, (2) metal products, (3) chemicals. For each industry there are three processes of production. The three possible activities for agriculture will be denoted by a_1, a_2, a_3. In monetary units, these activity vectors are

$$a_1 = [0.1, 0.2, 0.2], \qquad a_2 = [0.2, 0.3, 0.1], \qquad a_3 = [0.15, 0.25, 0.30].$$

The first component of each of these vectors refers to agriculture and the third to chemicals. The three activity vectors for metal products will be denoted by a_4, a_5, a_6; they are

$$a_4 = [0.05, 0.3, 0.3], \qquad a_5 = [0.03, 0.4, 0.2], \qquad a_6 = [0.07, 0.25, 0.35].$$

The three activity vectors for chemicals will be denoted by a_7, a_8, a_9; they are

$$a_7 = [0.25, 0.05, 0.15], \qquad a_8 = [0.30, 0.04, 0.13], \qquad a_9 = [0.10, 0.06, 0.25].$$

FIGURE 13–3

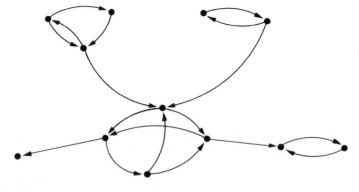

FIGURE 13–4

Let x_j be the level of activity j. Activity 4 has an upper bound of 4×10^6, and activity 7 has an upper bound of 3×10^6. The labor requirements u_j per unit level of each activity are $u_1 = 0.45$, $u_2 = 0.25$, $u_3 = 0.30$, $u_4 = 0.30$, $u_5 = 0.35$, $u_6 = 0.45$, $u_7 = 0.42$, $u_8 = 0.50$, $u_9 = 0.55$. Determine the level at which each activity should be operated in order to minimize labor requirements and to meet exactly the exogenous bill of goods:

$$\mathbf{b} = [18 \times 10^6, 10 \times 10^6, 6 \times 10^6].$$

13–17. Write down the dual of a gasoline-blending problem of the type discussed in Chapter 12. Can you provide an economic interpretation for the dual variables?

13–18. Consider the dual of the refinery routing problem discussed in Chapter 12. Can you provide an economic interpretation for all (or any) of the dual variables?

13–19. Consider an economy represented by the graph of Fig. 13–4. Write down the technology matrix for this economy in its decomposed form. Write down the form of $(\mathbf{I} - \mathbf{A})^{-1}$, indicating clearly which elements are zero. Evaluate explicitly $(\mathbf{I} - \mathbf{A})^{-1}$ in terms of the elements of $\mathbf{A}$ for an economy whose graph is shown in Fig. 13–5.

13–20. Give the form of the technology matrix for an economy whose graph is shown in Fig. 13–6. Compute $(\mathbf{I} - \mathbf{A})^{-1}$ in terms of the elements of $\mathbf{A}$.

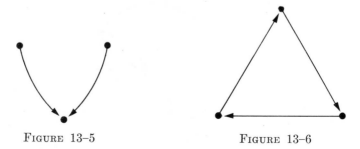

FIGURE 13–5   FIGURE 13–6

13–21. Show that for any linear programming problem $\mathbf{Ax} = \mathbf{b}$, $\mathbf{x} \geq \mathbf{0}$, max $z = \mathbf{cx}$, the dual variable w_k can be interpreted as $\partial z_{\max}/\partial b_k$, provided that b_k can be varied independently of the other b_i's. For the transportation problem, is it possible to change an a_i without changing a b_j? Hint: $\sum a_i = \sum b_j$.

13–22. For the formulation of the transportation problem used in Chapter 9, where the dual variables were unrestricted in sign, we noted that any one of the dual variables could be assigned arbitrarily and the others would be uniquely determined. Show that for the formulation of the transportation problem given by Eq. (13–19), where the dual variables are non-negative, it is not possible to assign arbitrarily a value to one of the dual variables. Why is this so? Hint: In Eq. (13–19) there are surplus variables which must be added. Will one of the surplus vectors appear in an optimal basis?

13–23. Consider a simple economy consisting of three industries: (1) metals, (2) electronics, (3) missiles. It is desired to study the dynamic behavior of this economy over a five-year period, the object being to maximize the production of missiles. To increase missile production, it may also be necessary to increase the capacities of the metals and electronics industries. The natural units for measuring production are number of missiles, tons of metal, and "equivalent computers" in the electronics industry. In natural units, the technological coefficients for the economy are given in the following table. The last row of the table gives the labor coefficients a_{0j} in man-years.

	Missiles	Electronics	Metals
Missiles	0	0	0
Electronics	3	0.1	0.05
Metals	2	0.4	0.1
Labor	500	25	0.2

The capacities of each industry are measured in the same units as production. The coefficients d_{ij} which give the units of i required for increasing the capacity of industry j by one unit are given in the following table:

	Missiles	Electronics	Metals
Missiles	0	0	0
Electronics	2	3	0.5
Metals	5	1	2
Labor	7	2	0.5

Any increased capacity obtained in one period cannot be used until the beginning of the next. The initial capacities of the industries in their natural units are (1) missiles: 100, (2) electronics: 4000, (3) metals: 100,000. One million man-years of labor are available in the first year. The labor force is expected to increase at the rate of 10% per year. The exogenous demand for electronics in the first year is 3000 and for metals 60,000. The exogenous demand for electronics is expected to increase at the rate of 10% per year and for metals at the rate of 5% per year. Assume that electronics and metals can be inventoried and that the initial stocks of metals and electronics are respectively 5000 and 100. Set up on a large sheet of paper the linear programming problem whose solution will maximize the output of missiles over the next five years while at the same time meeting the exogenous demands. If the reader has access to a digital computer, he will find it instructive to solve the above problem and do a parameter study determining how the missile production depends on the initial electronics capacity.

INDEX

INDEX